Functions Modeling Change:
A Preparation for Calculus

Third & Fourth Editions

CONNALLY

Data, Functions and Graphs – Math 105
University of Michigan

Wiley Custom Learning Solutions

To order books or for customer service, please call 1(800)-CALL-WILEY (225-5945).

Printed in the United States of America.

ISBN 978-1-118-80915-0
Printed and bound by IPAK.

10 9 8 7 6 5 4 3

Custom Brief Contents

FORMULA SUMMARY: ALGEBRA

Lines

Slope of line through (x_1, y_1) and (x_2, y_2):

$$m = \frac{y_2 - y_1}{x_2 - x_1}$$

Point-slope equation of line through (x_1, y_1) with slope m:

$$y - y_1 = m(x - x_1)$$

Slope-intercept equation of line with slope m and y-intercept b:

$$y = b + mx$$

Distance from (x_1, y_1) to (x_2, y_2):

$$\text{Distance} = \sqrt{(x_2 - x_1)^2 + (y_2 - y_1)^2}$$

Midpoint of a line segment whose ends are at (x_1, y_1) and (x_2, y_2):

$$\text{Midpoint} = \left(\frac{x_1 + x_2}{2}, \frac{y_1 + y_2}{2} \right)$$

Definition of Zero, Negative, and Fractional Exponents

$$a^0 = 1, \quad a^{-1} = \frac{1}{a}, \quad \text{and, in general, } a^{-x} = \frac{1}{a^x}$$

$$a^{1/2} = \sqrt{a}, \quad a^{1/3} = \sqrt[3]{a}, \quad \text{and, in general, } a^{1/n} = \sqrt[n]{a}.$$

$$\text{Also, } a^{m/n} = \sqrt[n]{a^m} = (\sqrt[n]{a})^m.$$

Rules of Exponents

1. $a^x \cdot a^t = a^{x+t}$ For example, $2^4 \cdot 2^3 = (2 \cdot 2 \cdot 2 \cdot 2) \cdot (2 \cdot 2 \cdot 2) = 2^7$.

2. $\dfrac{a^x}{a^t} = a^{x-t}$ For example, $\dfrac{2^4}{2^3} = \dfrac{2 \cdot 2 \cdot 2 \cdot 2}{2 \cdot 2 \cdot 2} = 2^1$.

3. $(a^x)^t = a^{xt}$ For example, $(2^3)^2 = 2^3 \cdot 2^3 = 2^6$.

Definition of Log

$y = \ln x$ means $e^y = x$; for example: $\ln 1 = 0$, since $e^0 = 1$.

$y = \log x$ means $10^y = x$; for example: $\log 10 = 1$, since $10^1 = 10$.

Rules of Logarithms

$$\log(AB) = \log A + \log B \qquad\qquad \ln(AB) = \ln A + \ln B$$

$$\log\left(\frac{A}{B}\right) = \log A - \log B \qquad\qquad \ln\left(\frac{A}{B}\right) = \ln A - \ln B$$

$$\log A^p = p \log A \qquad\qquad \ln A^p = p \ln A$$

Identities

$$\log 10^x = x \qquad\qquad \ln e^x = x$$

$$10^{\log x} = x \qquad\qquad e^{\ln x} = x$$

FUNCTIONS MODELING CHANGE:
A Preparation for Calculus

Fourth Edition

FUNCTIONS MODELING CHANGE:
A Preparation for Calculus

Fourth Edition

Produced by the Calculus Consortium and initially funded by a National Science Foundation Grant.

Eric Connally
Harvard University Extension

Deborah Hughes-Hallett
The University of Arizona

Andrew M. Gleason
Harvard University

Philip Cheifetz
Nassau Community College

Ann Davidian
Gen. Douglas MacArthur HS

Daniel E. Flath
Macalester College

Selin Kalaycıoğlu
New York University

Brigitte Lahme
Sonoma State University

Patti Frazer Lock
St. Lawrence University

William G. McCallum
The University of Arizona

Jerry Morris
Sonoma State University

Karen Rhea
University of Michigan

Ellen Schmierer
Nassau Community College

Pat Shure
University of Michigan

Adam H. Spiegler
Loyola University Chicago

Carl Swenson
Seattle University

Elliot J. Marks

with the assistance of

Frank Avenoso
Nassau Community College

Douglas Quinney
University of Keele

Katherine Yoshiwara
Los Angeles Pierce College

John Wiley & Sons, Inc.

Dedicated to Ben, Jonah, and Isabel

PUBLISHER	Laurie Rosatone
ACQUISITIONS EDITOR	Joanna Dingle
PROJECT EDITOR	Shannon Corliss
MARKETING MANAGER	Jonathan Cottrell
MEDIA EDITOR	Melissa Edwards
PRODUCTION MANAGER	Micheline Frederick
SENIOR PRODUCTION EDITOR	Ken Santor
FREELANCE DEVELOPMENTAL EDITOR	Anne Scanlan-Rohrer
EDITORIAL ASSISTANT	Beth Pearson
MARKETING ASSISTANT	Patrick Flatley
COVER DESIGNER	Maureen Eide
COVER AND CHAPTER OPENING PHOTO	©Patrick Zephyr/Patrick Zephyr Nature Photography

This book was set in Times Roman by the Consortium using TeX, Mathematica, and the package AsTeX, which was written by Alex Kasman. It was printed and bound by Courier Kendallville. The cover was printed by Courier Kendallville. The process was managed by Elliot Marks.

This material is based upon work supported by the National Science Foundation under Grant No. DUE-9352905. Opinions expressed are those of the authors and not necessarily those of the Foundation.

ISBN-13 978-0-470-48474-6 (Cloth)
ISBN-13 978-0-470-48475-3 (Paper)
ISBN-13 978-0-470-91760-2 (BRV)

PREFACE

Mathematics has the extraordinary power to reduce complicated problems to simple rules and procedures. Therein lies the danger in teaching mathematics: it is possible to teach the subject as nothing but the rules and procedures—thereby losing sight of both the mathematics and its practical value. The fourth edition of *Functions Modeling Change: A Preparation for Calculus* continues our effort to refocus the teaching of mathematics on concepts as well as procedures.

Fourth Edition: Focus

The focus of this edition remains the same as in previous editions: a balance of understanding and skills. We stress conceptual understanding and multiple ways of representing mathematical ideas. Our goal is to provide students with a clear understanding of functions as a solid foundation for subsequent courses in mathematics and other disciplines. When we designed this curriculum under an NSF grant, we started with a clean slate. We focused on the key concepts, emphasizing depth of understanding.

Skills are developed in the context of problems and reinforced in a variety of settings, thereby encouraging retention. This balance of skills and understanding enables students to realize the power of mathematics in modeling.

Fourth Edition: Flexibility

Precalculus courses are taken by a wide range of students and are taught in a wide variety of styles. As instructors ourselves, we know that the balance we choose depends on the students we have: sometimes a focus on conceptual understanding is best; sometimes more skill-building is needed.

To enable instructors to select the balance appropriate for their students, we have increased the options available in the fourth edition. Instructors will find that by selecting sections and exercises that reflect their goals, they can tailor the materials to their students and their institution.

Origin of Text: The Calculus Consortium for Higher Education

This book is the work of faculty at a diverse consortium of institutions, and was originally generously supported by the National Science Foundation. It represents the first consensus among such a diverse group of faculty to have shaped a mainstream precalculus text. Bringing together the results of research and experience with the views of many users, this text is designed to be used in a wide range of institutions.

Guiding Principles: Varied Problems and the Rule of Four

Since students usually learn most when they are active, the exercises in a text are of central importance. In addition, we have found that multiple representations encourage students to reflect on the meaning of the material. Consequently, we have been guided by the following principles.

- Problems should be varied and some should be challenging. Many of our problems cannot be done by following a template in the text.

- The Rule of Four: each concept and function should be represented symbolically, numerically, graphically, and verbally. This principle, originally introduced by the consortium, promotes multiple representations.

- Students and instructors should have a quick way to pinpoint misunderstandings before moving on. To this end, we include Check Your Understanding true-false problems at the end of each chapter.

- The components of a precalculus curriculum should be tied together by clearly defined themes. Functions as models of change is our central theme, and algebra is integrated where appropriate.

- Topics should be fewer in number than is customary so that they can be treated in greater depth. The core syllabus of precalculus should include only those topics that are essential to the study of calculus.

- Problems involving real data should be included to prepare students to use mathematics in other fields.

- To use mathematics effectively, students should develop skill in both symbolic manipulation and the use of technology. The exact proportions of each may vary widely, depending on the preparation of the student and the wishes of the instructor.

- Materials for precalculus should allow for a broad range of teaching styles. They should be flexible enough to use in large lecture halls, small classes, or in group or lab settings.

Changes in the Fourth Edition

The fourth edition retains the hallmarks of earlier editions and reflects the many helpful suggestions from users in the following changes.

- **Algebraic Skills Refreshers** are introduced in two formats, both integrated with the text:
  · **Skills Refresher exercises** are included at the start of many exercise sets, identified by **S1, S2**, etc.
  · **Skills Refresher sections** are included at the end of some chapters.

- A new **Chapter 3** on **Quadratic Functions** brings together and expands the material on quadratics in the former Sections 2.6 and 5.5.

- **Section 4.4** on **Compound Interest** and **Section 4.5** on **the Number** e have been reorganized to give instructors more flexibility in deciding how to introduce e.

- **Limit Notation** has been moved to the end of **Section 5.3** to provide additional flexibility in how, or whether, limit notation is introduced.

- A new **Section 6.5** on **Combining Transformations** investigates the effect of varying the order in which transformations are applied to functions and their graphs.

- The material on **trigonometry** in the former Chapters 6 and 7 has been expanded and reorganized into three chapters, allowing instructors to tailor their approach to the needs of their students.

  · **Chapter 7 defines the trigonometric functions** in circles and triangles.
  · **Chapter 8 studies the behavior of the trigonometric functions** and their graphs, and introduces trigonometric identities, polar coordinates, and complex numbers.
  · **Chapter 9 investigates trigonometric identities** and their applications to modeling.

- **Data and problems** have been updated and revised as appropriate. Many new problems have been added.

- **ConcepTests** for precalculus are available for instructors looking for innovative ways to promote active learning in the classroom. Further information is provided under Supplementary Materials on page ix.

What Student Background is Expected?

Students using this book should have successfully completed a course in intermediate algebra or high school algebra II. The book is thought-provoking for well-prepared students while still accessible to students with weaker backgrounds. Providing numerical and graphical approaches as well as algebraic gives students various ways to master the material. This encourages students to persist, thereby lowering failure rates.

Our Experiences

Previous editions of this book were used by hundreds of schools around the country. In this diverse group of schools, the first three editions were successfully used with many different types of students in semester and quarter systems, in large lectures and small classes, as well as in full-year courses in secondary schools. They were used in computer labs, small groups, and traditional settings, and with a number of different technologies.

Content

The central theme of this course is functions as models of change. We emphasize that functions can be grouped into families and that functions can be used as models for real-world behavior. Because linear, quadratic, exponential, power, and periodic functions are more frequently used to model physical phenomena, they are introduced before polynomial and rational functions. Once introduced, a family of functions is compared and contrasted with other families of functions.

A large number of the examples and problems that students see in this precalculus course are given in the context of real-world problems. Indeed, we hope that students will be able to create mathematical models that help them understand the world in which they live. The inclusion of non-routine problems is intended to establish the idea that such problems are not only part of mathematics, but in some sense are the point of mathematics.

The book does not require any specific software or technology. Instructors have used the material with graphing calculators and graphing software. Any technology with the ability to graph functions will suffice.

Chapter 1: Linear Functions and Change

This chapter introduces the concept of a function and graphical, tabular, symbolic, and verbal representations of functions, discussing the advantages and disadvantages of each representation. It introduces rates of change and uses them to characterize linear functions. A section on fitting a linear function to data is included.

The **Skills Refresher** section for Chapter 1 reviews linear equations and the coordinate plane.

Chapter 2: Functions

This chapter studies function notation in more detail, after its introduction in Chapter 1. It introduces domain, range, and the concepts of composite and inverse functions and investigates the idea of concavity using rates of change. A section on piecewise functions is included.

Chapter 3: Quadratic Functions

This chapter introduces the standard, factored, and vertex forms of a quadratic function and explores their relationship to graphs. The family of quadratic functions provides an opportunity to see the effect of parameters on functional behavior.

The **Skills Refresher** section for Chapter 3 reviews factoring, completing the square, and quadratic equations.

Chapter 4: Exponential Functions

This chapter introduces the family of exponential functions and the number e. It compares exponential and linear functions, solves exponential equations graphically, and gives applications to compound interest.

The **Skills Refresher** section for Chapter 4 reviews the properties of exponents.

Chapter 5: Logarithmic Functions

This chapter introduces logarithmic functions with base 10 and base e, both in order to solve exponential equations and as inverses of exponential functions. After discussing manipulations with logarithms, the chapter focuses on modeling with exponential functions and logarithms. Logarithmic scales and a section on linearizing data conclude the chapter.

The **Skills Refresher** section for Chapter 5 reviews the properties of logarithms.

Chapter 6: Transformations of Functions and Their Graphs

This chapter investigates transformations—shifting, reflecting, and stretching. The last section investigates the effect of changing the order of transformations and suggests a standard way of writing transformations.

Chapter 7: Trigonometry in Circles and Triangles

This chapter, which opens with modeling periodic phenomena, introduces the trigonometric functions of an angle measured in degrees: sine, cosine, tangent, and, briefly, secant, cosecant, and cotangent. Definitions of these functions use the unit circle and are related to definitions using right triangles. The graphs of sine, cosine, and tangent are introduced. The treatment of triangles includes both right and non-right triangles and the inverse trigonometric functions for angles in a right triangle.

The **Skills Refresher** section for Chapter 7 reviews the special angles in $30°$-$60°$-$90°$ and $45°$-$45°$-$90°$ triangles.

Chapter 8: The Trigonometric Functions

This chapter opens with the definition of radians and then studies sinusoidal behavior. It introduces basic identities and revisits inverse trigonometric functions. It also introduces polar coordinates and complex numbers, including Euler's and de Moivre's formulas.

Chapter 9: Trigonometric Identities and Their Applications

The first two sections of this chapter provide a thorough treatment of identities, including double-angle identities and identities involving the sum and difference of angles. The third section shows the uses of trigonometry in mathematical modeling.

Chapter 10: Compositions, Inverses, and Combinations of Functions

This chapter discusses combinations of functions. It investigates composite and inverse functions, which were introduced in Chapter 2, in more detail.

Chapter 11: Polynomial and Rational Functions

This chapter discusses power functions, polynomials, and rational functions. The chapter concludes by comparing several families of functions, including polynomial and exponential functions, and by fitting functions to data.

The **Skills Refresher** section for Chapter 11 reviews algebraic fractions.

Chapter 12: Vectors

This chapter contains material on vectors and operations involving vectors. An introduction to matrices is included in the last section.

Chapter 13: Sequences and Series

This chapter introduces arithmetic and geometric sequences and series and their applications.

Chapter 14: Parametric Equations and Conic Sections

The concluding chapter looks at parametric equations, implicit functions, hyperbolic functions, and conic sections: circles, ellipses, and hyperbolas. The chapter includes a section on the geometrical properties of the conic sections and their applications to orbits.

Supplementary Materials

The following supplementary materials are available for the Fourth Edition:

- **The Instructor's Manual** contains teaching tips, lesson plans, syllabi, and worksheets. It has been expanded and revised to include worksheets, identification of technology-oriented problems, and new syllabi. (ISBN 978-0-470-93904-8)

- **The Printed Test Bank** contains test questions arranged by section. (ISBN 978-0-470-54738-0)

- **The Instructor's Solution Manual** has complete solutions to all problems. (ISBN 978-0-470-54736-6)

- **The Student Solution Manual** has complete solutions to half the odd-numbered problems. (ISBN 978-0-470-54735-9)

- **The Student Study Guide** includes study tips, learning objectives, practice problems, and solutions. The topics are tied directly to the book.

- **The Getting Started Graphing Calculator Manual** instructs students on how to use their TI-83 and TI-84 series calculators with the text. It contains samples, tips, and trouble-shooting sections to answer students' questions.

- **The Computerized Test Bank**, available in both PC and Macintosh formats, allows instructors to create, customize, and print a test containing any combinations of questions from a large bank of questions. Instructors can also customize the questions or create their own.

- **Classroom Activities** are posted at the book companion website. These activities were developed to facilitate in-class group work as well as to introduce new concepts and to practice skills. In addition to the blank copies for each activity that can be handed out to the students, a copy of the activity with fully worked out solutions is also available.

- **The Book Companion Site** contains all instructor supplements.

- **WileyPLUS** is a powerful and highly integrated suite of online teaching and learning resources providing course management options to instructors and students. Instructors can automate the process of assigning, delivering, and grading algorithmically generated homework exercises, and giving hints and solutions, while providing students with immediate feedback. In addition, WileyPLUS provides student tutorials, an instructor gradebook, integrated links to the electronic version of the text, and all of the text supplemental materials. For more information, visit www.wiley.com/college/wileyplus or contact your local Wiley representative for more details.

- **The Faculty Resource Network** is a peer network of academic faculty dedicated to the effective use of technology in the classroom. This group can help you apply innovative classroom techniques, implement specific software packages, and tailor the technology experience to the specific needs of each individual class. Ask your Wiley representative for more details.

ConcepTests

ConcepTests, modeled on the pioneering work of Harvard physicist Eric Mazur, are questions designed to promote active learning during class, particularly (but not exclusively) in large lectures. Our evaluation data show students taught with ConcepTests outperformed students taught by traditional lecture methods 73% versus 17% on conceptual questions, and 63% versus 54% on computational problems. ConcepTests arranged by section are available in print, PowerPoint, and Classroom Response System-ready formats from your Wiley representative. (ISBN 978-0-470-93902-4)

Acknowledgments

We would like to thank the many people who made this book possible. First, we would like to thank the National Science Foundation for their trust and their support; we are particularly grateful to Jim Lightbourne and Spud Bradley.

We are also grateful to our Advisory Board for their guidance: Benita Albert, Lida Barrett, Simon Bernau, Robert Davis, Lovenia Deconge-Watson, John Dossey, Ronald Douglas, Eli Fromm, Bill Haver, Don Lewis, Seymour Parter, John Prados, and Stephen Rodi.

Working with Laurie Rosatone, Anne Scanlan-Rohrer, Ken Santor, Shannon Corliss, Joanna Dingle, Jonathan Cottrell, Beth Pearson, and Maureen Eide at John Wiley is a pleasure. We appreciate their patience and imagination.

Many people have contributed significantly to this text. They include: Lauren Akers, Fahd Alshammari, David Arias, Tim Bean, Charlotte Bonner, Bill Bossert, Brian Bradie, Noah S. Brannen, Mike Brilleslyper, Donna Brouillette, Jo Cannon, Ray Cannon, Kenny Ching, Anna Chung, Pierre Cressant, Laurie Delitsky, Bob Dobrow, Helen M. Doerr, Ian Dowker, Carolyn Edmond, Maryann Faller, Aidan Flanagan, Brendan Fry, Brad Garner, Carrie Garner, John Gerke, Christie Gilliland, Wynne Guy, Donnie Hallstone, David Halstead, Larry Henly, Dean Hickerson, Jo Ellen Hillyer, Bob Hoburg, Phil Hotchkiss, Mike Huffman, Mac Hyman, Rajini Jesudason, Loren Johnson, Scott Kaplowitch, Thomas Kershaw, Mary Kilbride, Steve Kinholt, Kandace Kling, Rob LaQuaglia, Barbara Leasher, Richard Little, David Lovelock, Guadalupe Lozano Terán, Nicholas Lyktey, Chaimaa Makoudi, Len Malinowski, Nancy Marcus, Kate McGivney, Gowri Meda, Bob Megginson, Deborah Moore, Eric Motylinski, Bill Mueller, Kyle Niedzwiecki, Kathryn Oswald, Igor Padure, Bridget Neale Paris, Janet Ray, Ritam Ray, Ken Richardson, Halip Saifi, Sharon Sanders, Mary Schumacher, Mike Seery, Mike Sherman, Donna Sherrill, Max Shuchman, Fred Shure, Kanwal Singh, Myra Snell, Natasha Speer, Sonya Stanley, Michael Steuer, Jim Stone, Peggy Tibbs, Jeff Taft, Elias Toubassi, Jerry Uhl, Pat Wagener, Benjamin West, Dale Winter, and Xianbao Xu.

Reports from the following reviewers were most helpful in shaping the second, third, and fourth editions: Victor Akatsa, Jeffrey Anderson, Beth Borel, Linda Braddy, Michael Brassington, Ingrid Brown-Scott, Linda Casper, Kim Chudnick, Ted Coe, Ray Collings, Joe Coyle, Pam Crawford, Monica Davis, Phyllis Desormeaux, Helen Doerr, Diane Downie, Peter Dragnev, Patricia Dueck, Julie Fisher, Jennifer Fowler, Alyne Fulte, David Gillette, Jack Green, Zdenka Guadarrama, Donnie Hallstone, Jeff Hoherz, Majid Hosseini, Rick Hough, Ann Humes, Pallavi Ketkar, William Kiele, Mile Krajcevski, John LaMaster, Phyllis Leonard, Daphne MacLean, Diane Mathios, Vince McGarry, Maria Miles, Laura Moore-Mueller, Ellen Musen, Dave Nolan, Linda O'Brien, Chris Parks, Scott Perry, Jeffrey S. Powell, Mary Rack, Emily Roth, Barbara Shabell Deirdre Smith, Ernie Solheid, Sandy Spears, Diana Staats, John Stadler, Mary Jane Sterling, Allison Sutton, John Thomason, Diane Van Nostrand, Jim Vicich, Linda Wagner, Nicole Williams, Jim Winston, Vauhn Wittman-Grahler, and Bruce Yoshiwara.

Special thanks are owed to Faye Riddle for administering the project and to Alex Kasman for his software support.

Eric Connally	Deborah Hughes-Hallett	Andrew M. Gleason	Philip Cheifetz
Ann Davidian	Dan Flath	Selin Kalaycıoğlu	Brigitte Lahme
Patti Frazer Lock	Elliot Marks	William G. McCallum	Jerry Morris
Karen Rhea	Ellen Schmierer	Pat Shure	Adam H. Spiegler
Carl Swenson			

To Students: How to Learn from this Book

- This book may be different from other math textbooks that you have used, so it may be helpful to know about some of the differences in advance. At every stage, this book emphasizes the *meaning* (in practical, graphical or numerical terms) of the symbols you are using. There is much less emphasis on "plug-and-chug" and using formulas, and much more emphasis on the interpretation of these formulas than you may expect. You will often be asked to explain your ideas in words or to explain an answer using graphs.

- The book contains the main ideas of precalculus in plain English. Success in using this book will depend on reading, questioning, and thinking hard about the ideas presented. It will be helpful to read the text in detail, not just the worked examples.

- There are few examples in the text that are exactly like the homework problems, so homework problems can't be done by searching for similar–looking "worked out" examples. Success with the homework will come by grappling with the ideas of precalculus.

- Many of the problems in the book are open-ended. This means that there is more than one correct approach and more than one correct solution. Sometimes, solving a problem relies on common-sense ideas that are not stated in the problem explicitly but which you know from everyday life.

- This book assumes that you have access to a calculator or computer that can graph functions and find (approximate) roots of equations. There are many situations where you may not be able to find an exact solution to a problem, but can use a calculator or computer to get a reasonable approximation. An answer obtained this way can be as useful as an exact one. However, the problem does not always state that a calculator is required, so use your own judgment.

- This book attempts to give equal weight to four methods for describing functions: graphical (a picture), numerical (a table of values), algebraic (a formula) and verbal (words). Sometimes it's easier to translate a problem given in one form into another. For example, you might replace the graph of a parabola with its equation, or plot a table of values to see its behavior. It is important to be flexible about your approach: if one way of looking at a problem doesn't work, try another.

- Students using this book have found discussing these problems in small groups helpful. There are a great many problems that are not cut-and-dried; it can help to attack them with the other perspectives your colleagues can provide. If group work is not feasible, see if your instructor can organize a discussion session in which additional problems can be worked on.

- You are probably wondering what you'll get from the book. The answer is, if you put in a solid effort, you will get a real understanding of functions as well as a real sense of how mathematics is used in the age of technology.

Table of Contents

4 EXPONENTIAL FUNCTIONS 129

5 LOGARITHMIC FUNCTIONS 179

6 TRANSFORMATIONS OF FUNCTIONS AND THEIR GRAPHS 223

10 COMPOSITIONS, INVERSES, AND COMBINATIONS OF FUNCTIONS   397

11 POLYNOMIAL AND RATIONAL FUNCTIONS   431

12 VECTORS AND MATRICES   495

Chapter One

LINEAR FUNCTIONS AND CHANGE

Contents

1.1 FUNCTIONS AND FUNCTION NOTATION

In everyday language, the word *function* expresses the notion of dependence. For example, a person might say that election results are a function of the economy, meaning that the winner of an election is determined by how the economy is doing. Someone else might claim that car sales are a function of the weather, meaning that the number of cars sold on a given day is affected by the weather.

In mathematics, the meaning of the word *function* is more precise, but the basic idea is the same. A function is a relationship between two quantities. If the value of the first quantity determines exactly one value of the second quantity, we say the second quantity is a function of the first. We make the following definition:

> A **function** is a rule that takes certain numbers as inputs and assigns to each input number exactly one output number. The output is a function of the input.

The inputs and outputs are also called *variables*.

Representing Functions: Words, Tables, Graphs, and Formulas

A function can be described using words, data in a table, points on a graph, or a formula.

Example 1   It is a surprising biological fact that most crickets chirp at a rate that increases as the temperature increases. For the snowy tree cricket (*Oecanthus fultoni*), the relationship between temperature and chirp rate is so reliable that this type of cricket is called the thermometer cricket. We can estimate the temperature (in degrees Fahrenheit) by counting the number of times a snowy tree cricket chirps in 15 seconds and adding 40. For instance, if we count 20 chirps in 15 seconds, then a good estimate of the temperature is $20 + 40 = 60°F$.

The rule used to find the temperature T (in °F) from the chirp rate R (in chirps per minute) is an example of a function. The input is chirp rate and the output is temperature. Describe this function using words, a table, a graph, and a formula.

Solution   • **Words**: To estimate the temperature, we count the number of chirps in fifteen seconds and add forty. Alternatively, we can count R chirps per minute, divide R by four and add forty. This is because there are one-fourth as many chirps in fifteen seconds as there are in sixty seconds. For instance, 80 chirps per minute works out to $\frac{1}{4} \cdot 80 = 20$ chirps every 15 seconds, giving an estimated temperature of $20 + 40 = 60°F$.
• **Table**: Table 1.1 gives the estimated temperature, T, as a function of R, the number of chirps per minute. Notice the pattern in Table 1.1: each time the chirp rate, R, goes up by 20 chirps per minute, the temperature, T, goes up by $5°F$.
• **Graph**: The data from Table 1.1 are plotted in Figure 1.1. For instance, the pair of values $R = 80$, $T = 60$ is plotted as the point P, which is 80 units along the horizontal axis and 60 units up the vertical axis. Data represented in this way are said to be plotted on the *Cartesian plane*. The precise position of P is shown by its coordinates, written $P = (80, 60)$.

Table 1.1   *Chirp rate and temperature*

R, chirp rate (chirps/minute)	T, predicted temperature (°F)
20	45
40	50
60	55
80	60
100	65
120	70
140	75
160	80

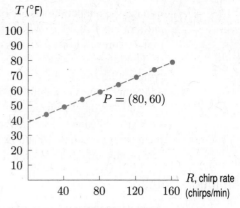

Figure 1.1: Chirp rate and temperature

- **Formula**: A formula is an equation giving T in terms of R. Dividing the chirp rate by four and adding forty gives the estimated temperature, so:

$$\underbrace{\text{Estimated temperature (in °F)}}_{T} = \frac{1}{4} \cdot \underbrace{\text{Chirp rate (in chirps/min)}}_{R} + 40.$$

Rewriting this using the variables T and R gives the formula:

$$T = \frac{1}{4}R + 40.$$

Let's check the formula. Substituting $R = 80$, we have

$$T = \frac{1}{4} \cdot 80 + 40 = 60,$$

which agrees with point $P = (80, 60)$ in Figure 1.1. The formula $T = \frac{1}{4}R + 40$ also tells us that if $R = 0$, then $T = 40$. Thus, the dashed line in Figure 1.1 crosses (or intersects) the T-axis at $T = 40$; we say the T-*intercept* is 40.

All the descriptions given in Example 1 provide the same information, but each description has a different emphasis. A relationship between variables is often given in words, as at the beginning of Example 1. Table 1.1 is useful because it shows the predicted temperature for various chirp rates. Figure 1.1 is more suggestive of a trend than the table, although it is harder to read exact values of the function. For example, you might have noticed that every point in Figure 1.1 falls on a straight line that slopes up from left to right. In general, a graph can reveal a pattern that might otherwise go unnoticed. Finally, the formula has the advantage of being both compact and precise. However, this compactness can also be a disadvantage since it may be harder to gain as much insight from a formula as from a table or a graph.

Mathematical Models

When we use a function to describe an actual situation, the function is referred to as a **mathematical model**. The formula $T = \frac{1}{4}R + 40$ is a mathematical model of the relationship between the temperature and the cricket's chirp rate. Such models can be powerful tools for understanding phenomena and making predictions. For example, this model predicts that when the chirp rate is 80 chirps per minute, the temperature is 60°F. In addition, since $T = 40$ when $R = 0$, the model predicts that the chirp rate is 0 at 40°F. Whether the model's predictions are accurate for chirp rates down to 0 and temperatures as low as 40°F is a question that mathematics alone cannot answer; an understanding of the biology of crickets is needed. However, we can safely say that the model does not apply for temperatures below 40°F, because the chirp rate would then be negative. For the range of chirp rates and temperatures in Table 1.1, the model is remarkably accurate.

In everyday language, saying that T is a function of R suggests that making the cricket chirp faster would somehow make the temperature change. Clearly, the cricket's chirping does not cause the temperature to be what it is. In mathematics, saying that the temperature "depends" on the chirp rate means only that knowing the chirp rate is sufficient to tell us the temperature.

Function Notation

To indicate that a quantity Q is a function of a quantity t, we abbreviate

$$Q \text{ is a function of } t \quad \text{to} \quad Q \text{ equals "} f \text{ of } t"$$

and, using function notation, to

$$Q = f(t).$$

Thus, applying the rule f to the input value, t, gives the output value, $f(t)$. In other words, $f(t)$ represents a value of Q. Here Q is called the *dependent variable* and t is called the *independent variable*. Symbolically,

$$\text{Output} = f(\text{Input})$$

or

$$\text{Dependent} = f(\text{Independent}).$$

We could have used any letter, not just f, to represent the rule.

Example 2   The number of gallons of paint needed to paint a house depends on the size of the house. A gallon of paint typically covers 250 square feet. Thus, the number of gallons of paint, n, is a function of the area to be painted, A ft². We write $n = f(A)$.

(a) Find a formula for f.
(b) Explain in words what the statement $f(10,000) = 40$ tells us about painting houses.

Solution   (a) If $A = 5000$ ft², then $n = 5000/250 = 20$ gallons of paint. In general, n and A are related by the formula

$$n = \frac{A}{250}.$$

(b) The input of the function $n = f(A)$ is an area and the output is an amount of paint. The statement $f(10,000) = 40$ tells us that an area of $A = 10,000$ ft² requires $n = 40$ gallons of paint.

The expressions "Q depends on t" or "Q is a function of t" do *not* imply a cause-and-effect relationship, as the snowy tree cricket example illustrates.

Example 3   Example 1 gives the following formula for estimating air temperature based on the chirp rate of the snowy tree cricket:

$$T = \frac{1}{4}R + 40.$$

In this formula, T depends on R. Writing $T = f(R)$ indicates that the relationship is a function.

Functions Don't Have to Be Defined by Formulas

People sometimes think that functions are always represented by formulas. However, the next example shows a function that is not given by a formula.

Example 4   The average monthly rainfall, R, at Chicago's O'Hare airport is given in Table 1.2, where time, t, is in months and $t = 1$ is January, $t = 2$ is February, and so on. The rainfall is a function of the month, so we write $R = f(t)$. However, there is no equation that gives R when t is known. Evaluate $f(1)$ and $f(11)$. Explain what your answers mean.

Table 1.2   *Average monthly rainfall at Chicago's O'Hare airport*

Month, t	1	2	3	4	5	6	7	8	9	10	11	12
Rainfall, R (inches)	1.8	1.8	2.7	3.1	3.5	3.7	3.5	3.4	3.2	2.5	2.4	2.1

Solution   The value of $f(1)$ is the average rainfall in inches at Chicago's O'Hare airport in a typical January. From the table, $f(1) = 1.8$ inches. Similarly, $f(11) = 2.4$ means that in a typical November, there are 2.4 inches of rain at O'Hare.

When Is a Relationship Not a Function?

It is possible for two quantities to be related and yet for neither quantity to be a function of the other.

Example 5   A national park contains foxes that prey on rabbits. Table 1.3 gives the two populations, F and R, over a 12-month period, where $t = 0$ means January 1, $t = 1$ means February 1, and so on.

Table 1.3   *Number of foxes and rabbits in a national park, by month*

t, month	0	1	2	3	4	5	6	7	8	9	10	11
R, rabbits	1000	750	567	500	567	750	1000	1250	1433	1500	1433	1250
F, foxes	150	143	125	100	75	57	50	57	75	100	125	143

(a) Is F a function of t? Is R a function of t?

(b) Is F a function of R? Is R a function of F?

Solution   (a) Both F and R are functions of t. For each value of t, there is exactly one value of F and exactly one value of R. For example, Table 1.3 shows that if $t = 5$, then $R = 750$ and $F = 57$. This means that on June 1 there are 750 rabbits and 57 foxes in the park. If we write $R = f(t)$ and $F = g(t)$, then $f(5) = 750$ and $g(5) = 57$.

(b) No, F is not a function of R. For example, suppose $R = 750$, meaning there are 750 rabbits. This happens both at $t = 1$ (February 1) and at $t = 5$ (June 1). In the first instance, there are 143 foxes; in the second instance, there are 57 foxes. Since there are R-values which correspond to more than one F-value, F is not a function of R.

Similarly, R is not a function of F. At time $t = 5$, we have $R = 750$ when $F = 57$, while at time $t = 7$, we have $R = 1250$ when $F = 57$ again. Thus, the value of F does not uniquely determine the value of R.

How to Tell if a Graph Represents a Function: Vertical Line Test

What does it mean graphically for y to be a function of x? Look at the graph of y against x. For a function, each x-value corresponds to exactly one y-value. This means that the graph intersects any vertical line at most once. If a vertical line cuts the graph twice, the graph would contain two points with different y-values but the same x-value; this would violate the definition of a function. Thus, we have the following criterion:

Vertical Line Test: If there is a vertical line that intersects a graph in more than one point, then the graph does not represent a function.

Example 6   In which of the graphs in Figures 1.2 and 1.3 could y be a function of x?

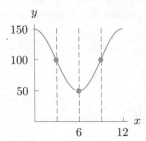

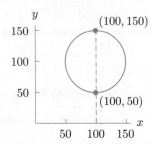

Figure 1.2: Since no vertical line intersects this curve at more than one point, y could be a function of x

Figure 1.3: Since one vertical line intersects this curve at more than one point, y is not a function of x

Solution   The graph in Figure 1.2 could represent y as a function of x because no vertical line intersects this curve in more than one point. The graph in Figure 1.3 does not represent a function because the vertical line shown intersects the curve at two points.

A graph fails the vertical line test if at least one vertical line cuts the graph more than once, as in Figure 1.3. However, if a graph represents a function, then *every* vertical line must intersect the graph at no more than one point.

Exercises and Problems for Section 1.1

Skill Refresher

In Exercises S1–S4, simplify each expression.

S1. $c + \frac{1}{2}c$

S2. $P + 0.07P + 0.02P$

S3. $2\pi r^2 + 2\pi r \cdot 2r$

S4. $\dfrac{12\pi - 2\pi}{6\pi}$

In Exercises S5–S8, find the value of the expressions for the given value of x and y.

S5. $x - 5y$ for $x = \frac{1}{2}$, $y = -5$.

S6. $1 - 12x + x^2$ for $x = 3$.

S7. $\dfrac{3}{2 - x^3}$ for $x = -1$.

S8. $\dfrac{4}{1 + 1/x}$ for $x = -\frac{3}{4}$.

The figures in Exercises S9–S10 are parallelograms. Find the coordinates of the labeled point(s).

S9.

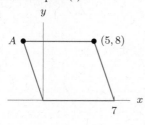

S10.

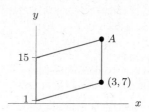

Exercises

1. Figure 1.4 gives the depth of the water at Montauk Point, New York, for a day in November.

   (a) How many high tides took place on this day?
   (b) How many low tides took place on this day?
   (c) How much time elapsed in between high tides?

Figure 1.4

In Exercises 2–3, write the relationship using function notation (that is, y is a function of x is written $y = f(x)$).

2. Number of molecules, m, in a gas, is a function of the volume of the gas, v.

3. Weight, w, is a function of caloric intake, c.

In Exercises 4–7, label the axes for a sketch to illustrate the given statement.

4. "Over the past century we have seen changes in the population, P (in millions), of the city. . ."

5. "Sketch a graph of the cost of manufacturing q items. . ."

6. "Graph the pressure, p, of a gas as a function of its volume, v, where p is in pounds per square inch and v is in cubic inches."

7. "Graph D in terms of y. . ."

8. Using Table 1.4, graph $n = f(A)$, the number of gallons of paint needed to cover a house of area A. Identify the independent and dependent variables.

Table 1.4

A	0	250	500	750	1000	1250	1500
n	0	1	2	3	4	5	6

9. Use Table 1.5 to fill in the missing values. (There may be more than one answer.)

   (a) $f(0) = ?$ **(b)** $f(?) = 0$
   (c) $f(1) = ?$ **(d)** $f(?) = 1$

Table 1.5

x	0	1	2	3	4
$f(x)$	4	2	1	0	1

10. Use Figure 1.5 to fill in the missing values:

   (a) $f(0) = ?$ **(b)** $f(?) = 0$

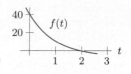

Figure 1.5

Exercises 11–14 use Figure 1.6.

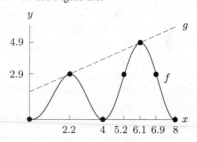

Figure 1.6

11. Find $f(6.9)$.

12. Give the coordinates of two points on the graph of g.

13. Solve $f(x) = 0$ for x.

14. Solve $f(x) = g(x)$ for x.

15. (a) You are going to graph $p = f(w)$. Which variable goes on the horizontal axis?

(b) If $10 = f(-4)$, give the coordinates of a point on the graph of f.

(c) If 6 is a solution of the equation $f(w) = 1$, give a point on the graph of f.

16. (a) Suppose x and y are the coordinates of a point on the circle $x^2 + y^2 = 1$. Is y a function of x? Why or why not?

(b) Suppose x and y are the coordinates of a point on the part of the circle $x^2 + y^2 = 1$ that is above the x-axis. Is y a function of x? Why or why not?

17. (a) Is the area, A, of a square a function of the length of one of its sides, s?

(b) Is the area, A, of a rectangle a function of the length of one of its sides, s?

18. Which of the following graphs represent functions?

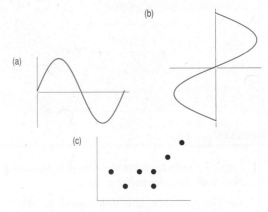

Figure 1.7

Problems

19. A buzzard is circling high overhead when it spies some road kill. It swoops down, lands, and eats. Later it takes off sluggishly, and resumes circling overhead, but at a lower altitude. Sketch a possible graph of the height of the buzzard as a function of time.

20. A person's blood sugar level at a particular time of the day is partially determined by the time of the most recent meal. After a meal, blood sugar level increases rapidly, then slowly comes back down to a normal level. Sketch a person's blood sugar level as a function of time over the course of a day. Label the axes to indicate normal blood sugar level and the time of each meal.

21. Let $f(t)$ be the number of people, in millions, who own cell phones t years after 1990. Explain the meaning of the following statements.

(a) $f(10) = 100.3$ (b) $f(a) = 20$

(c) $f(20) = b$ (d) $n = f(t)$

22. At the end of a semester, students' math grades are listed in a table which gives each student's ID number in the left column and the student's grade in the right column. Let N represent the ID number and the G represent the grade. Which quantity, N or G, must necessarily be a function of the other?

23. Table 1.6 gives the ranking r for three different names— Hannah, Alexis, and Madison. Of the three names, which was most popular and which was least popular in

(a) 1995?   (b) 2004?

Table 1.6   *Ranking of names—Hannah (r_h), Alexis (r_a), and Madison (r_m)—for girls born between 1995 ($t = 0$) and 2004 ($t = 9$)[1]*

t	0	1	2	3	4	5	6	7	8	9
r_h	7	7	5	2	2	2	3	3	4	5
r_a	14	8	8	6	3	6	5	5	7	11
r_m	29	15	10	9	7	3	2	2	3	3

24. Table 1.6 gives information about the popularity of the names Hannah, Madison, and Alexis. Describe in words what your answers to parts (a)–(c) tell you about these names.

(a) Evaluate $r_m(0) - r_h(0)$.

(b) Evaluate $r_m(9) - r_h(9)$.

(c) Solve $r_m(t) < r_a(t)$.

25. Figure 1.8 shows the fuel consumption (in miles per gallon, mpg) of a car traveling at various speeds.

(a) How much gas is used on a 300-mile trip at 40 mph?

(b) How much gas is saved by traveling 60 mph instead of 70 mph on a 200-mile trip?

(c) According to this graph, what is the most fuel-efficient speed to travel? Explain.

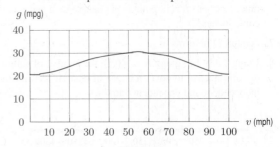

Figure 1.8

___
[1] Data from the SSA website at www.ssa.gov, accessed January 12, 2006.

26. (a) Ten inches of snow is equivalent to about one inch of rain.[2] Write an equation for the amount of precipitation, measured in inches of rain, $r = f(s)$, as a function of the number of inches of snow, s.
(b) Evaluate and interpret $f(5)$.
(c) Find s such that $f(s) = 5$ and interpret your result.

27. An 8-foot-tall cylindrical water tank has a base of diameter 6 feet.

(a) How much water can the tank hold?
(b) How much water is in the tank if the water is 5 feet deep?
(c) Write a formula for the volume of water as a function of its depth in the tank.

28. Match each story about a bike ride to one of the graphs (i)–(v), where d represents distance from home and t is time in hours since the start of the ride. (A graph may be used more than once.)

(a) Starts 5 miles from home and rides 5 miles per hour away from home.
(b) Starts 5 miles from home and rides 10 miles per hour away from home.
(c) Starts 10 miles from home and arrives home one hour later.
(d) Starts 10 miles from home and is halfway home after one hour.
(e) Starts 5 miles from home and is 10 miles from home after one hour.

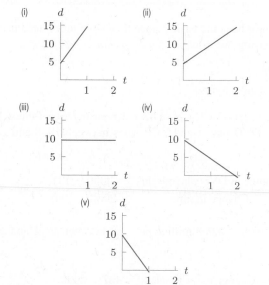

29. Table 1.7 shows the daily low temperature for a one-week period in New York City during July.

(a) What was the low temperature on July 19?
(b) When was the low temperature 73°F?
(c) Is the daily low temperature a function of the date?
(d) Is the date a function of the daily low temperature?

Table 1.7

Date	17	18	19	20	21	22	23
Low temp (°F)	73	77	69	73	75	75	70

30. Use the data from Table 1.3 on page 5.

(a) Plot R on the vertical axis and t on the horizontal axis. Use this graph to explain why you believe that R is a function of t.
(b) Plot F on the vertical axis and t on the horizontal axis. Use this graph to explain why you believe that F is a function of t.
(c) Plot F on the vertical axis and R on the horizontal axis. From this graph show that F is not a function of R.
(d) Plot R on the vertical axis and F on the horizontal axis. From this graph show that R is not a function of F.

31. Since Roger Bannister broke the 4-minute mile on May 6, 1954, the record has been lowered by over sixteen seconds. Table 1.8 shows the year and times (as min:sec) of new world records for the one-mile run.[3] The last time the record was broken was in 1999.

(a) Is the time a function of the year? Explain.
(b) Is the year a function of the time? Explain.
(c) Let $y(r)$ be the year in which the world record, r, was set. Explain what is meant by the statement $y(3{:}47.33) = 1981$.
(d) Evaluate and interpret $y(3{:}51.1)$.

Table 1.8

Year	Time	Year	Time	Year	Time
1954	3:59.4	1966	3:51.3	1981	3:48.53
1954	3:58.0	1967	3:51.1	1981	3:48.40
1957	3:57.2	1975	3:51.0	1981	3:47.33
1958	3:54.5	1975	3:49.4	1985	3:46.32
1962	3:54.4	1979	3:49.0	1993	3:44.39
1964	3:54.1	1980	3:48.8	1999	3:43.13
1965	3:53.6				

---

[2]http://mo.water.usgs.gov/outreach/rain, accessed May 7, 2006.
[3]www.infoplease.com/ipsa/A0112924.html, accessed January 15, 2006.

32. Table 1.9 gives $A = f(d)$, the amount of money in bills of denomination d circulating in US currency in 2008.[4] For example, there were $64.7 billion worth of $50 bills in circulation.

   (a) Find $f(100)$. What does this tell you about money?
   (b) Are there more $1 bills or $5 bills in circulation?

Table 1.9

Denomination ($)	1	2	5	10	20	50	100
Circulation ($bn)	9.5	1.7	11	16.3	125.1	64.7	625

33. There are x male job-applicants at a certain company and y female applicants. Suppose that 15% of the men are accepted and 18% of the women are accepted. Write an expression in terms of x and y representing each of the following quantities:

   (a) The total number of applicants to the company.
   (b) The total number of applicants accepted.
   (c) The percentage of all applicants accepted.

34. The sales tax on an item is 6%. Express the total cost, C, in terms of the price of the item, P.

35. Write a formula for the area of a circle as a function of its radius and determine the percent increase in the area if the radius is increased by 10%.

36. A price increases 5% due to inflation and is then reduced 10% for a sale. Express the final price as a function of the original price, P.

37. A chemical company spends $2 million to buy machinery before it starts producing chemicals. Then it spends $0.5 million on raw materials for each million liters of chemical produced.

   (a) The number of liters produced ranges from 0 to 5 million. Make a table showing the relationship between the number of million liters produced, l, and the total cost, C, in millions of dollars, to produce that number of million liters.
   (b) Find a formula that expresses C as a function of l.

38. A person leaves home and walks due west for a time and then walks due north.

   (a) The person walks 10 miles in total. If w represents the (variable) distance west she walks, and D represents her (variable) distance from home at the end of her walk, is D a function of w? Why or why not?
   (b) Suppose now that x is the distance that she walks in total. Is D a function of x? Why or why not?

1.2   RATE OF CHANGE

Sales of digital video disc (DVD) players have been increasing since they were introduced in early 1998. To measure how fast sales were increasing, we calculate a *rate of change* of the form

$$\frac{\text{Change in sales}}{\text{Change in time}}.$$

At the same time, sales of video cassette recorders (VCRs) have been decreasing. See Table 1.10.

Let us calculate the rate of change of DVD player and VCR sales between 1998 and 2003. Table 1.10 gives

$$\begin{array}{l}\text{Average rate of change of DVD} \\ \text{player sales from 1998 to 2003}\end{array} = \frac{\text{Change in DVD player sales}}{\text{Change in time}} = \frac{3050 - 421}{2003 - 1998} \approx 525.8 \frac{\text{mn \$/}}{\text{year}}.$$

Thus, DVD player sales increased on average by $525.8 million per year between 1998 and 2003. See Figure 1.9. Similarly, Table 1.10 gives

$$\begin{array}{l}\text{Average rate of change of VCR sales} \\ \text{from 1998 to 2003}\end{array} = \frac{\text{Change in VCR sales}}{\text{Change in time}} = \frac{407 - 2409}{2003 - 1998} \approx -400.4 \frac{\text{mn \$/}}{\text{year}}.$$

---

[4]www.visualeconomics.com/the-value-of-united-states-currency-in-circulation, The Value of United States Currency in Circulation, 2008, accessed November 16, 2009.

Thus, VCR sales decreased on average by \$400.4 million per year between 1998 and 2003. See Figure 1.10.

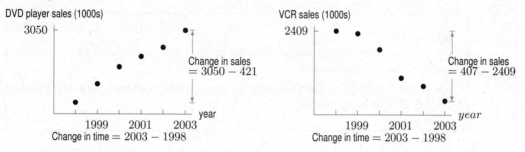

Figure 1.9: DVD player sales   Figure 1.10: VCR sales

Table 1.10 *Annual sales of VCRs and DVD players in millions of dollars*[5]

Year	1998	1999	2000	2001	2002	2003
VCR sales (million \$)	2409	2333	1869	1058	826	407
DVD player sales (million \$)	421	1099	1717	2097	2427	3050

Rate of Change of a Function

The rate of change of sales is an example of the rate of change of a function. In general, if $Q = f(t)$, we write ΔQ for a change in Q and Δt for a change in t. We define:[6]

> The **average rate of change**, or **rate of change**, of Q with respect to t over an interval is
>
> $$\begin{array}{c} \text{Average rate of change} \\ \text{over an interval} \end{array} = \frac{\text{Change in } Q}{\text{Change in } t} = \frac{\Delta Q}{\Delta t}.$$

The average rate of change of the function $Q = f(t)$ over an interval tells us how much Q changes, on average, for each unit change in t within that interval. On some parts of the interval, Q may be changing rapidly, while on other parts Q may be changing slowly. The average rate of change evens out these variations.

Increasing and Decreasing Functions

In the previous example, the average rate of change of DVD player sales is positive on the interval from 1998 to 2003 since sales of DVD players increased over this interval. Similarly, the average rate of change of VCR sales is negative on the same interval since sales of VCRs decreased over this interval. The annual sales of DVD players is an example of an *increasing function* and the annual sales of VCRs is an example of a *decreasing function*. In general we say the following:

> If $Q = f(t)$ for t in the interval $a \le t \le b$,
> * f is an **increasing function** if the values of f increase as t increases in this interval.
> * f is a **decreasing function** if the values of f decrease as t increases in this interval.

---

[5]www.census.gov/prod/2005pubs/06statab/manufact.pdf, accessed January 16, 2006.
[6]The Greek letter Δ, delta, is often used in mathematics to represent change. In this book, we use rate of change to mean average rate of change across an interval. In calculus, rate of change means something called instantaneous rate of change.

Looking at DVD player sales, we see that an increasing function has a positive rate of change. From the VCR sales, we see that a decreasing function has a negative rate of change. In general:

> If $Q = f(t)$,
> - If f is an increasing function, then the average rate of change of Q with respect to t is positive on every interval.
> - If f is a decreasing function, then the average rate of change of Q with respect to t is negative on every interval.

Example 1 The function $A = q(r) = \pi r^2$ gives the area, A, of a circle as a function of its radius, r. Graph q. Explain how the fact that q is an increasing function can be seen on the graph.

Solution The area increases as the radius increases, so $A = q(r)$ is an increasing function. We can see this in Figure 1.11 because the graph climbs as we move from left to right and the average rate of change, $\Delta A / \Delta r$, is positive on every interval.

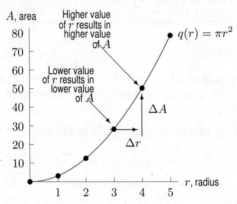

Figure 1.11: The graph of an increasing function, $A = q(r)$, rises when read from left to right

Example 2 Carbon-14 is a radioactive element that exists naturally in the atmosphere and is absorbed by living organisms. When an organism dies, the carbon-14 present at death begins to decay. Let $L = g(t)$ represent the quantity of carbon-14 (in micrograms, μg) in a tree t years after its death. See Table 1.11. Explain why we expect g to be a decreasing function of t. How is this represented on a graph?

Table 1.11   *Quantity of carbon-14 as a function of time*

t, time (years)	0	1000	2000	3000	4000	5000
L, quantity of carbon-14 (μg)	200	177	157	139	123	109

Solution Since the amount of carbon-14 is decaying over time, g is a decreasing function. In Figure 1.12, the graph falls as we move from left to right and the average rate of change in the level of carbon-14 with respect to time, $\Delta L / \Delta t$, is negative on every interval.

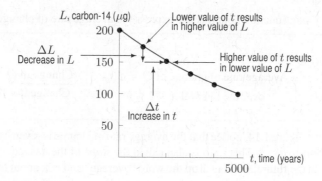

Figure 1.12: The graph of a decreasing function, $L = g(t)$, falls when read from left to right

In general, we can identify an increasing or decreasing function from its graph as follows:

> • The graph of an increasing function rises when read from left to right.
> • The graph of a decreasing function falls when read from left to right.

Many functions have some intervals on which they are increasing and other intervals on which they are decreasing. These intervals can often be identified from the graph.

Example 3   On what intervals is the function graphed in Figure 1.13 increasing? Decreasing?

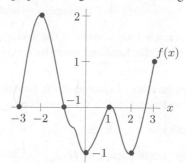

Figure 1.13: Graph of a function that is increasing on some intervals and decreasing on others

Solution   The function appears to be increasing for values of x between -3 and -2, for x between 0 and 1, and for x between 2 and 3. The function appears to be decreasing for x between -2 and 0 and for x between 1 and 2. Using inequalities, we say that f is increasing for $-3 < x < -2$, for $0 < x < 1$, and for $2 < x < 3$. Similarly, f is decreasing for $-2 < x < 0$ and $1 < x < 2$.

Function Notation for the Average Rate of Change

Suppose we want to find the average rate of change of a function $Q = f(t)$ over the interval $a \le t \le b$. On this interval, the change in t is given by

$$\Delta t = b - a.$$

At $t = a$, the value of Q is $f(a)$, and at $t = b$, the value of Q is $f(b)$. Therefore, the change in Q is given by

$$\Delta Q = f(b) - f(a).$$

Using function notation, we express the average rate of change as follows:

$$\begin{array}{c}\text{Average rate of change of } Q = f(t) \\ \text{over the interval } a \le t \le b\end{array} = \frac{\text{Change in } Q}{\text{Change in } t} = \frac{\Delta Q}{\Delta t} = \frac{f(b) - f(a)}{b - a}.$$

In Figure 1.14, notice that the average rate of change is given by the ratio of the rise, $f(b) - f(a)$, to the run, $b - a$. This ratio is also called the *slope* of the dashed line segment.[7]

In the future, we may drop the word "average" and talk about the rate of change over an interval.

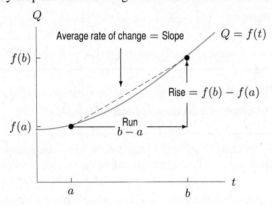

Figure 1.14: The average rate of change is the ratio Rise/Run

In previous examples we calculated the average rate of change from data. We now calculate average rates of change for functions given by formulas.

Example 4   Calculate the average rates of change of the function $f(x) = x^2$ between $x = 1$ and $x = 3$ and between $x = -2$ and $x = 1$. Show your results on a graph.

Solution   Between $x = 1$ and $x = 3$, we have

$$\begin{array}{c}\text{Average rate of change of } f(x) \\ \text{over the interval } 1 \le x \le 3\end{array} = \frac{\text{Change in } f(x)}{\text{Change in } x} = \frac{f(3) - f(1)}{3 - 1}$$

$$= \frac{3^2 - 1^2}{3 - 1} = \frac{9 - 1}{2} = 4.$$

Between $x = -2$ and $x = 1$, we have

$$\begin{array}{c}\text{Average rate of change of } f(x) \\ \text{over the interval } -2 \le x \le 1\end{array} = \frac{\text{Change in } f(x)}{\text{Change in } x} = \frac{f(1) - f(-2)}{1 - (-2)}$$

$$= \frac{1^2 - (-2)^2}{1 - (-2)} = \frac{1 - 4}{3} = -1.$$

The average rate of change between $x = 1$ and $x = 3$ is positive because $f(x)$ is increasing on this interval. See Figure 1.15. However, on the interval from $x = -2$ and $x = 1$, the function is partly decreasing and partly increasing. The average rate of change on this interval is negative because the decrease on the interval is larger than the increase.

----

[7] See Section 1.3 for further discussion of slope.

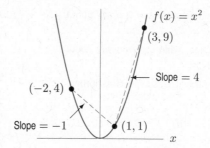

Figure 1.15: Average rate of change of $f(x)$ on an interval is the slope of the dashed line on that interval

Exercises and Problems for Section 1.2

Skill Refresher

In Exercises S1–S10, simplify each expression.

S1. $\dfrac{4-6}{3-2}$

S2. $\dfrac{1-3}{2^2-(-3)^2}$

S3. $\dfrac{-3-(-9)}{-1-2}$

S4. $\dfrac{(1-3^2)-(1-4^2)}{3-4}$

S5. $\dfrac{\left(\frac{1}{2}-(-4)^2\right)-\left(\frac{1}{2}-(5^2)\right)}{-4-5}$

S6. $2(x+a)-3(x-b)$

S7. $x^2-(2x+a)^2$

S8. $4x^2-(x-b)^2$

S9. $\dfrac{x^2-\frac{3}{4}-\left(y^2-\frac{3}{4}\right)}{x-y}$

S10. $\dfrac{2(x+h)^2-2x^2}{(x+h)-x}$

Exercises

1. In 2005, you have 40 CDs in your collection. In 2008, you have 120 CDs. In 2012, you have 40. What is the average rate of change in your CD collection's size between

(a) 2005 and 2008?   (b) 2008 and 2012?
(c) 2005 and 2012?

2. Table 1.10 on page 11 gives the annual sales (in millions) of VCRs and DVD players. What was the average rate of change of annual sales of each of them between

(a) 1998 and 2000?   (b) 2000 and 2003?
(c) Interpret these results in terms of sales.

3. Table 1.10 on page 11 shows that VCR sales are a function of DVD player sales. Is it an increasing or decreasing function?

4. Table 1.12 shows data for two populations (in hundreds) for five different years. Find the average rate of change of each population over the following intervals.

(a) 1990 to 2000   (b) 1995 to 2007
(c) 1990 to 2007

Table 1.12

Year	1990	1992	1995	2000	2007
P_1	53	63	73	83	93
P_2	85	80	75	70	65

Exercises 5–9 use Figure 1.16.

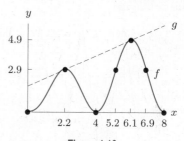

Figure 1.16

5. Find the average rate of change of f for $2.2 \le x \le 6.1$.

6. Give two different intervals on which $\Delta f(x)/\Delta x = 0$.

7. What is the average rate of change of g between $x = 2.2$ and $x = 6.1$?

8. What is the relation between the average rate of change of f and the average rate of change of g between $x = 2.2$ and $x = 6.1$?

9. Is the rate of change of f positive or negative on the following intervals?

(a) $2.2 \le x \le 4$ (b) $5 \le x \le 6$

10. If G is an increasing function, what can you say about $G(3) - G(-1)$?

11. If F is a decreasing function, what can you say about $F(-2)$ compared to $F(2)$?

12. Figure 1.17 shows distance traveled as a function of time.

   (a) Find ΔD and Δt between:

      (i) $t = 2$ and $t = 5$ (ii) $t = 0.5$ and $t = 2.5$
      (iii) $t = 1.5$ and $t = 3$

   (b) Compute the rate of change, $\Delta D/\Delta t$, over each of the intervals in part (a), and interpret its meaning.

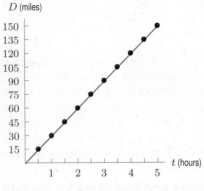

Figure 1.17

Problems

13. Figure 1.18 shows the percent of the side of the moon toward the earth illuminated by the sun at different times during the year 2008. Use the figure to answer the following questions.

   (a) Give the coordinates of the points A, B, C, D, E.
   (b) Plot the point $F = (15, 60)$ and $G = (60, 15)$. Which point is on the graph?
   (c) During which time intervals is the function increasing?
   (d) During which time intervals is the function decreasing?

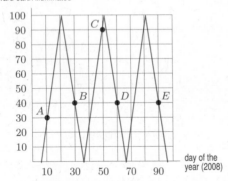

Figure 1.18: Moon phases

14. Imagine you constructed a list of the world record times for a particular event—such as the mile footrace, or the 100-meter freestyle swimming race—in terms of when they were established. Is the world record time a function of the date when it was established? If so, is this function increasing or decreasing? Explain. Could a world record be established twice in the same year? Is the world record time a function of the year it was established?

15. (a) What is the average rate of change of $g(x) = 2x - 3$ between the points $(-2, -7)$ and $(3, 3)$?
   (b) Based on your answer to part (a), is g increasing or decreasing on the given interval? Explain.
   (c) Graph the function and determine over what intervals g is increasing and over what intervals g is decreasing.

16. (a) Let $f(x) = 16 - x^2$. Compute each of the following expressions, and interpret each as an average rate of change.

      (i) $\dfrac{f(2) - f(0)}{2 - 0}$ (ii) $\dfrac{f(4) - f(2)}{4 - 2}$
      (iii) $\dfrac{f(4) - f(0)}{4 - 0}$

   (b) Graph $f(x)$. Illustrate each ratio in part (a) by sketching the line segment with the given slope. Over which interval is the average rate of decrease the greatest?

17. Figure 1.19 gives the population of two different towns over a 50-year period of time.

   (a) Which town starts (in year $t = 0$) with the most people?
   (b) Which town is growing faster over these 50 years?

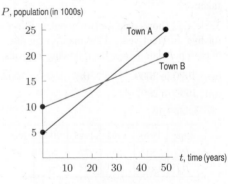

Figure 1.19

18. You have zero dollars now and the average rate of change in your net worth is $5000 per year. How much money will you have in forty years?

19. The most freakish change in temperature ever recorded was from $-4°F$ to $45°F$ between 7:30 am and 7:32 am on January 22, 1943 at Spearfish, South Dakota.[8] What was the average rate of change of the temperature for this time period?

20. The surface of the sun has dark areas known as sunspots, that are cooler than the rest of the sun's surface. The number of sunspots fluctuates with time, as shown in Figure 1.20. [9]

   (a) Explain how you know the number of sunspots, s, in year t is a function of t.

   (b) Approximate the time intervals on which s is an increasing function of t.

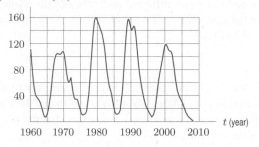

Figure 1.20

21. Table 1.13 shows the number of calories used per minute as a function of body weight for three sports.[10]

   (a) Determine the number of calories that a 200-lb person uses in one half-hour of walking.

   (b) Who uses more calories, a 120-lb person swimming for one hour or a 220-lb person bicycling for a half-hour?

   (c) Does the number of calories used by a person walking increase or decrease as weight increases?

Table 1.13

Activity	100 lb	120 lb	150 lb	170 lb	200 lb	220 lb
Walking	2.7	3.2	4.0	4.6	5.4	5.9
Bicycling	5.4	6.5	8.1	9.2	10.8	11.9
Swimming	5.8	6.9	8.7	9.8	11.6	12.7

22. Because scientists know how much carbon-14 a living organism should have in its tissues, they can measure the amount of carbon-14 present in the tissue of a fossil and then calculate how long it took for the original amount to decay to the current level, thus determining the time of the organism's death. A tree fossil is found to contain 130 μg of carbon-14, and scientists determine from the size of the tree that it would have contained 200 μg of carbon-14 at the time of its death. Using Table 1.11 on page 12, approximately how long ago did the tree die?

23. Find the average rate of change of $f(x) = 3x^2 + 1$ between the points

   (a) $(1, 4)$ and $(2, 13)$ **(b)** (j, k) and (m, n)

   (c) $(x, f(x))$ and $(x+h, f(x+h))$

24. Figure 1.21 shows the graph of the function $g(x)$.

   (a) Estimate $\dfrac{g(4) - g(0)}{4 - 0}$.

   (b) The ratio in part (a) is the slope of a line segment joining two points on the graph. Sketch this line segment on the graph.

   (c) Estimate $\dfrac{g(b) - g(a)}{b - a}$ for $a = -9$ and $b = -1$.

   (d) On the graph, sketch the line segment whose slope is given by the ratio in part (c).

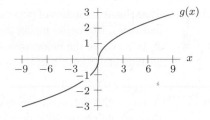

Figure 1.21

25. Table 1.14 gives the amount of garbage, G, in millions of tons, produced[11] in the US in year t.

   (a) What is the value of Δt for consecutive entries in this table?

   (b) Calculate the value of ΔG for each pair of consecutive entries in this table.

   (c) Are all the values of ΔG you found in part (b) the same? What does this tell you?

   (d) The function G changed from increasing to decreasing between 2007 and 2008. To what might this be attributed?

Table 1.14

t	1960	1970	1980	1990	2000	2007	2008
G	88.1	121.1	151.6	205.2	239.1	254.6	249.6

---

[8] *The Guinness Book of Records.* 1995.

[9] ftp://ftp.ngdc.noaa.gov/STP/SOLAR DATA/SUNSPOT NUMBERS/YEARLY.PLT, accessed November 30, 2009.

[10] From *1993 World Almanac.*

[11] http://www.epa.gov/osw/nonhaz/municipal/pubs/msw2008rpt.pdf, accessed November 23, 2009.

26. Table 1.15 shows the times, t, in sec, achieved every 10 meters by Carl Lewis in the 100-meter final of the World Championship in Rome in 1987.[12] Distance, d, is in meters.

(a) For each successive time interval, calculate the average rate of change of distance. What is a common name for the average rate of change of distance?

(b) Where did Carl Lewis attain his maximum speed during this race? Some runners are running their fastest as they cross the finish line. Does that seem to be true in this case?

Table 1.15

t	0.00	1.94	2.96	3.91	4.78	5.64
d	0	10	20	30	40	50

t	6.50	7.36	8.22	9.07	9.93	
d	60	70	80	90	100	

1.3 LINEAR FUNCTIONS

Constant Rate of Change

In the previous section, we introduced the average rate of change of a function on an interval. For many functions, the average rate of change is different on different intervals. For the remainder of this chapter, we consider functions that have the same average rate of change on every interval. Such a function has a graph that is a line and is called *linear*.

Population Growth

Mathematical models of population growth are used by city planners to project the growth of towns and states. Biologists model the growth of animal populations and physicians model the spread of an infection in the bloodstream. One possible model, a linear model, assumes that the population changes at the same average rate on every time interval.

Example 1   A town of 30,000 people grows by 2000 people every year. Since the population, P, is growing at the constant rate of 2000 people per year, P is a linear function of time, t, in years.

(a) What is the average rate of change of P over every time interval?

(b) Make a table that gives the town's population every five years over a 20-year period. Graph the population.

(c) Find a formula for P as a function of t.

Solution   (a) The average rate of change of population with respect to time is 2000 people per year.

(b) The initial population in year $t = 0$ is $P = 30,000$ people. Since the town grows by 2000 people every year, after five years it has grown by

$$\frac{2000 \text{ people}}{\text{year}} \cdot 5 \text{ years} = 10,000 \text{ people.}$$

Thus, in year $t = 5$ the population is given by

$$P = \text{Initial population} + \text{New population} = 30,000 + 10,000 = 40,000.$$

In year $t = 10$ the population is given by

$$P = 30,000 + \underbrace{2000 \text{ people/year} \cdot 10 \text{ years}}_{20,000 \text{ new people}} = 50,000.$$

---

[12]W. G. Pritchard, "Mathematical Models of Running", *SIAM Review.* 35, 1993, pp. 359–379.

Similar calculations for year $t = 15$ and year $t = 20$ give the values in Table 1.16. See Figure 1.22; the dashed line shows the trend in the data.

Table 1.16 *Population over 20 years*

t, years	P, population
0	30,000
5	40,000
10	50,000
15	60,000
20	70,000

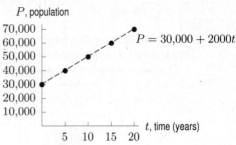

Figure 1.22: Town's population over 20 years

(c) From part (b), we see that the size of the population is given by

$$P = \text{Initial population} + \text{Number of new people}$$
$$= 30,000 + 2000 \text{ people/year} \cdot \text{Number of years},$$

so a formula for P in terms of t is

$$P = 30,000 + 2000t.$$

The graph of the population data in Figure 1.22 is a straight line. The average rate of change of the population over every interval is the same, namely 2000 people per year. Any linear function has the same average rate of change over every interval. Thus, we talk about *the* rate of change of a linear function. In general:

- A **linear function** has a constant rate of change.
- The graph of any linear function is a straight line.

Financial Models

Economists and accountants use linear functions for *straight-line depreciation*. For tax purposes, the value of certain equipment is considered to decrease, or depreciate, over time. For example, computer equipment may be state-of-the-art today, but after several years it is outdated. Straight-line depreciation assumes that the rate of change of value with respect to time is constant.

Example 2   A small business spends $20,000 on new computer equipment and, for tax purposes, chooses to depreciate it to $0 at a constant rate over a five-year period.

(a) Make a table and a graph showing the value of the equipment over the five-year period.

(b) Give a formula for value as a function of time.

Solution   (a) After five years, the equipment is valued at $0. If V is the value in dollars and t is the number of years, we see that

$$\begin{array}{l} \text{Rate of change of value} \\ \text{from } t = 0 \text{ to } t = 5 \end{array} = \frac{\text{Change in value}}{\text{Change in time}} = \frac{\Delta V}{\Delta t} = \frac{-\$20,000}{5 \text{ years}} = -\$4000 \text{ per year.}$$

Thus, the value drops at the constant rate of $4000 per year. (Notice that ΔV is negative because the value of the equipment decreases.) See Table 1.17 and Figure 1.23. Since V changes at a constant rate, $V = f(t)$ is a linear function and its graph is a straight line. The rate of change, $-\$4000$ per year, is negative because the function is decreasing and the graph slopes down.

Table 1.17   *Value of equipment depreciated over a 5-year period*

t, year	V, value (\$)
0	20,000
1	16,000
2	12,000
3	8,000
4	4,000
5	0

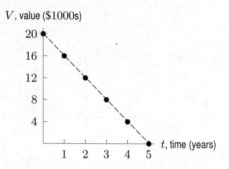

Figure 1.23: Value of equipment depreciated over a 5-year period

(b) After t years have elapsed,

$$\text{Decrease in value of equipment} = \$4000 \cdot \text{Number of years} = \$4000t.$$

The initial value of the equipment is $\$20,000$, so at time t,

$$V = 20,000 - 4000t.$$

The total cost of production is another application of linear functions in economics.

A General Formula for the Family of Linear Functions

Example 1 involved a town whose population is growing at a constant rate with formula

$$\underbrace{\text{Current}}_{\text{population}} = \underbrace{\text{Initial population}}_{\text{30,000 people}} + \underbrace{\text{Growth rate}}_{\text{2000 people per year}} \times \underbrace{\text{Number of years}}_{t}$$

so

$$P = 30,000 + 2000t.$$

In Example 2, the value, V, as a function of t is given by

$$\underbrace{\text{Total cost}} = \underbrace{\text{Initial value}}_{\$20,000} + \underbrace{\text{Change per year}}_{-\$4000 \text{ per year}} \times \underbrace{\text{Number of years}}_{t}$$

so

$$V = 20,000 + (-4000)t.$$

Using the symbols x, y, b, m, we see formulas for both of these linear functions follow the same pattern:

$$\underbrace{\text{Output}}_{y} = \underbrace{\text{Initial value}}_{b} + \underbrace{\text{Rate of change}}_{m} \times \underbrace{\text{Input}}_{x}.$$

Summarizing, we get the following results:

If $y = f(x)$ is a linear function, then for some constants b and m:

$$y = b + mx.$$

- m is called the **slope**, and gives the rate of change of y with respect to x. Thus,

$$m = \frac{\Delta y}{\Delta x}.$$

If (x_0, y_0) and (x_1, y_1) are any two distinct points on the graph of f, then

$$m = \frac{\Delta y}{\Delta x} = \frac{y_1 - y_0}{x_1 - x_0}.$$

- b is called the **vertical intercept**, or **y-intercept**, and gives the value of y for $x = 0$. In mathematical models, b typically represents an initial, or starting, value of the output.

Every linear function can be written in the form $y = b + mx$. Different linear functions have different values for m and b. These constants are known as *parameters*.

Example 3   In Example 1, the population function, $P = 30{,}000 + 2000t$, has slope $m = 2000$ and vertical intercept $b = 30{,}000$. In Example 2, the value of the computer equipment, $V = 20{,}000 - 4000t$, has slope $m = -4000$ and vertical intercept $b = 20{,}000$.

Tables for Linear Functions

A table of values could represent a linear function if the rate of change is constant, for all pairs of points in the table; that is,

$$\text{Rate of change of linear function} = \frac{\text{Change in output}}{\text{Change in input}} = \text{Constant}.$$

Thus, if the value of x goes up by equal steps in a table for a linear function, then the value of y goes up (or down) by equal steps as well. We say that changes in the value of y are *proportional* to changes in the value of x.

Example 4   Table 1.18 gives values of two functions, p and q. Could either of these functions be linear?

Table 1.18   *Values of two functions p and q*

x	50	55	60	65	70
$p(x)$	0.10	0.11	0.12	0.13	0.14
$q(x)$	0.01	0.03	0.06	0.14	0.15

Solution   The value of x goes up by equal steps of $\Delta x = 5$. The value of $p(x)$ also goes up by equal steps of $\Delta p = 0.01$, so $\Delta p / \Delta x$ is a constant. See Table 1.19. Thus, p could be a linear function.

Table 1.19   *Values of $\Delta p / \Delta x$*

x	$p(x)$	Δp	$\Delta p / \Delta x$
50	0.10		
		0.01	0.002
55	0.11		
		0.01	0.002
60	0.12		
		0.01	0.002
65	0.13		
		0.01	0.002
70	0.14		

Table 1.20   *Values of $\Delta q / \Delta x$*

x	$q(x)$	Δq	$\Delta q / \Delta x$
50	0.01		
		0.02	0.004
55	0.03		
		0.03	0.006
60	0.06		
		0.08	0.016
65	0.14		
		0.01	0.002
70	0.15		

In contrast, the value of $q(x)$ does not go up by equal steps. The value climbs by 0.02, then by 0.03, and so on. See Table 1.20. This means that $\Delta q / \Delta x$ is not constant. Thus, q could not be a linear function.

It is possible to have data from a linear function in which neither the x-values nor the y-values go up by equal steps. However the rate of change must be constant, as in the following example.

Example 5   The former Republic of Yugoslavia exported cars called Yugos to the US between 1985 and 1989. The car is now a collector's item.[13] Table 1.21 gives the quantity of Yugos sold, Q, and the price, p, for each year from 1985 to 1988.

(a) Using Table 1.21, explain why Q could be a linear function of p.
(b) What does the rate of change of this function tell you about Yugos?

Table 1.21   *Price and sales of Yugos in the US*

Year	Price in $, p	Number sold, Q
1985	3990	49,000
1986	4110	43,000
1987	4200	38,500
1988	4330	32,000

Solution   (a) We are interested in Q as a function of p, so we plot Q on the vertical axis and p on the horizontal axis. The data points in Figure 1.24 appear to lie on a straight line, suggesting a linear function.

---

[13] www.inet.hr/~pauric/epov.htm, accessed January 16, 2006.

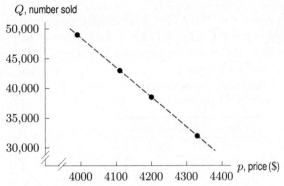

Figure 1.24: Since the data from Table 1.21 falls on a straight line, the table could represent a linear function

To provide further evidence that Q is a linear function, we check that the rate of change of Q with respect to p is constant for the points given. When the price of a Yugo rose from \$3990 to \$4110, sales fell from 49,000 to 43,000. Thus,

$$\Delta p = 4110 - 3990 = 120,$$

$$\Delta Q = 43{,}000 - 49{,}000 = -6000.$$

Since the number of Yugos sold decreased, ΔQ is negative. Thus, as the price increased from \$3990 to \$4110,

$$\text{Rate of change of quantity as price increases} = \frac{\Delta Q}{\Delta p} = \frac{-6000}{120} = -50 \text{ cars per dollar.}$$

Next, we calculate the rate of change as the price increased from \$4110 to \$4200 to see if the rate remains constant:

$$\text{Rate of change} = \frac{\Delta Q}{\Delta p} = \frac{38{,}500 - 43{,}000}{4200 - 4110} = \frac{-4500}{90} = -50 \text{ cars per dollar,}$$

and as the price increased from \$4200 to \$4330:

$$\text{Rate of change} = \frac{\Delta Q}{\Delta p} = \frac{32{,}000 - 38{,}500}{4330 - 4200} = \frac{-6500}{130} = -50 \text{ cars per dollar.}$$

Since the rate of change, -50, is constant, Q could be a linear function of p. Given additional data, $\Delta Q / \Delta p$ might not remain constant. However, based on the table, it appears that the function is linear.

(b) Since ΔQ is the change in the number of cars sold and Δp is the change in price, the rate of change is -50 cars per dollar. Thus the number of Yugos sold decreased by 50 each time the price increased by \$1.

Warning: Not All Graphs That Look Like Lines Represent Linear Functions

The graph of any linear function is a line. However, a function's graph can look like a line without actually being one. Consider the following example.

Example 6   The function $P = 100(1.02)^t$ approximates the population of Mexico in the early 2000s. Here P is the population (in millions) and t is the number of years since 2000. Table 1.22 and Figure 1.25 show values of P over a 5-year period. Is P a linear function of t?

Table 1.22 *Population of Mexico t years after 2000*

t (years)	P (millions)
0	100
1	102
2	104.04
3	106.12
4	108.24
5	110.41

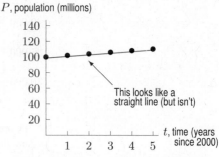

Figure 1.25: Graph of $P = 100(1.02)^t$ over 5-year period: Looks linear (but is not)

Solution   The formula $P = 100(1.02)^t$ is not of the form $P = b + mt$, so P is not a linear function of t. However, the graph of P in Figure 1.25 appears to be a straight line. We check P's rate of change in Table 1.22. When $t = 0$, $P = 100$ and when $t = 1$, $P = 102$. Thus, between 2000 and 2001,

$$\text{Rate of change of population} = \frac{\Delta P}{\Delta t} = \frac{102 - 100}{1 - 0} = 2.$$

For the interval from 2001 to 2002, we have

$$\text{Rate of change} = \frac{\Delta P}{\Delta t} = \frac{104.04 - 102}{2 - 1} = 2.04,$$

and for the interval from 2004 to 2005, we have

$$\text{Rate of change} = \frac{\Delta P}{\Delta t} = \frac{110.41 - 108.24}{5 - 4} = 2.17.$$

Thus, P's rate of change is not constant. In fact, P appears to be increasing at a faster and faster rate. Table 1.23 and Figure 1.26 show values of P over a longer (60-year) period. On this scale, these points do not appear to fall on a straight line. However, the graph of P curves upward so gradually at first that over the short interval shown in Figure 1.25, it barely curves at all. The graphs of many nonlinear functions, when viewed on a small scale, appear to be linear.

Table 1.23 *Population over 60 years*

t (years since 2000)	P (millions)
0	100
10	121.90
20	148.59
30	181.14
40	220.80
50	269.16
60	328.10

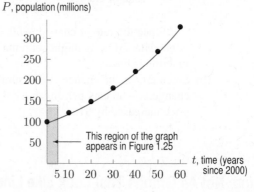

Figure 1.26: Graph of $P = 100(1.02)^t$ over 60 years: Not linear

Exercises and Problems for Section 1.3

Skill Refresher

In Exercises S1–S2, find $f(0)$ and $f(3)$.

S1. $f(x) = \frac{2}{3}x + 5$

S2. $f(t) = 17 - 4t$

In Exercises S3–S4, find $f(2) - f(0)$.

S3.

x	0	1	2	3
$f(x)$	-2	0	3	4

S4.

t	-1	0	1	2
$f(t)$	0	2	7	-1

In Exercises S5–S6, find the coordinates of the x and y intercepts.

S5. $y = -4x + 3$ **S6.** $5x - 2y = 4$

For each of the linear expressions in x in Exercises S7–S10, give the constant term and the coefficient of x.

S7. $3 - 2x + \frac{1}{2}$

S8. $4 - 3(x + 2) + 6(2x - 1)$

S9. $ax - ab - 3x + a + 3$

S10. $5(x - 1) + 3$

Exercises

Which of the tables in Exercises 1–6 could represent a linear function?

1.

x	0	100	300	600
$g(x)$	50	100	150	200

2.

x	0	10	20	30
$h(x)$	20	40	50	55

3.

t	1	2	3	4	5
$g(t)$	5	4	5	4	5

4.

x	0	5	10	15
$f(x)$	10	20	30	40

5.

γ	9	8	7	6	5
$p(\gamma)$	42	52	62	72	82

6.

x	-3	-1	0	3
$j(x)$	5	1	-1	-7

In Exercises 7–8, which line has the greater

(a) Slope?   (b) y-intercept?

7. $y = 7 + 2x$, $y = 8 - 15x$

8. $y = 5 - 2x$, $y = 7 - 3x$

In Exercises 9–12, identify the vertical intercept and the slope, and explain their meanings in practical terms.

9. The population of a town can be represented by the formula $P(t) = 54.25 - \frac{2}{7}t$, where $P(t)$ represents the population, in thousands, and t represents the time, in years, since 1970.

10. A stalactite grows according to the formula $L(t) = 17.75 + \frac{1}{250}t$, where $L(t)$ represents the length of the stalactite, in inches, and t represents the time, in years, since the stalactite was first measured.

11. The profit, in dollars, of selling n items is given by $P(n) = 0.98n - 3000$.

12. A phone company charges according to the formula $C(n) = 29.99 + 0.05n$, where n is the number of minutes, and $C(n)$ is the monthly phone charge, in dollars.

Problems

13. Table 1.24 gives the proposed fine $r = f(v)$ to be imposed on a motorist for speeding, where v is the motorist's speed and 55 mph is the speed limit.

    (a) Decide whether f appears to be linear.
    (b) What would the rate of change represent in practical terms for the motorist?
    (c) Plot the data points.

    Table 1.24

v (mph)	60	65	70	75	80	85
r (dollars)	75	100	125	150	175	200

14. In 2006, the population of a town was 18,310 and growing by 58 people per year. Find a formula for P, the town's population, in terms of t, the number of years since 2006.

15. A new Toyota RAV4 costs $21,500. The car's value depreciates linearly to $11,900 in three years time. Write a formula which expresses its value, V, in terms of its age, t, in years.

16. In 2003, the number, N, of cases of SARS (Severe Acute Respiratory Syndrome) reported in Hong Kong[14] was initially approximated by $N = 78.9 + 30.1t$, where t is the number of days since March 17. Interpret the constants 78.9 and 30.1.

17. Table 1.25 shows the cost C, in dollars, of selling x cups of coffee per day from a cart.

   (a) Using the table, show that the relationship appears to be linear.

   (b) Plot the data in the table.

   (c) Find the slope of the line. Explain what this means in the context of the given situation.

   (d) Why should it cost $50 to serve zero cups of coffee?

Table 1.25

x	0	5	10	50	100	200
C	50.00	51.25	52.50	62.50	75.00	100.00

18. In each case, graph a linear function with the given rate of change. Label and put scales on the axes.

   (a) Increasing at 2.1 inches/day

   (b) Decreasing at 1.3 gallons/mile

19. A flight costs $10,000 to operate, regardless of the number of passengers. Each ticket costs $127. Express profit, π, as a linear function of the number of passengers, n, on the flight.

20. A small café sells drip coffee for $0.95 per cup. On average, it costs the café $0.25 to make a cup of coffee (for grounds, hot water, filters). The café also has a fixed daily cost of $200 (for rent, wages, utilities).

   (a) Let R, C, and P be the café's daily revenue, costs, and profit, respectively, for selling x cups of coffee in a day. Find formulas for R, C, and P as functions of x. [Hint: The revenue, R, is the total amount of money that the café brings in. The cost, C, includes the fixed daily cost as well as the cost for all x cups of coffee sold. P is the café's profit after costs have been accounted for.]

   (b) Plot P against x. For what x-values is the graph of P below the x-axis? Above the x-axis? Interpret your results.

   (c) Interpret the slope and both intercepts of your graph in practical terms.

21. Owners of an inactive quarry in Australia have decided to resume production. They estimate that it will cost them $1000 per month to maintain and insure their equipment and that monthly salaries will be $3000. It costs $80 to mine a ton of rocks. Write a formula that expresses the total cost each month, c, as a function of r, the number of tons of rock mined per month.

22. Table 1.26 gives the area and perimeter of a square as a function of the length of its side.

   (a) From the table, decide if either area or perimeter could be a linear function of side length.

   (b) From the data make two graphs, one showing area as a function of side length, the other showing perimeter as a function of side length. Connect the points.

   (c) If you find a linear relationship, give its corresponding rate of change and interpret its significance.

Table 1.26

Length of side	0	1	2	3	4	5	6
Area of square	0	1	4	9	16	25	36
Perimeter of square	0	4	8	12	16	20	24

23. Make two tables, one comparing the radius of a circle to its area, the other comparing the radius of a circle to its circumference. Repeat parts (a), (b), and (c) from Problem 22, this time comparing radius with circumference, and radius with area.

24. Sri Lanka is an island that experienced approximately linear population growth from 1950 to 2000. On the other hand, Afghanistan was torn by warfare in the 1980s and did not experience linear nor near-linear growth.[15]

   (a) Table 1.27 gives the population of these two countries, in millions. Which of these two countries is A and which is B? Explain.

   (b) What is the approximate rate of change of the linear function? What does the rate of change represent in practical terms?

   (c) Estimate the population of Sri Lanka in 1988.

Table 1.27

Year	1950	1960	1970	1980	1990	2000
Population of country A	8.2	9.8	12.4	15.1	14.7	23.9
Population of country B	7.5	9.9	12.5	14.9	17.2	19.2

---

[14]World Health Organization, www.who.int/csr/sars/country/en.

[15]www.census.gov/ipc/www/idbsusum.html, accessed January 12, 2006.

25. Table 1.44 on page 54 gives the temperature-depth profile, $T = f(d)$, in a borehole in Belleterre, Quebec, where T is the average temperature at a depth d.

   (a) Could f be linear?
   (b) Graph f. What do you notice about the graph for $d \geq 150$?
   (c) What can you say about the average rate of change of f for $d \geq 150$?

26. The summit of Africa's largest peak, Mt. Kilimanjaro, consists of the northern and southern ice fields and the Furtwanger glacier. An article in the Proceedings of the National Academy of Sciences[16] indicates that in 2000 ($t = 0$) the area of the ice cover at the peak of Mt. Kilimanjaro was approximately 1951 m². By 2007, the area had shrunk to approximately 1555 m².

   (a) If this decline is modeled by a linear function, find $A = f(t)$, the equation of the ice-cover area as a function of time. Explain what the slope and A-intercept mean in terms of the ice cover.
   (b) Evaluate $f(11)$.
   (c) If this model is correct, when would you expect the ice cover to disappear?

27. Tuition cost T (in dollars) for part-time students at Stonewall College is given by $T = 300 + 200C$, where C represents the number of credits taken.

   (a) Find the tuition cost for eight credits.
   (b) How many credits were taken if the tuition was $1700?
   (c) Make a table showing costs for taking from one to twelve credits. For each value of C, give both the tuition cost, T, and the cost per credit, T/C. Round to the nearest dollar.
   (d) Which of these values of C has the smallest cost per credit?
   (e) What does the 300 represent in the formula for T?
   (f) What does the 200 represent in the formula for T?

28. A company finds that there is a linear relationship between the amount of money that it spends on advertising and the number of units it sells. If it spends no money on advertising, it sells 300 units. For each additional $5000 spent, an additional 20 units are sold.

   (a) If x is the amount of money that the company spends on advertising, find a formula for y, the number of units sold as a function of x.
   (b) How many units does the firm sell if it spends $25,000 on advertising? $50,000?

   (c) How much advertising money must be spent to sell 700 units?
   (d) What is the slope of the line you found in part (a)? Give an interpretation of the slope that relates units sold and advertising costs.

29. When each of the following equations are written in the form $y = b + mx$, the result is $y = 5 + 4x$. Find the constants r, s, k, j in these equations.

   (a) $y = 2r + x\sqrt{s}$
   (b) $y = \dfrac{1}{k} - (j - 1)x$.

30. Graph the following function in the window $-10 \leq x \leq 10, -10 \leq y \leq 10$. Is this graph a line? Explain.

$$y = -x\left(\frac{x - 1000}{900}\right)$$

31. Graph $y = 2x + 400$ using the window $-10 \leq x \leq 10, -10 \leq y \leq 10$. Describe what happens, and how you can fix it by using a better window.

32. Graph $y = 200x + 4$ using the window $-10 \leq x \leq 10, -10 \leq y \leq 10$. Describe what happens and how you can fix it by using a better window.

33. Figure 1.27 shows the graph of $y = x^2/1000 + 5$ in the window $-10 \leq x \leq 10, -10 \leq y \leq 10$. Discuss whether this is a linear function.

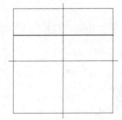

Figure 1.27

34. The cost of a cab ride is given by the function $C = 2.50 + 2d$, where d is the number of miles traveled and C is in dollars. Choose an appropriate window and graph the cost of a ride for a cab that travels no farther than a 10-mile radius from the center of the city.

---

[16]http://www.pnas.org/content/early/2009/10/30/0906029106.full.pdf+html, accessed November 27, 2009.

1.4 FORMULAS FOR LINEAR FUNCTIONS

To find a formula for a linear function we find values for the slope, m, and the vertical intercept, b, in the formula $y = b + mx$.

Finding a Formula for a Linear Function from a Table of Data

If a table of data represents a linear function, we first calculate m and then determine b.

Example 1   A grapefruit is thrown into the air. Its velocity, v, is a linear function of t, the time since it was thrown. A positive velocity indicates the grapefruit is rising and a negative velocity indicates it is falling. Check that the data in Table 1.28 corresponds to a linear function. Find a formula for v in terms of t.

Table 1.28 *Velocity of a grapefruit t seconds after being thrown into the air*

t, time (sec)	1	2	3	4
v, velocity (ft/sec)	48	16	−16	−48

Solution   Figure 1.28 shows the data in Table 1.28. The points appear to fall on a line. To check that the velocity function is linear, calculate the rates of change of v and see that they are constant. From time $t = 1$ to $t = 2$, we have

$$\text{Rate of change of velocity with time} = \frac{\Delta v}{\Delta t} = \frac{16 - 48}{2 - 1} = -32.$$

For the next second, from $t = 2$ to $t = 3$, we have

$$\text{Rate of change} = \frac{\Delta v}{\Delta t} = \frac{-16 - 16}{3 - 2} = -32.$$

You can check that the rate of change from $t = 3$ to $t = 4$ is also -32.

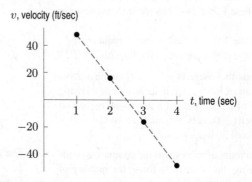

Figure 1.28: Velocity of a grapefruit is a linear function of time

A formula for v is of the form $v = b + mt$. Since m is the rate of change, we have $m = -32$ so $v = b - 32t$. The initial velocity (at $t = 0$) is represented by b. We are not given the value of v when $t = 0$, but we can use any data point to calculate b. For example, $v = 48$ when $t = 1$, so

$$48 = b - 32 \cdot 1,$$

which gives
$$b = 80.$$
Thus, a formula for the velocity is $v = 80 - 32t$.

What does the rate of change, m, in Example 1 tell us about the grapefruit? Think about the units:
$$m = \frac{\Delta v}{\Delta t} = \frac{\text{Change in velocity}}{\text{Change in time}} = \frac{-32 \text{ ft/sec}}{1 \text{ sec}} = -32 \text{ ft/sec per second.}$$
The value of m, -32 ft/sec per second, tells us that the grapefruit's velocity is decreasing by 32 ft/sec for every second that goes by. We say the grapefruit is accelerating at -32 ft/sec per second. (The units ft/sec per second are often written ft/sec^2. Negative acceleration is also called deceleration.)[17]

Finding a Formula for a Linear Function from a Graph

We can calculate the slope, m, of a linear function using two points on its graph. Having found m, we can use either of the points to calculate b, the vertical intercept.

Example 2   Figure 1.29 shows oxygen consumption as a function of heart rate for two people.

(a) Assuming linearity, find formulas for these two functions.
(b) Interpret the slope of each graph in terms of oxygen consumption.

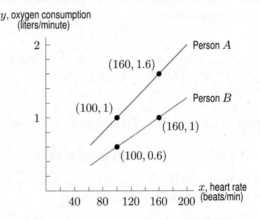

Figure 1.29: Oxygen consumption of two people running on treadmills

Solution   (a) Let x be heart rate and let y be oxygen consumption. Since we are assuming linearity, $y = b + mx$. The two points on person A's line, $(100, 1)$ and $(160, 1.6)$, give
$$\text{Slope of A's line} = m = \frac{\Delta y}{\Delta x} = \frac{1.6 - 1}{160 - 100} = 0.01.$$
Thus $y = b + 0.01x$. To find b, use the fact that $y = 1$ when $x = 100$:
$$1 = b + 0.01(100)$$
$$1 = b + 1$$
$$b = 0.$$

---

[17]The notation ft/sec^2 is shorthand for ft/sec per second; it does not mean a "square second" in the same way that areas are measured square feet or square meters.

Alternatively, b can be found using the fact that $x = 160$ if $y = 1.6$. Either way leads to the formula $y = 0.01x$.

For person B, we again begin with the formula $y = b + mx$. In Figure 1.29, two points on B's line are $(100, 0.6)$ and $(160, 1)$, so

$$\text{Slope of B's line} = m = \frac{\Delta y}{\Delta x} = \frac{1 - 0.6}{160 - 100} = \frac{0.4}{60} \approx 0.0067.$$

To find b, use the fact that $y = 1$ when $x = 160$:

$$1 = b + (0.4/60) \cdot 160$$
$$1 = b + 1.067$$
$$b = -0.067.$$

Thus, for person B, we have $y = -0.067 + 0.0067x$.

(b) The slope for person A is $m = 0.01$, so

$$m = \frac{\text{Change in oxygen consumption}}{\text{Change in heart rate}} = \frac{\text{Change in liters/min}}{\text{Change in beats/min}} = 0.01 \frac{\text{liters}}{\text{heartbeat}}.$$

Every additional heartbeat (per minute) for person A translates to an additional 0.01 liters (per minute) of oxygen consumed.

The slope for person B is $m = 0.0067$. Thus, for every additional beat (per minute), person B consumes an additional 0.0067 liter of oxygen (per minute). Since the slope for person B is smaller than for person A, person B consumes less additional oxygen than person A for the same increase in pulse.

What do the y-intercepts of the functions in Example 2 say about oxygen consumption? Often the y-intercept of a function is a starting value. In this case, the y-intercept would be the oxygen consumption of a person whose pulse is zero (i.e. $x = 0$). Since a person running on a treadmill must have a pulse, in this case it makes no sense to interpret the y-intercept this way. The formula for oxygen consumption is useful only for realistic values of the pulse.

Finding a Formula for a Linear Function from a Verbal Description

Sometimes the verbal description of a linear function is less straightforward than those we saw in Section 1.3. Consider the following example.

Example 3   We have \$24 to spend on soda and chips for a party. A six-pack of soda costs \$3 and a bag of chips costs \$2. The number of six-packs we can afford, y, is a function of the number of bags of chips we decide to buy, x.

(a) Find an equation relating x and y.

(b) Graph the equation. Interpret the intercepts and the slope in the context of the party.

Solution   (a) If we spend all \$24 on soda and chips, then we have the following equation:

$$\text{Amount spent on chips} + \text{Amount spent on soda} = \$24.$$

If we buy x bags of chips at \$2 per bag, then the amount spent on chips is \$2x. Similarly, if we buy y six-packs of soda at \$3 per six-pack, then the amount spent on soda is \$3y. Thus,

$$2x + 3y = 24.$$

We can solve for y, giving

$$3y = 24 - 2x$$
$$y = 8 - \frac{2}{3}x.$$

This is a linear function with slope $m = -2/3$ and y-intercept $b = 8$.

(b) The graph of this function is a discrete set of points, since the number of bags of chips and the number of six-packs of soda must be (nonnegative) integers.

To find the y-intercept, we set $x = 0$, giving

$$2 \cdot 0 + 3y = 24.$$

So $3y = 24$, giving $y = 8$.

Substituting $y = 0$ gives the x-intercept,

$$2x + 3 \cdot 0 = 24.$$

So $2x = 24$, giving $x = 12$. Thus the points $(0, 8)$ and $(12, 0)$ are on the graph.

The point $(0, 8)$ indicates that we can buy 8 six-packs of soda if we buy no chips. The point $(12, 0)$ indicates that we can buy 12 bags of chips if we buy no soda. The other points on the line describe affordable options between these two extremes. For example, the point $(6, 4)$ is on the line, because

$$2 \cdot 6 + 3 \cdot 4 = 24.$$

This means that if we buy 6 bags of chips, we can afford 4 six-packs of soda.

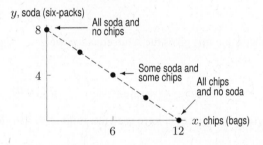

Figure 1.30: Relation between the number of six-packs, y, and the number of bags of chips, x

The points marked in Figure 1.30 represent affordable options. All affordable options lie on or below the line $2x + 3y = 24$. Not all points on the line are affordable options. For example, suppose we purchase one six-pack of soda for \$3.00. That leaves \$21.00 to spend on chips, meaning we would have to buy 10.5 bags of chips, which is not possible. Therefore, the point $(10.5, 1)$ is not an option, although it is a point on the line $2x + 3y = 24$.

To interpret the slope, notice that

$$m = \frac{\Delta y}{\Delta x} = \frac{\text{Change in number of six-packs}}{\text{Change in number of bags of chips}},$$

so the units of m are six-packs of soda per bags of chips. The fact that $m = -2/3$ means that for each additional 3 bags of chips purchased, we can purchase 2 fewer six-packs of soda. This occurs because 2 six-packs cost \$6, the same as 3 bags of chips. Thus, $m = -2/3$ is the rate at which the amount of soda we can buy decreases as we buy more chips.

Alternative Forms for the Equation of a Line

In Example 3, the equation $2x + 3y = 24$ represents a linear relationship between x and y even though the equation is not in the form $y = b + mx$. The following equations represent lines.

- The *slope-intercept form* is
$$y = b + mx \qquad \text{where } m \text{ is the slope and } b \text{ is the } y\text{-intercept.}$$
- The *point-slope form* is
$$y - y_0 = m(x - x_0) \quad \text{where } m \text{ is the slope and } (x_0, y_0) \text{ is a point on the line.}$$
- The *standard form* is
$$Ax + By + C = 0 \qquad \text{where } A, B, \text{ and } C \text{ are constants.}$$

If we know the slope of a line and the coordinates of a point on the line, it is often convenient to use the point-slope form of the equation.

Example 4   Use the point-slope form to find the equation of the line for the oxygen consumption of person A in Example 2.

Solution   In Example 2, we found the slope of person A's line to be $m = 0.01$. Since the point $(100, 1)$ lies on the line, the point-slope form gives the equation

$$y - 1 = 0.01(x - 100).$$

To check that this gives the same equation we got in Example 2, we multiply out and simplify:

$$y - 1 = 0.01x - 1$$
$$y = 0.01x.$$

Alternatively, we could have used the point $(160, 1.6)$ instead of $(100, 1)$, giving

$$y - 1.6 = 0.01(x - 160).$$

Multiplying out again gives $y = 0.01x$.

Exercises and Problems for Section 1.4

Skill Refresher

Solve the equations in Exercises S1–S5.

S1. $y - 5 = 21$

S2. $2x - 5 = 13$

S3. $2x - 5 = 4x - 9$

S4. $17 - 28y = 13y + 24$

S5. $\dfrac{5}{3}(y + 2) = \dfrac{1}{2} - y$

In Exercises S6–S10, solve for the indicated variable.

S6. $I = Prt$, for P.

S7. $C = \dfrac{5}{9}(F - 32)$, for F.

S8. $C = 2\pi r$, for r.

S9. $ab + ax = c - ax$, for x.

S10. $by - d = ay + c$, for y.

Exercises

If possible, rewrite the equations in Exercises 1–9 in slope-intercept form, $y = b + mx$.

1. $5(x + y) = 4$

2. $3x + 5y = 20$

3. $0.1y + x = 18$

4. $5x - 3y + 2 = 0$

5. $y - 0.7 = 5(x - 0.2)$

6. $y = 5$

7. $3x + 2y + 40 = x - y$

8. $x = 4$

9. $\dfrac{x + y}{7} = 3$

Is each function in Exercises 10–15 linear? If so, rewrite it the form $y = b + mx$.

10. $g(w) = -\dfrac{1 - 12w}{3}$

11. $F(P) = 13 - \dfrac{2^{-1}}{4}P$

12. $j(s) = 3s^{-1} + 7$

13. $C(r) = 2\pi r$

14. $h(x) = 3^x + 12$

15. $f(x) = m^2 x + n^2$

Find formulas for the linear functions in Exercises 16–23.

16. Slope -4 and x-intercept 7

17. Slope 3 and y-intercept 8

18. Passes through the points $(-1, 5)$ and $(2, -1)$

19. Slope $2/3$ and passes through the point $(5, 7)$

20. Has x-intercept 3 and y-intercept -5

21. Slope 0.1, passes through $(-0.1, 0.02)$

22. Function f has $f(0.3) = 0.8$ and $f(0.8) = -0.4$

23. Function f has $f(-2) = 7$ and $f(3) = -3$

Exercises 24–30 give data from a linear function. Find a formula for the function.

24.

Year, t	0	1	2
Value of computer, $\$V = f(t)$	2000	1500	1000

25.

Price per bottle, p (\$)	0.50	0.75	1.00
Number of bottles sold, $q = f(p)$	1500	1000	500

26.

Temperature, $y = f(x)$ (°C)	0	5	20
Temperature, x (°F)	32	41	68

27.

Temperature, $y = f(x)$, (°R)	459.7	469.7	489.7
Temperature, x (°F)	0	10	30

28.

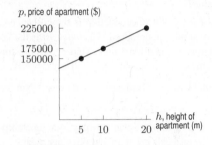

29.

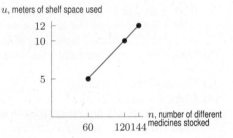

30.

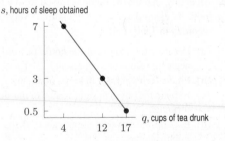

Problems

Find formulas for the linear functions in Problems 31–34.

31. The graph of f contains $(-3, -8)$ and $(5, -20)$.

32. $g(100) = 2000$ and $g(400) = 3800$

33. $P = h(t)$ gives the size of a population that begins with 12,000 members and grows by 225 members each year.

34. The graph of h intersects the graph of $y = x^2$ at $x = -2$ and $x = 3$.

Table 1.29 gives the cost, $C(n)$, of producing a certain good as a linear function of n, the number of units produced. Use the table to answer Problems 35–37.

Table 1.29

n (units)	100	125	150	175
$C(n)$ (dollars)	11000	11125	11250	11375

35. Evaluate the following expressions. Give economic interpretations for each.

(a) $C(175)$ (b) $C(175) - C(150)$

(c) $\dfrac{C(175) - C(150)}{175 - 150}$

36. Estimate $C(0)$. What is the economic significance of this value?

37. The *fixed cost* of production is the cost incurred before any goods are produced. The *unit cost* is the cost of producing an additional unit. Find a formula for $C(n)$ in terms of n, given that

Total cost = Fixed cost + Unit cost · Number of units

38. In a college meal plan you pay a membership fee; then all your meals are at a fixed price per meal.

(a) If 90 meals cost $1005 and 140 meals cost $1205, write a linear function that describes the cost of a meal plan, C, in terms of the number of meals, n.

(b) What is the cost per meal and what is the membership fee?

(c) Find the cost for 120 meals.

(d) Find n in terms of C.

(e) Use part (d) to determine the maximum number of meals you can buy on a budget of $1285.

39. An empty champagne bottle is tossed from a hot-air balloon. Its upward velocity is measured every second and recorded in Table 1.30.

(a) Describe the motion of the bottle in words. What do negative values of v represent?

(b) Find a formula for v in terms of t.

(c) Explain the physical significance of the slope of your formula.

(d) Explain the physical significance of the t-axis and v-axis intercepts.

Table 1.30

t (sec)	0	1	2	3	4	5
v (ft/sec)	40	8	−24	−56	−88	−120

40. John wants to buy a dozen rolls. The local bakery sells sesame and poppy-seed rolls for the same price.

(a) Make a table of all the possible combinations of rolls if he buys a dozen, where s is the number of sesame seed rolls and p is the number of poppy-seed rolls.

(b) Find a formula for p as a function of s.

(c) Graph this function.

41. The demand for gasoline can be modeled as a linear function of price. If the price of gasoline is $p = \$3.10$ per gallon, the quantity demanded in a fixed period is $q = 65$ gallons. If the price rises to $3.50 per gallon, the quantity demanded falls to 45 gallons in that period.

(a) Find a formula for q in terms of p.

(b) Explain the economic significance of the slope of your formula.

(c) Explain the economic significance of the q-axis and p-axis intercepts.

42. The solid waste generated each year in the cities of the US is increasing.[18] The solid waste generated, in millions of tons, was 88.1 in 1960 and 239.1 in 2000. The trend appears linear during this time.

(a) Construct a formula for the amount of municipal solid waste generated in the US by finding the equation of the line through these two points.

(b) Use this formula to predict the amount of municipal solid waste generated in the US, in millions of tons, in the year 2020.

43. Find the equation of the line l, shown in Figure 1.31, if its slope is $m = 4$.

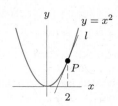

Figure 1.31

44. Find a formula for the line intersecting the graph of $f(x)$ at $x = 1$ and $x = 3$, where

$$f(x) = \frac{10}{x^2 + 1}.$$

[18] http://www.epa.gov/osw/nonhaz/municipal/pubs/msw2008rpt.pdf, accessed November 23, 2009.

45. Find the equation of line l in Figure 1.32.

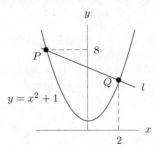

Figure 1.32

46. Find an equation for the line l in Figure 1.33 in terms of the constant A and values of the function f.

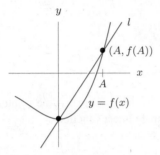

Figure 1.33

47. You can type four pages in 50 minutes and nine pages in an hour and forty minutes.

   (a) Find a linear function for the number of pages typed, p, as a function of time, t. If time is measured in minutes, what values of t make sense in this example?

   (b) How many pages can be typed in two hours?

   (c) Interpret the slope of the function in practical terms.

   (d) Use the result in part (a) to solve for time as a function of the number of pages typed.

   (e) How long does it take to type a 15-page paper?

   (f) Write a short paragraph explaining why it is useful to know both of the formulas obtained in part (a) and part (d).

48. Wire is sold by gauge size, where the diameter of the wire is a decreasing linear function of gauge. Gauge 2 wire has a diameter of 0.2656 inches and gauge 8 wire has a diameter of 0.1719 inches. Find the diameter for wires of gauge 12.5 and gauge 0. What values of the gauge do not make sense in this model?

49. A dose-response function can be used to describe the increase in risk associated with the increase in exposure to various hazards. For example, the risk of contracting lung cancer depends, among other things, on the number of cigarettes a person smokes per day. This risk can be described by a linear dose-response function. For example, it is known that smoking 10 cigarettes per day increases a person's probability of contracting lung cancer by a factor of 25, while smoking 20 cigarettes a day increases the probability by a factor of 50.

   (a) Find a formula for $i(x)$, the increase in the probability of contracting lung cancer for a person who smokes x cigarettes per day as compared to a non-smoker.

   (b) Evaluate $i(0)$.

   (c) Interpret the slope of the function i.

In Problems 50–51, write the functions in slope-intercept form. Identify the values of b and m.

50. $v(s) = \pi x^2 - 3xr - 4rs - s\sqrt{x}$

51. $w(r) = \pi x^2 - 3xr - 4rs - s\sqrt{x}$

52. The development time, t, of an organism is the number of days required for the organism to mature, and the development rate is defined as $r = 1/t$. In cold-blooded organisms such as insects, the development rate depends on temperature: the colder it is, the longer the organism takes to develop. For such organisms, the degree-day model[19] assumes that the development rate r is a linear function of temperature H (in $°C$):

$$r = b + kH.$$

   (a) According to the degree-day model, there is a minimum temperature H_{min} below which an organism never matures. Find a formula for H_{min} in terms of the constants b and k.

   (b) Define S as $S = (H - H_{min})t$, where S is the number of degree-days. That is, S is the number of days t times the number of degrees between H and H_{min}. Use the formula for r to show that S is a constant. In other words, find a formula for S that does not involve H. Your formula will involve k.

   (c) A certain organism requires $t = 25$ days to develop at a constant temperature of $H = 20°C$ and has $H_{min} = 15°C$. Using the fact that S is a constant, how many days does it take for this organism to develop at a temperature of $25°C$?

---

[19]Information drawn from a web site created by Dr. Alexei A. Sharov at the Virginia Polytechnic Institute, http://www.ento.vt.edu/ sharov/PopEcol/popecol.html.

(d) In part (c) we assumed that the temperature H is constant throughout development. If the temperature varies from day to day, the number of degree-days can be accumulated until they total S, at which point the organism completes development. For instance, suppose on the first day the temperature is $H = 20°C$ and that on the next day it is $H = 22°C$. Then for these first two days

Total number of degree days

$$= (20 - 15) \cdot 1 + (22 - 15) \cdot 1 = 12.$$

Based on Table 1.31, on what day does the organism reach maturity?

Table 1.31

Day	1	2	3	4	5	6	7	8	9	10	11	12
H (°C)	20	22	27	28	27	31	29	30	28	25	24	26

53. (Continuation of Problem 52.) Table 1.32 gives the development time t (in days) for an insect as a function of temperature H (in °C).

(a) Find a linear formula for r, the development rate, in terms of H.

(b) Find the value of S, the number of degree-days required for the organism to mature.

Table 1.32

H, °C	20	22	24	26	28	30
t, days	14.3	12.5	11.1	10.0	9.1	8.3

1.5 GEOMETRIC PROPERTIES OF LINEAR FUNCTIONS

Interpreting the Parameters of a Linear Function

The slope-intercept form for a linear function is $y = b + mx$, where b is the y-intercept and m is the slope. The parameters b and m can be used to compare linear functions.

Example 1   With time, t, in years, the populations of four towns, P_A, P_B, P_C and P_D, are given by the following formulas:

$$P_A = 20{,}000 + 1600t, \quad P_B = 50{,}000 - 300t, \quad P_C = 650t + 45{,}000, \quad P_D = 15{,}000(1.07)^t.$$

(a) Which populations are represented by linear functions?

(b) Describe in words what each linear model tells you about that town's population. Which town starts out with the most people? Which town is growing fastest?

Solution   (a) The populations of towns A, B, and C are represented by linear functions because they are written in the form $P = b + mt$. Town D's population does not grow linearly since its formula, $P_D = 15{,}000(1.07)^t$, cannot be expressed in the form $P_D = b + mt$.

(b) For town A, we have

$$P_A = \underbrace{20{,}000}_{b} + \underbrace{1600}_{m} \cdot t,$$

so $b = 20{,}000$ and $m = 1600$. This means that in year $t = 0$, town A has 20,000 people. It grows by 1600 people per year.

For town B, we have

$$P_B = \underbrace{50{,}000}_{b} + \underbrace{(-300)}_{m} \cdot t,$$

so $b = 50{,}000$ and $m = -300$. This means that town B starts with 50,000 people. The negative slope indicates that the population is decreasing at the rate of 300 people per year.

For town C, we have

$$P_C = \underbrace{45{,}000}_{b} + \underbrace{650}_{m} \cdot t,$$

so $b = 45{,}000$ and $m = 650$. This means that town C begins with 45,000 people and grows by 650 people per year.

Town B starts out with the most people, 50,000, but town A, with a rate of change of 1600 people per year, grows the fastest of the three towns that grow linearly.

The Effect of the Parameters on the Graph of a Linear Function

The graph of a linear function is a line. Changing the values of b and m gives different members of the family of linear functions. In summary:

Let $y = b + mx$. Then the graph of y against x is a line.
- The y-intercept, b, tells us where the line crosses the y-axis.
- If the slope, m, is positive, the line climbs from left to right. If the slope, m, is negative, the line falls from left to right.
- The slope, m, tells us how fast the line is climbing or falling.
- The larger the magnitude of m (either positive or negative), the steeper the graph of f.

Example 2 (a) Graph the three linear functions P_A, P_B, P_C from Example 1 and show how to identify the values of b and m from the graph.

(b) Graph P_D from Example 1 and explain how the graph shows P_D is not a linear function.

Solution (a) Figure 1.34 gives graphs of the three functions:

$$P_A = 20{,}000 + 1600t, \qquad P_B = 50{,}000 - 300t, \quad \text{and} \quad P_C = 45{,}000 + 650t.$$

The values of b identified in Example 1 tell us the vertical intercepts. Figure 1.34 shows that the graph of P_A crosses the P-axis at $P = 20{,}000$, the graph of P_B crosses at $P = 50{,}000$, and the graph of P_C crosses at $P = 45{,}000$.

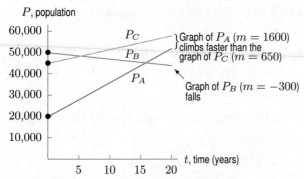

Figure 1.34: Graphs of three linear functions, P_A, P_B, and P_C, showing starting values and rates of climb

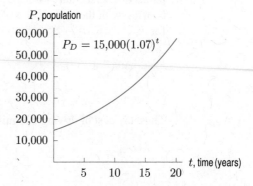

Figure 1.35: Graph of $P_D = 15{,}000(1.07)^t$ is not a line

Notice that the graphs of P_A and P_C are both climbing and that P_A climbs faster than P_C. This corresponds to the fact that the slopes of these two functions are positive ($m = 1600$ for P_A and $m = 650$ for P_C) and the slope of P_A is larger than the slope of P_C.

The graph of P_B falls when read from left to right, indicating that population decreases over time. This corresponds to the fact that the slope of P_C is negative ($m = -300$).

(b) Figure 1.35 gives a graph of P_D. Since it is not a line, P_D is not a linear function.

Intersection of Two Lines

To find the point at which two lines intersect, notice that the (x, y)-coordinates of such a point must satisfy the equations for both lines. Thus, in order to find the point of intersection algebraically, solve the equations simultaneously.[20]

If linear functions are modeling real quantities, their points of intersection often have practical significance. Consider the next example.

Example 3   The cost in dollars of renting a car for a day from three different rental agencies and driving it d miles is given by the following functions:

$$C_1 = 50 + 0.10d, \qquad C_2 = 30 + 0.20d, \qquad C_3 = 0.50d.$$

(a) Describe in words the daily rental arrangements made by each of these three agencies.
(b) Which agency is cheapest?

Solution   (a) Agency 1 charges $50 plus $0.10 per mile driven. Agency 2 charges $30 plus $0.20 per mile. Agency 3 charges $0.50 per mile driven.

(b) The answer depends on how far we want to drive. If we are not driving far, agency 3 may be cheapest because it only charges for miles driven and has no other fees. If we want to drive a long way, agency 1 may be cheapest (even though it charges $50 up front) because it has the lowest per-mile rate.

The three functions are graphed in Figure 1.36. The graph shows that for d up to 100 miles, the value of C_3 is less than C_1 and C_2 because its graph is below the other two. For d between 100 and 200 miles, the value of C_2 is less than C_1 and C_3. For d more than 200 miles, the value of C_1 is less than C_2 and C_3.

By graphing these three functions on a calculator, we can estimate the coordinates of the points of intersection by tracing. To find the exact coordinates, we solve simultaneous equations. Starting with the intersection of lines C_1 and C_2, we set the costs equal, $C_1 = C_2$, and solve for d:

$$50 + 0.10d = 30 + 0.20d$$
$$20 = 0.10d$$
$$d = 200.$$

Thus, the cost of driving 200 miles is the same for agencies 1 and 2. Solving $C_2 = C_3$ gives

$$30 + 0.20d = 0.50d$$
$$0.30d = 30$$
$$d = 100,$$

[20]If you have questions about the algebra in this section, see the Skills Refresher on page 61.

which means the cost of driving 100 miles is the same for agencies 2 and 3.

Thus, agency 3 is cheapest up to 100 miles. Agency 1 is cheapest for more than 200 miles. Agency 2 is cheapest between 100 and 200 miles. See Figure 1.36. Notice that the point of intersection of C_1 and C_3, $(125, 62.5)$, does not influence our decision as to which agency is the cheapest.

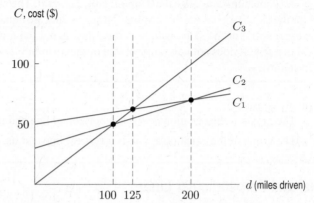

Figure 1.36: Cost of driving a car d miles when renting from three different agencies. Cheapest agency corresponds to the lowest graph for a given d value

Equations of Horizontal and Vertical Lines

An increasing linear function has positive slope and a decreasing linear function has negative slope. What about a line with slope $m = 0$? If the rate of change of a quantity is zero, then the quantity does not change. Thus, if the slope of a line is zero, the value of y must be constant. Such a line is horizontal.

Example 4 Explain why the equation $y = 4$ represents a horizontal line and the equation $x = 4$ represents a vertical line.

Solution The equation $y = 4$ represents a linear function with slope $m = 0$. To see this, notice that this equation can be rewritten as $y = 4 + 0 \cdot x$. Thus, the value of y is 4 no matter what the value of x is. See Figure 1.37. Similarly, the equation $x = 4$ means that x is 4 no matter what the value of y is. Every point on the line in Figure 1.38 has x equal to 4, so this line is the graph of $x = 4$.

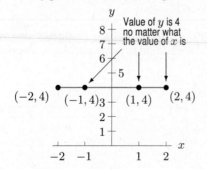

Figure 1.37: The horizontal line $y = 4$ has slope 0

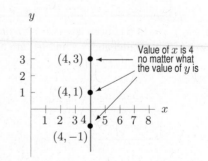

Figure 1.38: The vertical line $x = 4$ has an undefined slope

What is the slope of a vertical line? Figure 1.38 shows three points, $(4, -1)$, $(4, 1)$, and $(4, 3)$ on a vertical line. Calculating the slope, gives

$$m = \frac{\Delta y}{\Delta x} = \frac{3 - 1}{4 - 4} = \frac{2}{0}.$$

The slope is undefined because the denominator, Δx, is 0. The slope of every vertical line is undefined for the same reason. All the x-values on such a line are equal, so Δx is 0, and the denominator of the expression for the slope is 0. A vertical line is not the graph of a function, since it fails the vertical line test. It does not have an equation of the form $y = b + mx$.

In summary,

For any constant k:
- The graph of the equation $y = k$ is a horizontal line and its slope is zero.
- The graph of the equation $x = k$ is a vertical line and its slope is undefined.

Slopes of Parallel and Perpendicular Lines

Figure 1.39 shows two parallel lines. These lines are parallel because they have equal slopes.

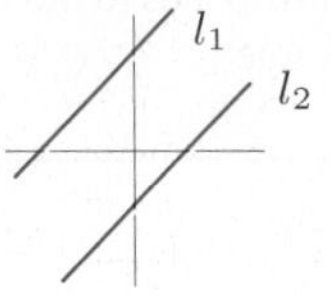

Figure 1.39: Parallel lines: l_1 and l_2 have equal slopes

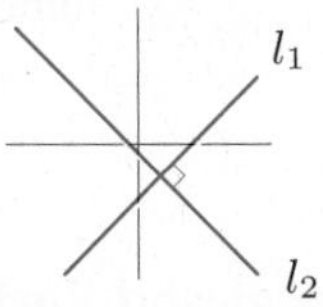

Figure 1.40: Perpendicular lines: l_1 has a positive slope and l_2 has a negative slope

What about perpendicular lines? Two perpendicular lines are graphed in Figure 1.40. We can see that if one line has a positive slope, then any perpendicular line must have a negative slope. Perpendicular lines have slopes with opposite signs.

We show that if l_1 and l_2 are two perpendicular lines with slopes, m_1 and m_2, then m_1 is the negative reciprocal of m_2. If m_1 and m_2 are not zero, we have the following result:

Let l_1 and l_2 be two lines having slopes m_1 and m_2, respectively. Then:
- These lines are parallel if and only if $m_1 = m_2$.
- These lines are perpendicular if and only if $m_1 = -\dfrac{1}{m_2}$.

In addition, any two horizontal lines are parallel and $m_1 = m_2 = 0$. Any two vertical lines are parallel and m_1 and m_2 are undefined. A horizontal line is perpendicular to a vertical line. See Figures 1.41–1.43.

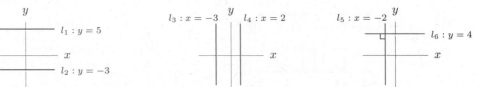

Figure 1.41: Any two horizontal lines are parallel

Figure 1.42: Any two vertical lines are parallel

Figure 1.43: A horizontal line and a vertical line are perpendicular

Justification of Formula for Slopes of Perpendicular Lines

Figure 1.44 shows l_1 and l_2, two perpendicular lines with slopes m_1 and m_2. Neither line is horizontal or vertical, so m_1 and m_2 are both defined and nonzero. We will show that

$$m_2 = -\frac{1}{m_1}.$$

Using right triangle $\triangle PQR$ with side lengths a and b we see that

$$m_1 = \frac{b}{a}.$$

Rotating $\triangle PQR$ by 90° about the point P produces triangle $\triangle PST$. Using $\triangle PST$ we see that

$$m_2 = -\frac{a}{b} = -\frac{1}{b/a} = -\frac{1}{m_1}.$$

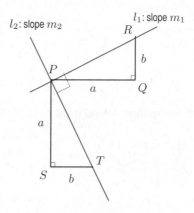

Figure 1.44

Exercises and Problems for Section 1.5

Skill Refresher

Solve the systems of equations in Exercises S1–S6, if possible.

Determine the points of intersection for Exercises S7–S8.

S1. $\begin{cases} x + y = 3 \\ y = 5 \end{cases}$

S2. $\begin{cases} x + y = 3 \\ x - y = 5 \end{cases}$

S3. $\begin{cases} x + y = 2 \\ 2x + 2y = 7 \end{cases}$

S4. $\begin{cases} y = x - 3 \\ 2y - 2x = -6 \end{cases}$

S5. $\begin{cases} 2x - y = 10 \\ x + 2y = 15 \end{cases}$

S6. $\begin{cases} 2(x + y) = 3 \\ x = y + 3(x - 5) \end{cases}$

S7.

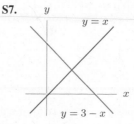

S8.

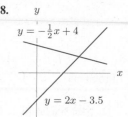

Exercises

1. Without using a calculator, match the equations (a) – (f) to the graphs (I) – (VI).

 (a) $y = -2.72x$ (b) $y = 0.01 + 0.001x$
 (c) $y = 27.9 - 0.1x$ (d) $y = 0.1x - 27.9$
 (e) $y = -5.7 - 200x$ (f) $y = x/3.14$

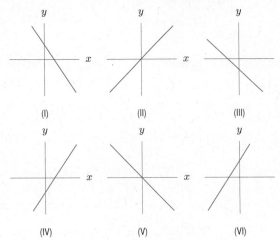

(I)   (II)   (III)

(IV)   (V)   (VI)

2. Without a calculator, match the equations (a)–(g) to the graphs (I)–(VII).

 (a) $y = x - 5$ (b) $-3x + 4 = y$
 (c) $5 = y$ (d) $y = -4x - 5$
 (e) $y = x + 6$ (f) $y = x/2$
 (g) $5 = x$

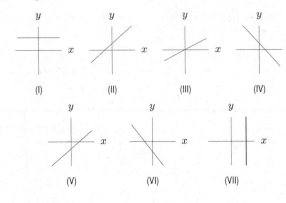

(I)   (II)   (III)   (IV)

(V)   (VI)   (VII)

3. Figure 1.45 gives lines, A, B, C, D, and E. Without a calculator, match each line to f, g, h, u or v:

$$f(x) = 20 + 2x$$
$$g(x) = 20 + 4x$$
$$h(x) = 2x - 30$$
$$u(x) = 60 - x$$
$$v(x) = 60 - 2x$$

Figure 1.45

4. Without a calculator, match the following functions to the lines in Figure 1.46:

$$f(x) = 5 + 2x$$
$$g(x) = -5 + 2x$$
$$h(x) = 5 + 3x$$
$$j(x) = 5 - 2x$$
$$k(x) = 5 - 3x$$

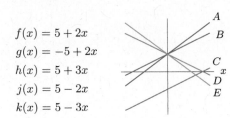

Figure 1.46

5. (a) By hand, graph $y = 3$ and $x = 3$.
   (b) Can the equations in part (a) be written in slope-intercept form?

Are the lines in Exercises 6–11 perpendicular? Parallel? Neither?

6. $y = 5x - 7; y = 5x + 8$

7. $y = 4x + 3; y = 13 - \frac{1}{4}x$

8. $y = 2x + 3; \quad y = 2x - 7$

9. $y = 4x + 7; \quad y = \frac{1}{4}x - 2$

10. $f(q) = 12q + 7; g(q) = \frac{1}{12}q + 96$

11. $2y = 16 - x; 4y = -8 - 2x$

Problems

12. Sketch a family of functions $y = -2 - ax$ for five different values of a with $a < 0$.

13. Find the equation of the line parallel to $3x + 5y = 6$ and passing through the point $(0, 6)$.

14. Find the equation of the line passing through the point $(2, 1)$ and perpendicular to the line $y = 5x - 3$.

15. Find the equations of the lines parallel to and perpendicular to the line $y + 4x = 7$, and through the point $(1, 5)$.

16. Estimate the slope of the line in Figure 1.47 and find an approximate equation for the line.

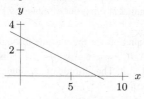

Figure 1.47

17. Line l in Figure 1.48 is parallel to the line $y = 2x + 1$. Find the coordinates of the point P.

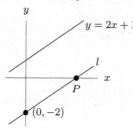

Figure 1.48

18. Find the equation of the line l_2 in Figure 1.49.

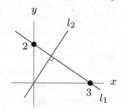

Figure 1.49

19. The cost of a Frigbox refrigerator is $950, and it depreciates $50 each year. The cost of an Arctic Air refrigerator is $1200, and it depreciates $100 per year.

(a) If a Frigbox and an Arctic Air are bought at the same time, when do the two refrigerators have equal value?

(b) If both refrigerators continue to depreciate at the same rates, what happens to the values of the refrigerators in 20 years' time? What does this mean?

20. You need to rent a car and compare the charges of three different companies. Company A charges 20 cents per mile plus $20 per day. Company B charges 10 cents per mile plus $35 per day. Company C charges $70 per day with no mileage charge.

(a) Find formulas for the cost of driving cars rented from companies A, B, and C, in terms of x, the distance driven in miles in one day.

(b) Graph the costs for each company for $0 \leq x \leq 500$. Put all three graphs on the same set of axes.

(c) What do the slope and the vertical intercept tell you in this situation?

(d) Use the graph in part (b) to find under what circumstances company A is the cheapest. What about Company B? Company C? Explain why your results make sense.

21. Line l is given by $y = 3 - \frac{2}{3}x$ and point P has coordinates $(6, 5)$.

(a) Find the equation of the line containing P and parallel to l.

(b) Find the equation of the line containing P and perpendicular to l.

(c) Graph the equations in parts (a) and (b).

22. Assume A, B, C are constants with $A \neq 0$, $B \neq 0$. Consider the equation

$$Ax + By = C.$$

(a) Show that $y = f(x)$ is linear. State the slope and the x- and y-intercepts of $f(x)$.

(b) Graph $y = f(x)$, labeling the x- and y-intercepts in terms of A, B, and C, assuming

(i) $A > 0, B > 0, C > 0$

(ii) $A > 0, B > 0, C < 0$

(iii) $A > 0, B < 0, C > 0$

23. Fill in the missing coordinates for the points in the following figures.

(a) The triangle in Figure 1.50.

(b) The parallelogram in Figure 1.51.

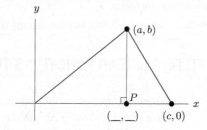

Figure 1.50

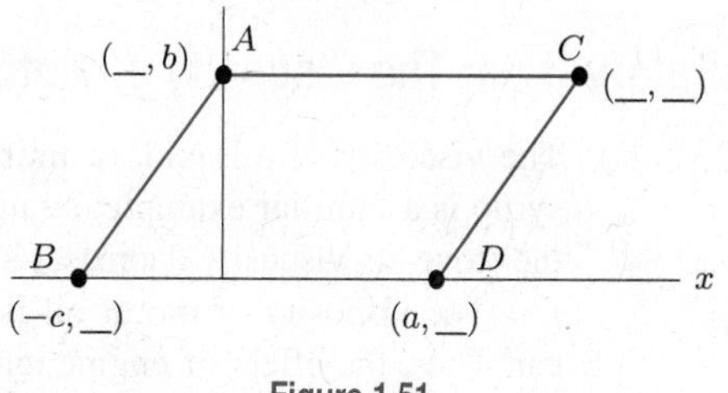

Figure 1.51

24. Using the window $-10 \leq x \leq 10, -10 \leq y \leq 10$, graph $y = x$, $y = 10x$, $y = 100x$, and $y = 1000x$.

   (a) Explain what happens to the graphs of the lines as the slopes become large.

   (b) Write an equation of a line that passes through the origin and is horizontal.

25. Graph $y = x + 1$, $y = x + 10$, and $y = x + 100$ in the window $-10 \leq x \leq 10, -10 \leq y \leq 10$.

   (a) Explain what happens to the graph of a line, $y = b + mx$, as b becomes large.

   (b) Write a linear equation whose graph cannot be seen in the window $-10 \leq x \leq 10, -10 \leq y \leq 10$ because all its y-values are less than the y-values shown.

26. The graphical interpretation of the slope is that it shows steepness. Using a calculator or a computer, graph the function $y = 2x - 3$ in the following windows:

   (a) $-10 \leq x \leq 10$ by $-10 \leq y \leq 10$
   (b) $-10 \leq x \leq 10$ by $-100 \leq y \leq 100$
   (c) $-10 \leq x \leq 10$ by $-1000 \leq y \leq 1000$
   (d) Write a sentence about how steepness is related to the window being used.

In Problems 27–28, what is true about the constant β in the following linear equation if its graph has the given property?

$$y = \frac{x}{\beta - 3} + \frac{1}{6 - \beta}.$$

27. Positive slope, positive y-intercept.

28. Perpendicular to the line $y = (\beta - 7)x - 3$.

29. A circle of radius 2 is centered at the origin and goes through the point $(-1, \sqrt{3})$.

   (a) Find an equation for the line through the origin and the point $(-1, \sqrt{3})$.

   (b) Find an equation for the tangent line to the circle at $(-1, \sqrt{3})$. [Hint: A tangent line is perpendicular to the radius at the point of tangency.]

30. Find an equation for the altitude through point A of the triangle ABC, where A is $(-4, 5)$, B is $(-3, 2)$, and C is $(9, 8)$. [Hint: The altitude of a triangle is perpendicular to the base.]

31. Fill in the missing coordinates in Figure 1.52. Write an equation for the line connecting the two points. Check your answer by solving the system of two equations.

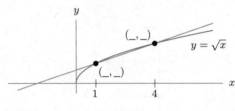

Figure 1.52

32. Two lines are given by $y = b_1 + m_1 x$ and $y = b_2 + m_2 x$, where b_1, b_2, m_1, and m_2 are constants.

   (a) What conditions are imposed on b_1, b_2, m_1, and m_2 if the two lines have no points in common?

   (b) What conditions are imposed on b_1, b_2, m_1, and m_2 if the two lines have all points in common?

   (c) What conditions are imposed on b_1, b_2, m_1, and m_2 if the two lines have exactly one point in common?

   (d) What conditions are imposed on b_1, b_2, m_1, and m_2 if the two lines have exactly two points in common?

1.6   FITTING LINEAR FUNCTIONS TO DATA

When real data are collected in the laboratory or the field, they are often subject to experimental error. Even if there is an underlying linear relationship between two quantities, real data may not fit this relationship perfectly. However, even if a data set does not perfectly conform to a linear function, we may still be able to use a linear function to help us analyze the data.

Laboratory Data: The Viscosity of Motor Oil

The viscosity of a liquid, or its resistance to flow, depends on the liquid's temperature. Pancake syrup is a familiar example: straight from the refrigerator, it pours very slowly. When warmed on the stove, its viscosity decreases and it becomes quite runny.

     The viscosity of motor oil is a measure of its effectiveness as a lubricant in the engine of a car. Thus, the effect of engine temperature is an important determinant of motor-oil performance. Table 1.33 gives the viscosity, v, of motor oil as measured in the lab at different temperatures, T.

Table 1.33 *The measured viscosity, v, of motor oil as a function of the temperature, T*

T, temperature (°F)	v, viscosity (lbs·sec/in^2)
160	28
170	26
180	24
190	21
200	16
210	13
220	11
230	9

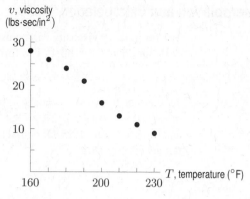

Figure 1.53: The viscosity data from Table 1.33

The *scatter plot* of the data in Figure 1.53 shows that the viscosity of motor oil decreases, approximately linearly, as its temperature rises. To find a formula relating viscosity and temperature, we fit a line to these data points.

Fitting the best line to a set of data is called *linear regression*. One way to fit a line is to draw a line "by eye." Alternatively, many computer programs and calculators compute regression lines. Figure 1.54 shows the data from Table 1.33 together with the computed regression line,

$$v = 75.6 - 0.293T.$$

Notice that none of the data points lie exactly on the regression line, although it fits the data well.

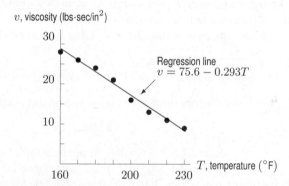

Figure 1.54: A graph of the viscosity data from Table 1.33, together with a regression line (provided by a calculator)

The Assumptions Involved In Finding a Regression Line

When we find a regression line for the data in Table 1.33, we are assuming that the value of v is related to the value of T. However, there may be experimental errors in our measurements. For example, if we measure viscosity twice at the same temperature, we may get two slightly different values. Alternatively, something besides engine temperature could be affecting the oil's viscosity (the oil pressure, for example). Thus, even if we assume that the temperature readings are exact, the viscosity readings include some degree of uncertainty.

Interpolation and Extrapolation

The formula for viscosity can be used to make predictions. Suppose we want to know the viscosity of motor oil at $T = 196°F$. The formula gives

$$v = 75.6 - 0.293 \cdot 196 \approx 18.2 \text{ lb} \cdot \text{sec/in}^2.$$

To see that this is a reasonable estimate, compare it to the entries in Table 1.33. At 190°F, the measured viscosity was 21, and at 200°F, it was 16; the predicted viscosity of 18.2 is between 16 and 21. See Figure 1.55. Of course, if we measured the viscosity at $T = 196°F$ in the lab, we might not get exactly 18.2.

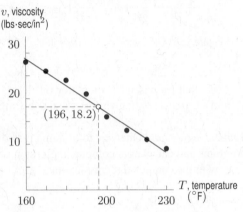

Figure 1.55: Regression line used to predict the viscosity at 196°F

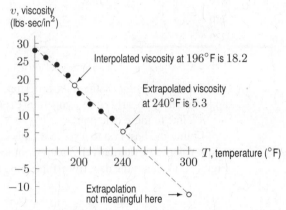

Figure 1.56: The data from Table 1.33 together with the predicted viscosity at $T = 196°F$, $T = 240°F$, and $T = 300°F$

Since the temperature $T = 196°F$ is between two temperatures for which v is known (190°F and 200°F), the estimate of 18.2 is said to be an *interpolation*. If instead we estimate the value of v at a temperature outside the values for T in Table 1.33, our estimate is called an *extrapolation*.

Example 1   Predict the viscosity of motor oil at 240°F and at 300°F.

Solution   At $T = 240°F$, the formula for the regression line predicts that the viscosity of motor oil is

$$v = 75.6 - 0.293 \cdot 240 = 5.3 \text{ lb} \cdot \text{sec/in}^2.$$

This is reasonable. Figure 1.56 shows that the predicted point—represented by an open circle on the graph—is consistent with the trend in the data points from Table 1.33.

On the other hand, at $T = 300°F$ the regression-line formula gives

$$v = 75.6 - 0.293 \cdot 300 = -12.3 \text{ lb} \cdot \text{sec/in}^2.$$

This is unreasonable because viscosity cannot be negative. To understand what went wrong, notice that in Figure 1.56, the open circle representing the point $(300, -12.3)$ is far from the plotted data points. By making a prediction at 300°F, we have assumed—incorrectly—that the trend observed in laboratory data extended as far as 300°F.

In general, interpolation tends to be more reliable than extrapolation because we are making a prediction on an interval we already know something about instead of making a prediction beyond the limits of our knowledge.

How Regression Works

How does a calculator or computer decide which line fits the data best? We assume that the value of y is related to the value of x, although other factors could influence y as well. Thus, we assume that we can pick the value of x exactly but that the value of y may be only partially determined by this x-value.

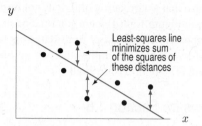

Figure 1.57: A given set of data and the corresponding least-squares regression line

One way to fit a line to the data is shown in Figure 1.57. The line shown was chosen to minimize the sum of the squares of the vertical distances between the data points and the line. Such a line is called a *least-squares line*. There are formulas which a calculator or computer uses to calculate the slope, m, and the y-intercept, b, of the least-squares line.

Correlation

When a computer or calculator calculates a regression line, it also gives a *correlation coefficient*, r. This number lies between -1 and $+1$ and measures how well a particular regression line fits the data. If $r = 1$, the data lie exactly on a line of positive slope. If $r = -1$, the data lie exactly on a line of negative slope. If r is close to 0, the data may be completely scattered, or there may be a nonlinear relationship between the variables. (See Figure 1.58.)

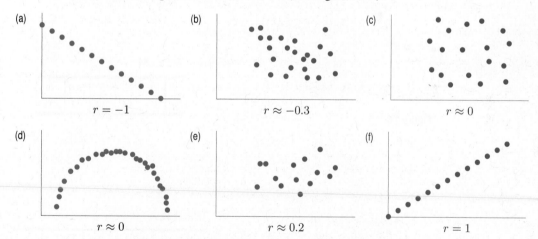

Figure 1.58: Various data sets and correlation coefficients

Example 2   The correlation coefficient for the viscosity data in Table 1.33 on page 45 is $r \approx -0.99$. The fact that r is negative tells us that the regression line has negative slope. The fact that r is close to -1 tells us that the regression line fits the data well.

The Difference Between Relation, Correlation, and Causation

It is important to understand that a high correlation (either positive or negative) between two quantities does *not* imply causation. For example, there is a high correlation between children's reading level and shoe size.[21] However, large feet do not cause a child to read better (or vice versa). Larger feet and improved reading ability are both a consequence of growing older.

Notice also that a correlation of 0 does not imply that there is no relationship between x and y. For example, in Figure 1.58(d) there is a relationship between x and y-values, while Figure 1.58(c) exhibits no apparent relationship. Both data sets have a correlation coefficient of $r \approx 0$. Thus a correlation of $r = 0$ usually implies there is no linear relationship between x and y, but this does not mean there is no relationship at all.

Exercises and Problems for Section 1.6

For data in Problems 1–6 is the given value of r reasonable? Give an explanation for your answer.

1. $r = 0.93$

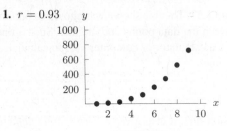

Figure 1.59

2. $r = -0.9$

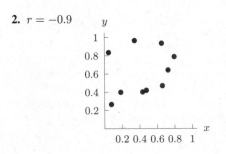

Figure 1.60

3. $r = 1$

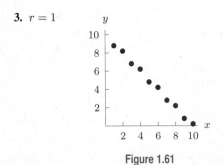

Figure 1.61

4. $r = 0.92$

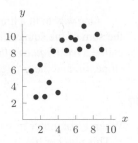

Figure 1.62

5. $r = 1$

Table 1.34

x	1	2	3	4	5
y	3.8	3.2	1.8	1.2	-0.2

6. $r = 0.343$

Table 1.35

x	1	2	3	4	5
y	3.477	5.531	14.88	5.924	8.049

---

[21]From *Statistics*, 2nd edition, by David Freedman, Robert Pisani, Roger Purves, Ani Adhikari, p. 142 (New York: W.W. Norton, 1991).

7. Match the r values with scatter plots in Figure 1.63.

$$r = -0.98, \quad r = -0.5, \quad r = -0.25,$$

$$r = 0, \quad r = 0.7, \quad r = 1.$$

(a)
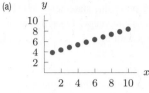

(b)
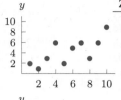

(c)
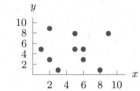

(d)
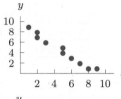

(e)
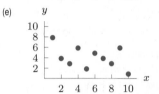

(f)
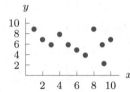

Figure 1.63

8. Table 1.36 shows the number of calories burned per minute by a person walking at 3 mph.

   (a) Make a scatter plot of this data.
   (b) Draw a regression line by eye.
   (c) Roughly estimate the correlation coefficient by eye.

Table 1.36

Body weight (lb)	100	120	150	170	200	220
Calories	2.7	3.2	4.0	4.6	5.4	5.9

9. An ecologist tracked 290 zebra that were born in 2000. The number of zebra, z, living each subsequent year is recorded in Table 1.37.

   (a) Make a scatter plot of this data. Let $t = 0$ represent 2000.
   (b) Draw by eye a line of good fit and estimate its equation. (Round the coefficients to integers.)
   (c) Use a calculator or computer to find the equation of the least squares line. (Round the coefficients to integers.)
   (d) Interpret the slope and each intercept of the line.

   (e) Interpret the correlation between the year and the number of zebra born in 2000 that are still alive.

Table 1.37

Year	2000	2001	2002	2003	2004	2005	2006	2007	2008
Zebra	290	288	268	206	140	90	64	44	8

10. The rate of oxygen consumption for Colorado beetles increases with temperature. See Table 1.38.

   (a) Make a scatter plot of this data.
   (b) Draw an estimated regression line by eye.
   (c) Use a calculator or computer to find the equation of the regression line. (Alternatively, find the equation of your line in part (b).) Round constants in the equation to the nearest integer.
   (d) Interpret the slope and each intercept of the regression equation.
   (e) Interpret the correlation between temperature and oxygen rate.

Table 1.38

°C	10	15	20	25	30
Oxygen consumption rate	90	125	200	300	375

11. Table 1.39 gives the data on hand strength collected from college freshman using a grip meter.

   (a) Make a scatter plot of these data treating the strength of the preferred hand as the independent variable.
   (b) Draw a line on your scatter plot that is a good fit for these data and use it to find an approximate equation for the regression line.
   (c) Using a graphing calculator or computer, find the equation of the least squares line.
   (d) What would the predicted grip strength in the non-preferred hand be for a student with a preferred hand strength of 37?
   (e) Discuss interpolation and extrapolation using specific examples in relation to this regression line.
   (f) Discuss why r, the correlation coefficient, is both positive and close to 1.
   (g) Why do the points tend to cluster into two groups on your scatter plot?

Table 1.39   *Hand strength for 20 students in kilograms*

Preferred	28	27	45	20	40	47	28	54	52	21
Nonpreferred	24	26	43	22	40	45	26	46	46	22
Preferred	53	52	49	45	39	26	25	32	30	32
Nonpreferred	47	47	41	44	33	20	27	30	29	29

12. Table 1.40 shows men's and women's world records for swimming distances from 50 meters to 1500 meters.[22]

(a) What values would you add to Table 1.40 to represent the time taken by both men and women to swim 0 meters?

(b) Plot men's time against distance, with time t in seconds on the vertical axis and distance d in meters on the horizontal axis. It is claimed that a straight line models this behavior well. What is the equation for that line? What does its slope represent? On the same graph, plot women's time against distance and find the equation of the straight line that models this behavior well. Is this line steeper or flatter than the men's line? What does that mean in terms of swimming? What are the values of the vertical intercepts? Do these values have a practical interpretation?

(c) On another graph plot the women's times against the men's times, with women's times, w, on the vertical axis and men's times, m, on the horizontal axis. It should look linear. How could you have predicted this linearity from the equations you found in part (b)? What is the slope of this line and how can it be interpreted? A newspaper reporter claims that the women's records are about 8% slower than the men's. Do the facts support this statement? What is the value of the vertical intercept? Does this value have a practical interpretation?

Table 1.40   *Men's and women's world swimming records*

Distance (m)	50	100	200	400	800	1500
Men (sec)	21.64	47.84	104.06	220.08	458.65	874.56
Women (sec)	24.13	53.62	116.64	243.85	496.22	952.10

CHAPTER SUMMARY

- **Functions**
  Definition: a rule which takes certain numbers as inputs and assigns to each input exactly one output number.
  Function notation, $y = f(x)$.
  Use of vertical line test.

- **Average Rate of Change**
  Average rate of change of $Q = f(t)$ on $[a, b]$ is
  $$\frac{\Delta Q}{\Delta t} = \frac{f(b) - f(a)}{b - a}.$$
  Increasing, decreasing functions; identifying from average rate of change.

- **Linear Functions**
  Value of y changes at constant rate.
  Tables for linear functions.

- **Formulas for Linear Functions**
  Slope-intercept form: $y = b + mx$.
  Point-slope form: $y - y_0 = m(x - x_0)$.
  Standard form: $Ax + By + C = 0$.

- **Properties of Linear Functions**
  Interpretation of slope, vertical and horizontal intercepts.
  Intersection of lines: Solution of equations.
  Horizontal and vertical lines.
  Parallel lines: $m_1 = m_2$.
  Perpendicular lines: $m_1 = -\dfrac{1}{m_2}$.

- **Fitting Lines to Data**
  Linear regression; correlation. Interpolation, extrapolation; dangers of extrapolation.

REVIEW EXERCISES AND PROBLEMS FOR CHAPTER ONE

Exercises

In Exercises 1–5 a relationship is given between two quantities. Are both quantities functions of the other one, or is one or neither a function of the other? Explain.

1. $7w^2 + 5 = z^2$ **2.** $y = x^4 - 1$ **3.** $m = \sqrt{t}$

4. The number of gallons of gas, g, at \$2 per gallon and the number of pounds of coffee, c, at \$10 per pound that can be bought for a total of \$100.

5.

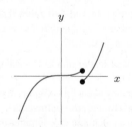

Figure 1.64

---

[22]Data from *The World Almanac and Book of Facts: 2006*, World Almanac Education Group, Inc., New York, 2006.

6. (a) Which of the graphs in Figure 1.65 represent y as a function of x? (Note that an open circle indicates a point that is not included in the graph; a solid dot indicates a point that is included in the graph.)

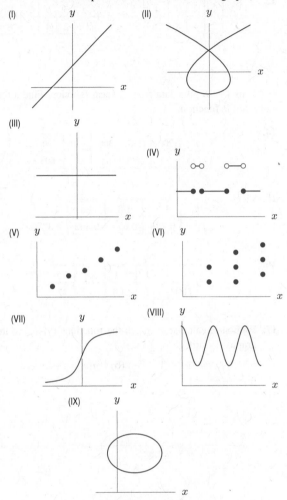

Figure 1.65

(b) Which of the graphs in Figure 1.65 could represent the following situations? Give reasons.

(i) SAT Math score versus SAT Verbal score for a small number of students.

(ii) Total number of daylight hours as a function of the day of the year, shown over a period of several years.

(c) Among graphs (I)–(IX) in Figure 1.65, find two which could give the cost of train fare as a function of the time of day. Explain the relationship between cost and time for both choices.

7. (a) Make a table of values for $f(x) = 10/(1 + x^2)$ for $x = 0, 1, 2, 3$.

(b) What x-value gives the largest $f(x)$ value in your table? How could you have predicted this before doing any calculations?

8. Table 1.41 gives the populations of two cities (in thousands) over a 17-year period.

(a) Find the average rate of change of each population on the following intervals:

(i) 1990 to 2000   (ii) 1990 to 2007

(iii) 1995 to 2007

(b) What do you notice about the average rate of change of each population? Explain what the average rate of change tells you about each population.

Table 1.41

Year	1990	1992	1995	2000	2007
P_1	42	46	52	62	76
P_2	82	80	77	72	65

9. The following tables represent the relationship between the button number, N, that you push, and the snack, S, delivered by three different vending machines.[23]

(a) One of these vending machines is not a good one to use, because S is not a function of N. Which one?

(b) For which vending machine(s) is S a function of N?

(c) For which of the vending machines is N not a function of S?

Vending Machine #1

N	S
1	M&Ms
2	pretzels
3	dried fruit
4	Hersheys
5	fat-free cookies
6	Snickers

Vending Machine #2

N	S
1	M&Ms or dried fruit
2	pretzels or Hersheys
3	Snickers or fat-free cookies

Vending Machine #3

N	S
1	M&Ms
2	M&Ms
3	pretzels
4	dried fruit
5	Hersheys
6	Hersheys
7	fat-free cookies
8	Snickers
9	Snickers

[23] For each N, vending machine #2 dispenses one or the other product at random.

10. Figure 1.66 shows the average monthly temperature in Albany, New York, over a twelve-month period. (January is month 1.)

   (a) Make a table showing average temperature as a function of the month of the year.

   (b) What is the warmest month in Albany?

   (c) Over what interval of months is the temperature increasing? Decreasing?

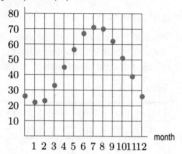

average temperature (°F)

month

Figure 1.66

11. In 1947, Jesse Owens, the US gold medal track star of the 1930s and 1940s, ran a 100-yard race against a horse. The race, "staged" in Havana, Cuba, is filled with controversy; some say Owens received a head start, others claim the horse was drugged. Owens himself revealed some years later that the starting gun was placed next to the horse's ear, causing the animal to rear and remain at the gate for a few seconds. Figure 1.67 depicts speeds measured against time for the race.

   (a) How fast were Owens and the horse going at the end of the race?

   (b) When were the participants both traveling at the same speed?

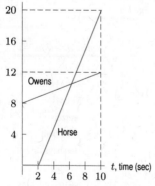

speed (yds/secs)

Owens

Horse

t, time (sec)

Figure 1.67

In Exercises 12–13, could the table represent a linear function?

12.

λ	1	2	3	4	5
$q(\lambda)$	2	4	8	16	32

13.

t	3	6	9	12	15
$a(t)$	2	4	6	8	10

Problems 14–16 give data from a linear function. Find a formula for the function.

14.

x	200	230	300	320	400
$g(x)$	70	68.5	65	64	60

15.

t	1.2	1.3	1.4	1.5
$f(t)$	0.736	0.614	0.492	0.37

16.

t	5.2	5.3	5.4	5.5
$f(t)$	73.6	61.4	49.2	37

17. Without a calculator, match the functions (a)–(c) to the graphs (i)–(iii).

   (a) $f(x) = 3x + 1$ (b) $g(x) = -2x + 1$

   (c) $h(x) = 1$

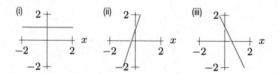

In Exercises 18–20, which line has the greater

   (a) Slope?   (b) y-intercept?

18. $y = -1 + 2x; \quad y = -2 + 3x$

19. $y = 3 + 4x; \quad y = 5 - 2x$

20. $y = \frac{1}{4}x; \quad y = 1 - 6x$

Are the lines in Exercises 21–24 perpendicular? Parallel? Neither?

21. $y = 5x + 2; \quad y = 2x + 5$

22. $y = 14x - 2; \quad y = -\frac{1}{14}x + 2$

23. $y = 3x + 3; \quad y = -\frac{1}{3}x + 3$

24. $7y = 8 + 21x; 9y = 77 - 3x$

Problems

In Problems 25–27, use Table 1.42, which gives values of $v = r(s)$, the eyewall wind profile of a typical hurricane.[24] The eyewall of a hurricane is the band of clouds that surrounds the eye of the storm. The eyewall wind speed v (in mph) is a function of the height above the ground s (in meters).

Table 1.42

s	0	100	200	300	400	500
v	90	110	116	120	121	122
s	600	700	800	900	1000	1100
v	121	119	118	117	116	115

25. Evaluate and interpret $r(300)$.

26. At what altitudes does the eyewall wind speed appear to equal or exceed 116 mph?

27. At what height is the eyewall wind speed greatest?

28. You are looking at the graph of y, a function of x.

   (a) What is the maximum number of times that the graph can intersect the y-axis? Explain.

   (b) Can the graph intersect the x-axis an infinite number of times? Explain.

29. A bug starts out ten feet from a light, flies closer to the light, then farther away, then closer than before, then farther away. Finally the bug hits the bulb and flies off. Sketch the distance of the bug from the light as a function of time.

30. Although there were 17 women in the Senate in 2009, the first woman elected to the Senate was Hattie Wyatt Caraway of Arkansas. She was appointed to fill the vacancy caused by the death of her husband, then won election in 1932, was reelected in 1938, and served until 1945. Table 1.43 shows the number of female senators at the beginning of the first session of each Congress.[25]

   (a) Is the number of female senators a function of the Congress's number, c? Explain.

   (b) Is the Congress's number a function of the number of female senators? Explain.

   (c) Let $S(c)$ represent the number of female senators serving in the cth Congress. What does the statement $S(104) = 8$ mean?

   (d) Evaluate and interpret $S(110)$.

Table 1.43 *Female senators, S, in Congress c*

c	96	98	100	102	104	106	108	110	111
S	1	2	2	2	8	9	14	16	17

31. A light is turned off for several hours. It is then turned on. After a few hours it is turned off again. Sketch the light bulb's temperature as a function of time.

32. According to Charles Osgood, CBS news commentator, it takes about one minute to read 15 double-spaced type-written lines on the air.[26]

   (a) Construct a table showing the time Charles Osgood is reading on the air in seconds as a function of the number of double-spaced lines read for $0, 1, 2, \ldots, 10$ lines. From your table, how long does it take Charles Osgood to read 9 lines?

   (b) Plot this data on a graph with the number of lines on the horizontal axis.

   (c) From your graph, estimate how long it takes Charles Osgood to read 9 lines. Estimate how many lines Charles Osgood can read in 30 seconds.

   (d) Construct a formula which relates the time T to n, the number of lines read.

33. The distance between Cambridge and Wellesley is 10 miles. A person walks part of the way at 5 miles per hour, then jogs the rest of the way at 8 mph. Find a formula that expresses the total amount of time for the trip, $T(d)$, as a function of d, the distance walked.

34. A cylindrical can is closed at both ends and its height is twice its radius. Express its surface area, S, as a function of its radius, r. [Hint: The surface of a can consists of a rectangle plus two circular disks.]

35. A lawyer does nothing but sleep and work during a day. There are 1440 minutes in a day. Write a linear function relating minutes of sleep, s, to minutes of work, w.

For the functions in Problems 36–38:

   (a) Find the average rate of change between the points

      (i) $(-1, f(-1))$ and $(3, f(3))$

      (ii) $(a, f(a))$ and $(b, f(b))$

      (iii) $(x, f(x))$ and $(x + h, f(x + h))$

   (b) What pattern do you see in the average rate of change between the three pairs of points?

36. $f(x) = 5x - 4$ **37.** $f(x) = \frac{1}{2}x + \frac{5}{2}$

38. $f(x) = x^2 + 1$

---

[24]Data from the National Hurricane Center, www.nhc.noaa.gov/aboutwindprofile.shtml, accessed October 7, 2004.

[25]http://en.wikipedia.org/wiki/111th United States Congress Members.

[26]T. Parker, *Rules of Thumb* (Boston: Houghton Mifflin, 1983).

39. Table 1.44 gives the average temperature, T, at a depth d, in a borehole in Belleterre, Quebec.[27] Evaluate $\Delta T/\Delta d$ on the following intervals, and explain what your answers tell you about borehole temperature.

(a) $25 \le d \le 150$
(b) $25 \le d \le 75$
(c) $100 \le d \le 200$

Table 1,44

d, depth (m)	25	50	75	100
T, temp (°C)	5.50	5.20	5.10	5.10
d, depth (m)	125	150	175	200
T, temp (°C)	5.30	5.50	5.75	6.00
d, depth (m)	225	250	275	300
T, temp (°C)	6.25	6.50	6.75	7.00

40. The population, $P(t)$, in millions, of a country in year t, is given by the formula $P(t) = 22 + 0.3t$.

(a) Construct a table of values for $t = 0, 10, 20, \ldots ,50$.
(b) Plot the points you found in part (a).
(c) What is the country's initial population?
(d) What is the average rate of change of the population, in millions of people/year?

41. A woodworker sells rocking horses. His start-up costs, including tools, plans, and advertising, total $5000. Labor and materials for each horse cost $350.

(a) Calculate the woodworker's total cost, C, to make 1, 2, 5, 10, and 20 rocking horses. Graph C against n, the number of rocking horses that he carves.
(b) Find a formula for C in terms of n.
(c) What is the rate of change of the function C? What does the rate of change tell us about the woodworker's expenses?

42. Outside the US, temperature readings are usually given in degrees Celsius; inside the US, they are often given in degrees Fahrenheit. The exact conversion from Celsius, C, to Fahrenheit, F, uses the formula

$$F = \frac{9}{5}C + 32.$$

An approximate conversion is obtained by doubling the temperature in Celsius and adding 30° to get the equivalent Fahrenheit temperature.

(a) Write a formula using C and F to express the approximate conversion.

(b) How far off is the approximation if the Celsius temperature is $-5°, 0°, 15°, 30°$?
(c) For what temperature (in Celsius) does the approximation agree with the actual formula?

43. Find a formula for the linear function $h(t)$ whose graph intersects the graph of $j(t) = 30(0.2)^t$ at $t = -2$ and $t = 1$.

44. Find the equation of the line l in Figure 1.68. The shapes under the line are squares.

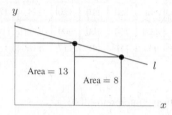

Figure 1.68

45. A bullet is shot straight up into the air from ground level. After t seconds, the velocity of the bullet, in meters per second, is approximated by the formula

$$v = f(t) = 1000 - 9.8t.$$

(a) Evaluate the following: $f(0)$, $f(1)$, $f(2)$, $f(3)$, $f(4)$. Compile your results in a table.
(b) Describe in words what is happening to the speed of the bullet. Discuss why you think this is happening.
(c) Evaluate and interpret the slope and both intercepts of $f(t)$.
(d) The gravitational field near the surface of Jupiter is stronger than that near the surface of the earth, which, in turn, is stronger than the field near the surface of the moon. How is the formula for $f(t)$ different for a bullet shot from Jupiter's surface? From the moon?

46. A theater manager graphed weekly profits as a function of the number of patrons and found that the relationship was linear. One week the profit was $11,328 when 1324 patrons attended. Another week 1529 patrons produced a profit of $13,275.50.

(a) Find a formula for weekly profit, y, as a function of the number of patrons, x.
(b) Interpret the slope and the y-intercept.
(c) What is the break-even point (the number of patrons for which there is zero profit)?

[27]Hugo Beltrami of St. Francis Xavier University and David Chapman of the University of Utah posted this data at http://geophysics.stfx.ca/public/borehole/borehole.html, accessed November 10, 2005.

(d) Find a formula for the number of patrons as a function of profit.

(e) If the weekly profit was \$17,759.50, how many patrons attended the theater?

47. Describe a linear (or nearly linear) relationship that you have encountered outside the classroom. Determine the rate of change and interpret it in practical terms.

48. In economics, the *demand* for a product is the amount of that product that consumers are willing to buy at a given price. The quantity demanded of a product usually decreases if the price of that product increases. Suppose that a company believes there is a linear relationship between the demand for its product and its price. The company knows that when the price of its product was \$3 per unit, the quantity demanded weekly was 500 units, and that when the unit price was raised to \$4, the quantity demanded weekly dropped to 300 units. Let D represent the quantity demanded weekly at a unit price of p dollars.

(a) Calculate D when $p = 5$. Interpret your result.

(b) Find a formula for D in terms of p.

(c) The company raises the price of the good and that the new quantity demanded weekly is 50 units. What is the new price?

(d) Give an economic interpretation of the slope of the function you found in part (b).

(e) Find D when $p = 0$. Find p when $D = 0$. Give economic interpretations of both these results.

49. In economics, the *supply* of a product is the quantity of that product suppliers are willing to provide at a given price. In theory, the quantity supplied of a product increases if the price of that product increases. Suppose that there is a linear relationship between the quantity supplied, S, of the product described in Problem 48 and its price, p. The quantity supplied weekly is 100 when the price is \$2 and the quantity supplied rises by 50 units when the price rises by \$0.50.

(a) Find a formula for S in terms of p.

(b) Interpret the slope of your formula in economic terms.

(c) Is there a price below which suppliers will not provide this product?

(d) The *market clearing price* is the price at which supply equals demand. According to theory, the free-market price of a product is its market clearing price. Using the demand function from Problem 48, find the market clearing price for this product.

50. When economists graph demand or supply equations, they place quantity on the horizontal axis and price on the vertical axis.

(a) On the same set of axes, graph the demand and supply equations you found in Problems 48 and 49, with price on the vertical axis.

(b) Indicate how you could estimate the market clearing price from your graph.

51. The figure gives graphs of g, a linear function, and of $f(x) = 12 - 0.5(x+4)^2$. Find a possible formula for g.

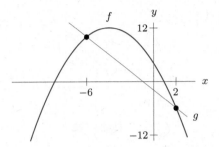

52. Write in slope-intercept form and identify the values of b and m:
$$f(r) = rx^3 + 3rx^2 + 2r + 4sx + 7s + 3.$$

53. Find an equation for the line intersecting the graph of f at $x = -2$ and $x = 5$ given that $f(x) = 2 + \dfrac{3}{x+5}$.

54. A business consultant works 10 hours a day, 6 days a week. She divides her time between meetings with clients and meetings with co-workers. A client meeting requires 3 hours while a co-worker meeting requires 2 hours. Let x be the number of co-worker meetings the consultant holds during a given week. If y is the number of client meetings for which she has time remaining, then y is a function of x. Assume this relationship is linear and that meetings can be split up and continued on different days.

(a) Graph the relationship between y and x. [Hint: Consider the maximum number of client and co-worker meetings that can be held.]

(b) Find a formula for y as a function of x.

(c) Explain what the slope and the x- and y-intercepts represent in the context of the consultant's meeting schedule.

(d) A change is made so that co-worker meetings take 90 minutes instead of 2 hours. Graph this situation. Describe those features of this graph that have changed from the one sketched in part (a) and those that have remained the same.

55. You start 60 miles east of Pittsburgh and drive east at a constant speed of 50 miles per hour. (Assume that the road is straight and permits you to do this.) Find a formula for d, your distance from Pittsburgh as a function of t, the number of hours of travel.

56. Find a formula for the line parallel to the line $y = 20 - 4x$ and containing the point $(3, 12)$.

57. Find the equation of the linear function g whose graph is perpendicular to the line $5x - 3y = 6$; the two lines intersect at $x = 15$.

58. Find the coordinates of point P in Figure 1.69.

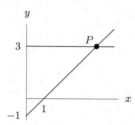

Figure 1.69

59. You want to choose one long-distance telephone company from the following options.

- Company A charges $0.37 per minute.
- Company B charges $13.95 per month plus $0.22 per minute.
- Company C charges a fixed rate of $50 per month.

Let Y_A, Y_B, Y_C represent the monthly charges using Company A, B, and C, respectively. Let x be the number of minutes per month spent on long-distance calls.

(a) Find formulas for Y_A, Y_B, Y_C as functions of x.

(b) Figure 1.70 gives the graphs of the functions in part (a). Which function corresponds to which graph?

(c) Find the x-values for which Company B is cheapest.

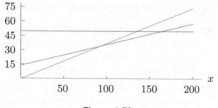

Figure 1.70

60. A commission is a payment made to an employee based on a percentage of sales made. For example, car salespeople earn commission on the selling price of a car. In parts (a)–(d), explain how to choose between the options for different levels of sales.

(a) A weekly salary of $100 or a weekly salary of $50 plus 10% commission.

(b) A weekly salary of $175 plus 7% commission or a weekly salary of $175 plus 8% commission.

(c) A weekly salary of $145 plus 7% commission or a weekly salary of $165 plus 7% commission.

(d) A weekly salary of $225 plus 3% commission or a weekly salary of $180 plus 6% commission.

61. Table 1.45 shows the IQ of ten students and the number of hours of TV each watches per week.

(a) Make a scatter plot of the data.

(b) By eye, make a rough estimate of the correlation coefficient.

(c) Use a calculator or computer to find the least squares regression line and the correlation coefficient. Your values should be correct to four decimal places.

Table 1.45

IQ	110	105	120	140	100	125	130	105	115	110
TV	10	12	8	2	12	10	5	6	13	3

62. For 35 years, major league baseball Hall of Fame member Henry Aaron held the record for the greatest number of career home runs. His record was broken by Barry Bonds in 2007. Table 1.46 shows Aaron's cumulative yearly record [28] from the start of his career, 1954, until 1973.

(a) Plot Aaron's cumulative number of home runs H on the vertical axis, and the time t in years along the horizontal axis, where $t = 1$ corresponds to 1954.

(b) By eye, draw a straight line that fits these data well and find its equation.

(c) Use a calculator or computer to find the equation of the regression line for these data. What is the correlation coefficient, r, to 4 decimal places? To 3 decimal places? What does this tell you?

(d) What does the slope of the regression line mean in terms of Henry Aaron's home-run record?

(e) From your answer to part (d), how many home runs do you estimate Henry Aaron hit in each of the years 1974, 1975, 1976, and 1977? If you were told that Henry Aaron retired at the end of the 1976 season, would this affect your answers?

Table 1.46   *Henry Aaron's cumulative home-run record, H, from 1954 to 1973, with t in years since 1953*

t	1	2	3	4	5	6	7	8	9	10
H	13	40	66	110	140	179	219	253	298	342
t	11	12	13	14	15	16	17	18	19	20
H	366	398	442	481	510	554	592	639	673	713

[28] Adapted from "Graphing Henry Aaron's home-run output" by H. Ringel, *The Physics Teacher*, January 1974, page 43.

63. The graph of a linear function $y = f(x)$ passes through the two points $(a, f(a))$ and $(b, f(b))$, where $a < b$ and $f(a) < f(b)$.

  (a) Graph the function labeling the two points.
  (b) Find the slope of the line in terms of f, a, and b.

64. Let $f(x) = 0.003 - (1.246x + 0.37)$.

  (a) Calculate the following average rates of change:

  (i) $\dfrac{f(2) - f(1)}{2 - 1}$ (ii) $\dfrac{f(1) - f(2)}{1 - 2}$

  (iii) $\dfrac{f(3) - f(4)}{3 - 4}$

  (b) Rewrite $f(x)$ in the form $f(x) = b + mx$.

Write the linear function $y = -3 - x/2$ in the forms given in Problems 65–66, assuming all constants are positive.

65. $y = \dfrac{p}{p - 1} - r^2 x$ **66.** $y = \dfrac{x + k}{z}$

67. You spend c dollars on x apples and y bananas. In Figure 1.71, line l gives y as a function of x.

  (a) If apples cost p dollars each and bananas cost q each, label the x- and y-intercepts of l. [Note: Your labels will involve the constants p, q or c.]
  (b) What is the slope of l?

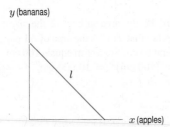

y (bananas)

l

x (apples)

Figure 1.71: Axes not necessarily to scale

68. The apples in Problem 67 cost more than bananas, so $p > q$. Which of the two lines, l_1 or l_2, in Figure 1.72 could represent $y = f(x)$?

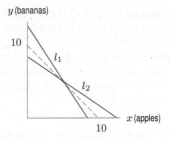

y (bananas)

10

l_1

l_2

10   x (apples)

Figure 1.72

69. Many people think that hair growth is stimulated by haircuts. In fact, there is no difference in the rate hair grows after a haircut, but there *is* a difference in the rate at which hair's ends break off. A haircut eliminates dead and split ends, thereby slowing the rate at which hair breaks. However, even with regular haircuts, hair will not grow to an indefinite length. The average life cycle of human scalp hair is 3-5 years, after which the hair is shed.[29]

Judy trims her hair once a year, when its growth is slowed by split ends. She cuts off just enough to eliminate dead and split ends, and then lets it grow another year. After 5 years, she realizes her hair won't grow any longer. Graph the length of her hair as a function of time. Indicate when she receives her haircuts.

70. Academics have suggested that loss of worker productivity can result from sleep deprivation. An article in the September 26, 1993, *New York Times* quotes David Poltrack, the senior vice president for planning and research at CBS, as saying that seven million Americans are staying up an hour later than usual to watch talk show host David Letterman. The article goes on to quote Timothy Monk, a professor at the University of Pittsburgh School of Medicine, as saying, ". . . my hunch is that the effect [on productivity due to sleep deprivation among this group] would be in the area of a 10 percent decrement." The article next quotes Robert Solow, a Nobel prize-winning professor of economics at MIT, who suggests the following procedure to estimate the impact that this loss in productivity will have on the US economy— an impact he dubbed "the Letterman loss." First, Solow says, we find the percentage of the work force who watch the program. Next, we determine this group's contribution to the gross domestic product (GDP). Then we reduce the group's contribution by 10% to account for the loss in productivity due to sleep deprivation. The amount of this reduction is "the Letterman loss."

  (a) The article estimated that the GDP is $6.325 trillion, and that 7 million Americans watch the show. Assume that the nation's work force is 118 million

---

[29]*Britannica Micropaedia* vol. 5 (Chicago: Encyclopaedia Britannica, Inc., 1989).

people and that 75% of David Letterman's audience belongs to this group. What percentage of the work force is in Dave's audience?

(b) What percent of the GDP would be expected to come from David Letterman's audience? How much money would they have contributed if they had not watched the show?

(c) How big is "the Letterman loss"?

71. Judging from the graph of $y = f(x)$ in the figure, find a possible formula for the line intersecting it at $x = -2\pi$ and $x = 3\pi$.

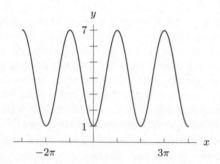

Problems 72–74 refer to Table 1.47, which describes a *boustrophedonic pairing function*. [30] We can use this table to list all the positive roots of the positive integers, such as $\sqrt{2}$, $\sqrt{3}$, $\sqrt[3]{2}$, $\sqrt[3]{3}$, $\sqrt[4]{2}$, $\sqrt[4]{3}$, ..., without omitting any. If n is an entry in the table, we let c stand for the column number and r the row number of the entry and define the function g by

$$g(n) = c^{1/r}.$$

For instance, if $n = 6$, then $c = 2$ and $r = 3$ so we have $g(6) = 2^{1/3}$, or $\sqrt[3]{2}$.

Table 1.47

	1	2	3	4	5	6	⋯
1	1	2	9	10	25	26	⋯
2	4	3	8	11	24	27	⋯
3	5	6	7	12	23	28	⋯
4	16	15	14	13	22	29	⋯
5	17	18	19	20	21	30	⋯
6	36	35	34	33	32	31	⋯
⋮	⋮	⋮	⋮	⋮	⋮	⋮	⋱

72. Evaluate $g(22)$.   **73.** Evaluate $g(54)$.

74. Find a solution to $g(n) = \sqrt{3}$. Is this solution unique? Explain your reasoning.

Problems 75–76 ask about the A series of paper. Many countries use A4 paper, which is somewhat different from the 8.5 by 11 inch paper standard in the US.[31] A4 is part of a series of paper sizes specified in ISO 216, an international standard. Two sheets of A4 paper, if laid side by side (not end to end), are the same size as one sheet of A3 paper. Likewise, two sheets of A3 are the same as one sheet of A2, and so on. See Figure 1.73. Each sheet in the series has the same proportions, length to width, and the largest sheet, A0, has an area of exactly 1 m².

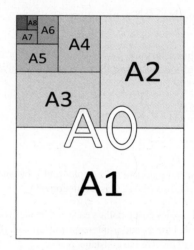

Figure 1.73

75. Let $f(n)$ be the area in cm² of the size n sheet in the A-series, so that $f(1)$ is the area of A1 paper, $f(2)$ of A2 paper, and so on. Since 1 m equals 100 cm, we know that $f(0) = (100 \text{ cm})^2 = 10{,}000 \text{ cm}^2$. Complete the table of values of f.

Table 1.48

n	0	1	2	3	4	5
$f(n)$	10,000					

---

[30] The term *boustrophedonic* means "ox-plowing": Notice how the entries in the table, 1, 2, 3, 4 ..., turn back and forth, like an ox plowing a field.

[31] http://en.wikipedia.org/wiki/ISO_216, accessed January 30, 2008. Note that the actual sizes of A-series paper are rounded to the nearest millimeter.

76. We know that A1 paper has the same proportion (length over width) as A0. Further, the length of A1 paper is the same as the width W of A0, and the width of A1 is half the length L of A0. (See the figure.)

    (a) Find a formula for L in terms of W. What does your formula tell you about the shape of A-series paper? How does the shape compare to US letter paper?

    (b) Given that A4 paper has area 625 cm^2, find its width and height.

CHECK YOUR UNDERSTANDING

Are the statements in Problems 1–54 true or false? Give an explanation for your answer.

1. $Q = f(t)$ means Q is equal to f times t.

2. A function must be defined by a formula.

3. If $P = f(x)$ then P is called the dependent variable.

4. Independent variables are always denoted by the letter x or t.

5. It is possible for two quantities to be related and yet neither be a function of the other.

6. A function is a rule that takes certain values as inputs and assigns to each input value exactly one output value.

7. It is possible for a table of values to represent a function.

8. If Q is a function of P, then P is a function of Q.

9. The graph of a circle is not the graph of a function.

10. If $n = f(A)$ is the number of angels that can dance on the head of a pin whose area is A square millimeters, then $f(10) = 100$ tells us that 10 angels can dance on the head of a pin whose area is 100 square millimeters.

11. Average speed can be computed by dividing the distance traveled by the time elapsed.

12. The average rate of change of a function Q with respect to t over an interval can be symbolically represented as $\dfrac{\Delta t}{\Delta Q}$.

13. If $y = f(x)$ and as x increases, y increases, then f is an increasing function.

14. If f is a decreasing function, then the average rate of change of f on any interval is negative.

15. The average rate of change of a function over an interval is the slope of a line connecting two points of the graph of the function.

16. The average rate of change of $y = 3x - 4$ between $x = 2$ and $x = 6$ is 7.

17. The average rate of change of $f(x) = 10 - x^2$ between $x = 1$ and $x = 2$ is the ratio $\dfrac{10 - 2^2 - 10 - 1^2}{2 - 1}$.

18. If $y = x^2$ then the slope of the line connecting the point $(2, 4)$ to the point $(3, 9)$ is the same as the slope of the line connecting the point $(-2, 4)$ to the point $(-3, 9)$.

19. A linear function can have different rates of change over different intervals.

20. The graph of a linear function is a straight line.

21. If a line has the equation $3x + 2y = 7$, then the slope of the line is 3.

22. A table of values represents a linear function if $\dfrac{\text{Change in output}}{\text{Change in input}} = \text{constant}$.

23. If a linear function is decreasing, then its slope is negative.

24. If $y = f(x)$ is linear and its slope is negative, then in the expression $\dfrac{\Delta y}{\Delta x}$ either Δx or Δy is negative, but not both.

25. A linear function can have a slope that is zero.

26. If a line has slope 2 and y-intercept -3, then its equation may be written $y = -3x + 2$.

27. The line $3x + 5y = 7$ has slope $3/5$.

28. A line that goes through the point $(-2, 3)$ and whose slope is 4 has the equation $y = 4x + 5$.

29. The line $4x + 3y = 52$ intersects the x-axis at $x = 13$.

30. If $f(x) = -2x + 7$ then $f(2) = 3$.

31. The line that passes through the points $(1, 2)$ and $(4, -10)$ has slope 4.

32. The linear equation $y - 5 = 4(x + 1)$ is equivalent to the equation $y = 4x + 6$.

33. The line $y - 4 = -2(x + 3)$ goes through the point $(4, -3)$.

34. The line whose equation is $y = 3 - 7x$ has slope -7.

35. The line $y = -5x + 8$ intersects the y-axis at $y = 8$.

36. The equation $y = -2 - \frac{2}{3}x$ represents a linear function.

37. The lines $y = 8 - 3x$ and $-2x + 16y = 8$ both cross the y-axis at $y = 8$.

38. The graph of $f(x) = 6$ is a line whose slope is six.

39. The lines $y = -\frac{4}{5}x + 7$ and $4x - 5y = 8$ are parallel.

40. The lines $y = 7 + 9x$ and $y - 4 = -\frac{1}{9}(x + 5)$ are perpendicular.

41. The lines $y = -2x + 5$ and $y = 6x - 3$ intersect at the point $(1, 3)$.

42. If two lines never intersect then their slopes are equal.

43. The equation of a line parallel to the y-axis could be $y = -\frac{3}{4}$.

44. A line parallel to the x-axis has slope zero.

45. The slope of a vertical line is undefined.

46. Fitting the best line to a set of data is called linear regression.

47. The process of estimating a value within the range for which we have data is called interpolation.

48. Extrapolation tends to be more reliable than interpolation.

49. If two quantities have a high correlation then one quantity causes the other.

50. If the correlation coefficient is zero, there is not a relationship between the two quantities.

51. A correlation coefficient can have a value of $-\frac{3}{7}$.

52. A value of a correlation coefficient is always between negative and positive one.

53. A correlation coefficient of one indicates that all the data points lie on a straight line.

54. A regression line is also referred to as a least squares line.

SKILLS REFRESHER FOR CHAPTER ONE: LINEAR EQUATIONS AND THE COORDINATE PLANE

Solving Linear Equations

To solve a linear equation, we isolate the variable.

Example 1   Solve $22 + 1.3t = 31.1$ for t.

Solution   We subtract 22 from both sides. Since $31.1 - 22 = 9.1$, we have

$$1.3t = 9.1.$$

We divide both sides by 1.3, so

$$t = \frac{9.1}{1.3} = 7.$$

Example 2   Solve $3 - [5.4 + 2(4.3 - x)] = 2 - (0.3x - 0.8)$ for x.

Solution   We begin by clearing the innermost parentheses on each side. Using the distributive law, this gives

$$3 - [5.4 + 8.6 - 2x] = 2 - 0.3x + 0.8.$$

Then

$$3 - 14 + 2x = 2 - 0.3x + 0.8$$
$$2.3x = 13.8,$$
$$x = 6.$$

Example 3   Solve $ax = c + bx$ for x. Assume $a \neq b$.

Solution   To solve for x, we first get all the terms involving x on the left side by subtracting bx from both sides

$$ax - bx = c.$$

Factoring on the left, $ax - bx = (a - b)x$, enables us to solve for x by dividing both sides by $(a - b)$:

$$x(a - b) = c$$
$$x = \frac{c}{(a - b)}.$$

Since $a \neq b$, division by $(a - b)$ is possible.

Example 4   Solve for q if $p^2 q + r(-q - 1) = 4(p + r)$.

Solution   We first collect all the terms containing q on the left side of the equation.

$$p^2 q - rq - r = 4p + 4r$$
$$p^2 q - rq = 4p + 5r.$$

To solve for q, we factor and then divide by the coefficient of q.

$$q(p^2 - r) = 4p + 5r$$
$$q = \frac{4p + 5r}{p^2 - r}.$$

Solving Exactly Versus Solving Approximately

Some equations can be solved exactly, often by using algebra. For example, the equation $7x - 1 = 0$ has the exact solution $x = 1/7$. Other equations can be hard or even impossible to solve exactly. However, it is often possible, and sometimes easier, to find an approximate solution to an equation by using a graph or a numerical method on a calculator. The equation $7x - 1 = 0$ has the approximate solution $x \approx 0.14$ (since $1/7 = 0.142857...$). We use the sign $\approx$, meaning approximately equal, when we want to emphasize that we are making an approximation.

Systems of Linear Equations

To solve for two unknowns, we must have two equations—that is, two relationships between the unknowns. Similarly, three unknowns require three equations, and n unknowns (n an integer) require n equations. The group of equations is known as a *system* of equations. To solve the system, we find the *simultaneous* solutions to all equations in the system.

We can solve these equations either by *substitution* (see Example 5) or by *elimination* (see Example 6).

Example 5   Solve for x and y in the following system of equations using substitution.

$$\begin{cases} y + \dfrac{x}{2} = 3 \\ 2(x + y) = 1 - y \end{cases}$$

Solution   Solving the first equation for y, we write $y = 3 - x/2$. Substituting for y in the second equation gives

$$2\left(x + \left(3 - \frac{x}{2}\right)\right) = 1 - \left(3 - \frac{x}{2}\right).$$

Then

$$2x + 6 - x = -2 + \frac{x}{2}$$
$$x + 6 = -2 + \frac{x}{2}$$
$$2x + 12 = -4 + x$$
$$x = -16.$$

Using $x = -16$ in the first equation to find the corresponding y, we have

$$y - \frac{16}{2} = 3$$
$$y = 3 + 8 = 11.$$

Thus, the solution that simultaneously solves both equations is $x = -16$, $y = 11$.

Example 6   Solve for x and y in the following system of equations using elimination.

$$\begin{cases} 8x - 5y = 11 \\ -2x + 10y = -1. \end{cases}$$

Solution   To eliminate y, we observe that if we multiply the first equation by 2, the coefficients of y are -10 and 10:

$$\begin{cases} 16x - 10y = 22 \\ -2x + 10y = -1. \end{cases}$$

Adding these two equations gives

$$14x = 21$$
$$x = 3/2.$$

We can substitute this value for x in either of the original equations to find y. For example,

$$8\left(\frac{3}{2}\right) - 5y = 11$$
$$12 - 5y = 11$$
$$-5y = -1$$
$$y = 1/5$$

Thus, the solution is $x = 3/2, y = 1/5$.

Intersection of Two Lines

The coordinates of the point of intersection of two lines satisfy the equations of both lines. Thus, the point can be found by solving the equations simultaneously.

Example 7   Find the point of intersection of the lines $y = 3 - \frac{2}{3}x$ and $y = -4 + \frac{3}{2}x$.

Solution   Since the y-values of the two lines are equal at the point of intersection, we have

$$-4 + \frac{3}{2}x = 3 - \frac{2}{3}x.$$

Notice that we have converted a pair of equations into a single equation by eliminating one of the two variables. This equation can be simplified by multiplying both sides by 6:

$$6\left(-4 + \frac{3}{2}x\right) = 6\left(3 - \frac{2}{3}x\right)$$
$$-24 + 9x = 18 - 4x$$
$$13x = 42$$
$$x = \frac{42}{13}.$$

We can evaluate either of the original equations at $x = \frac{42}{13}$ to find y. For example, $y = -4 + \frac{3}{2}x$ gives

$$y = -4 + \frac{3}{2}\left(\frac{42}{13}\right) = \frac{11}{13}.$$

Therefore, the point of intersection is $\left(\dfrac{42}{13}, \dfrac{11}{13}\right)$. You can check that this point also satisfies the other equation. The lines and their point of intersection are shown in Figure 1.74.

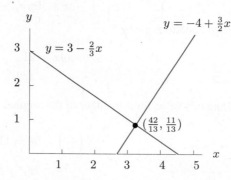

Figure 1.74: Intersection of lines is solution to simultaneous equations

Exercises Skills for Chapter 1

Solve the equations in Exercises 1–12.

1. $3x = 15$

2. $-2y = 12$

3. $4z = 22$

4. $x + 3 = 10$

5. $w - 23 = -34$

6. $7 - 3y = -14$

7. $13t + 2 = 47$

8. $0.5x - 3 = 7$

9. $3t - \dfrac{2(t-1)}{3} = 4$

10. $2(r + 5) - 3 = 3(r - 8) + 21$

11. $B - 4[B - 3(1 - B)] = 42$

12. $1.06s - 0.01(248.4 - s) = 22.67s$

In Exercises 13–22, solve for the indicated variable.

13. $A = l \cdot w$, for l.

14. $l = l_0 + \dfrac{k}{2}w$, for w.

15. $h = v_0 t + \dfrac{1}{2}at^2$, for a.

16. $3xy + 1 = 2y - 5x$, for y.

17. $u(v + 2) + w(v - 3) = z(v - 1)$, for v.

18. $S = \dfrac{rL - a}{r - 1}$, for r.

19. $\dfrac{a - cx}{b + dx} + a = 0$, for x.

20. $\dfrac{At - B}{C - B(1 - 2t)} = 3$, for t.

21. $y'y^2 + 2xyy' = 4y$, for y'.

22. $2x - (xy' + yy') + 2yy' = 0$, for y'.

Solve the systems of equations in Exercises 23–27.

23. $\begin{cases} 3x - 2y = 6 \\ y = 2x - 5 \end{cases}$

24. $\begin{cases} x = 7y - 9 \\ 4x - 15y = 26 \end{cases}$

25. $\begin{cases} 2x + 3y = 7 \\ y = -\frac{3}{5}x + 6 \end{cases}$

26. $\begin{cases} 3x - y = 17 \\ -2x - 3y = -4 \end{cases}$

27. $\begin{cases} ax + y = 2a \\ x + ay = 1 + a^2 \end{cases}$

Determine the points of intersection for Exercises 28–29.

28.

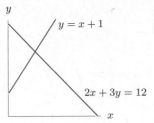

$y = x + 1$

$2x + 3y = 12$

29.

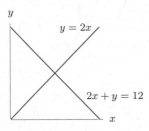

$y = 2x$

$2x + y = 12$

The figures in Problems 30–31 are parallelograms. Find the coordinates of the labeled point(s).

30.

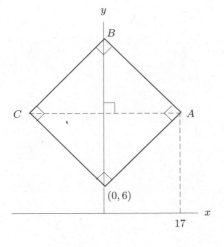

B

C A

$(0, 6)$

17

31.

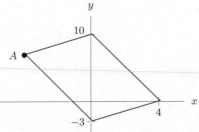

10

A

-3 4

The figures in Problems 32–35 contain a semicircle with the center marked. Find the coordinates of A, a point on the diameter, and B, an extreme point (highest, lowest, or farthest to the right).

32.

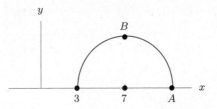

B

3 7 A

33.

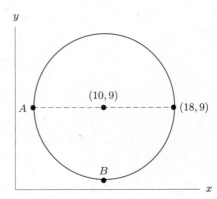

A $(10, 9)$ $(18, 9)$

B

34.

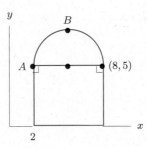

B

A $(8, 5)$

2

35.

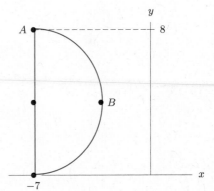

A 8

B

-7

Chapter Two

FUNCTIONS

Contents

2.1 INPUT AND OUTPUT

Finding Output Values: Evaluating a Function

Evaluating a function means calculating the value of a function's output from a particular value of the input.

In the housepainting example on page 4, the notation $n = f(A)$ indicates that the number of gallons of paint n is a function of area A. The expression $f(A)$ represents the output of the function—specifically, the amount of paint required to cover an area of A ft². For example, $f(20,000)$ represents the number of gallons of paint required to cover an area of 20,000 ft².

Example 1   Using the fact that 1 gallon of paint covers 250 ft², evaluate the expression $f(20,000)$.

Solution   To evaluate $f(20,000)$, calculate the number of gallons required to cover 20,000 ft²:

$$f(20,000) = \frac{20,000 \text{ ft}^2}{250 \text{ ft}^2/\text{gallon}} = 80 \text{ gallons of paint.}$$

Evaluating a Function Using a Formula

If we have a formula for a function, we evaluate it by substituting the input value into the formula.

Example 2   The formula for the area of a circle of radius r is $A = q(r) = \pi r^2$. Use the formula to evaluate $q(10)$ and $q(20)$. What do your results tell you about circles?

Solution   In the expression $q(10)$, the value of r is 10, so

$$q(10) = \pi \cdot 10^2 = 100\pi \approx 314.$$

Similarly, substituting $r = 20$, we have

$$q(20) = \pi \cdot 20^2 = 400\pi \approx 1257.$$

The statements $q(10) \approx 314$ and $q(20) \approx 1257$ tell us that a circle of radius 10 cm has an area of approximately 314 cm² and a circle of radius 20 cm has an area of approximately 1257 cm².

Example 3   Let $g(x) = \dfrac{x^2 + 1}{5 + x}$. Evaluate the following expressions.

(a) $g(3)$ (b) $g(-1)$ (c) $g(a)$

Solution   (a) To evaluate $g(3)$, replace every x in the formula with 3:

$$g(3) = \frac{3^2 + 1}{5 + 3} = \frac{10}{8} = 1.25.$$

(b) To evaluate $g(-1)$, replace every x in the formula with (-1):

$$g(-1) = \frac{(-1)^2 + 1}{5 + (-1)} = \frac{2}{4} = 0.5.$$

(c) To evaluate $g(a)$, replace every x in the formula with a:

$$g(a) = \frac{a^2 + 1}{5 + a}.$$

Evaluating a function may involve algebraic simplification, as the following example shows.

Example 4   Let $h(x) = x^2 - 3x + 5$. Evaluate and simplify the following expressions.

(a) $h(2)$ (b) $h(a-2)$ (c) $h(a) - 2$ (d) $h(a) - h(2)$

Solution   Notice that x is the input and $h(x)$ is the output. It is helpful to rewrite the formula as

$$\text{Output} = h(\text{Input}) = (\text{Input})^2 - 3 \cdot (\text{Input}) + 5.$$

(a) For $h(2)$, we have Input $= 2$, so

$$h(2) = (2)^2 - 3 \cdot (2) + 5 = 3.$$

(b) In this case, Input $= a - 2$. We substitute and multiply out

$$\begin{aligned} h(a-2) &= (a-2)^2 - 3(a-2) + 5 \\ &= a^2 - 4a + 4 - 3a + 6 + 5 \\ &= a^2 - 7a + 15. \end{aligned}$$

(c) First input a, then subtract 2:

$$\begin{aligned} h(a) - 2 &= a^2 - 3a + 5 - 2 \\ &= a^2 - 3a + 3. \end{aligned}$$

(d) Since we found $h(2) = 3$ in part (a), we subtract from $h(a)$:

$$\begin{aligned} h(a) - h(2) &= a^2 - 3a + 5 - 3 \\ &= a^2 - 3a + 2. \end{aligned}$$

Finding Input Values: Solving Equations

Given an input, we evaluate the function to find the output. Sometimes the situation is reversed; we know the output and we want to find a corresponding input. If the function is given by a formula, the input values are solutions to an equation.

Example 5   Use the cricket function $T = \frac{1}{4}R + 40$, introduced on page 3, to find the rate, R, at which the snowy tree cricket chirps when the temperature, T, is $76°$F.

Solution   We want to find R when $T = 76$. Substitute $T = 76$ into the formula and solve the equation

$$76 = \frac{1}{4}R + 40$$

$$36 = \frac{1}{4}R \quad \text{subtract 40 from both sides}$$

$$144 = R. \quad \text{multiply both sides by 4}$$

The cricket chirps at a rate of 144 chirps per minute when the temperature is $76°$F.

Example 6   Suppose $f(x) = \dfrac{1}{\sqrt{x-4}}$.

(a) Find an x-value that results in $f(x) = 2$.
(b) Is there an x-value that results in $f(x) = -2$?

Solution   (a) To find an x-value that results in $f(x) = 2$, solve the equation

$$2 = \frac{1}{\sqrt{x-4}}.$$

Square both sides:

$$4 = \frac{1}{x - 4}.$$

Now multiply by $(x - 4)$:

$$4(x - 4) = 1$$
$$4x - 16 = 1$$
$$x = \frac{17}{4} = 4.25.$$

The x-value is 4.25. (Note that the simplification $(x - 4)/(x - 4) = 1$ in the second step was valid because $x - 4 \neq 0$.)

(b) Since $\sqrt{x - 4}$ is nonnegative if it is defined, its reciprocal, $f(x) = \dfrac{1}{\sqrt{x - 4}}$ is also nonnegative if it is defined. Thus, $f(x)$ is not negative for any x input, so there is no x-value that results in $f(x) = -2$.

In the next example, we solve an equation for a quantity that is being used to model a physical quantity; we must choose the solutions that make sense in the context of the model.

Example 7   Let $A = q(r)$ be the area of a circle of radius r, where r is in cm. What is the radius of a circle whose area is 100 cm²?

Solution   The output $q(r)$ is an area. Solving the equation $q(r) = 100$ for r gives the radius of a circle whose area is 100 cm². Since the formula for the area of a circle is $q(r) = \pi r^2$, we solve

$$q(r) = \pi r^2 = 100$$
$$r^2 = \frac{100}{\pi}$$
$$r = \pm\sqrt{\frac{100}{\pi}} = \pm 5.642.$$

We have two solutions for r, one positive and one negative. Since a circle cannot have a negative radius, we take $r = 5.642$ cm. A circle of area 100 cm² has a radius of 5.642 cm.

Finding Output and Input Values From Tables and Graphs

The following two examples use function notation with a table and a graph respectively.

Example 8   Table 2.1 shows the revenue, $R = f(t)$, received, by the National Football League,[1] NFL, from network TV as a function of the year, t, since 1975.

(a) Evaluate and interpret $f(25)$.   (b) Solve and interpret $f(t) = 1159$.

Table 2.1

Year, t (since 1975)	0	5	10	15	20	25	30
Revenue, R (million $)	201	364	651	1075	1159	2200	2200

Solution   (a) Table 2.1 shows $f(25) = 2200$. Since $t = 25$ in the year 2000, we know that NFL's revenue from TV was $2200 million in the year 2000.

(b) Solving $f(t) = 1159$ means finding the year in which TV revenues were $1159 million; it is $t = 20$. In 1995, NFL's TV revenues were $1159 million.

---

[1]*Newsweek*, January 26, 1998.

Example 9   A man drives from his home to a store and back. The entire trip takes 30 minutes. Figure 2.1 gives his velocity $v(t)$ (in mph) as a function of the time t (in minutes) since he left home. A negative velocity indicates that he is traveling away from the store back to his home.

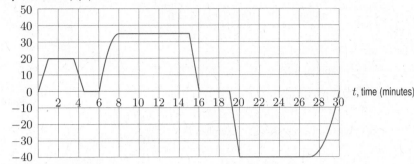

Figure 2.1: Velocity of a man on a trip to the store and back

Evaluate and interpret:

(a) $v(5)$ (b) $v(24)$ (c) $v(8) - v(6)$ (d) $v(-3)$

Solve for t and interpret:

(e) $v(t) = 15$ (f) $v(t) = -20$ (g) $v(t) = v(7)$

Solution   (a) To evaluate $v(5)$, look on the graph where $t = 5$ minutes. Five minutes after he left home, his velocity is 0 mph. Thus, $v(5) = 0$. Perhaps he had to stop at a light.

(b) The graph shows that $v(24) = -40$ mph. After 24 minutes, he is traveling at 40 mph away from the store, back to his home.

(c) From the graph, $v(8) = 35$ mph and $v(6) = 0$ mph. Thus, $v(8) - v(6) = 35 - 0 = 35$. This shows that the man's speed increased by 35 mph in the interval between $t = 6$ minutes and $t = 8$ minutes.

(d) The quantity $v(-3)$ is not defined since the graph only gives velocities for nonnegative times.

(e) To solve for t when $v(t) = 15$, look on the graph where the velocity is 15 mph. This occurs at $t \approx 0.75$ minute, 3.75 minutes, 6.5 minutes, and 15.5 minutes. At each of these four times the man's velocity was 15 mph.

(f) To solve $v(t) = -20$ for t, we see that the velocity is -20 mph (that is, 20 mph toward home) at $t \approx 19.5$ and $t \approx 29$ minutes.

(g) First we evaluate $v(7) \approx 27$. To solve $v(t) = 27$, we look for the values of t making the velocity 27 mph. One such t is of course $t = 7$; the other t is $t \approx 15$ minutes. These are the two times when the velocity is the same as it is at 7 minutes.

Exercises and Problems for Section 2.1

Skill Refresher

For Exercises S1–S6, expand and simplify.

S1. $5(x - 3)$

S2. $a(2a + 5)$

S3. $(m - 5)(4(m - 5) + 2)$

S4. $(x + 2)(3x - 8)$

S5. $3\left(1 + \dfrac{1}{x}\right)$

S6. $3 + 2\left(\dfrac{1}{x}\right)^2 - x$

Solve the equations in Exercises S7–S10.

S7. $x^2 - 9 = 0$

S8. $\sqrt{2x - 1} + 3 = 9$

S9. $\dfrac{21}{z - 5} - \dfrac{13}{z^2 - 5z} = 3$

S10. $2x^{\frac{3}{2}} - 1 = 7$

Exercises

1. If $f(t) = t^2 - 4$, (a) Find $f(0)$ (b) Solve $f(t) = 0$.
2. If $g(x) = x^2 - 5x + 6$, (a) Find $g(0)$ (b) Solve $g(x) = 0$.

3. If $g(t) = \dfrac{1}{t+2} - 1$, (a) Find $g(0)$ (b) Solve $g(t) = 0$.

4. If $h(x) = ax^2 + bx + c$, find $h(0)$.

5. If $g(x) = -\frac{1}{2}x^{1/3}$, find $g(-27)$.

6. Let $f(x) = \dfrac{2x+1}{x+1}$. For what value of x is $f(x) = 0.3$?

If $p(r) = r^2 + 5$, evaluate the expressions in Exercises 7–8.

7. $p(7)$
8. $p(x) + p(8)$

In Figure 2.2, mark the point(s) representing the statements in Exercises 9–12 and label their coordinates.

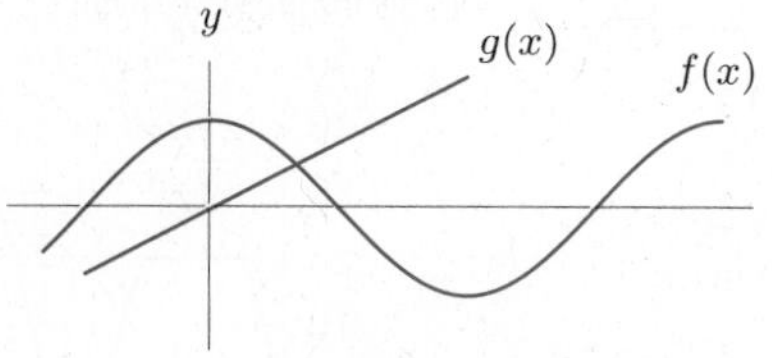

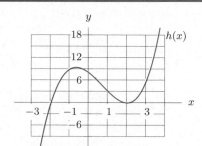

Figure 2.2

9. $f(0) = 2$
10. $f(-3) = f(3) = f(9) = 0$
11. $f(2) = g(2)$
12. $g(x) > f(x)$ for $x > 2$

Problems

13. Let $F = g(t)$ be the number of foxes in a park as a function of t, the number of months since January 1. Evaluate $g(9)$ using Table 1.3 on page 5. What does this tell us about the fox population?

14. Let $F = g(t)$ be the number of foxes in month t in the national park described in Example 5 on page 5. Solve the equation $g(t) = 75$. What does your solution tell you about the fox population?

15. Let $f(x) = 3 + 2x^2$. Find $f\left(\dfrac{1}{3}\right)$ and $\dfrac{f(1)}{f(3)}$. Are they equal?

16. Let $g(x) = x^2 + x$. Find formulas for the following functions. Simplify your answers.

   (a) $g(-3x)$ (b) $g(1-x)$ (c) $g(x+\pi)$
   (d) $g(\sqrt{x})$ (e) $g(1/(x+1))$ (f) $g(x^2)$

17. Let $f(x) = \dfrac{x}{x-1}$.

   (a) Find and simplify

   (i) $f\left(\dfrac{1}{t}\right)$ (ii) $f\left(\dfrac{1}{t+1}\right)$

   (b) Solve $f(x) = 3$.

18. (a) Using Figure 2.3, fill in Table 2.2.

   Table 2.2

x	-2	-1	0	1	2	3
$h(x)$						

   (b) Evaluate $h(3) - h(1)$ (c) Evaluate $h(2) - h(0)$
   (d) Evaluate $2h(0)$ (e) Evaluate $h(1) + 3$

Figure 2.3

19. A ball is thrown up from the ground with initial velocity 64 ft/sec. Its height at time t is

$$h(t) = -16t^2 + 64t.$$

   (a) Evaluate $h(1)$ and $h(3)$. What does this tell us about the height of the ball?
   (b) Sketch this function. Using a graph, determine when the ball hits the ground and the maximum height of the ball.

20. Let $v(t) = t^2 - 2t$ be the velocity, in ft/sec, of an object at time t, in seconds.

   (a) What is the initial velocity, $v(0)$?
   (b) When does the object have a velocity of zero?
   (c) What is the meaning of the quantity $v(3)$? What are its units?

21. Let $s(t) = 11t^2 + t + 100$ be the position, in miles, of a car driving on a straight road at time t, in hours. The car's velocity at any time t is given by $v(t) = 22t + 1$.

   (a) Use function notation to express the car's position after 2 hours. Where is the car then?

(b) Use function notation to express the question, "When is the car going 65 mph?"

(c) Where is the car when it is going 67 mph?

22. Use the letters a, b, c, d, e, h in Figure 2.4 to answer the following questions.

(a) What are the coordinates of the points P and Q?

(b) Evaluate $f(b)$.

(c) Solve $f(x) = e$ for x.

(d) Suppose $c = f(z)$ and $z = f(x)$. What is x?

(e) Suppose $f(b) = -f(d)$. What additional information does this give you?

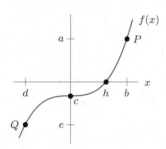

Figure 2.4

23. New York state income tax is based on taxable income, which is part of a person's total income. The tax owed to the state is calculated using the taxable income (not total income). In 2009, for a single person with a taxable income between \$20,000 and \$200,000, the tax owed was \$973 plus 6.85% of the taxable income over \$20,000.[2]

(a) Compute the tax owed by a lawyer whose taxable income is \$68,000.

(b) Consider a lawyer whose taxable income is 80% of her total income, $\$x$, where x is between \$85,000 and \$120,000. Write a formula for $T(x)$, the taxable income.

(c) Write a formula for $L(x)$, the amount of tax owed by the lawyer in part (b).

(d) Use $L(x)$ to evaluate the tax liability for $x = 85,000$ and compare your results to part (a).

24. (a) Complete Table 2.3 using

$$f(x) = 2x(x-3) - x(x-5) \quad \text{and} \quad g(x) = x^2 - x.$$

What do you notice? Graph these two functions. Are the two functions the same? Explain.

(b) Complete Table 2.4 using

$$h(x) = x^5 - 5x^3 + 6x + 1 \quad \text{and} \quad j(x) = 2x + 1.$$

What do you notice? Graph these two functions. Are the two functions the same? Explain.

[2] www.nystax.gov, accessed January 4, 2010.

Table 2.3

x	-2	-1	0	1	2
$f(x)$					
$g(x)$					

Table 2.4

x	-2	-1	0	1	2
$h(x)$					
$j(x)$					

Problems 25–26 concern $v = r(s)$, the eyewall wind profile of a hurricane at landfall, where v is the eyewall wind speed (in mph) as a function of s, the height (in meters) above the ground. (The eyewall is the band of clouds that surrounds the eye of the storm.) Let s_0 be the height at which the wind speed is greatest, and let $v_0 = r(s_0)$. Interpret the following in terms of the hurricanes.

25. $r(0.5s_0)$ **26.** $r(s) = 0.75v_0$

27. Let $h(x) = x^2 + bx + c$. Evaluate and simplify:

(a) $h(1)$ **(b)** $h(b+1)$

28. If $g(x) = x\sqrt{x} + 100x$, evaluate without a calculator

(a) $g(100)$ **(b)** $g(4/25)$ **(c)** $g(1.21 \cdot 10^4)$

In Problems 29–31, if $f(x) = \dfrac{ax}{a+x}$, find and simplify

29. $f(a)$ **30.** $f(1-a)$ **31.** $f\left(\dfrac{1}{1-a}\right)$

32. Values of f and g are given in Table 2.5.

(a) Evaluate $f(1)$ and $g(3)$.

(b) Describe in full sentences the patterns you see in the values for each function.

(c) Assuming that the patterns you observed in part (b) hold true for all values of x, calculate $f(5)$, $f(-2)$, $g(5)$, and $g(-2)$.

(d) Find possible formulas for $f(x)$ and $g(x)$.

Table 2.5

x	-1	0	1	2	3	4
$f(x)$	-4	-1	2	5	8	11
$g(x)$	4	1	0	1	4	9

33. Table 2.6 shows $N(s)$, the number of sections of Economics 101, as a function of s, the number of students in the course. If s is between two numbers listed in the table, then $N(s)$ is the higher number of sections.

Table 2.6

s	50	75	100	125	150	175	200
$N(s)$	4	4	5	5	6	6	7

(a) Evaluate and interpret:

(i) $N(150)$ (ii) $N(80)$ (iii) $N(55.5)$

(b) Solve for s and interpret:

(i) $N(s) = 4$ (ii) $N(s) = N(125)$

34. Figure 2.5 shows $y = f(x)$. Label the coordinates of any points on the graph where

(a) $f(c) = 0$.
(b) $f(0) = d$.

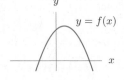

Figure 2.5

35. An epidemic of influenza spreads through a city. Figure 2.6 is the graph of $I = f(w)$, where I is the number of individuals (in thousands) infected w weeks after the epidemic begins.

(a) Evaluate $f(2)$ and explain its meaning in terms of the epidemic.

(b) Approximately how many people were infected at the height of the epidemic? When did that occur? Write your answer in the form $f(a) = b$.

(c) Solve $f(w) = 4.5$ and explain what the solutions mean in terms of the epidemic.

(d) The graph used $f(w) = 6w(1.3)^{-w}$. Use the graph to estimate the solution of the inequality $6w(1.3)^{-w} \geq 6$. Explain what the solution means in terms of the epidemic.

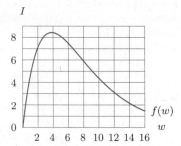

Figure 2.6

Problems 36–37 concern studies which indicate that as carbon dioxide (CO_2) levels rise, hurricanes will become more intense.[3] Hurricane intensity is measured in terms of the minimum central pressure P (in mb): the lower the pressure, the more powerful the storm. Since warm ocean waters fuel hurricanes, P is a decreasing function of H, sea surface temperature in °C. Let $P = n(H)$ be the hurricane-intensity function for present-day CO_2 levels, and let $P = N(H)$ be the hurricane-intensity function for future projected CO_2 levels. If H_0 is the average temperature in the Caribbean Sea, what do the following quantities tell you about hurricane intensity?

36. $N(H_0) - n(H_0)$ **37.** $n(H_0 + 1) - n(H_0)$

2.2 DOMAIN AND RANGE

In Example 4 on page 5, we defined R to be the average monthly rainfall at Chicago's O'Hare airport in month t. Although R is a function of t, the value of R is not defined for every possible value of t. For instance, it makes no sense to consider the value of R for $t = -3$, or $t = 8.21$, or $t = 13$ (since a year has 12 months). Thus, although R is a function of t, this function is defined only for certain values of t. Notice also that R, the output value of this function, takes only the values $\{1.8, 2.1, 2.4, 2.5, 2.7, 3.1, 3.2, 3.4, 3.5, 3.7\}$.

A function is often defined only for certain values of the independent variable. Also, the dependent variable often takes on only certain values. This leads to the following definitions:

> If $Q = f(t)$, then
> - the **domain** of f is the set of input values, t, which yield an output value.
> - the **range** of f is the corresponding set of output values, Q.

---

[3] *Journal of Climate*, September 14, 2004, pages 3477–3495.

Thus, the domain of a function is the set of input values, and the range is the set of output values.

If the domain of a function is not specified, we usually assume that it is as large as possible—that is, all numbers that make sense as inputs for the function. For example, if there are no restrictions, the domain of the function $f(x) = x^2$ is the set of all real numbers, because we can substitute any real number into the formula $f(x) = x^2$. Sometimes, however, we may restrict the domain to suit a particular application. If the function $f(x) = x^2$ is used to represent the area of a square of side x, we restrict the domain to positive numbers.

If a function is being used to model a real-world situation, the domain and range of the function are often determined by the constraints of the situation being modeled, as in the next example.

Example 1   The house-painting function $n = f(A)$ in Example 2 on page 4 has domain $A > 0$ because all houses have some positive paintable area. There is a practical upper limit to A because houses cannot be infinitely large, but in principle, A can be as large or as small as we like, as long as it is positive. Therefore we take the domain of f to be $A > 0$.

The range of this function is $n \geq 0$, because we cannot use a negative amount of paint.

Choosing Realistic Domains and Ranges

When a function is used to model a real situation, it may be necessary to modify the domain and range.

Example 2   Algebraically speaking, the formula

$$T = \frac{1}{4}R + 40$$

can be used for all values of R. If we know nothing more about this function than its formula, its domain is all real numbers. The formula for $T = \frac{1}{4}R + 40$ can return any value of T when we choose an appropriate R-value. (See Figure 2.7.) Thus, the range of the function is also all real numbers. However, if we use this formula to represent the temperature, T, as a function of a cricket's chirp rate, R, as we did in Example 1 on page 2, some values of R cannot be used. For example, it does not make sense to talk about a negative chirp rate. Also, there is some maximum chirp rate R_{max} that no cricket can physically exceed. Thus, to use this formula to express T as a function of R, we must restrict R to the interval $0 \leq R \leq R_{max}$ shown in Figure 2.8.

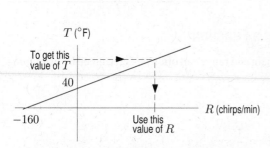

Figure 2.7: Graph showing that any T value can be obtained from some R value

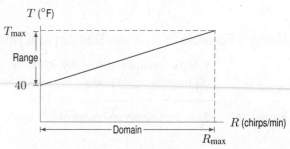

Figure 2.8: Graph showing that if $0 \leq R \leq R_{max}$, then $40 \leq T \leq T_{max}$

The range of the cricket function is also restricted. Since the chirp rate is nonnegative, the smallest value of T occurs when $R = 0$. This happens at $T = 40$. On the other hand, if the temperature gets too hot, the cricket will not be able to keep chirping faster. If the temperature T_{max} corresponds to the chirp rate R_{max}, then the values of T are restricted to the interval $40 \leq T \leq T_{max}$.

Using a Graph to Find the Domain and Range of a Function

A good way to estimate the domain and range of a function is to examine its graph. The domain is the set of input values on the horizontal axis that give rise to a point on the graph; the range is the corresponding set of output values on the vertical axis.

Example 3   A sunflower plant is measured every day t, for $t \geq 0$. The height, $h(t)$ centimeters, of the plant[4] can be modeled by using the *logistic function*

$$h(t) = \frac{260}{1 + 24(0.9)^t}.$$

(a) Using a graphing calculator or computer, graph the height over 80 days.
(b) What is the domain of this function? What is the range? What does this tell you about the height of the sunflower?

Solution   (a) The logistic function is graphed in Figure 2.9.

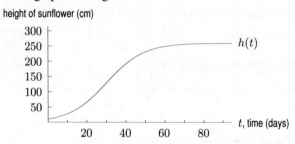

Figure 2.9: Height of sunflower as a function of time

(b) The domain of this function is $t \geq 0$. If we consider the fact that the sunflower dies at some point, then there is an upper bound on the domain, $0 \leq t \leq T$, where T is the day on which the sunflower dies.

To find the range, notice that the smallest value of h occurs at $t = 0$. Evaluating gives $h(0) = 10.4$ cm. This means that the plant was 10.4 cm high when it was first measured on day $t = 0$. Tracing along the graph, $h(t)$ increases. As t-values get large, $h(t)$-values approach, but never reach, 260. This suggests that the range is $10.4 \leq h(t) < 260$. This information tells us that sunflowers typically grow to a height of about 260 cm.

Using a Formula to Find the Domain and Range of a Function

When a function is defined by a formula, its domain and range can often be determined by examining the formula algebraically.

Example 4   State the domain and range of g, where

$$g(x) = \frac{1}{x}.$$

Solution   The domain is all real numbers except those which do not yield an output value. The expression $1/x$ is defined for any real number x except 0 (division by 0 is undefined). Therefore,

Domain: all real x, $\quad x \neq 0$.

---

[4] Adapted from H.S. Reed and R.H. Holland, "Growth of an Annual Plant Helianthus," *Proc. Nat. Acad. Sci.*, 5, 1919.

The range is all real numbers that the formula can return as output values. It is not possible for $g(x)$ to equal zero, since 1 divided by a real number is never zero. All real numbers except 0 are possible output values, since all nonzero real numbers have reciprocals. Thus

$$\text{Range: all real values,} \quad g(x) \neq 0.$$

The graph in Figure 2.10 indicates agreement with these values for the domain and range.

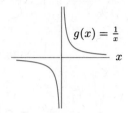

Figure 2.10: Domain and range of $g(x) = 1/x$

Example 5   Find the domain of the function $f(x) = \dfrac{1}{\sqrt{x-4}}$ by examining its formula.

Solution   The domain is all real numbers except those for which the function is undefined. The square root of a negative number is undefined (if we restrict ourselves to real numbers), and so is division by zero. Therefore we need

$$x - 4 > 0.$$

Thus, the domain is all real numbers greater than 4.

$$\text{Domain:} \quad x > 4.$$

In Example 6 on page 69, we saw that for $f(x) = 1/\sqrt{x-4}$, the output, $f(x)$, cannot be negative. Note that $f(x)$ cannot be zero either. (Why?) The range of $f(x) = 1/\sqrt{x-4}$ is $f(x) > 0$. See Exercise 9.

Exercises and Problems for Section 2.2

Skill Refresher

In Exercises S1–S4, for what value(s), if any, are the functions undefined?

S1. $f(x) = \dfrac{x-2}{x-3}$ **S2.** $g(x) = \dfrac{1}{x(x-3)}$

S3. $h(x) = \sqrt{x-15}$ **S4.** $k(x) = \sqrt{15-x}$

Solve the inequalities in Exercises S5–S10.

S5. $x - 8 > 0$ **S6.** $-x + 5 > 0$

S7. $-3(n-4) > 12$ **S8.** $12 \leq 24 - 4a$

S9. $x^2 - 25 > 0$ **S10.** $36 - x^2 \geq 0$

Exercises

In Exercises 1–4, use a graph to find the range of the function on the given domain.

1. $f(x) = \dfrac{1}{x}, \quad -2 \leq x \leq 2$

2. $f(x) = \dfrac{1}{x^2}, \quad -1 \leq x \leq 1$

3. $f(x) = x^2 - 4, \quad -2 \leq x \leq 3$

4. $f(x) = \sqrt{9 - x^2}, \quad -3 \leq x \leq 1$

Find the domain of the functions in Exercises 5–14 algebraically.

5. $f(x) = \dfrac{1}{x+3}$

6. $p(t) = \dfrac{1}{t^2 - 4}$

7. $f(t) = \dfrac{t-3}{3t+9}$

8. $n(q) = \dfrac{1}{q^4 + 2}$

9. $f(x) = \dfrac{1}{\sqrt{x-4}}$

10. $y(t) = \dfrac{1}{t^4}$

11. $f(x) = \sqrt{x^2 - 4}$

12. $q(r) = \sqrt[3]{r^2 - 16}$

13. $m(x) = x^2 - 9$

14. $t(a) = \sqrt[4]{a-2}$

Find the domain and range of the functions in Exercises 15–16 algebraically.

15. $m(q) = \dfrac{1}{5}q - 4$

16. $f(x) = \sqrt{15 - 4x}$

Given the domain D of the functions in Exercises 17–20, find possible values for the unknowns a and b (where applicable).

17. $f(x) = \dfrac{1}{x-a}$, D: all real numbers $\neq 3$

18. $p(t) = \dfrac{1}{(2t-a)(t+b)}$, D: all real numbers except 4 and 5.

19. $m(r) = \sqrt{r-a}$, D: all real numbers ≥ -3

20. $n(q) = \sqrt{r^2 + a}$, D: all real numbers

Problems

In Problems 21–22, estimate the domain and range of the function. Assume the entire graph is shown.

21.   **22.**

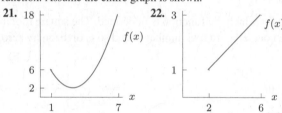

23. Give a formula for a function whose domain is all negative values of x except $x = -5$.

24. Give a formula for a function that is undefined for $x = -2$ and for $x < -4$, but is defined everywhere else.

25. A restaurant is open from 2 pm to 2 am each day, and a maximum of 200 clients can fit inside. If $f(t)$ is the number of clients in the restaurant t hours after 2 pm each day, what are a reasonable domain and range for $f(t)$?

26. What is the domain of the function f giving average monthly rainfall at Chicago's O'Hare airport? (See Table 1.2 on page 5.)

27. A movie theater seats 200 people. For any particular show, the amount of money the theater makes is a function of the number of people, n, in attendance. If a ticket costs $4.00, find the domain and range of this function. Sketch its graph.

28. A car gets the best mileage at intermediate speeds. Graph the gas mileage as a function of speed. Determine a reasonable domain and range for the function and justify your reasoning.

29. **(a)** Use Table 2.7 to determine the number of calories that a person weighing 200 lb uses in a half–hour of walking.[5]

(b) Table 2.7 illustrates a relationship between the number of calories used per minute walking and a person's weight in pounds. Describe in words what is true about this relationship. Identify the dependent and independent variables. Specify whether it is an increasing or decreasing function.

(c) (i) Graph the linear function for walking, as described in part (b), and estimate its equation.

(ii) Interpret the meaning of the vertical intercept of the graph of the function.

(iii) Specify a meaningful domain and range for your function.

(iv) Use your function to determine how many calories per minute a person who weighs 135 lb uses per minute of walking.

Table 2.7   *Calories per minute as a function of weight*

Activity	100 lb	120 lb	150 lb	170 lb	200 lb	220 lb
Walking	2.7	3.2	4.0	4.6	5.4	5.9
Bicycling	5.4	6.5	8.1	9.2	10.8	11.9
Swimming	5.8	6.9	8.7	9.8	11.6	12.7

In Problems 30–31, find the domain and range of the function.

30. $h(x) = \dfrac{a}{\sqrt{x}}$, where a is a constant

31. $p(x) = |x - b| + 6$, where b is a constant

---

[5] Source: 1993 World Almanac. Speeds assumed are 3 mph for walking, 10 mph for bicycling, and 2 mph for swimming.

32. The last digit, d, of a phone number is a function of n, its position in the phone book. Table 2.8 gives d for the first 10 listings in the 2009 New York State telephone directory.[6] The table shows that the last digit of the first listing is 1, the last digit of the second listing is 5, and so on. In principle we could use a phone book to figure out other values of d. For instance, if $n = 300$, we could count down to the 300th listing in order to determine d. So we write $d = f(n)$.

(a) What is the value of $f(6)$?

(b) Explain how you could use the phone book to find the domain of f.

(c) What is the range of f?

Table 2.8

n	1	2	3	4	5	6	7	8	9	10
d	1	2	1	5	9	9	0	1	1	7

33. In month $t = 0$, a small group of rabbits escapes from a ship onto an island where there are no rabbits. The island rabbit population, $p(t)$, in month t is given by

$$p(t) = \frac{1000}{1 + 19(0.9)^t}, \quad t \geq 0.$$

(a) Evaluate $p(0)$, $p(10)$, $p(50)$, and explain their meaning in terms of rabbits.

(b) Graph $p(t)$ for $0 \leq t \leq 100$. Describe the graph in words. Does it suggest the growth in population you would expect among rabbits on an island?

(c) Estimate the range of $p(t)$. What does this tell you about the rabbit population?

(d) Explain how you can find the range of $p(t)$ from its formula.

34. Bronze is an alloy or mixture of the metals copper and tin. The properties of bronze depend on the percentage of copper in the mix. A chemist decides to study the properties of a given alloy of bronze as the proportion of copper is varied. She starts with 9 kg of bronze that contain 3 kg of copper and 6 kg of tin and either adds or removes copper. Let $f(x)$ be the percentage of copper in the mix if x kg of copper are added ($x > 0$) or removed ($x < 0$).

(a) State the domain and range of f. What does your answer mean in the context of bronze?

(b) Find a formula in terms of x for $f(x)$.

(c) If the formula you found in part (b) was not intended to represent the percentage of copper in an alloy of bronze, but instead simply defined an abstract mathematical function, what would be the domain and range of this function?

35. Let t be time in seconds and let $r(t)$ be the rate, in gallons/second, that water enters a reservoir:

$$r(t) = 800 - 40t.$$

(a) Evaluate the expressions $r(0), r(15), r(25)$, and explain their physical significance.

(b) Graph $y = r(t)$ for $0 \leq t \leq 30$, labeling the intercepts. What is the physical significance of the slope and the intercepts?

(c) For $0 \leq t \leq 30$, when does the reservoir have the most water? When does it have the least water?

(d) What are the domain and range of $r(t)$?

36. The surface area of a cylindrical aluminum can is a measure of how much aluminum the can requires. If the can has radius r and height h, its surface area A and its volume V are given by the equations:

$$A = 2\pi r^2 + 2\pi rh \quad \text{and} \quad V = \pi r^2 h.$$

(a) The volume, V, of a 12 oz cola can is 355 cm^3. A cola can is approximately cylindrical. Express its surface area A as a function of its radius r, where r is measured in centimeters. [Hint: First solve for h in terms of r.]

(b) Graph $A = s(r)$, the surface area of a cola can whose volume is 355 cm^3, for $0 \leq r \leq 10$.

(c) What is the domain of $s(r)$? Based on your graph, what, approximately, is the range of $s(r)$?

(d) The manufacturers wish to use the smallest amount of aluminum (in cm^2) necessary to make a 12-oz cola can. Use your answer in (c) to find the minimum amount of aluminum needed. State the values of r and h that minimize the amount of aluminum used.

(e) The radius of a real 12-oz cola can is about 3.25 cm. Show that real cola cans use more aluminum than necessary to hold 12 oz of cola. Why do you think real cola cans are made in this way?

---

[6]www6.oft.state.ny.us/telecom/phones/techSubRange.do?type=INDIVIDUAL&prefix=A$D-1340452-P=1,   accessed February 10, 2010.

2.3 PIECEWISE-DEFINED FUNCTIONS

A function may employ different formulas on different parts of its domain. Such a function is said to be *piecewise defined*. For example, the function graphed in Figure 2.11 has the following formulas:

$$y = x^2 \quad \text{for } x \leq 2$$
$$y = 6 - x \text{ for } x > 2$$

or more compactly

$$y = \begin{cases} x^2 & \text{for } x \leq 2 \\ 6 - x & \text{for } x > 2. \end{cases}$$

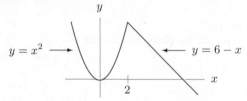

Figure 2.11: Piecewise defined function

Example 1   Graph the function $y = g(x)$ given by the following formulas:

$$g(x) = x + 1 \quad \text{for} \quad x \leq 2 \qquad \text{and} \qquad g(x) = 1 \quad \text{for} \quad x > 2.$$

Using bracket notation, this function is written:

$$g(x) = \begin{cases} x + 1 & \text{for } x \leq 2 \\ 1 & \text{for } x > 2. \end{cases}$$

Solution   For $x \leq 2$, graph the line $y = x + 1$. The solid dot at the point $(2, 3)$ shows that it is included in the graph. For $x > 2$, graph the horizontal line $y = 1$. See Figure 2.12. The open circle at the point $(2, 1)$ shows that it is not included in the graph. (Note that $g(2) = 3$, and $g(2)$ cannot have more than one value.)

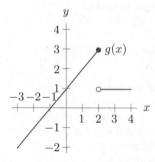

Figure 2.12: Graph of the piecewise defined function g

Example 2   A long-distance calling plan charges 99 cents for any call up to 20 minutes in length and 7 cents for each additional minute or part of a minute.

(a) Use bracket notation to write a formula for the cost, C, of a call as a function of its length t in minutes.
(b) Graph the function.
(c) State the domain and range of the function.

Solution

(a) For $0 < t \leq 20$, the value of C is 99 cents. If $t > 20$, we subtract 20 to find the additional minutes and multiply by the rate, 7 cents per minute.[7] The cost function in cents is thus

$$C = f(t) = \begin{cases} 99 & \text{for } 0 < t \leq 20 \\ 99 + 7(t - 20) & \text{for } t > 20, \end{cases}$$

or, after simplifying,

$$C = f(t) = \begin{cases} 99 & \text{for } 0 < t \leq 20 \\ 7t - 41 & \text{for } t > 20. \end{cases}$$

(b) See Figure 2.13.

(c) Because negative and zero call lengths do not make sense, the domain is $t > 0$. From the graph, we see that the range is $C \geq 99$.

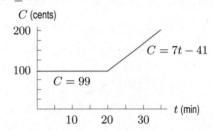

Figure 2.13: Cost of a long-distance phone call

Example 3   The Ironman Triathlon is a race that consists of three parts: a 2.4-mile swim followed by a 112-mile bike race and then a 26.2-mile marathon. A participant swims steadily at 2 mph, cycles steadily at 20 mph, and then runs steadily at 9 mph.[8] Assuming that no time is lost during the transition from one stage to the next, find a formula for the distance covered, d, in miles, as a function of the elapsed time t in hours, from the beginning of the race. Graph the function.

Solution   For each leg of the race, we use the formula Distance = Rate · Time. First, we calculate how long it took for the participant to cover each of the three parts of the race. The first leg took $2.4/2 = 1.2$ hours, the second leg took $112/20 = 5.6$ hours, and the final leg took $26.2/9 \approx 2.91$ hours. Thus, the participant finished the race in $1.2 + 5.6 + 2.91 = 9.71$ hours.

During the first leg, $t \leq 1.2$ and the speed is 2 mph, so

$$d = 2t \quad \text{for} \quad 0 \leq t \leq 1.2.$$

During the second leg, $1.2 < t \leq 1.2 + 5.6 = 6.8$ and the speed is 20 mph. The length of time spent in the second leg is $(t - 1.2)$ hours. Thus, by time t,

$$\text{Distance covered in the second leg} = 20(t - 1.2) \quad \text{for } 1.2 < t \leq 6.8.$$

When the participant is in the second leg, the total distance covered is the sum of the distance covered in the first leg (2.4 miles) plus the part of the second leg that has been covered by time t:

$$d = 2.4 + 20(t - 1.2)$$
$$= 20t - 21.6 \quad \text{for } 1.2 < t \leq 6.8.$$

In the third leg, $6.8 < t \leq 9.71$ and the speed is 9 mph. Since 6.8 hours were spent on the first two parts of the race, the length of time spent on the third leg is $(t - 6.8)$ hours. Thus, by time t,

$$\text{Distance covered in the third leg} = 9(t - 6.8) \quad \text{for } 6.8 < t \leq 9.71.$$

---

[7] In actuality, most calling plans round the call length to whole minutes or specified fractions of a minute.

[8] Personal communication Susan Reid, Athletics Department, University of Arizona.

When the participant is in the third leg, the total distance covered is the sum of the distances covered in the first leg (2.4 miles) and the second leg (112 miles), plus the part of the third leg that has been covered by time t:

$$d = 2.4 + 112 + 9(t - 6.8)$$
$$= 9t + 53.2 \qquad \text{for } 6.8 < t \le 9.71.$$

The formula for d is different on different intervals of t:

$$d = \begin{cases} 2t & \text{for} \quad 0 \le t \le 1.2 \\ 20t - 21.6 & \text{for} \quad 1.2 < t \le 6.8 \\ 9t + 53.2 & \text{for} \quad 6.8 < t \le 9.71 \end{cases}$$

Figure 2.14 gives a graph of the distance covered, d, as a function of time, t. Notice the three pieces.

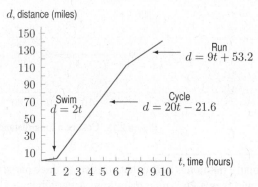

Figure 2.14: Ironman Triathlon: d as a function of t

The Absolute Value Function

The absolute value of a x, written $|x|$, is defined piecewise:

$$\text{For positive } x, \quad |x| = x.$$

$$\text{For negative } x, \quad |x| = -x.$$

(Remember that $-x$ is a positive number if x is a negative number.) For example, if $x = -3$, then

$$|-3| = -(-3) = 3.$$

For $x = 0$, we have $|0| = 0$. This leads to the following two-part definition:

> The **Absolute Value Function** is defined by
>
> $$f(x) = |x| = \begin{cases} x & \text{for} \quad x \ge 0 \\ -x & \text{for} \quad x < 0 \end{cases}.$$

Table 2.9 gives values of $f(x) = |x|$ and Figure 2.15 shows a graph of $f(x)$.

Table 2.9 *Absolute value function*

x	$\lvert x \rvert$
-3	3
-2	2
-1	1
0	0
1	1
2	2
3	3

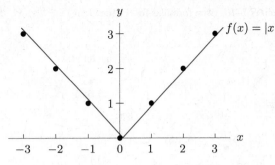

Figure 2.15:Graph of absolute value function

Exercises and Problems for Section 2.3

Skill Refresher

In Exercises S1–S6, write all the possible values for x that match the graph.

In Exercises S7–S10, determine the domain and range of the function.

S7.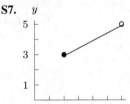

S8.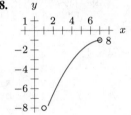

S1.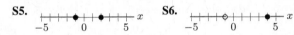

S2.

S3.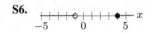

S4.

S9.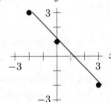

S10.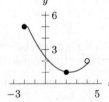

S5.

S6.

Exercises

Graph the piecewise defined functions in Exercises 1–4. Use an open circle to represent a point that is not included and a solid dot to indicate a point that is on the graph.

1. $f(x) = \begin{cases} -1, & -1 \le x < 0 \\ 0, & 0 \le x < 1 \\ 1, & 1 \le x < 2 \end{cases}$

2. $f(x) = \begin{cases} x+1, & -2 \le x < 0 \\ x-1, & 0 \le x < 2 \\ x-3, & 2 \le x < 4 \end{cases}$

3. $f(x) = \begin{cases} x+4, & x \le -2 \\ 2, & -2 < x < 2 \\ 4-x, & x \ge 2 \end{cases}$

4. $f(x) = \begin{cases} x^2, & x \le 0 \\ \sqrt{x}, & 0 < x < 4 \\ x/2, & x \ge 4 \end{cases}$

For Exercises 5–6, find the domain and range.

5. $G(x) = \begin{cases} x+1 & \text{for} \quad x < -1 \\ x^2+3 & \text{for} \quad x \ge -1 \end{cases}$

6. $F(x) = \begin{cases} x^3 & \text{for} \quad x \le 1 \\ 1/x & \text{for} \quad x > 1 \end{cases}$

In Exercises 7–10, write formulas for the functions.

7.

8.

9.

10.

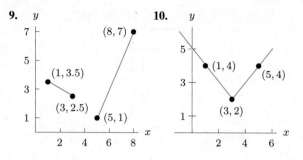

Problems

11. Consider the graph in Figure 2.16. An open circle represents a point that is not included.

  (a) Is y a function of x? Explain.
  (b) Is x a function of y? Explain.
  (c) The domain of $y = f(x)$ is $0 \le x < 4$. What is the range of $y = f(x)$?

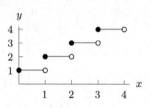

Figure 2.16

12. Many people believe that $\sqrt{x^2} = x$. We will investigate this claim graphically and numerically.

  (a) Graph the two functions x and $\sqrt{x^2}$ in the window $-5 \le x \le 5$, $-5 \le y \le 5$. Based on what you see, do you believe that $\sqrt{x^2} = x$? What function does the graph of $\sqrt{x^2}$ remind you of?
  (b) Complete Table 2.10. Based on this table, do you believe that $\sqrt{x^2} = x$? What function does the table for $\sqrt{x^2}$ remind you of? Is this the same function you found in part (a)?

Table 2.10

x	−5	−4	−3	−2	−1	0	1	2	3	4	5
$\sqrt{x^2}$											

  (c) Explain how you know that $\sqrt{x^2}$ is the same as the function $|x|$.
  (d) Graph the function $\sqrt{x^2} - |x|$ in the window $-5 \le x \le 5$, $-5 \le y \le 5$. Explain what you see.

13. **(a)** Graph $u(x) = |x|/x$ in the window $-5 \le x \le 5$, $-5 \le y \le 5$. Explain what you see.
  (b) Complete Table 2.11. Does this table agree with what you found in part (a)?

Table 2.11

x	−5	−4	−3	−2	−1	0	1	2	3	4	5
$|x|/x$											

  (c) Identify the domain and range of $u(x)$.
  (d) Comment on the claim that $u(x)$ can be written as
  $$u(x) = \begin{cases} -1 & \text{if } x < 0, \\ 0 & \text{if } x = 0, \\ 1 & \text{if } x > 0. \end{cases}$$

14. The charge for a taxi ride in New York City is $2.50 upon entry and $0.40 for each $1/5$ of a mile traveled (rounded up to the nearest $1/5$ mile), when the taxicab is traveling at 6 mph or more. In addition, a New York State Tax Surcharge of $0.50 is added to the fare. [9]

  (a) Make a table showing the cost of a trip as a function of its length. Your table should start at zero and go up to two miles in $1/5$-mile intervals.
  (b) What is the cost for a 1.2-mile trip?
  (c) How far can you go for $5.80?
  (d) Graph the cost function in part (a).

15. A museum charges $40 for a group of 10 or fewer people. A group of more than 10 people must, in addition to the $40, pay $2 per person for the number of people above 10. For example, a group of 12 pays $44 and a group of 15 pays $50. The maximum group size is 50.

  (a) Draw a graph that represents this situation.
  (b) What are the domain and range of the cost function?

[9] www.nyc.gov/html/tlc/html/passenger/taxicab_rate.shtml, accessed February 11, 2010.

16. A floor-refinishing company charges $1.83 per square foot to strip and refinish a tile floor for up to 1000 square feet. There is an additional charge of $350 for toxic waste disposal for any job that includes more than 150 square feet of tile.

   (a) Express the cost, y, of refinishing a floor as a function of the number of square feet, x, to be refinished.

   (b) Graph the function. Give the domain and range.

17. At a supermarket checkout, a scanner records the prices of the foods you buy. In order to protect consumers, the state of Michigan passed a "scanning law" that says something similar to the following:

> If there is a discrepancy between the price marked on the item and the price recorded by the scanner, the consumer is entitled to receive 10 times the difference between those prices; this amount given must be at least $1 and at most $5. Also, the consumer will be given the difference between the prices, in addition to the amount calculated above.

For example: If the difference is 5¢, you should receive $1 (since 10 times the difference is only 50¢ and you are to receive at least $1), plus the difference of 5¢. Thus, the total you should receive is $1.00 + $0.05 = $1.05.
If the difference is 25¢, you should receive 10 times the difference in addition to the difference, giving $(10)(0.25) + 0.25 = \$2.75$.
If the difference is 95¢, you should receive $5 (because $10(.95) = \$9.50$ is more than $5, the maximum penalty), plus 95¢, giving $5 + 0.95 = \$5.95$.

   (a) What is the lowest possible refund?

   (b) Suppose x is the difference between the price scanned and the price marked on the item, and y is the amount refunded to the customer. Write a formula for y in terms of x. [Hint: Look at the sample calculations.]

   (c) What would the difference between the price scanned and the price marked have to be in order to obtain a $9.00 refund?

   (d) Graph y as a function of x.

18. Seattle City Light charges residents for electricity on a daily basis. There is basic daily charge of 11.57 cents. For each day the first 10 kWh cost 4.59 cents per kWh and any additional kWhs are 9.55 cents per kWh. (A kWh is a unit of energy.)

   (a) Make a table showing the cost in dollars of usage from 0 to 40 kWh in increments of 5 kWh.

   (b) Write a piecewise defined function to describe the usage rate.

   (c) What is the cost for 33 kWh?

   (d) How many kWh can you burn on a day for $3?

19. Gore Mountain is a ski resort in the Adirondack mountains in upstate New York. Table 2.12 shows the cost of a weekday ski-lift ticket for various ages and dates.

   (a) Graph cost as a function of age for each time period given. (One graph will serve for times when rates are identical).

   (b) For which age group does the date affect cost?

   (c) Graph cost as a function of date for the age group mentioned in part (b).

   (d) Why does the cost fluctuate as a function of date?

Table 2.12 *Ski-lift ticket prices at Gore Mountain, 1998–1999*[10]

Age	Opening-Dec 12	Dec 13-Dec 24	Dec 25-Jan 3	Jan 4-Jan 15	Jan 16-Jan 18
Up to 6	Free	Free	Free	Free	Free
7–12	$19	$19	$19	$19	$19
13–69	$29	$34	$39	$34	$39
70+	Free	Free	Free	Free	Free

Age	Jan 19-Feb 12	Feb 13-Feb 21	Feb 22-Mar 28	Mar 29-Closing
Up to 6	Free	Free	Free	Free
7–12	$19	$19	$19	$19
13–69	$34	$39	$34	$29
70+	Free	Free	Free	Free

In Problems 20–21:

   (a) Use the definition of absolute value to write a piecewise formula for f.

   (b) Graph f.

20. $f(x) = |x^2 - 4|$　　　　　**21.** $f(x) = |2x - 6|$

22. If $f(x) = \begin{cases} 1/x & \text{for} \quad x < -1 \\ x^2 & \text{for} \quad -1 \le x \le 1 \\ \sqrt{x} & \text{for} \quad x > 1 \end{cases}$　evaluate:

   (a) $f(-2)$

   (b) $f(2)$

   (c) What is the range of f?

23. Let $f(x) = \begin{cases} 3x & \text{for} \quad -1 \le x \le 1 \\ -x + 4 & \text{for} \quad 1 < x \le 5 \end{cases}$

   (a) Find $f(0)$ and $f(3)$.

   (b) Find the domain and range of $f(x)$.

---

[10]The Olympic Regional Development Authority.

24. Let $g(x) = \begin{cases} -1 & \text{for} \quad x < 0 \\ x^3 & \text{for} \quad x \geq 0 \end{cases}$

(a) Find $g(-2)$, $g(2)$, and $g(0)$.

(b) Find the domain and range of $g(x)$.

25. Use bracket notation to write a formula for the piecewise function that is defined by $y = x^2$ for negative values of x and by $y = x - 1$ for x values that are greater than or equal to zero.

2.4 COMPOSITE AND INVERSE FUNCTIONS

Composition of Functions

Two functions may be connected by the fact that the output of one is the input of the other. For example, to find the cost, C, in dollars, to paint an area A square feet, we need to know the number, n, of gallons of paint required. Since one gallon covers 250 square feet, we have the function $n = f(A) = A/250$. If paint is \$30.50 a gallon, we have the function $C = g(n) = 30.5n$. We substitute $n = f(A)$ into $g(n)$ to find the cost C as a function of A.

Example 1   Find a formula for cost, C, as a function of area, A, to be painted.

Solution   Since we have

$$C = 30.5n \quad \text{and} \quad n = \frac{A}{250},$$

substituting for n in the formula for C gives

$$C = 30.5\frac{A}{250} = 0.122A.$$

We say that C is a "function of a function", or *composite function*. If the function giving C in terms of A is called h, so $C = h(A)$, then we write

$$C = h(A) = g(f(A)).$$

The function h is said to be the *composition* of the functions f and g. We say f is the *inside* function and g is the *outside* function. In this example, the composite function $C = h(A) = g(f(A))$ tells us the cost of painting an area of A square feet.

> For two functions $f(t)$ and $g(t)$, the function $f(g(t))$ is said to be a **composition** of f with g. The function $f(g(t))$ is defined by using the output of the function g as the input to f.

The composite function $f(g(t))$ is defined only for values in the domain of g whose $g(t)$ values are in the domain of f.

Example 2   The air temperature, T, in °F, is given in terms of the chirp rate, R, in chirps per minute, of a snowy tree cricket by the function

$$T = f(R) = \frac{1}{4}R + 40.$$

Suppose one night we record the chirp rate and find that it varies with time, x, according to the function

$$R = g(x) = 20 + x^2 \qquad \text{where } x \text{ is in hours since midnight and } 0 \leq x \leq 10.$$

Find how temperature varies with time by obtaining a formula for h, where $T = h(x)$.

Solution   Since $f(R)$ is a function of R and $R = g(x)$, we see that g is the inside function and f is the outside function. Thus we substitute $R = g(x)$ into f:

$$T = f(R) = f(g(x)) = \frac{1}{4}g(x) + 40 = \frac{1}{4}(20 + x^2) + 40 = \frac{1}{4}x^2 + 45.$$

Thus, for $0 \le x \le 10$, we have

$$T = h(x) = \frac{1}{4}x^2 + 45.$$

Example 3 shows another example of composition.

Example 3   Let $f(x) = 2x + 1$ and $g(x) = x^2 - 3$.
(a) Calculate $f(g(3))$ and $g(f(3))$.
(b) Find formulas for $f(g(x))$ and $g(f(x))$.

Solution   (a) We want

$$f(g(3)).$$

We start by evaluating $g(3)$. The formula for g gives $g(3) = 3^2 - 3 = 6$, so

$$f(g(3)) = f(6).$$

The formula for f gives $f(6) = 2 \cdot 6 + 1 = 13$, so

$$f(g(3)) = 13.$$

To calculate $g(f(3))$, we have

$$g(f(3)) = g(7) \qquad \text{Because } f(3) = 2 \cdot 3 + 1 = 7$$
$$= 46 \qquad \text{Because } g(7) = 7^2 - 3$$

Notice that, $f(g(3)) \ne g(f(3))$. The functions $f(g(x))$ and $g(f(x))$ are different.
(b) In the formula for $f(g(x))$,

$$f(\ \underbrace{g(x)}_{\text{Input for } f}\ ) = f(x^2 - 3) \qquad \text{Because } g(x) = x^2 - 3$$

$$= 2(x^2 - 3) + 1 \qquad \text{Because } f(\text{Input}) = 2 \cdot \text{Input} + 1$$
$$= 2x^2 - 5.$$

Check this formula by evaluating $f(g(3))$, which we know to be 13:

$$f(g(3)) = 2 \cdot 3^2 - 5 = 13.$$

In the formula for $g(f(x))$,

$$g(\ \underbrace{f(x)}_{\text{Input for } g}\ ) = g(2x + 1) \qquad \text{Because } f(x) = 2x + 1$$

$$= (2x + 1)^2 - 3 \qquad \text{Because } g(\text{Input}) = \text{Input}^2 - 3$$
$$= 4x^2 + 4x - 2.$$

Check this formula by evaluating $g(f(3))$, which we know to be 46:

$$g(f(3)) = 4 \cdot 3^2 + 4 \cdot 3 - 2 = 46.$$

Inverse Functions

The roles of a function's input and output can sometimes be reversed. For example, the population, P, of birds on an island is given, in thousands, by $P = f(t)$, where t is the number of years since 2007. In this function, t is the input and P is the output. If the population is increasing, knowing the population enables us to calculate the year. Thus we can define a new function, $t = g(P)$, which tells us the value of t given the value of P instead of the other way round. For this function, P is the input and t is the output. The functions f and g are called *inverses* of each other. A function which has an inverse is said to be *invertible*.

The fact that f and g are inverse functions means that they go in "opposite directions." The function f takes t as input and outputs P, while g takes P as input and outputs t.

Inverse Function Notation

In the preceding discussion, there was nothing about the names of the two functions that stressed their special relationship. If we want to emphasize that g is the inverse of f, we call it f^{-1} (read "f-inverse"). To express the fact that the population of birds, P, is a function of time, t, we write

$$P = f(t).$$

To express the fact that the time t is also determined by P, so that t is a function of P, we write

$$t = f^{-1}(P).$$

The symbol f^{-1} is used to represent the function that gives the output t for a given input P.

Warning: The -1 that appears in the symbol f^{-1} for the inverse function is not an exponent. Unfortunately, the notation $f^{-1}(x)$ might lead us to interpret it as $(f(x))^{-1} = \frac{1}{f(x)}$. The two expressions are not the same in general: $f^{-1}(x)$ is the output when x is fed into the inverse of f, while $(f(x))^{-1} = \frac{1}{f(x)}$ is the reciprocal of the number we get when x is fed into f.

Example 4   Using $P = f(t)$, where P represents the population, in thousands, of birds on an island and t is the number of years since 2007:

(a)   What does $f(4)$ represent?   (b)   What does $f^{-1}(4)$ represent?

Solution   (a) The expression $f(4)$ is the bird population (in thousands) in the year 2011.

(b) Since f^{-1} is the inverse function, f^{-1} is a function which takes population as input and returns time as output. Therefore, $f^{-1}(4)$ is the number of years after 2007 at which there were 4,000 birds on the island.

Example 5   Suppose that g is an invertible function, with $g(10) = -26$ and $g^{-1}(0) = 7$. What other values of g and g^{-1} do you know?

Solution   Because $g(10) = -26$, we know that $g^{-1}(-26) = 10$; because $g^{-1}(0) = 7$, we know that $g(7) = 0$.

Finding a Formula for the Inverse Function

In the next example, we find the formula for an inverse function.

Example 6   The cricket function, which gives temperature, T, in terms of chirp rate, R, is

$$T = f(R) = \frac{1}{4} \cdot R + 40.$$

Find a formula for the inverse function, $R = f^{-1}(T)$.

Solution   The inverse function gives the chirp rate in terms of the temperature, so we solve the following equation for R:

$$T = \frac{1}{4} \cdot R + 40,$$

giving

$$T - 40 = \frac{1}{4} \cdot R$$
$$R = 4(T - 40).$$

Thus, $R = f^{-1}(T) = 4(T - 40)$.

Domain and Range of an Inverse Function

The input values of the inverse function f^{-1} are the output values of the function f. Thus, the domain of f^{-1} is the range of f. For the cricket function, $T = f(R) = \frac{1}{4}R + 40$, if a realistic domain is $0 \leq R \leq 160$, then the range of f is $40 \leq T \leq 80$. The domain of f^{-1} is then $40 \leq T \leq 80$ and the range is $0 \leq R \leq 160$. See Figure 2.17.

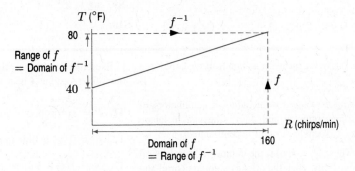

Figure 2.17: Domain and range of an inverse function

A Function and Its Inverse Undo Each Other

Example 7   Calculate the composite functions $f^{-1}(f(R))$ and $f(f^{-1}(T))$ for the cricket example. Interpret the results.

Solution   Since $f(R) = \frac{1}{4}R + 40$. and $f^{-1}(T) = 4(T - 40)$, we have

$$f^{-1}(f(R)) = f^{-1}\left(\frac{1}{4} \cdot R + 40\right) = 4\left(\left(\frac{1}{4} \cdot R + 40\right) - 40\right) = R.$$
$$f(f^{-1}(T)) = f(4(T - 40)) = \frac{1}{4}(4(T - 40)) + 40 = T.$$

To interpret these results, we use the fact that $f(R)$ gives the temperature corresponding to chirp rate R, and $f^{-1}(T)$ gives the chirp rate corresponding to temperature T. Thus $f^{-1}(f(R))$ gives the chirp rate at temperature $f(R)$, which is R. Similarly, $f(f^{-1}(T))$ gives the temperature at chirp rate $f^{-1}(T)$, which is T.

In Example 7, we see that $f^{-1}(f(R)) = R$ and $f(f^{-1}(T)) = T$. This illustrates the following result, which we see is true in general in Chapter 10.

> The functions f and f^{-1} are called inverses because they "undo" each other when composed.

Exercises and Problems for Section 2.4
Skill Refresher

Solve the equations in Exercises S1–S6 for y.

S1. $x = 3y - 4$

S2. $4x - 3y = 7$

S3. $x = \dfrac{2y + 1}{y - 2}$

S4. $x = \sqrt{y} - 2$

S5. $x = y^3 - 4$

S6. $x = 5 - (2y)^3$

Simplify the expressions in Exercises S7–S10.

S7. $5\left(\frac{1}{5}x - 1\right) + 5$

S8. $(2x + 1)^2 - 4$

S9. $3(y - 2)^2 - 7$

S10. $(1 - t)^2 - (1 - t)$

Exercises

In Exercises 1–3, give the meaning and units of the composite function.

1. $A(f(t))$, where $r = f(t)$ is the radius, in centimeters, of a circle at time t minutes, and $A(r)$ is the area, in square centimeters, of a circle of radius r centimeters.

2. $R(f(p))$, where $Q = f(p)$ is the number of barrels of oil sold by a company when the price is p dollars/barrel and $R(Q)$ is the revenue earned in millions of dollars from a sale of Q barrels.

3. $C(A(d))$, where $A(d)$ is the area of a circular pizza with diameter d, and $C(x)$ is the price of pizza with area x.

In Exercises 4–10, use $f(x) = 3x - 1$ and $g(x) = 1 - x^2$.

4. $f(g(0))$

5. $g(f(0))$

6. $g(f(2))$

7. $f(g(2))$

8. $f(g(x))$

9. $f(f(x))$

10. $g(g(x))$

In Exercises 11–15, give the meaning and units of the inverse function. (Assume f is invertible.)

11. $P = f(t)$ is population in millions in year t.

12. $T = f(H)$ is time in minutes to bake a cake at $H°$F.

13. $N = f(t)$ is number of inches of snow in the first t days of January.

14. $x = C(w)$ is calories for w ounces of almonds.

15. $c = P(d)$ is the price, in dollars, for a pizza of diameter d inches.

In Exercises 16–19, find the inverse function.

16. $y = f(t) = 2t + 3$

17. $Q = f(x) = x^3 + 3$

18. $A = f(r) = \pi r^2, r \geq 0$

19. $y = g(s) = 1 + \dfrac{1}{s}$

20. Use the graph in Figure 2.18 to fill in the missing values:

   (a) $f(0) =?$ **(b)** $f(?) = 0$

   (c) $f^{-1}(0) =?$ **(d)** $f^{-1}(?) = 0$

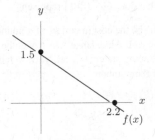

Figure 2.18

21. Use the graph in Figure 2.19 to fill in the missing values:

   (a) $f(0) =?$ **(b)** $f(?) = 0$

   (c) $f^{-1}(0) =?$ **(d)** $f^{-1}(?) = 0$

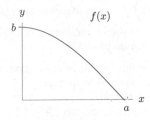

Figure 2.19

Problems

In Problems 22–24, let $n = f(A) = A/250$, where n is the number of gallons of paint needed to paint an area of A square feet.

22. Find a formula for the inverse function $A = f^{-1}(n)$.

23. Interpret and evaluate $f(100)$ and $f^{-1}(100)$.

24. Calculate the composite functions $f^{-1}(f(A))$ and $f(f^{-1}(n))$. Explain the results.

25. Table 2.13 gives values of an invertible function, f.

   (a) Using the table, fill in the missing values:

      (i) $f(0) =?$ (ii) $f(?) = 0$

      (iii) $f^{-1}(0) =?$ (iv) $f^{-1}(?) = 0$

   (b) How do the answers to (i)–(iv) in part (a) relate to one another? In particular, how could you have obtained the answers to (iii) and (iv) from the answers to (i) and (ii)?

Table 2.13

x	-2	-1	0	1	2
$f(x)$	5	4	2	0	-3

26. The cost (in dollars) of producing x air conditioners is $C = g(x) = 600 + 45x$. Find a formula for the inverse function $g^{-1}(C)$.

27. The cost of producing q thousand loaves of bread is $C(q)$ dollars. Interpret the following statements in terms of bread; give units.

   (a) $C(5) = 653$

   (b) $C^{-1}(80) = 0.62$

   (c) The solution to $C(q) = 790$ is 6.3

   (d) The solution to $C^{-1}(x) = 1.2$ is 150

28. The cost, C, in thousands of dollars, of producing q kg of a chemical is given by $C = f(q) = 100 + 0.2q$. Find and interpret

   (a) $f(10)$ **(b)** $f^{-1}(200)$ **(c)** $f^{-1}(C)$

29. The perimeter of a square of side s is given by $P = f(s) = 4s$. Find and interpret

   (a) $f(3)$ **(b)** $f^{-1}(20)$ **(c)** $f^{-1}(P)$

30. The gross domestic product (GDP) of the US is given by $G(t)$ where t is the number of years since 1990 and the units of G are billions of dollars.[11]

   (a) What is meant by $G(15) = 12{,}638.4$?

   (b) What is meant by $G^{-1}(14{,}441.4) = 18$?

In Problems 31–33, let $H = f(t) = \frac{5}{9}(t - 32)$, where H is temperature in degrees Celsius and t is in degrees Fahrenheit.

31. Find and interpret the inverse function, $f^{-1}(H)$.

32. Using the results of Problem 31, evaluate and interpret:

   (a) $f(0)$ **(b)** $f^{-1}(0)$

   (c) $f(100)$ **(d)** $f^{-1}(100)$

---

[11]www.bea.gov/national/xls/gdplev.xls, accessed December 21, 2009.

33. The temperature, $t = g(n) = 68 + 10 \cdot 2^{-n}$, in degrees Fahrenheit of a room is a function of the number, n, of hours that the air conditioner has been running. Find and interpret $f(g(n))$. Give units.

34. The period, T, of a pendulum of length l is given by $T = f(l) = 2\pi\sqrt{l/g}$, where g is a constant. Find a formula for $f^{-1}(T)$ and explain its meaning.

35. The area, in square centimeters, of a circle whose radius is r cm is given by $A = \pi r^2$.

    (a) Write this formula using function notation, where f is the name of the function.
    (b) Evaluate $f(0)$.
    (c) Evaluate and interpret $f(r + 1)$.
    (d) Evaluate and interpret $f(r) + 1$.
    (e) What are the units of $f^{-1}(4)$?

36. The area, $A = f(d)$ in^2, of a circular pizza is a function of the diameter d, in inches. A package of pepperoni costs $2.99 and covers 250 square inches of pizza.

    (a) Write the formula for $f(d)$.
    (b) Find a formula for $C = g(A)$, the cost in dollars of adding pepperoni to a pizza of area A in^2.
    (c) Find and interpret $C = g(f(d))$.
    (d) Evaluate and interpret $f(11)$ and $g(11)$.

37. The radius, r, in centimeters, of a melting snowball is given by $r = 50 - 2.5t$, where t is time in hours. The snowball is spherical, with volume $V = \frac{4}{3}\pi r^3$ cm^3. Find a formula for $V = f(t)$, the volume of the snowball as a function of time.

38. Suppose that $f(x)$ is invertible and that both f and f^{-1} are defined for all values of x. Let $f(2) = 3$ and $f^{-1}(5) = 4$. Evaluate the following expressions, or, if the given information is insufficient, write unknown.

    (a) $f^{-1}(3)$ (b) $f^{-1}(4)$ (c) $f(4)$

39. A circular oil slick is expanding with radius, r in yards, at time t in hours given by $r = 2t - 0.1t^2$, for $0 \leq t \leq 10$. Find a formula for the area in square yards, $A = f(t)$, as a function of time.

40. Carbon dioxide is one of the greenhouse gases that are believed to affect global warming. Between 2004 and 2008, the concentration of carbon dioxide in the earth's atmosphere increased steadily from 375 parts per million (ppm) to 383 ppm.[12] Let $C(t)$ be the concentration in ppm of carbon dioxide t years after 2004 during these four years.

    (a) State the domain and range of $C(t)$.
    (b) What is the practical meaning of $C(4)$? What is its value?
    (c) What does $C^{-1}(381)$ represent?

41. Let $f(a)$ be the cost in dollars of a pounds of organic apples at Fresh Abundance[13] in November 2009. What do the following statements tell you? What are the units of each of the numbers?

    (a) $f(2) = 2.80$ (b) $f(0.5) = 0.70$
    (c) $f^{-1}(0.35) = 0.25$ (d) $f^{-1}(7) = 5$

42. For $h(x) = \frac{x}{4} + 2$, evaluate $h\left(-\frac{1}{2}\right)$ and $h^{-1}(8)$.

43. For $g(x) = 2x^3 - 1$, evaluate $g(\frac{3}{2})$ and $g^{-1}(-17)$.

In Problems 44–45, find the inverse function.

44. $y = f(x) = 3x - 7$ 45. $y = g(x) = x^3 + 1$

Find the domain and range of the functions in Problems 46–49 algebraically.

46. $t(a) = \sqrt[3]{a + 1}$ 47. $n(r) = r^3 + 2$

48. $m(x) = \dfrac{1}{\sqrt{x - 2}}$ 49. $p(x) = \dfrac{1}{\sqrt{3 - x}}$

50. Table 2.14 gives values for $d = f(v)$, where d, in meters, is the stopping distance for a car traveling at velocity v kilometers per hour.

    (a) Evaluate and interpret $f(60)$.
    (b) Estimate $f(70)$.
    (c) Evaluate and interpret $f^{-1}(70)$.

Table 2.14

v (km/hr)	20	30	40	50	60	80	90	100	120
d (m)	6	10	16	23	30	50	60	70	100

---

[12]The World Almanac and Book of Facts 2010, page 297.

[13]www.freshabundance.com/index.php?main_page=product_info&products_id=254, accessed November 5, 2009.

2.5 CONCAVITY

Concavity and Rates of Change

The graph of a linear function is a straight line because the average rate of change is constant. However, not all graphs are straight lines; they may bend up or down. Consider the salary function $S(t)$ shown in Table 2.15 and Figure 2.20, where t is time in years since being hired. Since the rate of change increases with time, the slope of the graph increases as t increases, so the graph bends upward. We say such graphs are *concave up*.

Table 2.15 *Salary: Increasing rate of change*

t (years)	S ($1000s)	Rate of change $\Delta S/\Delta t$
0	40	
		3.2
10	72	
		5.6
20	128	
		10.2
30	230	
		18.1
40	411	

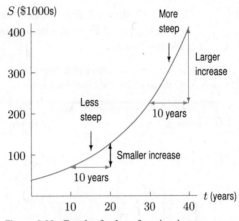

Figure 2.20: Graph of salary function is concave up because rate of change increases

The next example shows that a decreasing function can also be concave up.

Example 1 Table 2.16 shows Q, the quantity of carbon-14 (in μg) in a 200 μg sample remaining after t thousand years. We see from Figure 2.21 that Q is a decreasing function of t, so its rate of change is always negative. What can we say about the concavity of the graph, and what does this mean about the rate of change of the function?

Table 2.16 *Carbon-14: Increasing rate of change*

t (thousand years)	Q (μg)	Rate of change $\Delta Q/\Delta t$
0	200	
		−18.2
5	109	
		−9.8
10	60	
		−5.4
15	33	

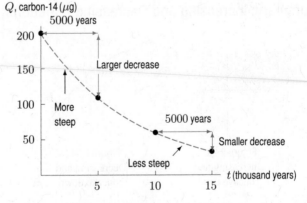

Figure 2.21: Graph of the quantity of carbon-14 is concave up

Solution   The graph bends upward, so it is concave up. Table 2.17 shows that the rate of change of the function is increasing, because the rate is becoming less negative. Figure 2.21 shows how the increasing rate of change can be visualized on the graph: the slope is negative and increasing.

Graphs can bend downward; we call such graphs *concave down*.

Example 2   Table 2.17 gives the distance traveled by a cyclist, Karim, as a function of time. What is the concavity of the graph? Was Karim's speed (that is, the rate of change of distance with respect to time) increasing, decreasing, or constant?

Solution   Table 2.17 shows Karim's speed was decreasing throughout the trip. Figure 2.22 shows how the decreasing speed leads to a decreasing slope and a graph which bends downward; thus the graph is concave down.

Table 2.17   *Karim's distance as a function of time, with the average speed for each hour*

t, time (hours)	d, distance (miles)	Average speed, $\Delta d/\Delta t$ (mph)
0	0	
		20 mph
1	20	
		15 mph
2	35	
		10 mph
3	45	
		7 mph
4	52	
		5 mph
5	57	

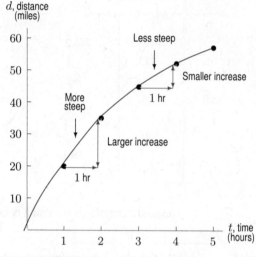

Figure 2.22: Karim's distance as a function of time

Summary: Increasing and Decreasing Functions; Concavity

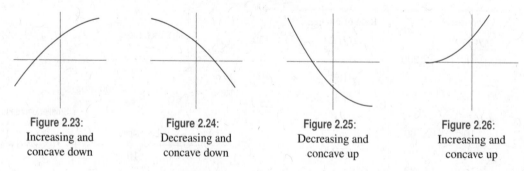

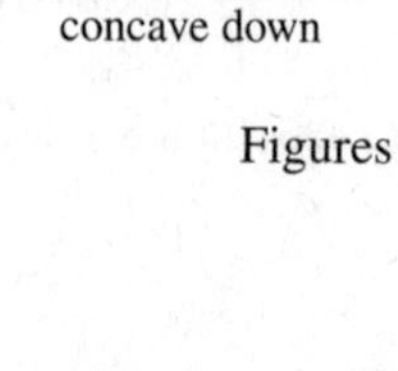

Figure 2.23:
Increasing and
concave down

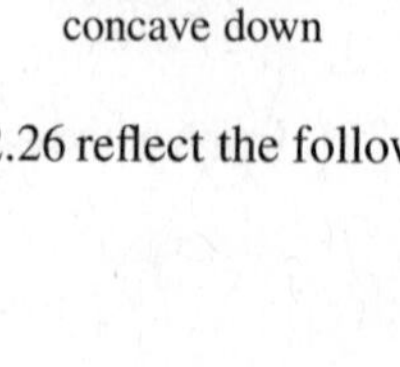

Figure 2.24:
Decreasing and
concave down

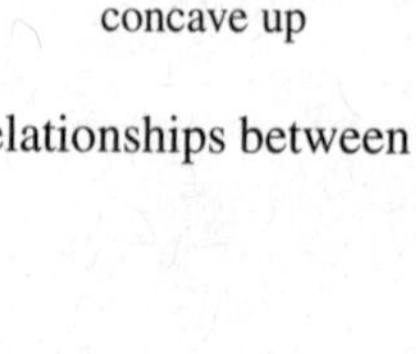

Figure 2.25:
Decreasing and
concave up

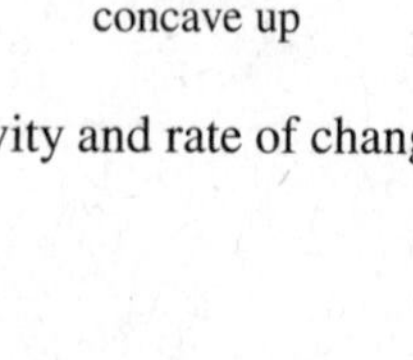

Figure 2.26:
Increasing and
concave up

Figures 2.23–2.26 reflect the following relationships between concavity and rate of change:

- If f is a function whose rate of change increases (gets less negative or more positive as we move from left to right[14]), then the graph of f is **concave up**. That is, the graph bends upward.
- If f is a function whose rate of change decreases (gets less positive or more negative as we move from left to right), then the graph of f is **concave down**. That is, the graph bends downward.

If a function has a constant rate of change, its graph is a line and it is neither concave up nor concave down.

Exercises and Problems for Section 2.5

Exercises

Do the graphs of the functions in Exercises 1–8 appear to be concave up, concave down, or neither?

1.

x	0	1	3	6
$f(x)$	1.0	1.3	1.7	2.2

2.

t	0	1	2	3	4
$f(t)$	20	10	6	3	1

3.
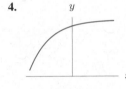

4.

5. $y = x^2$

6. $y = -x^2$

7. $y = x^3, x > 0$

8. $y = x^3, x < 0$

9. Calculate successive rates of change for the function, $R(t)$, in Table 2.18 to decide whether you expect the graph of $R(t)$ to be concave up or concave down.

Table 2.18
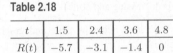

t	1.5	2.4	3.6	4.8
$R(t)$	−5.7	−3.1	−1.4	0

10. Calculate successive rates of change for the function, $H(x)$, in Table 2.19 to decide whether you expect the graph of $H(x)$ to be concave up or concave down.

Table 2.19

x	12	15	18	21
$H(x)$	21.40	21.53	21.75	22.02

11. Sketch a graph that is everywhere negative, increasing, and concave down.

12. Sketch a graph that is everywhere positive, increasing, and concave up.

Problems

Are the functions in Problems 13–17 increasing or decreasing? What does the scenario tell you about the concavity of the graph modeling it?

13. When money is deposited in the bank, the amount of money increases slowly at first. As the size of the account increases, the amount of money increases more rapidly, since the account is earning interest on the new interest, as well as on the original amount.

14. After a cup of hot chocolate is poured, the temperature cools off very rapidly at first, and then cools off more

slowly, until the temperature of the hot chocolate eventually reaches room temperature.

15. When a rumor begins, the number of people who have heard the rumor increases slowly at first. As the rumor spreads, the rate of increase gets greater (as more people continue to tell their friends the rumor), and then slows down again (when almost everyone has heard the rumor).

16. When a drug is injected into a person's bloodstream, the amount of the drug present in the body increases rapidly at first. If the person receives daily injections, the

---

[14]In fact, we need to take the average rate of change over an arbitrarily small interval.

body metabolizes the drug so that the amount of the drug present in the body continues to increase, but at a decreasing rate. Eventually, the quantity levels off at a saturation level.

17. When a new product is introduced, the number of people who use the product increases slowly at first, and then the rate of increase is faster (as more and more people learn about the product). Eventually, the rate of increase slows down again (when most people who are interested in the product are already using it).

18. Graph $f(x)$ with all of these properties:

- $f(0) = 4$
- f is decreasing and concave up for $-\infty < x < 0$
- f is increasing and concave up for $0 < x < 6$
- f is increasing and concave down for $6 < x < 8$
- f is decreasing and concave down for $x > 8$

19. Match each story with the table and graph which best represent it.

(a) When you study a foreign language, the number of new verbs you learn increases rapidly at first, but slows almost to a halt as you approach your saturation level.

(b) You board an airplane in Philadelphia heading west. Your distance from the Atlantic Ocean, in kilometers, increases at a constant rate.

(c) The interest on your savings plan is compounded annually. At first your balance grows slowly, but its rate of growth continues to increase.

(E)

x	0	5	10	15	20	25
y	20	275	360	390	395	399

(F)

x	0	5	10	15	20	25
y	20	36	66	120	220	400

(G)

x	0	5	10	15	20	25
y	20	95	170	245	320	395

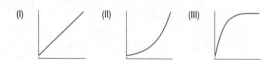

(I)   (II)   (III)

20. Match each of the following descriptions with an appropriate graph and table of values.

(a) The weight of your jumbo box of Fruity Flakes decreases by an equal amount every week.

(b) The machinery depreciated rapidly at first, but its value declined more slowly as time went on.

(c) In free fall, your distance from the ground decreases faster and faster.

(d) For a while it looked as if the decline in profits was slowing down, but then they began declining ever more rapidly.

(E)

x	0	1	2	3	4	5
y	400	384	336	256	144	0

(F)

x	0	1	2	3	4	5
y	400	320	240	160	80	0

(G)

x	0	1	2	3	4	5
y	400	184	98	63	49	43

(H)

x	0	1	2	3	4	5
y	412	265	226	224	185	38

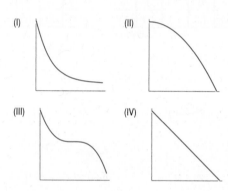

(I)   (II)   (III)   (IV)

21. An incumbent politician running for reelection declared that the number of violent crimes is no longer rising and is presently under control. Does the graph shown in Figure 2.27 support this claim? Why or why not?

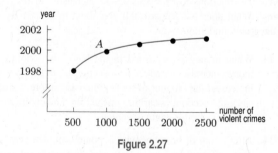

Figure 2.27

22. The rate at which water is entering a reservoir is given for time $t > 0$ by the graph in Figure 2.28. A negative rate means that water is leaving the reservoir. In parts (a)–(d), give the largest interval on which:

(a) The volume of water is increasing.
(b) The volume of water is constant.
(c) The volume of water is increasing fastest.
(d) The volume of water is decreasing.

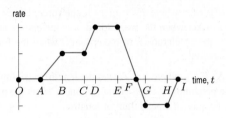

Figure 2.28

23. The relationship between the swimming speed U (in cm/sec) of a salmon to the length l of the salmon (in cm) is given by the function[15]

$$U = 19.5\sqrt{l}.$$

(a) If one salmon is 4 times the length of another salmon, how are their swimming speeds related?
(b) Graph the function $U = 19.5\sqrt{l}$. Describe the graph using words such as increasing, decreasing, concave up, concave down.
(c) Using a property that you described in part (b), answer the question "Do larger salmon swim faster than smaller ones?"
(d) Using a property that you described in part (b), answer the question "Imagine four salmon—two small and two large. The smaller salmon differ in length by 1 cm, as do the two larger. Is the difference in speed between the two smaller fish, greater than, equal to, or smaller than the difference in speed between the two larger fish?"

24. The graph of f is concave down for $0 \leq x \leq 6$. Which is bigger: $\dfrac{f(3) - f(1)}{3 - 1}$ or $\dfrac{f(5) - f(3)}{5 - 3}$? Why?

CHAPTER SUMMARY

- **Input and Output**
  Evaluating functions: finding $f(a)$ for given a.
  Solving equations: finding x if $f(x) = b$ for given b.

- **Domain and Range**
  Domain: set of input values.
  Range: set of output values
  Piecewise defined functions: different formulas on different intervals.

- **Composite Functions**
  Finding $f(g(x))$ given $f(x)$ and $g(x)$.

- **Inverse Functions**
  If $y = f(x)$, then $f^{-1}(y) = x$.
  Evaluating $f^{-1}(b)$. Interpretation of $f^{-1}(b)$.
  Formula for $f^{-1}(y)$ given formula for $f(x)$.

- **Concavity**
  Concave up: increasing rate of change.
  Concave down: decreasing rate of change.

REVIEW EXERCISES AND PROBLEMS FOR CHAPTER TWO

Exercises

In Exercises 1–2, evaluate the function for $x = -7$.

1. $f(x) = x/2 - 1$

2. $f(x) = x^2 - 3$

For Exercises 3–6, calculate exactly the values of y when $y = f(4)$ and of x when $f(x) = 6$.

3. $f(x) = \dfrac{6}{2 - x^3}$

4. $f(x) = \sqrt{20 + 2x^2}$

5. $f(x) = 4x^{3/2}$

6. $f(x) = x^{-3/4} - 2$

7. If $f(x) = 2x + 1$,   **(a)** Find $f(0)$ **(b)** Solve $f(x) = 0$.

8. If $f(x) = \dfrac{x}{1 - x^2}$, find $f(-2)$.

9. If $P(t) = 170 - 4t$, find $P(4) - P(2)$.

[15]From K. Schmidt-Nielsen, *Scaling, Why is Animal Size so Important?* (Cambridge: CUP, 1984).

10. Let $h(x) = 1/x$. Find

   (a) $h(x + 3)$ **(b)** $h(x) + h(3)$

11. **(a)** Using Table 2.20, evaluate $f(1)$, $f(-1)$, and $-f(1)$.
   (b) Solve $f(x) = 0$ for x.

Table 2.20

x	-1	0	1	2
$f(x)$	0	-1	2	1

12. **(a)** In Figure 2.29, estimate $f(0)$.
   (b) For what x-value(s) is $f(x) = 0$?
   (c) For what x-value(s) is $f(x) > 0$?

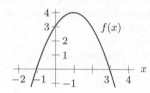

Figure 2.29

Find the domain and range of functions in Exercises 13–18 algebraically.

13. $q(x) = \sqrt{x^2 - 9}$ **14.** $m(r) = \dfrac{1}{\sqrt{r^2 - 1}}$

15. $m(x) = 9 - x$ **16.** $n(x) = 9 - x^4$

17. $m(t) = \dfrac{t}{3} + 2$ **18.** $s(q) = \dfrac{2q + 3}{5 - 4q}$

19. **(a)** How can you tell from the graph of a function that an x-value is not in the domain? Sketch an example.
   (b) How can you tell from the formula for a function that an x-value is not in the domain? Give an example.

20. Let $g(x) = x^2 + x$. Evaluate and simplify the following.

   (a) $-3g(x)$ **(b)** $g(1) - x$
   (c) $g(x) + \pi$ **(d)** $\sqrt{g(x)}$
   (e) $g(1)/(x + 1)$ **(f)** $(g(x))^2$

21. Let $f(x) = 1 - x$. Evaluate and simplify the following.

   (a) $2f(x)$ **(b)** $f(x) + 1$ **(c)** $f(1 - x)$
   (d) $(f(x))^2$ **(e)** $f(1)/x$ **(f)** $\sqrt{f(x)}$

In Exercises 22–23, let $f(x) = 3x - 7$ and $g(x) = x^3 + 1$ to find a formula for the function.

22. $f(g(x))$ **23.** $g(f(x))$

In Exercises 24–25, give the meaning and units of the composite function.

24. $a(g(w))$, where $F = g(w)$ is the force, in newtons, on a rocket when the wind speed is w meters/sec and $a(F)$ is the acceleration, in meters/sec^2, when the force is F newtons.

25. $P(f(t))$, where $l = f(t)$ is the length, in centimeters, of a pendulum at time t minutes, and $P(l)$ is the period, in seconds, of a pendulum of length l.

In Exercises 26–33, use $f(x) = x^2 + 1$ and $g(x) = 2x + 3$.

26. $f(g(0))$ **27.** $f(g(1))$ **28.** $g(f(0))$ **29.** $g(f(1))$

30. $f(g(x))$ **31.** $g(f(x))$ **32.** $f(f(x))$ **33.** $g(g(x))$

In Exercises 34–35, give the meaning and units of the inverse function. (Assume f is invertible.)

34. $V = f(t)$ is the speed in km/hr of an accelerating car t seconds after starting.

35. $I = f(r)$ is the interest earned, in dollars, on a $10,000 deposit at an interest rate of r% per year, compounded annually.

In Exercises 36–37, find the domain and range of the function.

36. $g(x) = a + 1/x$, where a is a constant

37. $q(x) = (x - b)^{1/2} + 6$, where b is a constant

In Exercises 38–39, find the inverse function.

38. $y = g(t) = \sqrt{t} + 1$ **39.** $P = f(q) = 14q - 2$

In Exercises 40–42, let $P = f(t)$ be the population, in millions, of a country at time t in years and let $E = g(P)$ be the daily electricity consumption, in megawatts, when the population is P. Give the meaning and units of the function. Assume both f and g are invertible.

40. $g(f(t))$ **41.** $f^{-1}(P)$ **42.** $g^{-1}(E)$

43. Calculate successive rates of change for the function, $p(t)$, in Table 2.21 to decide whether you expect the graph of $p(t)$ to be concave up or concave down.

Table 2.21

t	0.2	0.4	0.6	0.8
$p(t)$	-3.19	-2.32	-1.50	-0.74

44. If $p(x) = \dfrac{12}{\sqrt{x}}$, evaluate $p(8)$ and $p^{-1}(\sqrt{2})$

45. For $f(x) = 12 - \sqrt{x}$, evaluate $f(16)$ and $f^{-1}(3)$.

In Exercises 46–47, graph the function.

46. $f(x) = \begin{cases} x^2 & \text{for} \quad x \le 1 \\ 2 - x & \text{for} \quad x > 1 \end{cases}$

47. $g(x) = \begin{cases} x + 5 & \text{for} \quad x < 0 \\ x^2 + 1 & \text{for} \quad 0 \le x \le 2 \\ 3 & \text{for} \quad x > 2 \end{cases}$

Problems

48. If $V = \frac{1}{3}\pi r^2 h$ gives the volume of a cone, what is the value of V when $r = 3$ inches and $h = 2$ inches? Give units.

49. Let $q(x) = 3 - x^2$. Evaluate and simplify:

   (a) $q(5)$ **(b)** $q(a)$

   (c) $q(a - 5)$ **(d)** $q(a) - 5$

   (e) $q(a) - q(5)$

50. Let $p(x) = x^2 + x + 1$. Find $p(-1)$ and $-p(1)$. Are they equal?

51. Chicago's average monthly rainfall, $R = f(t)$ inches, is given as a function of month, t, in Table 2.22. (January is $t = 1$.) Solve and interpret:

   (a) $f(t) = 3.7$ **(b)** $f(t) = f(2)$

Table 2.22

t	1	2	3	4	5	6	7	8
R	1.8	1.8	2.7	3.1	3.5	3.7	3.5	3.4

52. Use the graph of $f(x)$ in Figure 2.30 to estimate:

   (a) $f(0)$ **(b)** $f(1)$ **(c)** $f(b)$ **(d)** $f(c)$ **(e)** $f(d)$

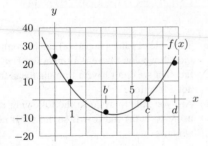

Figure 2.30

53. Let $f(x) = \sqrt{x^2 + 16} - 5$.

   (a) Find $f(0)$
   (b) For what values of x is $f(x)$ zero?
   (c) Find $f(3)$
   (d) What is the vertical intercept of the graph of $f(x)$?
   (e) Where does the graph cross the x-axis?

54. Use the graph in Figure 2.31 to fill in the missing values:

   (a) $f(0) =?$ **(b)** $f(?) = 0$

   (c) $f^{-1}(0) =?$ **(d)** $f^{-1}(?) = 0$

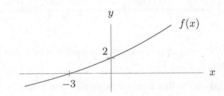

Figure 2.31

55. Use the values of the invertible function in Table 2.23 to find as many values of g^{-1} as possible.

Table 2.23

t	1	2	3	4	5
$y = g(t)$	7	12	13	19	22

56. The formula $V = f(r) = \frac{4}{3}\pi r^3$ gives the volume of a sphere of radius r. Find a formula for the inverse function, $f^{-1}(V)$, giving radius as a function of volume.

57. The formula for the volume of a cube with side s is $V = s^3$. The formula for the surface area of a cube is $A = 6s^2$.

(a) Find and interpret the formula for the function $s = f(A)$.

(b) If $V = g(s)$, find and interpret the formula for $g(f(A))$.

58. The area, $A = f(s)$ ft^2, of a square wooden deck is a function of the side s feet. A can of stain costs \$29.50 and covers 200 square feet of wood.

(a) Write the formula for $f(s)$.

(b) Find a formula for $C = g(A)$, the cost in dollars of staining an area of A ft^2.

(c) Find and interpret $C = g(f(s))$.

(d) Evaluate and interpret, giving units:

(i) $f(8)$ (ii) $g(80)$ (iii) $g(f(10))$

59. Table 2.24 shows the cost, $C(m)$, in dollars, of a taxi ride as a function of the number of miles, m, traveled.

(a) Estimate and interpret $C(3.5)$ in practical terms.

(b) Assume C is invertible. What does $C^{-1}(3.5)$ mean in practical terms? Estimate $C^{-1}(3.5)$.

Table 2.24

m	0	1	2	3	4	5
$C(m)$	0	2.50	4.00	5.50	7.00	8.50

60. The perimeter, in meters, of a square whose side is s meters is given by $P = 4s$.

(a) Write this formula using function notation, where f is the name of the function.

(b) Evaluate $f(s + 4)$ and interpret its meaning.

(c) Evaluate $f(s) + 4$ and interpret its meaning.

(d) What are the units of $f^{-1}(6)$?

61. **(a)** Find the side, $s = f(d)$, of a square as a function of its diagonal d.

(b) Find the area, $A = g(s)$, of a square as a function of its side s.

(c) Find the area $A = h(d)$ as a function of d.

(d) What is the relation between f, g, and h?

62. Suppose that $j(x) = h^{-1}(x)$ and that both j and h are defined for all values of x. Let $h(4) = 2$ and $j(5) = -3$. Evaluate if possible:

(a) $j(h(4))$ **(b)** $j(4)$ **(c)** $h(j(4))$

(d) $j(2)$ **(e)** $h^{-1}(-3)$ **(f)** $j^{-1}(-3)$

(g) $h(5)$ **(h)** $(h(-3))^{-1}$ **(i)** $(h(2))^{-1}$

63. Let $k(x) = 6 - x^2$.

(a) Find a point on the graph of $k(x)$ whose x-coordinate is -2.

(b) Find two points on the graph whose y-coordinates are -2.

(c) Graph $k(x)$ and locate the points in parts (a) and (b).

(d) Let $p = 2$. Calculate $k(p) - k(p-1)$.

64. **(a)** Find a point on the graph of $h(x) = \sqrt{x+4}$ whose x-coordinate is 5.

(b) Find a point on the graph whose y-coordinate is 5.

(c) Graph $h(x)$ and mark the points in parts (a) and (b).

(d) Let $p = 2$. Calculate $h(p+1) - h(p)$.

65. Let $t(x)$ be the time required, in seconds, to melt 1 gram of a compound at $x°C$.

(a) Express the following statement as an equation using $t(x)$: It takes 272 seconds to melt 1 gram of the compound at $400°C$.

(b) Explain the following equations in words:

(i) $t(800) = 136$ (ii) $t^{-1}(68) = 1600$

(c) Above a certain temperature, doubling the temperature, x, halves the melting time. Express this fact with an equation involving $t(x)$.

66. **(a)** The Fibonacci sequence is a sequence of numbers that begins 1, 1, 2, 3, 5, …. Each term in the sequence is the sum of the two preceding terms. For example,

$$2 = 1 + 1, \quad 3 = 2 + 1, \quad 5 = 2 + 3, \dots.$$

Based on this observation, complete the following table of values for $f(n)$, the nth term in the Fibonacci sequence.

n	1	2	3	4	5	6	7	8	9	10	11	12
$f(n)$	1	1	2	3	5							

(b) The table of values in part (a) can be completed even though we don't have a formula for $f(n)$. Does the fact that we don't have a formula mean that $f(n)$ is not a function?

(c) Are you able to evaluate the following expressions using parts (a) and (b)? If so, do so; if not, explain why not.

$$f(0), \quad f(-1), \quad f(-2), \quad f(0.5).$$

67. A psychologist conducts an experiment to determine the effect of sleep loss on job performance. Let $p = f(t)$ be the number of minutes it takes the average person to complete a particular task if he or she has lost t minutes of sleep, where $t = 0$ represents exactly 8 hours of sleep. For instance, $f(60)$ is the amount of time it takes the average person to complete the task after sleeping for only 7 hours. Let $p_0 = f(0)$ and let t_1, t_2, and t_3 be positive constants. Explain what the following statements tell you about sleep loss and job performance.

   (a) $f(30) = p_0 + 5$
   (b) $f(t_1) = 2p_0$
   (c) $f(2t_1) = 1.5f(t_1)$
   (d) $f(t_2 + 60) = f(t_2 + 30) + 10$

68. Give a formula for a function whose domain is all non-negative values of x except $x = 3$.

69. Give a formula for a function that is undefined for $x = 8$ and for $x < 4$, but is defined everywhere else.

70. Many printing presses are designed with large plates that print a fixed number of pages as a unit. Each unit is called a signature. A particular press prints signatures of 16 pages each. Suppose $C(p)$ is the cost of printing a book of p pages, assuming each signature printed costs $0.14.

   (a) What is the cost of printing a book of 128 pages? 129 pages? p pages?
   (b) What are the domain and range of C?
   (c) Graph $C(p)$ for $0 \leq p \leq 128$.

71. Table 2.25 shows the population, P, in millions, of Ireland[16] at various times between 1780 and 1910, with t in years since 1780.

   (a) When was the population increasing? Decreasing?
   (b) For each successive time interval, construct a table showing the average rate of change of the population.
   (c) From the table you constructed in part (b), when is the graph of the population concave up? Concave down?
   (d) When was the average rate of change of the population the greatest? The least? How is this related to part (c)? What does this mean in human terms?
   (e) Graph the data in Table 2.25 and join the points by a curve to show the trend in the data. From this graph identify where the curve is increasing, decreasing, concave up and concave down. Compare your answers to those you got in parts (a) and (c). Identify the region you found in part (d).
   (f) Something catastrophic happened in Ireland between 1780 and 1910. When? What happened in Ireland at that time to cause this catastrophe?

Table 2.25 *The population of Ireland from 1780 to 1910, where $t = 0$ corresponds to 1780*

t	0	20	40	60	70	90	110	130
P	4.0	5.2	6.7	8.3	6.9	5.4	4.7	4.4

CHECK YOUR UNDERSTANDING

Are the statements in Problems 1–42 true or false? Give an explanation for your answer.

1. If $f(t) = 3t^2 - 4$ then $f(2) = 0$.

2. If $f(x) = x^2 - 9x + 10$ then $f(b) = b^2 - 9b + 10$.

3. If $f(x) = x^2$ then $f(x + h) = x^2 + h^2$.

4. If $q = \dfrac{1}{\sqrt{z^2 + 5}}$ then the values of z that make $q = \frac{1}{3}$ are $z = \pm 2$.

5. If $W = \dfrac{t + 4}{t - 4}$ then when $t = 8$, $W = 1$.

6. If $f(t) = t^2 + 64$ then $f(0) = 64$.

7. If $f(x) = 0$ then $x = 0$.

8. If $f(x) = x^2 + 2x + 7$ then $f(-x) = f(x)$.

9. If $g(x) = \dfrac{3}{\sqrt{x^2 + 4}}$ then $g(x)$ can never be zero.

10. If $h(p) = -6p + 9$ then $h(3) + h(4) = h(7)$.

11. The domain of a function is the set of input values.

12. If a function is being used to model a real-world situation, the domain and range are often determined by the constraints of the situation being modeled.

13. The domain of $f(x) = \dfrac{4}{x - 3}$ consists of all real numbers x, $x \neq 0$.

14. If $f(x) = \sqrt{2 - x}$, the domain of f consists of all real numbers $x \geq 2$.

15. The range of $f(x) = \dfrac{1}{x}$ is all real numbers.

---

[16]Adapted from D. N. Burghes and A. D. Wood, *Mathematical Models in the Social, Management and Life Science*, p. 104 (Ellis Horwood, 1980).

16. The range of $y = 4 - \dfrac{1}{x}$ is $0 < y < 4$.

17. If $f(x) = \frac{2}{5}x + 6$ and its domain is $15 \leq x \leq 20$ then the range of f is $12 \leq x \leq 14$.

18. The domain of $f(x) = \dfrac{x}{\sqrt{x^2 + 1}}$ is all real numbers.

19. The graph of the absolute value function $y = |x|$ has a V shape.

20. The domain of $f(x) = |x|$ is all real numbers.

21. If $f(x) = |x|$ and $g(x) = |-x|$ then for all x, $f(x) = g(x)$.

22. If $f(x) = |x|$ and $g(x) = -|x|$ then for all x, $f(x) = g(x)$.

23. If $y = \dfrac{x}{|x|}$ then $y = 1$ for $x \neq 0$.

24. If $f(x) = \begin{cases} 3 & \text{if } x < 0 \\ x^2 & \text{if } 0 \leq x \leq 4 \\ 7 & \text{if } x > 4 \end{cases}$, then $f(3) = 0$.

25. Let $f(x) = \begin{cases} x & \text{if } x < 0 \\ x^2 & \text{if } 0 \leq x \leq 4 \\ -x & \text{if } x > 4 \end{cases}$. If $f(x) = 4$ then $x = 2$.

26. If $f(3) = 5$ and f is invertible, then $f^{-1}(3) = 1/5$.

27. If $h(7) = 4$ and h is invertible, then $h^{-1}(4) = 7$.

28. If $f(x) = \frac{3}{4}x - 6$ then $f^{-1}(8) = 0$.

29. If $R = f(S) = \frac{2}{3}S + 8$ then $S = f^{-1}(R) = \frac{3}{2}(R - 8)$.

30. In general $f^{-1}(x) = (f(x))^{-1}$.

31. If $f(x) = \dfrac{x}{x + 1}$ then $f(t^{-1}) = \dfrac{1/t}{1/t + 1}$.

32. The units of the output of a function are the same as the units of output of its inverse.

33. The functions $f(x) = 2x + 1$ and $g(x) = \frac{1}{2}x - 1$ are inverses.

34. If $q = f(x)$ is the quantity of rice in tons required to feed x million people for a year and $p = g(q)$ is the cost, in dollars, of q tons of rice, then $g(f(x))$ is the dollar cost of feeding x million people for a year.

35. If $f(t) = t + 2$ and $g(t) = 3t$, then $g(f(t)) = 3(t + 2) = 3t + 6$.

36. A fireball has radius $r = f(t)$ meters t seconds after an explosion. The volume of the ball is $V = g(r)$ meter^3 when it has radius r meters. Then the units of measurement of $g(f(t))$ are meter^3/sec.

37. If the graph of a function is concave up, then the average rate of change of a function over an interval of length 1 increases as the interval moves from left to right.

38. The function f in the table could be concave up.

x	−2	0	2	4
$f(x)$	5	6	8	12

39. The function g in the table could be concave down.

t	−1	1	3	5
$g(t)$	9	8	6	3

40. A straight line is concave up.

41. A function can be both decreasing and concave down.

42. If a function is concave up, it must be increasing.

Chapter Three

QUADRATIC FUNCTIONS

Contents

3.1 INTRODUCTION TO THE FAMILY OF QUADRATIC FUNCTIONS

A baseball is "popped" straight up by a batter. The height of the ball above the ground is given by the function $y = f(t) = -16t^2 + 47t + 3$, where t is time in seconds after the ball leaves the bat and y is in feet. See Figure 3.1. Note that the path of the ball is straight up and down, although the graph of height against time is a curve. The ball goes up fast at first and then more slowly because of gravity; thus the graph of its height as a function of time is concave down.

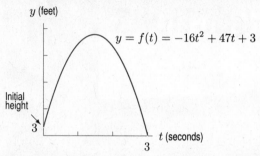

Figure 3.1: The height of a ball t seconds after being "popped up". (Note: This graph does not represent the ball's path.)

The baseball height function is an example of a *quadratic function*, whose general form is $y = ax^2 + bx + c$. The graph of a quadratic function is a *parabola*. Notice that the function in Figure 3.1 is concave down and has a maximum corresponding to the time at which the ball stops rising and begins to fall back to the earth. The maximum point on the parabola is called the *vertex*. The intersection of the parabola with the horizontal axis gives the times when the height of the ball is zero; these times are the *zeros* of the height function. The horizontal intercepts of a graph occur at the zeros of the function. In this section we examine the zeros and concavity of a quadratic functions, and in the next section we see how to find the vertex.

Finding the Zeros of a Quadratic Function

A natural question to ask is when the ball hits the ground. The graph suggests that $y = 0$ when t is approximately 3. In symbols, the question is: For what value(s) of t does $f(t) = 0$? These are the zeros of the function.

It is easy to find the zeros of a quadratic function if it can be expressed in *factored form*,

$$q(x) = a(x - r)(x - s),$$

where a, r, and s are constants, $a \neq 0$. Then r and s are zeros of the function q.

The baseball function factors as $y = -1(16t + 1)(t - 3)$, so the zeros of f are $t = 3$ and $t = -\frac{1}{16}$. In this problem we are interested in positive values of t, so the ball hits the ground 3 seconds after it was hit. (For more on factoring, see the Skills Review on page 120.)

Example 1   Find the zeros of $f(x) = x^2 - x - 6$.

Solution   To find the zeros, set $f(x) = 0$ and solve for x by factoring:

$$x^2 - x - 6 = 0$$
$$(x - 3)(x + 2) = 0.$$

Thus the zeros are $x = 3$ and $x = -2$.

We can also find the zeros of a quadratic function by using the quadratic formula. (See the Skills Review on page 120 to review the quadratic formula.)

Example 2   Find the zeros of $f(x) = x^2 - x - 6$ by using the quadratic formula.

Solution   We solve the equation $x^2 - x - 6 = 0$. For this equation, $a = 1$, $b = -1$, and $c = -6$. Thus

$$x = \frac{-b \pm \sqrt{b^2 - 4ac}}{2a} = \frac{-(-1) \pm \sqrt{(-1)^2 - 4(1)(-6)}}{2(1)}$$

$$= \frac{1 \pm \sqrt{25}}{2} = 3 \text{ or } -2.$$

The zeros are $x = 3$ and $x = -2$, the same as we found by factoring.

Since the zeros of a function occur at the horizontal intercepts of its graph, quadratic functions without horizontal intercepts (such as in the next example) have no zeros.

Example 3   Figure 3.2 shows a graph of $h(x) = -\dfrac{1}{2}x^2 - 2$. What happens if we try to use algebra to find the zeros of h?

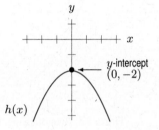

Figure 3.2: Zeros of $h(x) = -(x^2/2) - 2$?

Solution   To find the zeros, we solve the equation

$$-\frac{1}{2}x^2 - 2 = 0$$

$$-\frac{1}{2}x^2 = 2$$

$$x^2 = -4$$

$$x = \pm\sqrt{-4}.$$

Since $\sqrt{-4}$ is not a real number, there are no real solutions, so h has no real zeros. This corresponds to the fact that the graph of h in Figure 3.2 does not cross the x-axis.

Concavity and Quadratic Functions

A quadratic function has a graph that is either concave up or concave down.

Example 4   Let $f(x) = x^2$. Find the average rate of change of f over the consecutive intervals of length 2 starting at $x = -4$ and ending at $x = 4$. What do these rates tell you about the concavity of the graph of f?

Solution   Between $x = -4$ and $x = -2$, we have

$$\text{Average rate of change} \atop \text{of } f = \frac{f(-2) - f(-4)}{-2 - (-4)} = \frac{(-2)^2 - (-4)^2}{-2 + 4} = -6.$$

Between $x = -2$ and $x = 0$, we have

$$\text{Average rate of change} \atop \text{of } f = \frac{f(0) - f(-2)}{0 - (-2)} = \frac{0^2 - (-2)^2}{0 + 2} = -2.$$

Between $x = 0$ and $x = 2$, we have

$$\text{Average rate of change} \atop \text{of } f = \frac{f(2) - f(0)}{2 - 0} = \frac{2^2 - 0^2}{2 - 0} = 2.$$

Between $x = 2$ and $x = 4$, we have

$$\text{Average rate of change} \atop \text{of } f = \frac{f(4) - f(2)}{4 - 2} = \frac{4^2 - 2^2}{4 - 2} = 6.$$

Since the rates of change are increasing, the graph is concave up. See Figure 3.3.

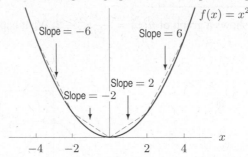

Figure 3.3: Rate of change and concavity of $f(x) = x^2$

Example 5   A high-diver jumps off a 10-meter platform. For t in seconds after the diver leaves the platform until she hits the water, her height h in meters above the water is given by

$$h = f(t) = -4.9t^2 + 8t + 10.$$

The graph of this function is shown in Figure 3.4.

(a) Estimate and interpret the domain and range of the function, and the intercepts of the graph.
(b) Identify the concavity.

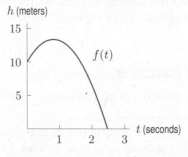

Figure 3.4: Height of diver above water as a function of time

Solution   (a) The diver enters the water when her height above the water is 0. This occurs when

$$h = f(t) = -4.9t^2 + 8t + 10 = 0.$$

Using the quadratic formula to solve this equation, we find the only positive solution is $t = 2.462$ seconds. The domain is the interval of time the diver is in the air, which is approximately $0 \le t \le 2.462$. To find the range of f, we look for the largest and smallest outputs for h. From the graph, the diver's maximum height appears to occur at about $t = 1$, so we estimate the largest output value for f to be about

$$f(1) = -4.9 \cdot 1^2 + 8 \cdot 1 + 10 = 13.1 \text{ meters.}$$

Thus, the range of f is approximately $0 \le f(t) \le 13.1$. Methods to find the exact maximum height are found in Section 3.2.

The vertical intercept of the graph is

$$f(0) = -4.9 \cdot 0^2 + 8 \cdot 0 + 10 = 10 \text{ meters.}$$

The diver's initial height is 10 meters (the height of the diving platform). The horizontal intercept is the point where $f(t) = 0$, which we found in part (a). The diver enters the water approximately 2.462 seconds after leaving the platform.

(b) In Figure 3.4, we see that the graph is bending downward over its entire domain, so it is concave down. This is reflected in Table 3.1, where the rate of change, $\Delta h / \Delta t$, is decreasing.

Table 3.1 *Slope of $f(t) = -4.9t^2 + 8t + 10$*

t (sec)	h (meters)	Rate of change $\Delta h / \Delta t$
0	10	
		5.55
0.5	12.775	
		0.65
1.0	13.100	
		−4.25
1.5	10.975	
		−9.15
2.0	6.400	

Finding a Formula From the Zeros and Vertical Intercept

If we know the zeros and the vertical intercept of a quadratic function, we can use the factored form to find a formula for the function.

Example 6   Find the equation of the parabola in Figure 3.5 using the factored form.

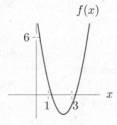

Figure 3.5: Finding a formula for a quadratic from the zeros

Solution   Since the parabola has x-intercepts at $x = 1$ and $x = 3$, its formula can be written as

$$f(x) = a(x - 1)(x - 3).$$

Substituting $x = 0, y = 6$ gives

$$6 = a(3)$$
$$a = 2.$$

Thus, the formula is

$$f(x) = 2(x - 1)(x - 3).$$

Multiplying out gives $f(x) = 2x^2 - 8x + 6$.

Formulas for Quadratic Functions

The function f in Example 6 can be written in at least two different ways.

The form $f(x) = 2x^2 - 8x + 6$ shows the the parabola opens upward, since the coefficient of x^2 is positive and the constant 6 gives the vertical intercept. The form $f(x) = 2(x - 1)(x - 3)$ shows that the parabola crosses the x-axis at $x = 1$ and $x = 3$. In general, we have the following:

The graph of a **quadratic function** is a **parabola**.

The **standard form** for a quadratic function is

$$y = ax^2 + bx + c, \quad \text{where } a, b, c \text{ are constants, } a \neq 0.$$

The parabola opens upward if $a > 0$ or downward if $a < 0$, and it intersects the y-axis at c.

The **factored form**, when it exists, is

$$y = a(x - r)(x - s), \quad \text{where } a, r, s \text{ are constants, } a \neq 0.$$

The parabola intersects the x-axis at $x = r$ and $x = s$.

In the next section we look at another form for quadratic functions which shows the vertex of the graph.

Exercises and Problems for Section 3.1

Skill Refresher

Multiply and write the expressions in Problems S1–S2 without parentheses. Gather like terms.

S1. $\left(t^2 + 1\right) 50t - \left(25t^2 + 125\right) 2t$

S2. $\left(A^2 - B^2\right)^2$

For Exercises S3–S8, factor completely if possible.

S3. $u^2 - 2u$

S4. $x^2 + 3x + 2$

S5. $3x^2 - x - 4$

S6. $(s + 2t)^2 - 4p^2$

S7. $16x^2 - 1$

S8. $y^3 - y^2 - 12y$

Solve the equations in Exercises S9–S10.

S9. $x^2 + 7x + 6 = 0$

S10. $2w^2 + w - 10 = 0$

Exercises

Are the functions in Exercises 1–7 quadratic? If so, write the function in the form $f(x) = ax^2 + bx + c$.

1. $f(x) = 2(7 - x)^2 + 1$

2. $L(P) = (P + 1)(1 - P)$

3. $g(m) = m(m^2 - 2m) + 3\left(14 - \dfrac{m^3}{3}\right) + \sqrt{3}m$

4. $h(t) = -16(t - 3)(t + 1)$

5. $R(q) = \dfrac{1}{q^2}(q^2 + 1)^2$

6. $K(x) = 13^2 + 13^x$

7. $T(n) = \sqrt{5} + \sqrt{3n^4} - \sqrt{\dfrac{n^4}{4}}$

8. Find the zeros of $Q(r) = 2r^2 - 6r - 36$ by factoring.

9. Find the zeros of $Q(x) = 5x - x^2 + 3$ using the quadratic formula.

10. Solve for x using the quadratic formula and demonstrate your solution graphically:

    (a) $6x - \frac{1}{3} = 3x^2$ **(b)** $2x^2 + 7.2 = 5.1x$

In Exercises 11–18, find the zeros (if any) of the function algebraically.

11. $y = (2 - x)(3 - 2x)$ **12.** $y = 2x^2 + 5x + 2$

13. $y = 4x^2 - 4x - 8$ **14.** $y = 7x^2 + 16x + 4$

15. $y = 5x^2 + 2x - 1$ **16.** $y = -17x^2 + 23x + 19$

17. $y = x^4 + 5x^2 + 6$ **18.** $y = x - \sqrt{x} - 12$

Problems

In Problems 19–20, find a formula for the quadratic function whose graph has the given properties.

19. A y-intercept of $y = 7$ and x-intercepts at $x = 1, 4$.

20. A y-intercept of $y = 7$ and only one zero at $x = -2$.

21. Use the quadratic formula to find the time at which the baseball in Figure 3.1 on page 104 hits the ground.

22. Is there a quadratic function with zeros $x = 1$, $x = 2$ and $x = 3$?

23. Find two quadratic functions with zeros $x = 1$, $x = 2$.

24. Determine the concavity of the graph of $f(x) = 4 - x^2$ between $x = -1$ and $x = 5$ by calculating average rates of change over intervals of length 2.

25. Graph a quadratic function which has all the following properties: concave up, y-intercept is -6, zeros at $x = -2$ and $x = 3$.

26. Without a calculator, graph $y = 3x^2 - 16x - 12$ by factoring and plotting zeros.

27. Without a calculator, graph the following function by factoring and plotting zeros:

$$y = -4cx + x^2 + 4c^2 \quad \text{for} \quad c > 0.$$

In Problems 28–29, find a formula for the parabola.

30. Using the factored form, find the formula for the parabola whose zeros are $x = -1$ and $x = 5$, and which passes through the point $(-2, 6)$.

31. Write $y = 3(0.5x - 4)(4 - 20x)$ in the form $y = k(x - r)(x - s)$ and give the values of k, r, s.

32. A ball is thrown into the air. Its height (in feet) t seconds later is given by $h(t) = 80t - 16t^2$.

    (a) Evaluate and interpret $h(2)$.

    (b) Solve the equation $h(t) = 80$. Interpret your solutions and illustrate them on a graph of $h(t)$.

33. Let $V(t) = t^2 - 4t + 4$ represent the velocity of an object in meters per second.

    (a) What is the object's initial velocity?

    (b) When is the object not moving?

    (c) Identify the concavity of the velocity graph.

34. A snowboarder slides up from the bottom of a half-pipe and comes down again, sliding with little resistance on the snow. Her height above the edge t seconds after starting up the side is $-4.9t^2 + 14t - 5$ meters.

    (a) What is her height at $t = 0$?

    (b) After how many seconds does she reach the air? Return to the edge of the pipe?

    (c) How long is she in the air?

28.

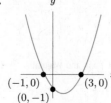

29.

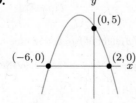

35. The percentage of schools with interactive videodisc players[1] each year from 1992 to 1996 is shown in Table 3.2. If x is in years since 1992, show that this data set can be approximated by the quadratic function $p(x) = -0.8x^2 + 8.8x + 7.2$. What does this model predict for the year 2004? How good is this model for predicting the future?

Table 3.2

Year	1992	1993	1994	1995	1996
Percentage	8	14	21	29.1	29.3

36. Let $f(x) = x^2$ and $g(x) = x^2 + 2x - 8$.

(a) Graph f and g in the window $-10 \leq x \leq 10$, $-10 \leq y \leq 10$. How are the two graphs similar? How are they different?

(b) Graph f and g in the window $-10 \leq x \leq 10$, $-10 \leq y \leq 100$. Why do the two graphs appear more similar on this window than on the window from part (a)?

(c) Graph f and g in the window $-20 \leq x \leq 20$, $-10 \leq y \leq 400$, the window $-50 \leq x \leq 50$, $-10 \leq y \leq 2500$, and the window $-500 \leq x \leq 500$, $-2500 \leq y \leq 250,000$. Describe the change in appearance of f and g on these three successive windows.

37. A relief package is dropped from a moving airplane. The package has an initial forward horizontal velocity and follows a quadratic graph path (instead of dropping straight down). Figure 3.6 shows the height of the package, h, in km, as a function of the horizontal distance, d, in meters, as it drops.

(a) From what height was the package released?

(b) How far away from the spot above which it was released does the package hit the ground?

(c) Write a formula for $h(d)$. [Hint: The package starts falling at the highest point on the graph].

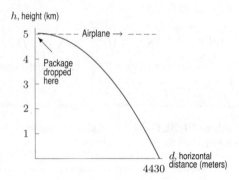

Figure 3.6

3.2   THE VERTEX OF A PARABOLA

In Section 3.1, we looked at the example of a baseball popped upward by a batter. The height of the ball above the ground is given by the quadratic function $y = f(t) = -16t^2 + 47t + 3$, where t is time in seconds after the ball leaves the bat, and y is in feet. See Figure 3.7.

The point on the graph with the largest y value appears to be approximately $(1.5, 37.5)$. (We find the exact value in Example 4 on page 114.) This means that the baseball reaches its maximum

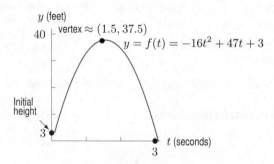

Figure 3.7: Height of baseball at time t

---

[1] Data from R. Famighetti, ed., *The World Almanac and Book of Facts: 1999* (New Jersey: Funk and Wagnalls, 1998).

height of about 37.5 feet about 1.5 seconds after being hit. The maximum point on the parabola is called the *vertex*. For quadratic functions the vertex shows where the function reaches either its maximum value or, in the case of a concave-up parabola, its minimum value.

The vertex of a parabola can be easily determined exactly if the quadratic function is written in the form $y = a(x - h)^2 + k$.

Example 1   (a) Sketch $f(x) = (x + 3)^2 - 4$, and indicate the vertex.
             (b) Estimate the coordinates of the vertex from the graph.
             (c) Explain how the formula for f can be used to obtain the minimum of f.

Solution   (a) Figure 3.8 shows a sketch of $f(x)$; the vertex gives the minimum value of the function.
             (b) The vertex of f appears to be about at the point $(-3, -4)$.
             (c) Note that $(x + 3)^2$ is always positive or zero, so $(x + 3)^2$ takes on its smallest value when $x + 3 = 0$, that is, at $x = -3$. At this point $(x + 3)^2 - 4$ takes on its smallest value,

$$f(-3) = (-3 + 3)^2 - 4 = 0 - 4 = -4.$$

Thus, we see that the vertex is exactly at the point $(-3, -4)$.

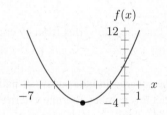

Figure 3.8: A graph of $f(x) = (x + 3)^2 - 4$

Notice that if we select x-values that are equally spaced to the left and the right of the vertex, the y-values of the function are equal. For example, $f(-2) = f(-4) = -3$. The graph is symmetric about a vertical line that passes through the vertex. This line is called the *axis of symmetry*. The function in Example 1 has axis of symmetry $x = -3$.

The Vertex Form of a Quadratic Function

Writing the function f in Example 1 in the form

$$f(x) = (x + 3)^2 - 4$$

enables us to find the vertex of the graph and the location and value for the minimum of the function.
In general, we have the following:

The **vertex form** of a quadratic function is

$$y = a(x - h)^2 + k, \quad \text{where } a, \ h, \ k \text{ are constants, } a \neq 0.$$

The graph of this quadratic function has vertex (h, k) and axis of symmetry $x = h$.

A quadratic function can always be expressed in both standard form and vertex form. For example, for the function $f(x) = (x + 3)^2 - 4$ in Example 1, we convert to standard form by expanding $(x + 3)^2$ and gather like terms, so that f can be written as

$$f(x) = x^2 + 6x + 5.$$

This form shows that the parabola opens upward and that the vertical intercept is 5.

In this case we can also factor f and write it as

$$f(x) = (x + 1)(x + 5).$$

This form shows that the parabola crosses the x-axis at $x = -1$ and $x = -5$. In fact, all three forms share the same constant a, which tells us whether the parabola opens upward or downward. In the function f, we see that $a = 1$.

To convert from vertex form to standard form, we multiply out the squared term. To convert from standard form to vertex form, we *complete the square*.[2]

Example 2   Put each quadratic function into vertex form by completing the square and then graph it.

(a) $s(x) = x^2 - 6x + 8$ (b) $t(x) = -4x^2 - 12x - 8$

Solution   (a) To complete the square, find the square of half of the coefficient of the x-term, $(-6/2)^2 = 9$. Add and subtract this number after the x-term:

$$s(x) = \underbrace{x^2 - 6x + 9}_{\text{Perfect square}} - 9 + 8,$$

so

$$s(x) = (x - 3)^2 - 1.$$

The vertex of s is $(3, -1)$ and the axis of symmetry is the vertical line $x = 3$. The parabola opens upward. See Figure 3.9.

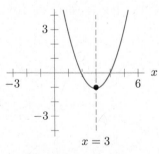

Figure 3.9: $s(x) = x^2 - 6x + 8$

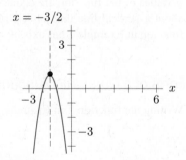

Figure 3.10: $t(x) = -4x^2 - 12x - 8$

[2] A more detailed explanation of this method is in the Skills Review on page 125.

(b) To complete the square, first factor out -4, the coefficient of x^2, giving

$$t(x) = -4(x^2 + 3x + 2).$$

Now add and subtract the square of half the coefficient of the x-term, $(3/2)^2 = 9/4$, inside the parentheses. This gives

$$t(x) = -4\left(\underbrace{x^2 + 3x + \frac{9}{4}}_{\text{Perfect square}} - \frac{9}{4} + 2 \right)$$

$$t(x) = -4\left(\left(x + \frac{3}{2}\right)^2 - \frac{1}{4} \right)$$

$$t(x) = -4\left(x + \frac{3}{2}\right)^2 + 1.$$

The vertex of t is $(-3/2, 1)$, the axis of symmetry is $x = -3/2$, and the parabola opens downward. See Figure 3.10.

Finding a Formula Given the Vertex and Another Point

If we know the vertex of a quadratic function and one other point, we can use the vertex form to find its formula.

Example 3   Find the formula for the quadratic function graphed in Figure 3.11.

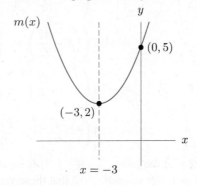

Figure 3.11: Finding a formula for a quadratic from the vertex

Solution   Since the vertex is given, we use the form $m(x) = a(x - h)^2 + k$ to find a, h, and k. The vertex is $(-3, 2)$, so $h = -3$ and $k = 2$. Thus,

$$m(x) = a(x - (-3))^2 + 2,$$

so

$$m(x) = a(x + 3)^2 + 2.$$

To find a, use the y-intercept $(0, 5)$. Substitute $x = 0$ and $y = m(0) = 5$ into the formula for $m(x)$ and solve for a:

$$5 = a(0 + 3)^2 + 2$$
$$3 = 9a$$
$$a = \frac{1}{3}.$$

Thus, the formula is

$$m(x) = \frac{1}{3}(x+3)^2 + 2.$$

If we want the formula in standard form, we multiply out:

$$m(x) = \frac{1}{3}x^2 + 2x + 5.$$

Modeling with Quadratic Functions

In applications, it is often useful to find the maximum or minimum value of a quadratic function. In the next example, we return to the baseball example that started this section.

Example 4   For t in seconds, the height of a baseball in feet is given by the formula

$$y = f(t) = -16t^2 + 47t + 3.$$

Using algebra, find the maximum height reached by the baseball and the time that height is reached.

Solution   The maximum height is at the vertex, so we complete the square to write the function in vertex form:

$$
\begin{aligned}
y = f(t) &= -16\left(t^2 - \frac{47}{16}t - \frac{3}{16}\right) \\
&= -16\left(t^2 - \frac{47}{16}t + \left(-\frac{47}{32}\right)^2 - \left(-\frac{47}{32}\right)^2 - \frac{3}{16}\right) \\
&= -16\left(\left(t - \frac{47}{32}\right)^2 - \frac{2209}{1024} - \frac{192}{1024}\right) \\
&= -16\left(\left(t - \frac{47}{32}\right)^2 - \frac{2401}{1024}\right) \\
&= -16\left(t - \frac{47}{32}\right)^2 + \frac{2401}{64}.
\end{aligned}
$$

Thus, the vertex is at the point $\left(\frac{47}{32}, \frac{2401}{64}\right)$. This means that the ball reaches it maximum height of 37.516 feet at $t = 1.469$ seconds. Note that these values are in line with the the graphical estimate $(1.5, 37.5)$ from the beginning of the section.

Example 5   A city decides to make a park by fencing off a section of riverfront property. Funds are allotted for 80 meters of fence. The area enclosed will be a rectangle, but only three sides will be enclosed by fence—the other side will be bounded by the river. What is the maximum area that can be enclosed?

Solution   Two sides are perpendicular to the bank of the river and have equal length, which we call h. The other side is parallel to the bank of the river; its length is b. See Figure 3.12. The area, A, of the park is the product of the lengths of adjacent sides, so $A = bh$.

Since the fence is 80 meters long, we have

$$2h + b = 80$$
$$b = 80 - 2h.$$

Thus,

$$A = bh = (80 - 2h)h$$
$$A = -2h^2 + 80h.$$

The function $A = -2h^2 + 80h$ is quadratic. Since the coefficient of h^2 is negative, the parabola opens downward and we have a maximum at the vertex. The factored form of the quadratic is $A = -2h(h - 40)$, so the zeros are $h = 0$ and $h = 40$. The vertex of the parabola occurs on its axis of symmetry, midway between the zeros at $h = 20$. Substituting $h = 20$ gives the maximum area:

$$A = -2 \cdot 20(20 - 40) = -40(-20) = 800 \text{ meters}^2.$$

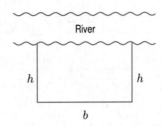

Figure 3.12: A park next to a river

Exercises and Problems for Section 3.2

Skill Refresher

For Exercises S1–S4, complete the square for each expression.

S1. $y^2 - 12y$ **S2.** $s^2 + 6s - 8$

S3. $c^2 + 3c - 7$ **S4.** $4s^2 + s + 2$

In Exercises S5–S7, solve by completing the square.

S5. $r^2 - 6r + 8 = 0$ **S6.** $n^2 = 3n + 18$

S7. $5q^2 - 8 = 2q$

In Exercises S8–S10, solve using factoring, completing the square, or the quadratic formula.

S8. $-3t^2 + 4t + 9 = 0$ **S9.** $n^2 + 4n - 3 = 2$

S10. $2q^2 + 4q - 5 = 8$

Exercises

For the quadratic functions in Exercises 1–2, state the coordinates of the vertex, the axis of symmetry, and whether the parabola opens upward or downward.

1. $f(x) = 3(x - 1)^2 + 2$

2. $g(x) = -(x + 3)^2 - 4$

3. Find the vertex and axis of symmetry of the graph of $v(t) = t^2 + 11t - 4$.

4. Find the vertex and axis of symmetry of the graph of $w(x) = -3x^2 - 30x + 31$.

5. Sketch the quadratic functions given in standard form. Identify the values of the parameters a, b, and c. Label the zeros, axis of symmetry, vertex, and y-intercept.

(a) $g(x) = x^2 + 3$ (b) $f(x) = -2x^2 + 4x + 16$

6. Show that the function $y = -x^2 + 7x - 13$ has no real zeros.

7. Find the value of k so that the graph of $y = (x - 3)^2 + k$ passes through the point $(6, 13)$.

8. The parabola $y = ax^2 + k$ has vertex $(0, -2)$ and passes through the point $(3, 4)$. Find its equation.

In Exercises 9–12, find a formula for the parabola.

9.

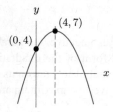

10.

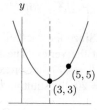

11.

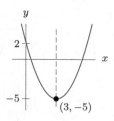

12.

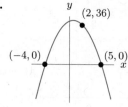

For Exercises 13–16, convert the quadratic functions to vertex form by completing the square. Identify the vertex and the axis of symmetry.

13. $f(x) = x^2 + 8x + 3$

14. $g(x) = -2x^2 + 12x + 4$

15. $p(t) = 2t^2 - 0.12t + 0.1$

16. $w(z) = -3z^2 + 9z - 2$

In Exercises 17–19, write the quadratic function in its standard, vertex, and factored forms.

17. $y = -6 + \dfrac{x^2 - x}{2}$

18. $f(t) = \dfrac{5t^2 - 20}{2}$

19. $g(s) = (s - 5)(2s + 3)$

Problems

20. Using the vertex form, find a formula for the parabola with vertex $(2, 5)$ that passes through the point $(1, 2)$.

In Problems 21–24, find a formula for the quadratic function whose graph has the given properties.

21. A vertex at $(4, 2)$ and a y-intercept of $y = 6$.

22. A vertex at $(4, 2)$ and a y-intercept of $y = -4$.

23. A vertex at $(4, 2)$ and zeros at $x = -3, 11$.

24. A vertex at $(-7, -3)$ and contains the point $(-3, -7)$.

25. Let f be a quadratic function whose graph is a concave up parabola with a vertex at $(1, -1)$, and a zero at the origin.

   (a) Graph $y = f(x)$.
   (b) Determine a formula for $f(x)$.
   (c) Determine the range of f.
   (d) Find any other zeros.

26. Find the vertex of $y = 0.03x^2 + 1.8x + 2$ exactly. Graph the function, labeling all intercepts.

27. Find the vertex of $y = 26 + 0.4x - 0.01x^2$ exactly. Graph the function, labeling all intercepts.

28. If we know a quadratic function f has a zero at $x = -1$ and vertex at $(1, 4)$, do we have enough information to find a formula for this function? If your answer is yes, find it; if not, give your reasons.

29. If you have a string of length 50 cm, what are the dimensions of the rectangle of maximum area that you can enclose with your string? Explain your reasoning. What about a string of length k cm?

30. A football player kicks a ball at an angle of $37°$ above the ground with an initial speed of 20 meters/second. The height, h, as a function of the horizontal distance traveled, d, is given by:

$$h = 0.75d - 0.0192d^2.$$

   (a) Graph the path the ball follows.
   (b) When the ball hits the ground, how far is it from the spot where the football player kicked it?
   (c) What is the maximum height the ball reaches during its flight?
   (d) What is the horizontal distance the ball has traveled when it reaches its maximum height?[3]

---

[3] Adapted from R. Halliday, D. Resnick, and K. Krane, *Physics* (New York: Wiley, 1992), p. 58.

31. A ballet dancer jumps in the air. The height, $h(t)$, in feet, of the dancer at time t, in seconds since the start of the jump, is given by[4]

$$h(t) = -16t^2 + 16Tt,$$

where T is the total time in seconds that the ballet dancer is in the air.

(a) Why does this model apply only for $0 \le t \le T$?

(b) When, in terms of T, does the maximum height of the jump occur?

(c) Show that the time, T, that the dancer is in the air is related to H, the maximum height of the jump, by the equation

$$H = 4T^2.$$

CHAPTER SUMMARY

- **General Formulas for Quadratic Functions**
  Standard form:

  $$y = ax^2 + bx + c, a \neq 0$$

  Factored form:

  $$y = a(x - r)(x - s)$$

  Vertex form:
  $$y = a(x - h)^2 + k$$

- **Graphs of Quadratic Functions**
  Graphs are parabolas
  Vertex (h, k)
  Axis of symmetry, $x = h$

Effect of parameter a

Opens upward (concave up) if $a > 0$, minimum at (h, k)

Opens downward (concave down) if $a < 0$, maximum at (h, k)

Factored form displays zeros at $x = r$ and $x = s$

- **Solving Quadratic Equations**
  Factoring
  Quadratic formula

  $$x = \frac{-b \pm \sqrt{b^2 - 4ac}}{2a}$$

  Completing the square

REVIEW EXERCISES AND PROBLEMS FOR CHAPTER THREE

Exercises

Are the functions in Exercises 1–4 quadratic? If so, write the function in the form $f(x) = ax^2 + bx + c$.

1. $f(x) = (2x - 3)(5 - x)$

2. $g(t) = 3(t - 2)^2 + 7$

3. $w(n) = n(n - 3)(n - 2) - n^2(n - 8)$

4. $r(v) = \dfrac{v^2 + \sqrt{2}}{3} + \dfrac{v - 3}{5} + \pi v^2$

In Exercises 5–10, find the zeros (if any) of the function algebraically.

5. $y = 9x^2 + 6x + 1$

6. $y = 6x^2 - 17x + 12$

7. $y = 89x^2 + 55x + 34$

8. $y = 3x^2 - 2x + 6$

9. $N(t) = t^2 - 7t + 10$

10. $Q(r) = 2r^2 - 6r - 36$

11. Show that $y = x^2 - x + 41$ has no real zeros.

12. Find the vertex and axis of symmetry for the parabola whose equation is $y = 3x^2 - 6x + 5$.

In Exercises 13–18, find a possible formula for the parabola with the given conditions.

13. The vertex is $(1, -2)$ and the y-intercept is $y = -5$.

14. The vertex is $(4, -2)$ and the y-intercept is $y = -3$.

15. The vertex is $(7, 3)$ and the parabola contains the point $(3, 7)$.

16. The parabola goes through the origin and its vertex is $(1, -1)$.

17. The x-intercepts are at $x = -1$ and $x = 2$ and $(-2, 16)$ is on the function's graph.

18. The parabola has only one x-intercept at $x = 1/2$ and has a y-intercept at 3.

---

[4] K. Laws, *The Physics of Dance* (Schirmer, 1984).

In Exercises 19–22, find a formula for the parabola.

19.

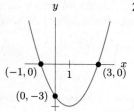

20.

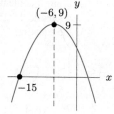

21.   **22.**

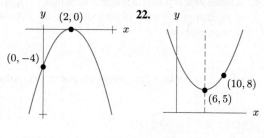

Problems

For each parabola in Problems 23–26, state the coordinates of the vertex, the axis of symmetry, the y-intercept, and whether the curve is concave up or concave down.

23. $y = 2(x - 3/4)^2 - 2/3$ **24.** $y = -1/2(x + 6)^2 - 4$

25. $y = (x - 0.6)^2$ **26.** $y = -0.3x^2 - 7$

In Problems 27–30, write each function in factored form or vertex form and then state its vertex and zeros.

27. $y = 0.3x^2 - 0.6x - 7.2$

28. $y = 2x^2 - 4x - 2$

29. $y = -3x^2 + 24x - 36$

30. $y = 2x^2 + (7/3)x + 1$

31. For x between $x = -2$ and $x = 4$, determine the concavity of the graph of $f(x) = (x-1)^2 + 2$ by calculating average rates of change over intervals of length 2.

32. A tomato is thrown vertically into the air at time $t = 0$. Its height, $d(t)$ (in feet), above the ground at time t (in seconds) is given by

$$d(t) = -16t^2 + 48t.$$

(a) Graph $d(t)$.
(b) Find t when $d(t) = 0$. What is happening to the tomato the first time $d(t) = 0$? The second time?
(c) When does the tomato reach its maximum height?
(d) What is the maximum height that the tomato reaches?

33. When slam-dunking, a basketball player seems to hang in the air at the height of his jump. The height $h(t)$, in feet above the ground, of a basketball player at time t, in seconds since the start of a jump, is given by

$$h(t) = -16t^2 + 16Tt,$$

where T is the total time in seconds that it takes to complete the jump. For a jump that takes 1 second to complete, how much of this time does the basketball player spend at the top 25% of the trajectory? [Hint: Find the maximum height reached. Then find the times at which the height is 75% of this maximum.]

CHECK YOUR UNDERSTANDING

Are the statements in Problems 1–15 true or false? Give an explanation for your answer.

1. The quadratic function $f(x) = x(x + 2)$ is in factored form.

2. If $f(x) = (x + 1)(x + 2)$, then the zeros of f are 1 and 2.

3. A quadratic function whose graph is concave up has a maximum.

4. All quadratic equations have the form $f(x) = ax^2$.

5. If the height above the ground of an object at time t is given by $s(t) = at^2 + bt + c$, then $s(0)$ tells us when the object hits the ground.

6. To find the zeros of $f(x) = ax^2 + bx + c$, solve the equation $ax^2 + bx + c = 0$ for x.

7. Every quadratic equation has two real solutions.

8. There is only one quadratic function with zeros at $x = -2$ and $x = 2$.

9. A quadratic function has exactly two zeros.

10. The graph of every quadratic equation is a parabola.

11. The maximum or minimum point of a parabola is called its vertex.

12. If a parabola is concave up its vertex is a maximum point.

13. If the equation of a parabola is written as $y = a(x - h)^2 + k$, then the vertex is located at the point $(-h, k)$.

14. If the equation of a parabola is written as $y = a(x - h)^2 + k$, then the axis of symmetry is found at $x = h$.

15. If the equation of a parabola is $y = ax^2 + bx + c$ and $a < 0$, then the parabola opens downward.

SKILLS REFRESHER FOR CHAPTER 3: QUADRATIC EQUATIONS

SKILLS FOR FACTORING

Expanding an Expression

The *distributive property* for real numbers a, b, and c tells us that

$$a(b + c) = ab + ac,$$

and

$$(b + c)a = ba + ca.$$

We use the distributive property and the rules of exponents to multiply algebraic expressions involving parentheses. This process is sometimes referred to as *expanding* the expression.

Example 1 Multiply the following expressions and simplify.

(a) $3x^2 \left(x + \frac{1}{6}x^{-3} \right)$

(b) $\left((2t)^2 - 5 \right) \sqrt{t}$

Solution

(a) $3x^2 \left(x + \frac{1}{6}x^{-3} \right) = \left(3x^2\right)(x) + \left(3x^2\right)\left(\frac{1}{6}x^{-3}\right) = 3x^3 + \frac{1}{2}x^{-1}$

(b) $\left((2t)^2 - 5 \right) \sqrt{t} = (2t)^2(\sqrt{t}) - 5\sqrt{t} = \left(4t^2\right)\left(t^{1/2}\right) - 5t^{1/2} = 4t^{5/2} - 5t^{1/2}$

If there are two terms in each factor, then there are four terms in the product:

$$(a + b)(c + d) = a(c + d) + b(c + d) = ac + ad + bc + bd.$$

The following special cases of the above product occur frequently. Learning to recognize their forms aids in factoring.

$$(a + b)(a - b) = a^2 - b^2$$
$$(a + b)^2 = a^2 + 2ab + b^2$$
$$(a - b)^2 = a^2 - 2ab + b^2$$

Example 2 Expand the following and simplify by gathering like terms.

(a) $(5x^2 + 2)(x - 4)$

(b) $(2\sqrt{r} + 2)(4\sqrt{r} - 3)$

(c) $\left(3 - \frac{1}{2}x \right)^2$

Solution

(a) $\left(5x^2 + 2\right)(x - 4) = \left(5x^2\right)(x) + \left(5x^2\right)(-4) + (2)(x) + (2)(-4) = 5x^3 - 20x^2 + 2x - 8$

(b) $(2\sqrt{r} + 2)(4\sqrt{r} - 3) = (2)(4)(\sqrt{r})^2 + (2)(-3)(\sqrt{r}) + (2)(4)(\sqrt{r}) + (2)(-3) = 8r + 2\sqrt{r} - 6$

(c) $\left(3 - \frac{1}{2}x \right)^2 = 3^2 - 2(3)\left(\frac{1}{2}x\right) + \left(-\frac{1}{2}x\right)^2 = 9 - 3x + \frac{1}{4}x^2$

Factoring

To write an expanded expression in factored form, we "un-multiply" the expression. Some techniques for factoring are given in this section. We can check factoring by multiplying the factors.

Removing a Common Factor

It is sometimes useful to factor out the same factor from each of the terms in an expression. This is basically the distributive law in reverse:

$$ab + ac = a(b + c).$$

One special case is removing a factor of -1, which gives

$$-a - b = -(a + b)$$

Another special case is

$$(a - b) = -(b - a)$$

Example 3   Factor the following:

(a) $\dfrac{2}{3}x^2y + \dfrac{4}{3}xy$ (b) $(2p + 1)p^3 - 3p(2p + 1)$ (c) $-\dfrac{s^2t}{8w} - \dfrac{st^2}{16w}$

Solution

(a) $\dfrac{2}{3}x^2y + \dfrac{4}{3}xy = \dfrac{2}{3}xy(x + 2)$

(b) $(2p + 1)p^3 - 3p(2p + 1) = (p^3 - 3p)(2p + 1) = p(p^2 - 3)(2p + 1)$
   (Note that the expression $(2p + 1)$ was one of the factors common to both terms.)

(c) $-\dfrac{s^2t}{8w} - \dfrac{st^2}{16w} = -\dfrac{st}{8w}\left(s + \dfrac{t}{2}\right)$

Grouping Terms

Even though all the terms may not have a common factor, we can sometimes factor by first grouping the terms and then removing a common factor.

Example 4   Factor $x^2 - hx - x + h$.

Solution $x^2 - hx - x + h = \left(x^2 - hx\right) - (x - h) = x(x - h) - (x - h) = (x - h)(x - 1)$

Factoring Quadratics

One way to factor quadratics is to mentally multiply out the possibilities.

Example 5   Factor $t^2 - 4t - 12$.

Solution   If the quadratic factors, it will be of the form

$$t^2 - 4t - 12 = (t + ?)(t + ?).$$

We are looking for two numbers whose product is -12 and whose sum is -4. By trying combinations, we find

$$t^2 - 4t - 12 = (t - 6)(t + 2).$$

Example 6   Factor $4 - 2M - 6M^2$.

Solution   By a similar method to the previous example, we find $4 - 2M - 6M^2 = (2 - 3M)(2 + 2M)$.

Perfect Squares and the Difference of Squares

Recognition of the special products $(x + y)^2$, $(x - y)^2$ and $(x + y)(x - y)$ in expanded form is useful in factoring. Reversing the results given on page 120, we have

$$a^2 + 2ab + b^2 = (a + b)^2,$$
$$a^2 - 2ab + b^2 = (a - b)^2,$$
$$a^2 - b^2 = (a - b)(a + b).$$

When we see squared terms in an expression to be factored, it is often useful to look for one of these forms. The difference of squares identity (the third one listed above) is especially useful.

Example 7   Factor: (a) $16y^2 - 24y + 9$ (b) $25S^2R^4 - T^6$ (c) $x^2(x - 2) + 16(2 - x)$

Solution   (a) $16y^2 - 24y + 9 = (4y - 3)^2$
(b) $25S^2R^4 - T^6 = \left(5SR^2\right)^2 - \left(T^3\right)^2 = \left(5SR^2 - T^3\right)\left(5SR^2 + T^3\right)$
(c) $x^2(x - 2) + 16(2 - x) = x^2(x - 2) - 16(x - 2) = (x - 2)\left(x^2 - 16\right) = (x - 2)(x - 4)(x + 4)$

Solving Quadratic Equations

Example 8   Give exact and approximate solutions to $x^2 = 3$.

Solution   The exact solutions are $x = \pm\sqrt{3}$; approximate ones are $x \approx \pm 1.73$, or $x \approx \pm 1.732$, or $x \approx \pm 1.73205$. (since $\sqrt{3} = 1.732050808\ldots$). Notice that the equation $x^2 = 3$ has only two exact solutions, but many possible approximate solutions, depending on how much accuracy is required.

Solving by Factoring

Some equations can be put into factored form such that the product of the factors is zero. Then we solve by using the fact that if $a \cdot b = 0$, then either a or b (or both) is zero.

Example 9   Solve $(x + 1)(x + 3) = 15$.

Solution   Although it is true that if $a \cdot b = 0$, then $a = 0$ or $b = 0$, it is *not* true that $a \cdot b = 15$ means that $a = 15$ or $b = 15$, or that a and b are 3 and 5. To solve this equation, we expand the left-hand side and rearrange so that the right-hand side is equal to zero:

$$x^2 + 4x + 3 = 15,$$
$$x^2 + 4x - 12 = 0.$$

Then, factoring gives

$$(x - 2)(x + 6) = 0.$$

Thus $x = 2$ and $x = -6$ are solutions.

Example 10   Solve $2(x + 3)^2 = 5(x + 3)$.

Solution   You might be tempted to divide both sides by $(x + 3)$. However, if you do this you will overlook one of the solutions. Instead, write

$$2(x + 3)^2 - 5(x + 3) = 0$$
$$(x + 3)\,(2(x + 3) - 5) = 0$$
$$(x + 3)(2x + 6 - 5) = 0$$
$$(x + 3)(2x + 1) = 0.$$

Thus, $x = -1/2$ and $x = -3$ are solutions.

Note that if we had divided by $(x + 3)$ at the start, we would have lost the solution $x = -3$, which was obtained by setting $x + 3 = 0$.

Solving with the Quadratic Formula

Instead of factoring, we can solve the equation $ax^2 + bx + c = 0$ by using the quadratic formula:

$$x = \frac{-b \pm \sqrt{b^2 - 4ac}}{2a}.$$

The quadratic formula is derived by completing the square for $y = ax^2 + bx + c$. See page 125.

Example 11   Solve $11 + 2x = x^2$.

Solution   The equation is

$$-x^2 + 2x + 11 = 0.$$

The expression on the left does not factor using integers, so we use

$$x = \frac{-2 + \sqrt{4 - 4(-1)(11)}}{2(-1)} = \frac{-2 + \sqrt{48}}{-2} = \frac{-2 + \sqrt{16 \cdot 3}}{-2} = \frac{-2 + 4\sqrt{3}}{-2} = 1 - 2\sqrt{3},$$

$$x = \frac{-2 - \sqrt{4 - 4(-1)(11)}}{2(-1)} = \frac{-2 - \sqrt{48}}{-2} = \frac{-2 - \sqrt{16 \cdot 3}}{-2} = \frac{-2 - 4\sqrt{3}}{-2} = 1 + 2\sqrt{3}.$$

The exact solutions are $x = 1 - 2\sqrt{3}$ and $x = 1 + 2\sqrt{3}$.

The decimal approximations to these numbers $x = 1 - 2\sqrt{3} = -2.464$ and $x = 1 + 2\sqrt{3} = 4.464$ are approximate solutions to this equation. The approximate solutions could also be found directly from a graph or calculator.

Exercises to Skills for Factoring

For Exercises 1–15, expand and simplify.

1. $2(3x - 7)$

2. $-4(y + 6)$

3. $12(x + y)$

4. $-7(5x - 8y)$

5. $x(2x + 5)$

6. $3z(2x - 9z)$

7. $-10r(5r + 6rs)$

8. $x(3x - 8) + 2(3x - 8)$

9. $5z(x - 2) - 3(x - 2)$

10. $(x+1)(x+3)$

11. $(x-2)(x+6)$

12. $(5x-1)(2x-3)$

13. $(y+1)(z+3)$

14. $(12y-5)(8w+7)$

15. $(5z-3)(x-2)$

Multiply and write the expressions in Problems 16–22 without parentheses. Gather like terms.

16. $-(x-3)-2(5-x)$

17. $(x-5)6-5(1-(2-x))$

18. $\left(3x-2x^2\right)4+(5+4x)(3x-4)$

19. $P(p-3q)^2$

20. $4(x-3)^2+7$

21. $-\left(\sqrt{2x}+1\right)^2$

22. $u\left(u^{-1}+2^u\right)2^u$

For Exercises 23–67, factor completely if possible.

23. $2x+6$

24. $3y+15$

25. $5z-30$

26. $4t-6$

27. $10w-25$

28. $3u^4-4u^3$

29. $3u^7+12u^2$

30. $12x^3y^2-18x$

31. $14r^4s^2-21rst$

32. x^2+3x-2

33. x^2-3x+2

34. x^2-3x-2

35. x^2+2x+3

36. x^2-2x-3

37. x^2-2x+3

38. x^2+2x-3

39. $2x^2+5x+2$

40. $2x^2-10x+12$

41. $x^2+3x-28$

42. x^3-2x^2-3x

43. x^3+2x^2-3x

44. $ac+ad+bc+bd$

45. $x^2+2xy+3xz+6yz$

46. $x^2-1.4x-3.92$

47. $a^2x^2-b^2$

48. $\pi r^2+2\pi rh$

49. $B^2-10B+24$

50. c^2+x^2-2cx

51. x^2+y^2

52. a^4-a^2-12

53. $(t+3)^2-16$

54. $x^2+4x+4-y^2$

55. a^3-2a^2+3a-6

56. $b^3-3b^2-9b+27$

57. $c^2d^2-25c^2-9d^2+225$

58. $hx^2+12-4hx-3x$

59. $r(r-s)-2(s-r)$

60. $y^2-3xy+2x^2$

61. $x^2e^{-3x}+2xe^{-3x}$

62. $t^2e^{5t}+3te^{5t}+2e^{5t}$

63. $P(1+r)^2+P(1+r)^2r$

64. $x^2-6x+9-4z^2$

65. $dk+2dm-3ek-6em$

66. $\pi r^2-2\pi r+3r-6$

67. $8gs-12hs+10gm-15hm$

Solve the equations in Exercises 68–93.

68. $y^2-5y-6=0$

69. $4s^2+3s-15=0$

70. $\dfrac{2}{x}+\dfrac{3}{2x}=8$

71. $\dfrac{3}{x-1}+1=5$

72. $\sqrt{y-1}=13$

73. $-16t^2+96t+12=60$

74. $g^3-4g=3g^2-12$

75. $8+2x-3x^2=0$

76. $2p^3+p^2-18p-9=0$

77. $N^2-2N-3=2N(N-3)$

78. $\dfrac{1}{64}t^3=t$

79. $x^2-1=2x$

80. $4x^2-13x-12=0$

81. $60=-16t^2+96t+12$

82. $n^5+80=5n^4+16n$

83. $5a^3+50a^2=4a+40$

84. $y^2 + 4y - 2 = 0$

85. $\dfrac{2}{z - 3} + \dfrac{7}{z^2 - 3z} = 0$

86. $\dfrac{x^2 + 1 - 2x^2}{(x^2 + 1)^2} = 0$

87. $4 - \dfrac{1}{L^2} = 0$

88. $2 + \dfrac{1}{q + 1} - \dfrac{1}{q - 1} = 0$

89. $\sqrt{r^2 + 24} = 7$

90. $\dfrac{1}{\sqrt[3]{x}} = -2$

91. $3\sqrt{x} = \dfrac{1}{2}x$

92. $10 = \sqrt{\dfrac{v}{7\pi}}$

93. $\dfrac{(3x + 4)(x - 2)}{(x - 5)(x - 1)} = 0$

In Exercises 94–97, solve for the indicated variable.

94. $T = 2\pi\sqrt{\dfrac{l}{g}}$, for l.

95. $Ab^5 = C$, for b.

96. $|2x + 1| = 7$, for x.

97. $\dfrac{x^2 - 5mx + 4m^2}{x - m} = 0$, for x

Solve the systems of equations in Exercises 98–102.

98. $\begin{cases} y = 2x - x^2 \\ y = -3 \end{cases}$

99. $\begin{cases} y = 1/x \\ y = 4x \end{cases}$

100. $\begin{cases} x^2 + y^2 = 36 \\ y = x - 3 \end{cases}$

101. $\begin{cases} y = 4 - x^2 \\ y - 2x = 1 \end{cases}$

102. $\begin{cases} y = x^3 - 1 \\ y = e^x \end{cases}$

103. Let ℓ be the line of slope 3 passing through the origin. Find the points of intersection of the line ℓ and the parabola whose equation is $y = x^2$. Sketch the line and the parabola, and label the points of intersection.

Determine the points of intersection for Problems 104–105.

104.

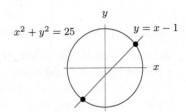

$x^2 + y^2 = 25$, $y = x - 1$

105.

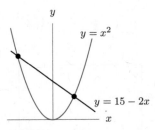

$y = x^2$, $y = 15 - 2x$

COMPLETING THE SQUARE

An example of changing the form of an expression is the conversion of $ax^2 + bx + c$ into the form $a(x - h)^2 + k$. We make this conversion by *completing the square*, a method for producing a perfect square within a quadratic expression. A perfect square is an expression of the form:

$$(x + n)^2 = x^2 + 2nx + n^2.$$

In order to complete the square in an expression, we must find that number n, which is half the coefficient of x. Before giving a general procedure, let's work through an example.

Example 1   Complete the square to rewrite $x^2 - 10x + 4$ in the form $a(x - h)^2 + k$.

Solution   Step 1: We divide the coefficient of x by 2, giving $\frac{1}{2}(-10) = -5$.
Step 2: We square the result of step 1, giving $(-5)^2 = 25$.
Step 3: Now add and subtract the 25 after the x-term:

$$x^2 - 10x + 4 = x^2 - 10x + 25 - 25 + 4$$
$$= \underbrace{(x^2 - 10x + 25)}_{\text{Perfect square}} -25 + 4.$$

Step 4: Notice that we have created a perfect square, $x^2 - 10x + 25$. The next step is to factor the perfect square and combine the constant terms, $-25 + 4$, giving the final result:

$$x^2 - 10x + 4 = (x - 5)^2 - 21.$$

Thus, $a = +1$, $h = +5$, and $k = -21$.

Visualizing The Process of Completing The Square

We can visualize how to find the constant that needs to be added to $x^2 + bx$ in order to obtain a perfect square by thinking of $x^2 + bx$ as the area of a rectangle. For example, the rectangle in Figure 3.13 has area $x(x + b) = x^2 + bx$. Now imagine cutting the rectangle into pieces as in Figure 3.14 and trying to rearrange them to make a square, as in Figure 3.15. The corner piece, whose area is $(b/2)^2$, is missing. By adding this piece to our expression, we "complete" the square: $x^2 + bx + (b/2)^2 = (x + b/2)^2$.

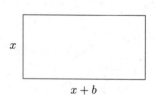

Figure 3.13: Rectangle with sides x and $x + b$

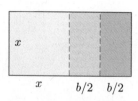

Figure 3.14: Cut off 2 strips of width $b/2$

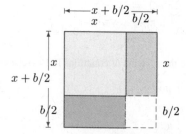

Figure 3.15: Rearrange to see a square with missing corner of area $(b/2)^2$

The procedure we followed can be summarized as follows:

To complete the square in the expression $x^2 + bx + c$, divide the coefficient of x by 2, giving $b/2$. Then add and subtract $(b/2)^2 = b^2/4$ and factor the perfect square:

$$x^2 + bx + c = \left(x + \frac{b}{2}\right)^2 - \frac{b^2}{4} + c.$$

To complete the square in the expression $ax^2 + bx + c$, factor out a first.

The next example has a coefficient a with $a \neq 1$. After factoring out the coefficient, we follow the same steps as in Example 1.

Example 2   Complete the square in the formula $h(x) = 5x^2 + 30x - 10$.

Solution   We first factor out 5:

$$h(x) = 5(x^2 + 6x - 2).$$

Now we complete the square in the expression $x^2 + 6x - 2$.
Step 1: Divide the coefficient of x by 2, giving 3.
Step 2: Square the result: $3^2 = 9$.
Step 3: Add the result after the x term, then subtract it:

$$h(x) = 5(\underbrace{x^2 + 6x + 9}_{\text{Perfect square}} - 9 - 2).$$

Step 4: Factor the perfect square and simplify the rest:

$$h(x) = 5\left((x+3)^2 - 11\right).$$

Now that we have completed the square, we can multiply by the 5:

$$h(x) = 5(x+3)^2 - 55.$$

Deriving the Quadratic Formula

We derive a general formula to find the zeros of $q(x) = ax^2 + bx + c$, with $a \neq 0$, by completing the square. To find the zeros, set $q(x) = 0$:

$$ax^2 + bx + c = 0.$$

Before we complete the square, we factor out the coefficient of x^2:

$$a\left(x^2 + \frac{b}{a}x + \frac{c}{a}\right) = 0.$$

Since $a \neq 0$, we can divide both sides by a:

$$x^2 + \frac{b}{a}x + \frac{c}{a} = 0.$$

To complete the square, we add and then subtract $((b/a)/2)^2 = b^2/(4a^2)$:

$$\underbrace{x^2 + \frac{b}{a}x + \frac{b^2}{4a^2}}_{\text{Perfect square}} - \frac{b^2}{4a^2} + \frac{c}{a} = 0.$$

We factor the perfect square and simplify the constant term, giving:

$$\left(x + \frac{b}{2a}\right)^2 - \left(\frac{b^2 - 4ac}{4a^2}\right) = 0 \qquad\qquad \text{since } \frac{-b^2}{4a^2} + \frac{c}{a} = \frac{-b^2}{4a^2} + \frac{4ac}{4a^2} = -\left(\frac{b^2 - 4ac}{4a^2}\right)$$

$$\left(x + \frac{b}{2a}\right)^2 = \frac{b^2 - 4ac}{4a^2} \qquad \text{adding } \frac{b^2 - 4ac}{4a^2} \text{ to both sides}$$

$$x + \frac{b}{2a} = \pm\sqrt{\frac{b^2 - 4ac}{4a^2}} = \frac{\pm\sqrt{b^2 - 4ac}}{2a} \qquad \text{taking the square root}$$

$$x = \frac{-b}{2a} \pm \frac{\sqrt{b^2 - 4ac}}{2a} \qquad \text{subtracting } b/2a$$

$$x = \frac{-b \pm \sqrt{b^2 - 4ac}}{2a}.$$

Exercises to Skills for Completing the Square

For Exercises 1–8, complete the square for each expression.

1. $x^2 + 8x$

2. $w^2 + 7w$

3. $2r^2 + 20r$

4. $3t^2 + 24t - 13$

5. $a^2 - 2a - 4$

6. $n^2 + 4n - 5$

7. $3r^2 + 9r - 4$

8. $12g^2 + 8g + 5$

In Exercises 9–12, rewrite in the form $a(x - h)^2 + k$.

9. $x^2 - 2x - 3$

10. $10 - 6x + x^2$

11. $-x^2 + 6x - 2$

12. $3x^2 - 12x + 13$

In Exercises 13–22, complete the square to find the vertex of the parabola.

13. $y = x^2 + 6x + 3$

14. $y = x^2 - x + 4$

15. $y = -x^2 - 8x + 2$

16. $y = x^2 - 3x - 3$

17. $y = -x^2 + x - 6$

18. $y = 3x^2 + 12x$

19. $y = -4x^2 + 8x - 6$

20. $y = 5x^2 - 5x + 7$

21. $y = 2x^2 - 7x + 3$

22. $y = -3x^2 - x - 2$

In Exercises 23–29, solve by completing the square.

23. $g^2 = 2g + 24$

24. $p^2 - 2p = 6$

25. $d^2 - d = 2$

26. $2r^2 + 4r - 5 = 0$

27. $2s^2 = 1 - 10s$

28. $7r^2 - 3r - 6 = 0$

29. $5p^2 + 9p = 1$

In Exercises 30–35, solve by using the quadratic formula.

30. $n^2 - 4n - 12 = 0$

31. $2y^2 + 5y = -2$

32. $6k^2 + 11k = -3$

33. $w^2 + w = 4$

34. $z^2 + 4z = 6$

35. $2q^2 + 6q - 3 = 0$

In Exercises 36–46, solve using factoring, completing the square, or the quadratic formula.

36. $r^2 - 2r = 8$

37. $s^2 + 3s = 1$

38. $z^3 + 2z^2 = 3z + 6$

39. $25u^2 + 4 = 30u$

40. $v^2 - 4v - 9 = 0$

41. $3y^2 = 6y + 18$

42. $2p^2 + 23 = 14p$

43. $2w^3 + 24 = 6w^2 + 8w$

44. $4x^2 + 16x - 5 = 0$

45. $49m^2 + 70m + 22 = 0$

46. $8x^2 - 1 = 2x$

Chapter Four

EXPONENTIAL FUNCTIONS

Contents

4.1 INTRODUCTION TO THE FAMILY OF EXPONENTIAL FUNCTIONS

Growing at a Constant Percent Rate

Linear functions represent quantities that change at a constant rate. In this section we introduce functions that change at a constant *percent* rate, the *exponential functions*.

Salary Raises

Example 1   After graduation from college, you will probably be looking for a job. Suppose you are offered a job at a starting salary of $40,000 per year. To strengthen the offer, the company promises annual raises of 6% per year for at least the first five years after you are hired. Let's compute your salary for the first few years.

If t represents the number of years since the beginning of your contract, then for $t = 0$, your salary is $40,000. At the end of the first year, when $t = 1$, your salary increases by 6% so

$$\begin{aligned}\text{Salary when } t = 1 &= \text{Original salary} + 6\% \text{ of Original salary} \\ &= 40{,}000 + 0.06 \cdot 40{,}000 \\ &= 42{,}400 \text{ dollars.}\end{aligned}$$

After the second year, your salary again increases by 6%, so

$$\begin{aligned}\text{Salary when } t = 2 &= \text{Former salary} + 6\% \text{ of Former salary} \\ &= 42{,}400 + 0.06 \cdot 42{,}400 \\ &= 44{,}944 \text{ dollars.}\end{aligned}$$

Notice that your raise is higher in the second year than in the first since the second 6% increase applies both to the original $40,000 salary and to the $2400 raise given in the first year.

Salary calculations for four years have been rounded and recorded in Table 4.1. At the end of the third and fourth years your salary again increases by 6%, and your raise is larger each year. Not only are you given the 6% increase on your original salary, but your raises earn raises as well.

Table 4.1   *Raise amounts and resulting salaries for a person earning 6% annual salary increases*

Year	Raise amount ($)	Salary ($)
0		40,000.00
1	2400.00	42,400.00
2	2544.00	44,944.00
3	2696.64	47,640.64
4	2858.44	50,499.08

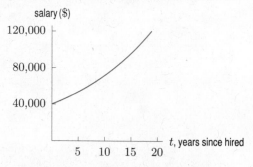

Figure 4.1: Salary over a 20-year period

Figure 4.1 shows salary over a 20-year period assuming that the annual increase remains 6%. Since the rate of change of your salary (in dollars per year) is not constant, the graph of this function is not a line. The salary increases at an increasing rate, giving the graph its upward curve. A function that increases at a constant percent rate is said to increase exponentially.

Population Growth

Exponential functions provide a reasonable model for many growing populations.

Example 2   During the 2000s, the population of Mexico increased at a constant annual percent rate of 1.2%.[1] Since the population grew by the same percent each year, it can be modeled by an exponential function.

Let's calculate the population of Mexico for the years after 2000. In 2000, the population was 100 million. The population grew by 1.2%, so

$$\text{Population in 2001} = \text{Population in 2000} + 1.2\% \text{ of Population in 2000}$$
$$= 100 + 0.012(100)$$
$$= 100 + 1.2 = 101.2 \text{ million.}$$

Similarly,

$$\text{Population in 2002} = \text{Population in 2001} + 1.2\% \text{ of Population in 2001}$$
$$= 101.2 + 0.012(101.2)$$
$$= 101.2 + 1.2144 = 102.4144 \text{ million.}$$

The calculations for years 2000 through 2007 have been rounded and recorded in Table 4.2. The population of Mexico increased by slightly more each year than it did the year before, because each year the increase is 1.2% of a larger number.

Table 4.2   *Calculated values for the population of Mexico*

Year	ΔP, increase in population	P, population (millions)
2000	—	100
2001	1.2	101.2
2002	1.21	102.41
2003	1.23	103.64
2004	1.25	104.89
2005	1.26	106.15
2006	1.27	107.42
2007	1.29	108.71

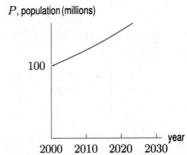

Figure 4.2: The projected population of Mexico, assuming 1.2% annual growth

Figure 4.2 gives a graph of the population of Mexico over a 30-year period, assuming a 1.2% annual growth rate. Notice that this graph curves upward like the graph in Figure 4.1.

Radioactive Decay

Exponential functions can also model decreasing quantities. A quantity which decreases at a constant percent rate is said to be decreasing exponentially.

Example 3   Carbon-14 is used to estimate the age of organic compounds. Over time, radioactive carbon-14 decays into a stable form. The decay rate is 11.4% every 1000 years. For example, if we begin with a 200-microgram (μg) sample of carbon-14 then

---

[1] http://www.census.gov/ipc/www/idb/country.php, accessed May 23, 2010.

$$\begin{array}{rl}\text{Amount remaining} & = \text{Initial amount} - 11.4\% \text{ of Initial amount} \\ \text{after 1000 years} & \\ & = 200 - 0.114 \cdot 200 \\ & = 177.2 \ \mu\text{g}.\end{array}$$

Similarly,

$$\begin{array}{rl}\text{Amount remaining} & \text{Amount remaining} \\ \text{after 2000 years} & = \text{after 1000 years} - 11.4\% \text{ of } \text{after 1000 years} \\ & = 177.2 - 0.114 \cdot 177.2 \approx 156.999 \ \mu\text{g},\end{array}$$

and

$$\begin{array}{rl}\text{Amount remaining} & \text{Amount remaining} \\ \text{after 3000 years} & = \text{after 2000 years} - 11.4\% \text{ of } \text{after 2000 years} \\ & = 156.999 - 0.114 \cdot 156.999 \approx 139.101 \ \mu\text{g}.\end{array}$$

These calculations are recorded in Table 4.3. During each 1000-year period, the amount of carbon-14 that decays is smaller than in the previous period. This is because we take 11.4% of a smaller quantity each time.

Table 4.3   *The amount of carbon-14 remaining over time*

Years elapsed	Amount decayed (μg)	Amount remaining (μg)
0	—	200.0
1000	22.8	177.2
2000	20.201	156.999
3000	17.898	139.101

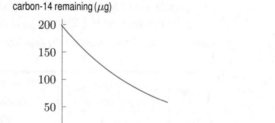

Figure 4.3: Amount of carbon-14 over 10,000 years

Figure 4.3 shows the amount of carbon-14 left from a 200 μg sample over 10,000 years. Because the amount decreases by a smaller amount over each successive time interval, the graph is not linear but bends upward, hence is concave up.

Growth Factors and Percent Growth Rates

The Growth Factor of an Increasing Exponential Function

The salary in Example 1 increases by 6% every year. We say that the annual percent growth rate is 6%. But there is another way to think about the growth of this salary. We know that each year,

$$\text{New salary} = \text{Old salary} + 6\% \text{ of Old salary}.$$

We can rewrite this as follows:

$$\text{New salary} = 100\% \text{ of Old salary} + 6\% \text{ of Old salary}.$$

So

$$\text{New salary} = 106\% \text{ of Old salary}.$$

Since $106\% = 1.06$, we have

$$\text{New salary} = 1.06 \cdot \text{Old salary}.$$

We call 1.06 the *growth factor*.

The Growth Factor of a Decreasing Exponential Function

In Example 3, the carbon-14 changes by -11.4% every 1000 years. The negative growth rate tells us that the quantity of carbon-14 decreases over time. We have

$$\text{New amount} = \text{Old amount} - 11.4\% \text{ of Old amount},$$

which can be rewritten as

$$\text{New amount} = 100\% \text{ of Old amount} - 11.4\% \text{ of Old amount}.$$

So,

$$\text{New amount} = 88.6\% \text{ of Old amount}.$$

Since $88.6\% = 0.886$, we have

$$\text{New amount} = 0.886 \cdot \text{Old amount}.$$

We call 0.886 the growth factor even though the amount of carbon-14 is decreasing. Although it may sound strange to refer to 0.886 as the growth factor, rather than the decay factor, we use "growth factor" to describe both increasing and decreasing quantities.

A General Formula for the Family of Exponential Functions

Because it grows at a constant percentage rate each year, the salary, S, in Example 1 is an example of an exponential function. We want a formula for S in terms of t, the number of years since being hired. Since the annual growth factor is 1.06, we know that for each year,

$$\text{New salary} = \text{Old salary} \cdot 1.06.$$

Thus, after one year, or when $t = 1$,

$$S = \underbrace{40,000}_{\text{Old salary}}(1.06).$$

Similarly, when $t = 2$,

$$S = \underbrace{40,000(1.06)}_{\text{Old salary}}(1.06) = 40,000(1.06)^2.$$

Here there are *two* factors of 1.06 because the salary has increased by 6% twice. When $t = 3$,

$$S = \underbrace{40,000(1.06)^2}_{\text{Old salary}}(1.06) = 40,000(1.06)^3$$

and continues in this pattern so that after t years have elapsed,

$$S = 40,000 \underbrace{(1.06)(1.06)\ldots(1.06)}_{t \text{ factors of } 1.06} = 40,000(1.06)^t.$$

After t years the salary has increased by a factor of 1.06 a total of t times. Thus,

$$S = 40{,}000(1.06)^t.$$

These results, which are summarized in Table 4.4, are the same as in Table 4.1. Notice that in this formula we assume that t is an integer, $t \geq 0$, since the raises are given only once a year.

Table 4.4 *Salary after t years*

t (years)	S, salary ($)
0	40,000
1	$40{,}000(1.06) = 42{,}400.00$
2	$40{,}000(1.06)^2 = 44{,}944.00$
3	$40{,}000(1.06)^3 = 47{,}640.64$
t	$40{,}000(1.06)^t$

This salary formula can be written as

$$S = \text{Initial salary} \cdot (\text{Growth factor})^t.$$

In general, we have:

An **exponential function** $Q = f(t)$ has the formula

$$f(t) = ab^t, \quad a \neq 0, b > 0,$$

where a is the initial value of Q (at $t = 0$) and b, the base, is the growth factor. The growth factor is given by

$$b = 1 + r$$

where r is the decimal representation of the percent rate of change.
- If there is exponential growth, then $r > 0$ and $b > 1$.
- If there is exponential decay, then $r < 0$ and $0 < b < 1$.

The constants a and b are called *parameters.*. The base b is restricted to positive values because if $b < 0$ then b^t is undefined for some exponents t, for example, $t = 1/2$.

Every function in the form $f(t) = ab^t$ with the input, t, in the exponent is an exponential function, provided $a \neq 0$. Note that if $b = 1$, then $f(t) = a \cdot 1^t = a$ and $f(t)$ is a constant, so when $b = 1$, the function is generally not considered exponential. Graphs showing exponential growth and decay are in Figures 4.4 and 4.5. Notice that in both cases the graph is concave up.

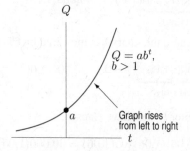
Figure 4.4: Exponential growth: $b > 1$

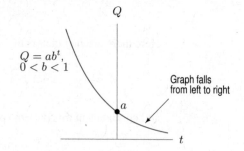
Figure 4.5: Exponential decay: $0 < b < 1$

Example 4   Use the formula $S = 40,000(1.06)^t$ to calculate your salary after 4 years, 12 years, and 40 years.

Solution   After 4 years, $t = 4$, and we have

$$S = 40,000(1.06)^4 \approx \$50,499.08.$$

Notice that this agrees with Table 4.1 on page 130. After 12 years, $t = 12$, and we have

$$S = 40,000(1.06)^{12} \approx \$80,487.86.$$

After 12 years, the salary has more than doubled from the initial salary of $\$40,000$. When $t = 40$ we have

$$S = 40,000(1.06)^{40} \approx \$411,428.72.$$

Thus if you work for 40 years and consistently earn 6% annual raises, your salary will be over $\$400,000$ a year.

Example 5   Carbon-14 decays at a rate of 11.4% every 1000 years. Write a formula for the quantity, Q, of a $200\text{-}\mu\text{g}$ sample remaining as a function of time, t, in thousands of years.

Solution   The growth factor of carbon-14 over 1000 years is $1 - 0.114 = 0.886$. Originally, there are 200 μg, so the quantity remaining after t thousand years is given by

$$Q = 200(0.886)^t.$$

Example 6   Using Example 2 on page 131, find a formula for P, the population of Mexico (in millions), in year t where $t = 0$ represents the year 2000.

Solution   In 2000, the population of Mexico was 100 million, and it was growing at a constant 1.2% annual rate. The growth factor is $b = 1 + 0.012 = 1.012$, and $a = 100$, so

$$P = 100(1.012)^t.$$

Because the growth factor may change eventually, this formula may not give accurate results for large values of t.

Example 7   What does the formula $P = 100(1.012)^t$ predict when $t = 0$? When $t = -5$? What do these values tell you about the population of Mexico?

Solution   If $t = 0$, then , since $(1.012)^0 = 1$, we have

$$P = 100(1.012)^0 = 100.$$

This makes sense because $t = 0$ stands for 2000, and in 2000 the population was 100 million. When $t = -5$ we have

$$P = 100(1.012)^{-5} \approx 94.210.$$

To make sense of this number, we must interpret the year $t = -5$ as five years before 2000; that is, as the year 1995. If the population of Mexico had been growing at a 1.2% annual rate from 1995 onward, then it was 94.21 million in 1995.

Example 8   On August 2, 1988, a US District Court judge imposed a fine on the city of Yonkers, New York, for defying a federal court order involving housing desegregation.[2] The fine started at $\$100$ for the first day and was to double daily until the city chose to obey the court order.

(a) What was the daily percent growth rate of the fine?
(b) Find a formula for the fine as a function of t, the number of days since August 2, 1988.
(c) If Yonkers waited 30 days before obeying the court order, what would the fine have been?

[2]*The Boston Globe*, August 27, 1988.

Solution   (a) Since the fine increased each day by a factor of 2, the fine grew exponentially with growth factor $b = 2$. To find the percent growth rate, we set $b = 1 + r = 2$, from which we find $r = 1$, or 100%. Thus the daily percent growth rate is 100%. This makes sense because when a quantity increases by 100%, it doubles in size.

(b) If t is the number of days since August 2, the formula for the fine, P in dollars, is

$$P = 100 \cdot 2^t.$$

(c) After 30 days, the fine is $P = 100 \cdot 2^{30} \approx 1.074 \cdot 10^{11}$ dollars, or \$107,374,182,400.

Exercises and Problems for Section 4.1

Skill Refresher

In Exercises S1–S2, express the percentages in decimal form.   In Exercises S3–S4, express the decimals as a percent.

S1. 6% **S2.** 0.6% **S3.** 0.0012 **S4.** 1.23

Exercises

Are the functions in Exercises 1–9 exponential? If so, write the function in the form $f(t) = ab^t$.

1. $g(w) = 2\left(2^{-w}\right)$ **2.** $m(t) = (2 \cdot 3^t)^3$

3. $f(x) = \dfrac{3^{2x}}{4}$ **4.** $G(t) = 3(t)^t$

5. $q(r) = \dfrac{-4}{3^r}$ **6.** $j(x) = 2^x 3^x$

7. $Q(t) = 8^{t/3}$ **8.** $K(x) = \dfrac{2^x}{3 \cdot 3^x}$

9. $p(r) = 2^r + 3^r$

What is the growth factor in Exercises 10–13? Assume time is measured in the units given.

10. Water usage is increasing by 3% per year.
11. A city grows by 28% per decade.
12. A diamond mine is depleted by 1% per day.
13. A forest shrinks 80% per century.

In Exercises 14–17, give the starting value a, the growth factor b, and the growth rate r if $Q = ab^t = a(1 + r)^t$.

14. $Q = 1750(1.593)^t$ **15.** $Q = 34.3(0.788)^t$

16. $Q = 79.2(1.002)^t$ **17.** $Q = 0.0022(2.31)^{-3t}$

Problems

18. The populations, P, of six towns with time t in years are given by

(i) $P = 1000(1.08)^t$ (ii) $P = 600(1.12)^t$
(iii) $P = 2500(0.9)^t$ (iv) $P = 1200(1.185)^t$
(v) $P = 800(0.78)^t$ (vi) $P = 2000(0.99)^t$

(a) Which towns are growing in size? Which are shrinking?
(b) Which town is growing the fastest? What is the annual percent growth rate for that town?
(c) Which town is shrinking the fastest? What is the annual percent "decay" rate for that town?

(d) Which town has the largest initial population (at $t = 0$)? Which town has the smallest?

19. The value, V, of a \$100,000 investment that earns 3% annual interest is given by $V = f(t)$ where t is in years. How much is the investment worth in 3 years?

20. An investment decreases by 5% per year for 4 years. By what total percent does it decrease?

21. Without a calculator, match each of the formulas to one of the graphs in Figure 4.6.

(a) $y = 0.8^t$ (b) $y = 5(3)^t$
(c) $y = -6(1.03)^t$ (d) $y = 15(3)^{-t}$

(e) $y = -4(0.98)^t$ **(f)** $y = 82(0.8)^{-t}$

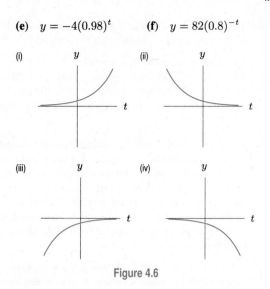

Figure 4.6

In Problems 22–27, the initial value (at year $t = 0$) and the percent change per year of a quantity Q are given.

(a) Write a formula for Q as a function of t.

(b) What is the value of Q when $t = 10$?

22. Initial amount 2000; increasing by 5% per year

23. Initial amount 35; decreasing by 8% per year

24. Initial amount 112.8; decreasing by 23.4% per year

25. Initial amount 5.35; increasing by 0.8% per year

26. Initial amount 5; increasing by 100% per year

27. Initial amount 0.2; decreasing by 0.5% per year

28. Figure 4.7 is the graph of $f(x) = 4 \cdot b^x$. Find the slope of the line segment PQ in terms of b.

Figure 4.7

29. In 2010, the population of a country was 70 million and growing at a rate of 1.9% per year. Assuming the percentage growth rate remains constant, express the population, P, as a function of t, the number of years after 2010.

30. The mass, Q, of a sample of tritium (a radioactive isotope of hydrogen), decays at a rate of 5.626% per year. Write a function giving the mass of a 726-gram sample after a time, t, in years. Graph this decay function.

31. In 2010 the number of people infected by a virus was P_0. Due to a new vaccine, the number of infected people has decreased by 20% each year since 2010. In other words, only 80% as many people are infected each year as were infected the year before. Find a formula for $P = f(n)$, the number of infected people n years after 2010. Graph $f(n)$. Explain, in terms of the virus, why the graph has the shape it does.

32. Every year, a lake becomes more polluted, and 2% fewer organisms can live in it. If in 2011 there are one million organisms, write an equation relating O, the number of organisms, to time, t, in years since 2011.

33. **(a)** The annual inflation rate is 3.5% per year. If a movie ticket costs \$7.50, find a formula for p, the price of the ticket t years from today, assuming that movie tickets keep up with inflation.
   (b) According to your formula, how much will movie tickets cost in 20 years?

34. The value \$$V$ of an investment in year t is given by $V = 2500(1.0325)^t$. Describe the investment in words.

35. A typical cup of coffee contains about 100 mg of caffeine and every hour approximately 16% of the amount of caffeine in the body is metabolized and eliminated.

   (a) Write C, the amount of caffeine in the body in mg, as a function of t, the number of hours since the coffee was consumed.
   (b) How much caffeine is in the body after 5 hours?

36. Grinnell Glacier in Glacier National Park in the US covered about 142 acres in 2007 and was shrinking at a rate of about 4.4% per year.[3]

   (a) Write a formula for the size, S, of the Grinnell Glacier, in acres, as a function of years t since 2007.
   (b) Use the model to predict the size of the glacier in the year 2015.
   (c) According to the model, how many acres of ice were lost from the glacier between 2007 and 2010?

37. In January 2005, the population of California was 36.8 million and growing at an annual rate of 1.3%. Assume that growth continues at the same rate.

   (a) By how much will the population increase between 2005 and 2030? Between 2030 and 2055?
   (b) Explain how you can tell before doing the calculations which of the two answers in part (a) is larger.

38. A cold yam is placed in a hot oven. Newton's Law of Heating tells us that the difference between the oven's temperature and the yam's temperature decays exponentially with time. The yam's temperature is initially 0°F,

---

[3] "Warming climate shrinking Glacier Park's glaciers", www.usatoday.com, October 15, 2007.

the oven's temperature is $300°$F, and the temperature difference decreases by 3% per minute. Find a formula for $Y(t)$, the yam's temperature at time t.

39. The population of India was about 1.15 billion people in 2010 and was growing at a rate of about 1.35% per year.

   (a) Write a formula for the population, P, of India, in billions, as a function of years t since 2010.
   (b) If the growth rate stays constant, predict the population of India in the year 2015 and the year 2020.
   (c) Find the rate of change of India's population, in million people per year, during the year 2010.
   (d) Find the rate of change of India's population, in people per minute, during the year 2010.

40. Polluted water is passed through a series of filters. Each filter removes 85% of the remaining impurities. Initially, the untreated water contains impurities at a level of 420 parts per million (ppm). Find a formula for L, the remaining level of impurities, after the water has been passed through a series of n filters.

41. In 2007, world solar photovoltaic (PV) market installations totaled 2826 megawatts and were growing at a rate of 62% per year. In the same year, Japan's PV market installations totaled 230 megawatts and were declining at a rate of 23% per year.[4]

   (a) Use the information given to predict PV market installations in the world and in Japan in the year 2012.
   (b) What percent of world PV market installations were in Japan in 2007? In 2012?

Write the exponential function $y = 5(0.5)^{t/3}$ in the forms given in Problems 42–43. Give the values of all constants.

42. $y = ab^t$

43. $y = a \cdot 4^{kt}$

44. Write the following exponential function in standard form, $f(t) = ab^t$, giving the values of a and b:

$$f(t) = \frac{60}{5 \cdot 2^{t/11.2}}.$$

45. In the year 2009, a total of 13.4 million passengers took a cruise vacation.[5] The global cruise industry has been growing at a rate of approximately 5% per year for the last five years.

   (a) Write a formula to approximate the number, N, of cruise passengers (in millions) t years after 2009.
   (b) How many cruise passengers are predicted in the year 2015? Approximately how many passengers went on a cruise in the year 2005?

46. The amount (in milligrams) of a drug in the body t hours after taking a pill is given by $A(t) = 25(0.85)^t$.

   (a) What is the initial dose given?
   (b) What percent of the drug leaves the body each hour?
   (c) What is the amount of drug left after 10 hours?
   (d) After how many hours is there less than 1 milligram left in the body?

47. Every year, teams from 64 colleges qualify to compete in the NCAA basketball playoffs. For each round, every team is paired with an opponent. A team is eliminated from the tournament once it loses a round. So, at the end of a round, only one half the number of teams move on to the next round. Let $N(r)$ be the number of teams remaining in competition after r rounds of the tournament have been played.

   (a) Find a formula for $N(r)$ and graph $y = N(r)$.
   (b) In 2009 the North Carolina Tar Heels defeated the Michigan State Spartans 89-72. How many rounds did #1 seed North Carolina have to go through to win the championship game?

48. The UN Food and Agriculture Organization estimates that 2.17% of the world's natural forests existing in 1990 were gone by the end of the decade. In 1990, the world's forest cover stood at 4077 million hectares.[6]

   (a) How many million hectares of natural forests were lost during the 1990s?
   (b) How many million hectares of natural forests existed in the year 2000?
   (c) Write an exponential formula approximating the number of million hectares of natural forest in the world t years after 1990.
   (d) What was the annual percent decay rate during the 1990s?
   (e) During the years 2000 through 2005, the world's natural forests decreased by approximately 0.18% per year. Approximately how many million hectares of natural forests existed in the year 2005?

49. Forty percent of a radioactive substance decays in five years. By what percent does the substance decay each year?

50. The population of a small town increases by a growth factor of 1.134 over a two-year period.

   (a) By what percent does the town increase in size during the two-year period?
   (b) If the town grows by the same percent each year, what is its annual percent growth rate?

---

[4]www.solarbuzz.com/marketbuzz2008. Accessed February, 2010.
[5]http://www.f-cca.com, accessed May 25, 2010.
[6]www.fao.org/forestry/fra/fra/2005/en/, accessed January 2, 2010.

51. The *Home* section of many Sunday newspapers includes a mortgage table similar to Table 4.5.[7] The table gives the monthly payment per $1000 borrowed for loans at various interest rates and time periods. Determine the monthly payment on a

(a) $60,000 mortgage at 4% for fifteen years.
(b) $60,000 mortgage at 4% for thirty years.
(c) $60,000 mortgage at 6% for fifteen years.
(d) Over the life of the loan, how much money would be saved on a 15-year mortgage of $60,000 if the rate were 4% instead of 6%?
(e) Over the life of the loan, how much money would be saved on an 4% mortgage of $60,000 if the term of the loan was fifteen years rather than thirty years?

Table 4.5

Interest rate (%)	15-year loan	20-year loan	25-year loan	30-year loan
4.00	7.40	6.06	5.28	4.77
4.50	7.65	6.33	5.56	5.07
5.00	7.91	6.60	5.85	5.37
5.50	8.17	6.88	6.14	5.68
6.00	8.44	7.16	6.44	6.00
6.50	8.71	7.46	6.75	6.32
7.00	8.99	7.75	7.07	6.65
7.50	9.27	8.06	7.39	6.99
8.00	9.56	8.36	7.72	7.34

52. You owe $2000 on a credit card. The card charges 1.5% monthly interest on your balance, and requires a minimum monthly payment of 2.5% of your balance. All transactions (payments and interest charges) are recorded at the end of the month. You make only the minimum required payment every month and incur no additional debt.

(a) Complete Table 4.6 for a twelve-month period.
(b) What is your unpaid balance after one year has passed? At that time, how much of your debt have you paid off? How much money in interest charges have you paid your creditors?

Table 4.6

Month	Balance	Interest	Minimum payment
0	$2000.00	$30.00	$50.00
1	$1980.00	$29.70	$49.50
2	$1960.20		
⋮			

53. A one-page letter is folded into thirds to go into an envelope. If it were possible to repeat this kind of tri-fold 20 times, how many miles thick would the letter be? (A stack of 150 pieces of stationery is one inch thick; 1 mile = 5280 feet.)

Problems 54–55 concern ISO A-series paper, commonly used in many countries. $A0$ is the largest sheet, $A1$ next largest, and so on, with $A4$ being somewhat similar to the 8.5 by 11 inch paper standard in the US. The width in millimeters (mm) of a sheet of A_n paper in this series is given by the formula[8]

$$f(n) = 1000 \cdot 2^{-\frac{1}{4} - \frac{n}{2}}.$$

54. Show that this is an exponential function by writing it in standard form, $f(n) = ab^n$, . What do the values of a and b tell you about A-series paper?

55. Evaluate and simplify the ratio $f(n + 2)/f(n)$. What does your answer tell you about A-series paper?

Use Figure 4.8 in Problems 56–59.

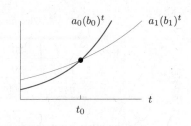

Figure 4.8

56. Which is greater, a_0 or a_1?

57. Which is greater, b_0 or b_1?

58. What happens to t_0 if a_0 is increased while the other quantities remain fixed?

59. What happens to t_0 if b_1 is decreased while the other quantities remain fixed?

---

[7]http://www.drcalculator.com, accessed January 1, 2010.
[8]Actual paper sizes are rounded to the nearest mm, so this formula is only approximate. See /www.cl.cam.ac.uk/~mgk25/iso-paper.html, accessed February 24, 2008.

60. The figure shows graphs of two functions:

$$f(t) = a_0 \cdot 2^{-t/\tau_0}$$
$$g(t) = a_1 \cdot 2^{-t/\tau_1}.$$

Which is larger, a_0 or a_1? τ_0 or τ_1?

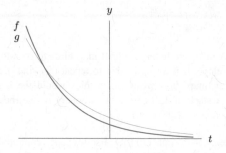

61. Let P be the number of students in a school district, N be the size of the tax base (in households), and r be the average annual tax rate (in \$/household).

(a) Find a formula for R, the total tax revenue, in terms of N and r.

(b) Find a formula for A, the average revenue per student.

(c) Suppose the tax base goes up by 2% and the tax rate is raised by 3%. Find formulas for the new tax base and tax rate in terms of N and r.

(d) Using your answer to part (c), find a formula for the new total tax revenue in terms of R. By what percent did R increase?

(e) Over the time period in part (c), the student population rises by 8%. Find a formula for the new average revenue in terms of A. Did the average revenue rise or fall? By how much?

4.2 COMPARING EXPONENTIAL AND LINEAR FUNCTIONS

The exponential function $Q = ab^t$ represents a quantity changing at a constant percent rate. In this section we compare exponential and linear models and we fit exponential models to data from tables and graphs.

Identifying Linear and Exponential Functions From a Table

Table 4.7 gives values of a linear and an exponential function. Notice that the value of x changes by equal steps of $\Delta x = 5$. The function f could be linear because the difference between consecutive values of $f(x)$ is constant: $f(x)$ increases by 15 each time x increases by 5.

Table 4.7   *Two functions, one linear and one exponential*

x	20	25	30	35	40	45
$f(x)$	30	45	60	75	90	105
$g(x)$	1000	1200	1440	1728	2073.6	2488.32

On the other hand, the difference between consecutive values of $g(x)$ is *not* constant:

$$1200 - 1000 = 200$$
$$1440 - 1200 = 240$$
$$1728 - 1440 = 288.$$

Thus, g is not linear. However, the *ratio* of consecutive values of $g(x)$ is constant:

$$\frac{1200}{1000} = 1.2, \quad \frac{1440}{1200} = 1.2, \quad \frac{1728}{1440} = 1.2,$$

and so on. Note that $1200 = 1.2(1000)$, $1440 = 1.2(1200)$, $1728 = 1.2(1440)$. Thus, each time x increases by 5, the value of $g(x)$ increases by a factor of 1.2. This pattern of constant ratios is indicative of exponential functions. In general:

> For a table of data that gives y as a function of x and in which Δx is constant:
> - If the *difference* of consecutive y-values is constant, the table could represent a linear function.
> - If the *ratio* of consecutive y-values is constant, the table could represent an exponential function.

Finding a Formula for an Exponential Function

To find a formula for the exponential function in Table 4.7, we must determine the values of a and b in the formula $g(x) = ab^x$. The table tells us that $ab^{20} = 1000$ and that $ab^{25} = 1200$. Taking the ratio gives

$$\frac{ab^{25}}{ab^{20}} = \frac{1200}{1000} = 1.2.$$

Notice that the value of a cancels in this ratio, so

$$\frac{ab^{25}}{ab^{20}} = b^5 = 1.2.$$

We solve for b by raising each side to the $(1/5)^{\text{th}}$ power:

$$(b^5)^{1/5} = b = 1.2^{1/5} \approx 1.03714.$$

Now that we have the value of b, we can solve for a. Since $g(20) = ab^{20} = 1000$, we have

$$a(1.03714)^{20} = 1000$$
$$a = \frac{1000}{1.03714^{20}} \approx 482.253.$$

Thus, a formula for g is $g(x) = 482.253(1.037)^x$. (Note: We could have used $g(25)$ or any other value from the table to find a.)

Modeling Linear and Exponential Growth Using Two Data Points

If we are given two data points, we can fit either a line or an exponential function to the points. The following example compares the predictions made by a linear model and an exponential model fitted to the same data.

Example 1   At time $t = 0$ years, a species of turtle is released into a wetland. When $t = 4$ years, a biologist estimates there are 300 turtles in the wetland. Three years later, the biologist estimates there are 450 turtles. Let P represent the size of the turtle population in year t.

(a) Find a formula for $P = f(t)$ assuming linear growth. Interpret the slope and P-intercept of your formula in terms of the turtle population.

(b) Now find a formula for $P = g(t)$ assuming exponential growth. Interpret the parameters of your formula in terms of the turtle population.

(c) In year $t = 12$, the biologist estimates that there are 900 turtles in the wetland. What does this indicate about the two population models?

Solution

(a) Assuming linear growth, we have $P = f(t) = b + mt$, and

$$m = \frac{\Delta P}{\Delta t} = \frac{450 - 300}{7 - 4} = \frac{150}{3} = 50.$$

Calculating b gives

$$300 = b + 50 \cdot 4$$
$$b = 100,$$

so $P = f(t) = 100 + 50t$. This formula tells us that 100 turtles were originally released into the wetland and that the number of turtles increases at the constant rate of 50 turtles per year.

(b) Assuming exponential growth, we have $P = g(t) = ab^t$. The values of a and b are calculated from the ratio

$$\frac{ab^7}{ab^4} = \frac{450}{300},$$

so

$$b^3 = 1.5.$$

Thus,

$$b = (1.5)^{1/3} \approx 1.145.$$

Using the fact that $g(4) = ab^4 = 300$ to find a gives

$$a(1.145)^4 = 300$$
$$a = \frac{300}{1.145^4} \approx 175, \quad \text{Rounding to the nearest whole turtle}$$

so $P = g(t) = 175(1.145)^t$. This formula tells us that 175 turtles were originally released into the wetland and the number increases at about 14.5% per year.

(c) In year $t = 12$, there are approximately 900 turtles. The linear function from part (a) predicts

$$P = 100 + 50 \cdot 12 = 700 \text{ turtles.}$$

The exponential formula from part (b), however, predicts

$$P = 175(1.145)^{12} \approx 889 \text{ turtles.}$$

The fact that 889 is closer to the observed value of 900 turtles suggests that, during the first 12 years, exponential growth is a better model of the turtle population than linear growth. The two models are graphed in Figure 4.9.

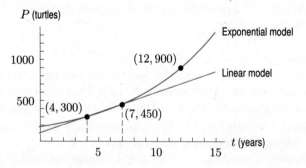

Figure 4.9: Comparison of the linear and exponential models of the turtle population

Similarities and Differences Between Linear and Exponential Functions

In some ways the general formulas for linear and exponential functions are similar. If y is a linear function of x and x is a positive integer, we can write $y = b + mx$ as

$$y = b + \underbrace{m + m + m + \ldots + m}_{x \text{ times}}.$$

Similarly, if y is an exponential function of x, so that $y = a \cdot b^x$ and x is a positive integer, we can write

$$y = a \cdot \underbrace{b \cdot b \cdot b \cdot \ldots \cdot b}_{x \text{ times}}.$$

So linear functions involve repeated sums whereas exponential functions involve repeated products. In both cases, x determines the number of repetitions.

There are other similarities between the formulas for linear and exponential functions. In the formula $y = b + mx$, b tells us the y-intercept and m tells us how the function is changing. In the formula $y = a \cdot b^x$, a tells us the y-intercept and b tells us how the function is changing.

Example 2　The following tables contain values from an exponential or linear function. For each table, decide if the function is linear or exponential, and find a possible formula for the function.

(a)

x	$f(x)$
0	65
1	75
2	85
3	95
4	105

(b)

x	$g(x)$
0	400
1	600
2	900
3	1350
4	2025

Solution　(a) The function values increase by 10 as x increases by 1, so this is a linear function with slope $m = 10$. Since $f(0) = 65$, the vertical intercept is 65. A possible formula is

$$f(x) = 65 + 10x.$$

(b) The function is not linear, since $g(x)$ increases by different amounts as x increases by 1. To determine whether g might be exponential, we look at ratios of consecutive values:

$$\frac{600}{400} = 1.5, \quad \frac{900}{600} = 1.5, \quad \frac{1350}{900} = 1.5, \quad \frac{2025}{1350} = 1.5.$$

Each time x increases by 1, the value of $g(x)$ increases by a factor of 1.5. This is an exponential function with growth factor 1.5. Since $g(0) = 400$, the vertical intercept is 400. A possible formula is

$$g(x) = 400(1.5)^x.$$

Exponential Growth Will Always Outpace Linear Growth in the Long Run

Figure 4.9 shows the graphs of the linear and exponential models for the turtle population from Example 1. The graphs highlight the fact that, although these two graphs remain fairly close for the first ten or so years, the exponential model predicts explosive growth later on.

It can be shown that an exponentially increasing quantity will, in the long run, always outpace a linearly increasing quantity. This fact led the 19th-century clergyman and economist Thomas Malthus to make some rather gloomy predictions, which are illustrated in the next example.

Example 3 The population of a country is initially 2 million people and is increasing at 4% per year. The country's annual food supply is initially adequate for 4 million people and is increasing at a constant rate adequate for an additional 0.5 million people per year.

    (a) Based on these assumptions, in approximately what year will this country first experience shortages of food?

    (b) If the country doubled its initial food supply, would shortages still occur? If so, when? (Assume the other conditions do not change).

    (c) If the country doubled the rate at which its food supply increases, in addition to doubling its initial food supply, would shortages still occur? If so, when? (Again, assume the other conditions do not change.)

Solution Let P represent the country's population (in millions) and N the number of people the country can feed (in millions). The population increases at a constant percent rate, so it can be modeled by an exponential function. The initial population is $a = 2$ million people and the annual growth factor is $b = 1 + 0.04 = 1.04$, so a formula for the population is

$$P = 2(1.04)^t.$$

In contrast, the food supply increases by a constant amount each year and is therefore modeled by a linear function. The initial food supply is adequate for $b = 4$ million people and the growth rate is $m = 0.5$ million per year, so the number of people that can be fed is

$$N = 4 + 0.5t.$$

    (a) Figure 4.10(a) gives the graphs of P and N over a 105-year span. For many years, the food supply is far in excess of the country's needs. However, after about 78 years the population has begun to grow so rapidly that it catches up to the food supply and then outstrips it. After that time, the country will suffer from shortages.

    (b) If the country can initially feed eight million people rather than four, the formula for N is

$$N = 8 + 0.5t.$$

However, as we see from Figure 4.10(b), this measure only buys the country three or four extra years with an adequate food supply. After 81 years, the population is growing so rapidly that the head start given to the food supply makes little difference.

    (c) If the country doubles the rate at which its food supply increases, from 0.5 million per year to 1.0 million per year, the formula for N is

$$N = 8 + 1.0t.$$

Unfortunately the country still runs out of food eventually. Judging from Figure 4.10(c), this happens in about 102 years.

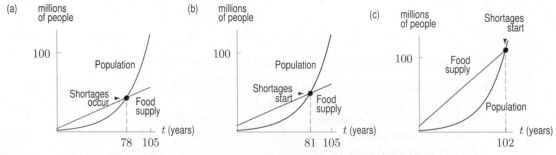

Figure 4.10: These graphs illustrate the fact that an exponentially growing population eventually outstrips a linearly growing food supply

Malthus believed that populations increase exponentially while food production increases linearly. The last example explains his gloomy predictions: Malthus believed that any population eventually outstrips its food supply, leading to famine and war.

Exercises and Problems for Section 4.2

Skill Refresher

In Exercises S1–S4, write each of the following with single positive exponents.

S1. $b^4 \cdot b^6$

S2. $8g^3 \cdot (-4g)^2$

S3. $\dfrac{18a^{10}b^6}{6a^3b^{-4}}$

S4. $\dfrac{(2a^3b^2)^3}{(4ab^{-4})^2}$

In Exercises S5–S6, evaluate the functions for $t = 0$ and $t = 3$.

S5. $f(t) = 5.6(1.043)^t$

S6. $g(t) = 12{,}837(0.84)^t$

In Exercises S7–S10, solve for x.

S7. $4x^3 = 20$

S8. $\dfrac{5x^3}{x^5} = 125$

S9. $\dfrac{4x^8}{3x^3} = 7$

S10. $\sqrt{4x^3} = 5$

Exercises

1. Write a formula for the price p of a gallon of gas in t days if the price is $2.50 on day $t = 0$ and the price is:

   (a) Increasing by $0.03 per day.
   (b) Decreasing by $0.07 per day.
   (c) Increasing by 2% per day.
   (d) Decreasing by 4% per day.

2. A population has size 5000 at time $t = 0$, with t in years.

   (a) If the population decreases by 100 people per year, find a formula for the population, P, at time t.
   (b) If the population decreases by 8% per year, find a formula for the population, P, at time t.

3. The following formulas give the populations (in 1000s) of four different cities, A, B, C, and D, where t is in years. Which are changing exponentially? Describe in words how each of these populations is changing over time. Graph those that are exponential.

$$P_A = 200 + 1.3t, \quad P_B = 270(1.021)^t,$$

$$P_C = 150(1.045)^t, \quad P_D = 600(0.978)^t.$$

4. In an environment with unlimited resources and no predators, a population tends to grow by the same percentage each year. Should a linear or exponential function be used to model such a population? Why?

5. Find $g(t) = ab^t$ if $g(10) = 50$ and $g(30) = 25$.

6. Find a formula for $f(x)$, an exponential function such that $f(-8) = 200$ and $f(30) = 580$.

7. Suppose that $f(x)$ is exponential and that $f(-3) = 54$ and $f(2) = \frac{2}{9}$. Find a formula for $f(x)$.

8. Find a formula for $f(x)$, an exponential function such that $f(2) = 1/27$ and $f(-1) = 27$.

9. Find the equation of an exponential curve through the points $(-1, 2)$, $(1, 0.3)$.

For Exercises 10–15, find a formula for the exponential function.

10.
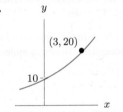

11.
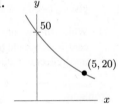

12.
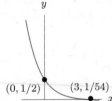

13.
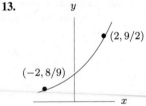

14.

15.

16. (a) Make a table of values for $P = f(t) = 1000(1.2)^t$, for $t = 0, 1, 2, 3, 4, 5$.

  (b) Calculate each of the ratios of successive terms:

$$\frac{f(1)}{f(0)}, \quad \frac{f(2)}{f(1)}, \quad \frac{f(3)}{f(2)}, \quad \frac{f(4)}{f(3)}, \quad \frac{f(5)}{f(4)}.$$

  (c) Discuss the results. Why is this outcome to be expected?

In Exercises 17–18, find exponential functions for the graphs shown in the figures, or explain why this is not possible.

17.

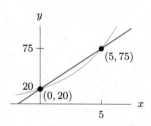

18.

19. Find a possible formula for the exponential function g given that the points $(2.3, 0.4)$ and $(3.5, 0.1)$ are on its graph.

20. Find a possible formula for the exponential function f given $f(-5) = 22$ and $f(17) = 46$.

21. Which (if any) of the functions in the table could be linear? Which could be exponential? (Note that table values may reflect rounding.)

x	0	5	10	15	20
$f(x)$	95.4	85.9	77.3	69.6	62.6
$g(x)$	44.8	40.9	36.8	32.5	28.0
$h(x)$	37.3	36.6	35.9	35.2	34.5

The tables in Exercises 22–25 contain values from an exponential or a linear function. In each problem:

  (a) Decide if the function is linear or exponential.
  (b) Find a possible formula for each function and graph it.

22.

x	$f(x)$
0	12.5
1	13.75
2	15.125
3	16.638
4	18.301

23.

x	$g(x)$
0	0
1	2
2	4
3	6
4	8

24.

x	$h(x)$
0	14
1	12.6
2	11.34
3	10.206
4	9.185

25.

x	$i(x)$
0	18
1	14
2	10
3	6
4	2

Problems

26. Graphs of a linear and an exponential function are shown in Figure 4.11. Find formulas for each of the functions.

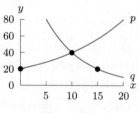

Figure 4.11

27. Let $p(x) = 2 + x$ and $q(x) = 2^x$. Estimate the values of x such that $p(x) < q(x)$.

28. If $f(x) = 12 + 20x$ and $g(x) = \frac{1}{2} \cdot 3^x$, for what values of x is $g(x) < f(x)$?

29. Find formulas for the exponential functions in Figure 4.12.

Figure 4.12

Decide whether the functions in Problems 30–32 could be approximately linear, approximately exponential, or are neither. For those that could be nearly linear or nearly exponential, find a formula.

30.

t	3	10	14
$Q(t)$	7.51	8.7	9.39

31.

t	5	9	15
$R(t)$	2.32	2.61	3.12

32.

t	5	12	16
$S(t)$	4.35	6.72	10.02

33. Figure 4.13 shows the balance, P, in a bank account.

   (a) Find a possible formula for $P = f(t)$ assuming the balance grows exponentially.
   (b) What was the initial balance?
   (c) What annual interest rate does the account pay?

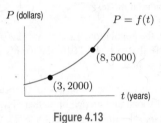

Figure 4.13

34. Suppose the city of Yonkers is offered two alternative fines by the judge. (See Example 8 on page 135.)

   Penalty A: $1 million on August 2 and the fine increases by $10 million each day thereafter.

   Penalty B: 1¢ on August 2 and the fine doubles each day thereafter.

   (a) If the city of Yonkers plans to defy the court order until the end of the month (August 31), compare the fines incurred under Penalty A and Penalty B.
   (b) If t represents the number of days after August 2, express the fine incurred as a function of t under

   (i)   Penalty A   (ii)   Penalty B

   (c) Assume your formulas in part (b) holds for $t \geq 0$, is there a time such that the fines incurred under both penalties are equal? If so, estimate that time.

35. A 1987 treaty to protect the ozone layer produced dramatic declines in global production, P, of chlorofluorocarbons (CFCs). See Figure 4.14.[9] Find a formula for P as an exponential function of the number of years, t, since 1989. What was the annual percent decay rate?

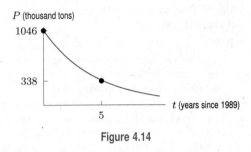

Figure 4.14

36. Figure 4.15 gives the voltage, $V(t)$, across a circuit element at time t seconds. For $t < 0$, the voltage is a constant 80 volts; for $t \geq 0$, the voltage decays exponentially.

   (a) Find a piecewise formula for $V(t)$.
   (b) At what value of t will the voltage reach 0.1?

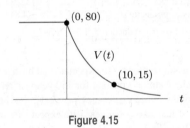

Figure 4.15

37. Short track 500m speed skating became a Winter Olympic event in 1994, and Chae Ji-Hoon of Korea won the event that year with a time of 43.45 seconds. In 2006, Apolo Ohno of the US won the event with a time of 41.94 seconds. Find a formula for the predicted winning time in the 500m speed skating event as a function of the number of years since 1994, and predict the winning time in 2018, if we assume the decrease in time is

   (a)   Linear   **(b)**   Exponential

---

[9]These numbers reflect the volume of the major CFCs multiplied by their respective ozone-depleting potentials (ODPs), as reported by the U. N. Environmental Programme Ozone Secretariat. See hq.uncp.org/ozone, accessed November, 2001.

38. There were 178.8 million licensed drivers in the US in 1989 and 187.2 million in 1999.[10] Find a formula for the number, N, of licensed drivers in the US as a function of t, the number of years since 1989, assuming growth is

(a) Linear   (b) Exponential

39. In year $t = 0$ a lake is estimated to have about 3500 trout in it. Ten years later, at $t = 10$, the population of trout is believed to be about 1700.

(a) Write a formula for the size of the population P as a function of year t if we assume the decrease is linear. What is the rate of change, in fish per year, of the function over the ten-year period?

(b) Write a formula for the size of the population P as a function of year t if we assume the decrease is exponential. What is the percent rate of change, in percent per year, of the function over the ten-year period?

(c) Graph the two functions on the same coordinate system. Indicate the points at $t = 0$ and $t = 10$.

40. Cocoa production[11] is shown in Table 4.8 for the world and the Ivory Coast, in millions of tons, as a function of the number of years since 2000. In each case, determine if production is better modeled with a linear or an exponential function and find a formula for the function.

Table 4.8

Years since 2000	0	1	2	3	4
World cocoa production	3.1	3.875	4.844	6.055	7.568
Ivory Coast cocoa production	1.3	1.34	1.38	1.42	1.46

41. The average gain in life expectancy at birth in the US has remained almost constant for 150 years, at an increase of 3 months in life expectancy per year.[12] Assume that this rate of increase continues. Life expectancy in the US in 2009 was 78.1 years.

(a) Is life expectancy increasing linearly or exponentially?

(b) Find a formula for life expectancy, L, in years, in the US at birth as a function of the number of years t since 2000.

(c) What is the predicted life expectancy for babies born in 2050?

42. In terms of the initial population P_0, what is the value of the population at the end of 10 years, given each of the following assumptions? Graph each population against time.

(a) A population decreases linearly and the decrease is 10% in the first year.

(b) A population decreases exponentially at the rate of 10% a year.

43. The number of asthma sufferers in the world was about 84 million in 1990 and 300 million in 2009.[13] Let N represent the number of asthma sufferers (in millions) worldwide t years after 1990.

(a) Write N as a linear function of t. What is the slope? What does it tell you about asthma sufferers?

(b) Write N as an exponential function of t. What is the growth factor? What does it tell you about asthma sufferers?

(c) How many asthma sufferers are predicted worldwide in the year 2020 with the linear model? With the exponential model?

44. In 2000, the population of a town was 20,000, and it grew by 4.14% that year. By 2010, the town's population had reached 30,000.

(a) Can this population be best described by a linear or an exponential model, or neither? Explain.

(b) If possible, find a formula for $P(t)$, this population t years after 2000.

45. In 2000, the population of a town was 18,500 and it grew by 250 people by the end of the year. By 2010, its population had reached 22,500.

(a) Can this population be best described by a linear or an exponential model, or neither? Explain.

(b) If possible, find a formula for $P(t)$, the population t years after 2000.

4.3   GRAPHS OF EXPONENTIAL FUNCTIONS

As with linear functions, an understanding of the significance of the parameters a and b in the formula $Q = ab^t$ helps us analyze and compare exponential functions.

---

[10]*The World Almanac* 2002 (New York: World Almanac Education Group, Inc., 2002), p. 228.
[11]Adapted from www.treecrops.org/crops/cocoaoutlook, accessed November, 2009.
[12]"The Science of Living Longer", Time Magazine, February 22, 2010.
[13]www.healthylifestyle-solutions.blogspot.com, accessed January 2, 2010.

Graphs of the Exponential Family: The Effect of the Parameter a

In the formula $Q = ab^t$, the value of a tells us where the graph crosses the Q-axis, since a is the value of Q when $t = 0$. In Figure 4.16 each graph has the same value of b but different values of a and thus different vertical intercepts.

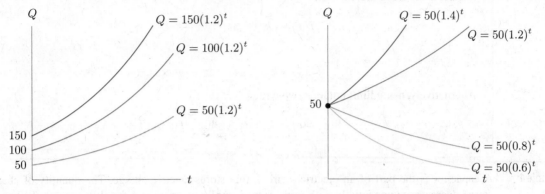

Figure 4.16: Graphs of $Q = a(1.2)^t$ for $a = 50$, 100, and 150 **Figure 4.17:** Graphs of $Q = 50b^t$ for $b = 0.6, 0.8, 1.2$ and 1.4

Graphs of the Exponential Family: The Effect of the Parameter b

The growth factor, b, is called the *base* of an exponential function. Provided a is positive, if $b > 1$, the graph climbs when read from left to right, and if $0 < b < 1$, the graph falls when read from left to right.

Figure 4.17 shows how the value of b affects the steepness of the graph of $Q = ab^t$. Each graph has a different value of b but the same value of a (and thus the same Q-intercept). For $b > 1$, the greater the value of b, the more rapidly the graph rises. For $0 < b < 1$, the smaller the value of b, the more rapidly the graph falls. In every case, however, the graph is concave up.

Horizontal Asymptotes

The t-axis is a *horizontal asymptote* for the graph of $Q = ab^t$, because Q approaches 0 as t gets large, either positively or negatively. For exponential decay, such as $Q = f(t) = a(0.6)^t$ in Figure 4.17, the value of Q approaches 0 as t gets large and positive. We write

$$Q \to 0 \quad \text{as} \quad t \to \infty.$$

This means that Q is as close to 0 as we like for all sufficiently large values of t. We say that the *limit* of $f(t)$ as t goes to infinity is 0, and we write

$$\lim_{t \to \infty} f(t) = 0.$$

For exponential growth, the value of Q approaches zero as t grows more negative. (See Figure 4.29 on page 159.) In this case, we write

$$Q \to 0 \quad \text{as} \quad t \to -\infty.$$

This means that Q is as close to 0 as we like for all sufficiently large negative values of t. Using limit notation, we write

$$\lim_{t \to -\infty} f(t) = 0.$$

We make the following definition:

The horizontal line $y = k$ is a **horizontal asymptote** of a function, f, if the function values get arbitrarily close to k as x gets large (either positively or negatively or both). We describe this behavior using the notation

$$f(x) \to k \qquad \text{as} \qquad x \to \infty$$

or

$$f(x) \to k \qquad \text{as} \qquad x \to -\infty.$$

Alternatively, using limit notation, we write

$$\lim_{x \to \infty} f(x) = k \quad \text{or} \quad \lim_{x \to -\infty} f(x) = k.$$

Example 1 A capacitor is the part of an electrical circuit that stores electric charge. The quantity of charge stored decreases exponentially with time. Stereo amplifiers provide a familiar example: When an amplifier is turned off, the display lights fade slowly because it takes time for the capacitors to discharge. (Thus, it can be unsafe to open a stereo or a computer immediately after it is turned off.)

If t is the number of seconds after the circuit is switched off, suppose that the quantity of stored charge (in micro-coulombs) is given by

$$Q = 200(0.9)^t, \quad t \geq 0.$$

(a) Describe in words how the stored charge changes over time.

(b) What quantity of charge remains after 10 seconds? 20 seconds? 30 seconds? 1 minute? 2 minutes? 3 minutes?

(c) Graph the charge over the first minute. What does the horizontal asymptote of the graph tell you about the charge?

Solution (a) The charge is initially 200 micro-coulombs. Since $b = 1 + r = 0.9$, we have $r = -0.10$, which means that the charge level decreases by 10% each second.

(b) Table 4.9 gives the value of Q at $t = 0, 10, 20, 30, 60, 120$, and 180. Notice that as t increases, Q gets closer and closer to, but does not quite reach, zero. The charge stored by the capacitor is getting smaller, but never completely vanishes.

(c) Figure 4.18 shows Q over a 60-second interval. The horizontal asymptote at $Q = 0$ corresponds to the fact that the charge gets very small as t increases. After 60 seconds, for all practical purposes, the charge is zero.

Table 4.9 *Charge (in micro-coulombs) stored by a capacitor over time*

t (seconds)	Q, charge level
0	200
10	69.736
20	24.315
30	8.478
60	0.359
120	0.000646
180	0.00000116

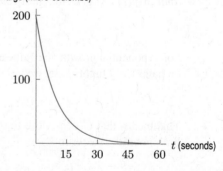

Figure 4.18: The charge stored by a capacitor over one minute

Solving Exponential Equations Graphically

We are often interested in solving equations involving exponential functions. In the following examples, we do this graphically. In Section 5.1, we will see how to solve equations using logarithms.

Example 2   In Example 8 on page 135, the fine, P, imposed on the city of Yonkers is given by $P = 100 \cdot 2^t$ where t is the number of days after August 2. In 1988, the annual budget of the city was $337 million. If the city chose to disobey the court order, at what point would the fine have wiped out the entire annual budget?

Solution   We need to find the day on which the fine reaches $337 million. That is, we must solve the equation

$$100 \cdot 2^t = 337,000,000.$$

Using a computer or graphing calculator we can graph $P = 100 \cdot 2^t$ to find the point at which the fine reaches 337 million. From Figure 4.19, we see that this occurs between $t = 21$ and $t = 22$. At day $t = 21$, August 23, the fine is:

$$P = 100 \cdot 2^{21} = 209,715,200$$

or just over $200 million. On day $t = 22$, the fine is

$$P = 100 \cdot 2^{22} = 419,430,400$$

or almost $420 million—quite a bit more than the city's entire annual budget!

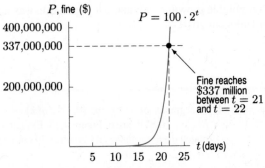

Figure 4.19: The fine imposed on Yonkers exceeds $337 million after 22 days

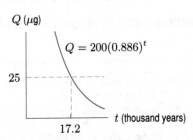

Figure 4.20: Solving the equation $200(0.886)^t = 25$

Example 3   A 200-μg sample of carbon-14 decays according to the formula

$$Q = 200(0.886)^t$$

where t is in thousands of years. Estimate when there is 25 μg of carbon-14 left.

Solution   We must solve the equation

$$200(0.886)^t = 25.$$

At the moment, we cannot find a formula for the solution to this equation. However, we can estimate the solution graphically. Figure 4.20 shows a graph of $Q = 200(0.886)^t$ and the line $Q = 25$. The amount of carbon-14 decays to 25 micrograms at $t \approx 17.180$. Since t is measured in thousands of years, this means in about 17,180 years.

Finding an Exponential Function for Data

The data in Table 4.10 gives population data for the Houston Metro Area since 1900. (2010 is estimated.) In Section 1.6, we saw how to fit a linear function to data, but the data points shown in Figure 4.21 suggests that it may make more sense to fit the data using an exponential function.

Table 4.10 *Population (in thousands) of Houston Metro Area, t years after 1900*

t	N	t	N
0	184	60	1583
10	236	70	2183
20	332	80	3122
30	528	90	3733
40	737	100	4672
50	1070	110	5937

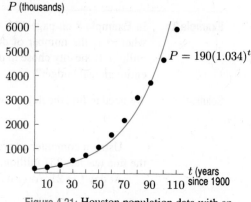

Figure 4.21: Houston population data with an exponential model

Using an exponential regression feature on a calculator or computer, the following exponential function was found:

$$P = 190(1.034)^t.$$

This equation fits the data nicely, with $a = 190$ being close to the initial data value of 184. The graph in Figure 4.21 shows that $b = 1.034$ is a suitable growth factor and the population was increasing at a rate of about 3.4% per year between 1900 and 2010.

Exercises and Problems for Section 4.3

Exercises

1. (a) Make a table of values for $f(x) = 2^x$ for $x = -3, -2, -1, 0, 1, 2, 3$.
   (b) Graph $f(x)$. Describe the graph in words.

2. (a) Make a table of values for $f(x) = \left(\frac{1}{2}\right)^x$ for $x = -3, -2, -1, 0, 1, 2, 3$.
   (b) Graph $f(x)$. Describe the graph in words.

3. The graphs of $f(x) = (1.1)^x$, $g(x) = (1.2)^x$, and $h(x) = (1.25)^x$ are in Figure 4.22. Explain how you can match these formulas and graphs without a calculator.

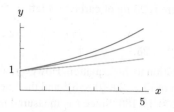

Figure 4.22

4. The graphs of $f(x) = (0.7)^x$, $g(x) = (0.8)^x$, and $h(x) = (0.85)^x$ are in Figure 4.23. Explain how you can match these formulas and graphs without a calculator.

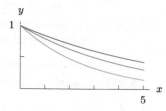

Figure 4.23

In Problems 5–10, will the graphs of the two functions cross in the first quadrant? Explain your reasoning without using a calculator.

5. $f(x) = 10(1.03)^x$; $g(x) = 2(1.05)^x$
6. $f(x) = 250(1.2)^x$; $g(x) = 300(1.3)^x$
7. $f(x) = 10(1.05)^x$; $g(x) = 9(0.95)^x$
8. $f(x) = 5(0.8)^x$; $g(x) = 2(1.05)^x$

9. $f(x) = 500(0.8)^x$; $g(x) = 450(0.7)^x$

10. $f(x) = 1000(0.9)^x$; $g(x) = 875(0.95)^x$

For Exercises 11–14, use Figure 4.24. Assume the equations for A, B, C, and D can all be written in the form $y = ab^t$.

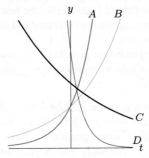

Figure 4.24

11. Which function has the largest value for a?

12. Which two functions have the same value for a?

13. Which function has the smallest value for b?

14. Which function has the largest value for b?

15. The volume of biodegradable material in a compost pile is shown in Figure 4.25, with time t measured in weeks. Use the graph to estimate:

(a) The volume after 5 weeks.

(b) The number of weeks until the volume is 20 ft³.

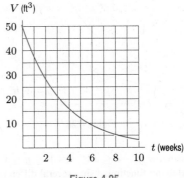

Figure 4.25

16. Solve $y = 46(1.1)^x$ graphically for x if $y = 91$.

17. Solve $p = 22(0.87)^q$ graphically for q if $p = 10$.

18. Solve $4m = 17(2.3)^w$ graphically for w if $m = 12$.

19. Solve $P/7 = (0.6)^t$ graphically for t if $P = 2$.

20. If $b > 1$, what is the horizontal asymptote of $y = ab^t$ as $t \to -\infty$?

21. If $0 < b < 1$, what is the horizontal asymptote of $y = ab^t$ as $t \to \infty$?

22. If the exponential function ab^x has the property that $\lim_{x \to \infty} ab^x = 0$, what can you say about the value of b?

Problems

In Problems 23–27, graph $f(x)$, a function defined for all real numbers and satisfying the condition.

23. $f(x) \to 3$ as $x \to -\infty$

24. $\lim_{x \to \infty} f(x) = 5$

25. $\lim_{x \to -\infty} f(x) = 2$ and $\lim_{x \to \infty} f(x) = -1$

26. $f(x) \to 0$ as $x \to -\infty$ and $f(x) \to -\infty$ as $x \to \infty$

27. $f(x)$ has a horizontal asymptote of $y = 5$.

In Problems 28–29, assume that all important features are shown in the graph of $y = f(x)$. Estimate

(a) $\lim_{x \to -\infty} f(x)$ (b) $\lim_{x \to \infty} f(x)$

28.

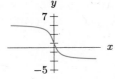

29.

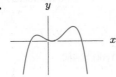

30. Let $f(x) = 5 + 3(0.9)^x$. As $x \to \infty$, what happens to $f(x)$? Does this function have a horizontal asymptote, and if so, what is it? Justify your answer both analytically and graphically.

31. Consider the exponential functions graphed in Figure 4.26 and the six constants a, b, c, d, p, q.

(a) Which of these constants are definitely positive?

(b) Which of these constants are definitely between 0 and 1?

(c) Which of these constants could be between 0 and 1?

(d) Which two of these constants are definitely equal?

(e) Which one of the following pairs of constants could be equal?

    a and p b and d b and q d and q

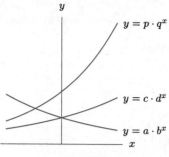

Figure 4.26

32. Set a window of $-4 \leq x \leq 4, -1 \leq y \leq 6$ and graph the following functions using several different values of a for each. Include some values of a with $a < 1$.

(a) $y = a2^x$, $0 < a < 5$.
(b) $y = 2a^x$, $0 < a < 5$.

33. For which value(s) of a and b is $y = ab^x$ an increasing function? A decreasing function? Concave up?

34. What are the domain and range of the exponential function $Q = ab^t$ where a and b are both positive constants?

Problems 35–36 use Figure 4.27, where y_0 is the y-coordinate of the point of intersection of the graphs. Describe what happens to y_0 if the following changes are made, assuming the other quantities remain the same.

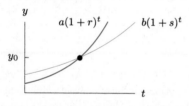

Figure 4.27

35. r is increased   **36.** a is increased

37. The city of Baltimore has been declining in population for the last fifty years.[14] In the year 2000, the population of Baltimore was 651 thousand and declining at a rate of 0.75% per year. If this trend continues:

(a) Give a formula for the population of Baltimore, P, in thousands, as a function of years, t, since 2000.
(b) What is the predicted population in 2010?
(c) To two decimal places, estimate t when the population is 550 thousand.

38. Let $P = f(t) = 1000(1.04)^t$ be the population of a community in year t.

(a) Evaluate $f(0)$ and $f(10)$. What do these expressions represent in terms of the population?
(b) Using a calculator or a computer, find appropriate viewing windows on which to graph the population for the first 10 years and for the first 50 years. Give the viewing windows you used and sketch the resulting graphs.
(c) If the percentage growth rate remains constant, approximately when will the population reach 2500 people?

39. Suppose you use your calculator to graph $y = 1.04^{5x}$. You correctly enter $y = 1.04\char`\^(5x)$ and see the graph in Figure 4.28. A friend graphed the function by entering $y = 1.04\char`\^5x$ and said, "The graph is a straight line, so I must have the wrong window." Explain why changing the window will not correct your friend's error.

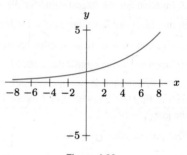

Figure 4.28

40. Suppose y, the number of cases of a disease, is reduced by 10% each year.

(a) If there are initially 10,000 cases, express y as a function of t, the number of years elapsed.
(b) How many cases will there be 5 years from now?
(c) How long does it take to reduce the number of cases to 1000?

41. The earth's atmospheric pressure, P, in terms of height above sea level is often modeled by an exponential decay function. The pressure at sea level is 1013 millibars and that the pressure decreases by 14% for every kilometer above sea level.

(a) What is the atmospheric pressure at 50 km?
(b) Estimate the altitude h at which the pressure equals 900 millibars.

---

[14]*The World Almanac and Book of Facts 2006* (New York), p. 480.

42. The population of a colony of rabbits grows exponentially. The colony begins with 10 rabbits; five years later there are 340 rabbits.

    (a) Give a formula for the population of the colony of rabbits as a function of the time.
    (b) Use a graph to estimate how long it takes for the population of the colony to reach 1000 rabbits.

43. Let f be a piecewise-defined function given by

$$f(x) = \begin{cases} 2^x, & x < 0 \\ 0, & x = 0 \\ 1 - \frac{1}{2}x, & x > 0. \end{cases}$$

    (a) Graph f for $-3 \leq x \leq 4$.
    (b) The domain of $f(x)$ is all real numbers. What is its range?
    (c) What are the intercepts of f?
    (d) What happens to $f(x)$ as $x \to \infty$ and $x \to -\infty$?
    (e) Over what intervals is f increasing? Decreasing?

44. Table 4.11 shows the concentration of theophylline, a common asthma drug, in the blood stream as a function of time after injection of a 300-mg initial dose.[15] It is claimed that this data set is consistent with an exponential decay model $C = ab^t$ where C is the concentration and t is the time.

    (a) Estimate the values of a and b, using ratios to estimate b. How good is this model?
    (b) Use a calculator or computer to find the exponential regression function for concentration as a function of time. Compare answers from parts (a) and (b).

Table 4.11

Time (hours)	0	1	3	5	7	9
Concentration (mg/l)	12.0	10.0	7.0	5.0	3.5	2.5

45. Table 4.12 shows global wind energy generating capacity, W (in megawatts), as a function of the number of years, t, since 1995.[16]

    (a) Plot the data and explain why it is reasonable to approximate these data with an exponential function.

    (b) Use a calculator or computer to fit an exponential function to these data.
    (c) What annual percent growth rate does the exponential model show?

Table 4.12

t	0	1	2	3	4
W	4780	6070	7640	10,150	13,930
t	5	6	7	8	9
W	18,450	24,930	32,037	39,664	47,760

46. Three scientists, working independently of each other, arrive at the following formulas to model the spread of a species of mussel in a system of fresh water lakes:

$$f_1(x) = 3(1.2)^x, \quad f_2(x) = 3(1.21)^x, \quad f_3(x) = 3.01(1.2)^x,$$

where $f_n(x)$, $n = 1, 2, 3$, is the number of individual mussels (in 1000s) predicted by model number n to be living in the lake system after x months have elapsed.

    (a) Graph these three functions for $0 \leq x \leq 60$, $0 \leq y \leq 40,000$.
    (b) The graphs of these three models do not seem all that different from each other. But do the three functions make significantly different predictions about the future mussel population? To answer this, graph the difference function, $f_2(x) - f_1(x)$, of the population sizes predicted by models 1 and 2, as well as the difference functions, $f_3(x) - f_1(x)$ and $f_3(x) - f_2(x)$. (Use the same window as in part (a).)
    (c) Based on your graphs in part (b), discuss the assertion that all three models are in good agreement as far as long-range predictions of mussel population are concerned. What conclusions can you draw about exponential functions in general?

4.4 APPLICATIONS TO COMPOUND INTEREST

What is the difference between a bank account that pays 12% interest once per year and one that pays 1% interest every month? Imagine we deposit $1000 into the first account. Then, after 1 year, we have (assuming no other deposits or withdrawals)

$$\$1000(1.12) = \$1120.$$

[15]Based on D. N. Burghes, I. Huntley, and J. McDonald, *Applying Mathematics* (Ellis Horwood, 1982).
[16]The Worldwatch Institute, *Vital Signs 2005* (New York: W.W. Norton & Company, 2005), p. 35.

But if we deposit $1000 into the second account, then after 1 year, or 12 months, we have

$$\$1000 \underbrace{(1.01)(1.01)\dots(1.01)}_{\text{12 months of 1\% monthly interest}} = 1000(1.01)^{12} = \$1126.83.$$

Thus, we earn $6.83 more in the second account than in the first. To see why this happens, notice that the 1% interest we earn in January itself earns interest at a rate of 1% per month. Similarly, the 1% interest we earn in February earns interest, and so does the interest earned in March, April, May, and so on. The extra $6.83 comes from interest earned on interest. This effect is known as *compounding*. We say that the first account earns 12% interest *compounded annually* and the second account earns 12% interest *compounded monthly*.

Nominal Versus Effective Rate

The expression 12% compounded monthly means that interest is added twelve times per year and that $12\%/12 = 1\%$ of the current balance is added each time. We refer to the 12% as the *nominal rate* (nominal means "in name only"). When the interest is compounded more frequently than once a year, the account effectively earns more than the nominal rate. Thus, we distinguish between nominal rate and *effective annual rate*, or *effective rate*. The effective annual rate tells you how much interest the investment actually earns. In the US, the effective annual rate is sometimes called the APY (annual percentage yield).

Example 1   What are the nominal and effective annual rates of an account paying 12% interest, compounded annually? Compounded monthly?

Solution   Since an account paying 12% annual interest, compounded annually, grows by exactly 12% in one year, we see that its nominal rate is the same as its effective rate: both are 12%.

The account paying 12% interest, compounded monthly, also has a nominal rate of 12%. On the other hand, since it pays 1% interest every month, after 12 months, its balance increases by a factor of

$$\underbrace{(1.01)(1.01)\dots(1.01)}_{\text{12 months of 1\% monthly growth}} = 1.01^{12} \approx 1.1268250.$$

Thus, effectively, the account earns 12.683% interest in a year, so its effective rate is 12.683%.

Example 2   What is the effective annual rate of an account that pays interest at the nominal rate of 6% per year, compounded daily? Compounded hourly?

Solution   Since there are 365 days in a year, daily compounding pays interest at the rate of

$$\frac{6\%}{365} = 0.0164384\% \text{ per day.}$$

Thus, the daily growth factor is

$$1 + \frac{0.06}{365} = 1.000164384.$$

If at the beginning of the year the account balance is P, after 365 days the balance is

$$P \cdot \underbrace{\left(1 + \frac{0.06}{365}\right)^{365}}_{\substack{\text{365 days of} \\ \text{0.0164384\% daily interest}}} = P \cdot (1.0618313).$$

Thus, this account earns interest at the effective annual rate of 6.18313%.

Notice that daily compounding results in a higher rate than yearly compounding (6.183% versus 6%), because with daily compounding the interest has the opportunity to earn interest.

If interest is compounded hourly, since there are $24 \cdot 365$ hours in a year, the balance at year's end is

$$P \cdot \left(1 + \frac{0.06}{24 \cdot 365}\right)^{24 \cdot 365} = P \cdot (1.0618363).$$

The effective rate is now 6.18363% instead of 6.18313%—that is, just slightly better than the rate of the account that compounds interest daily. The effective rate increases with the frequency of compounding.

In the previous examples, we computed the growth factor for one year. We now compute the growth factor over t years.

Example 3 At the beginning of the year you deposit P dollars in an account paying interest at the nominal rate of 4% per year compounded quarterly. By what factor does P grow in 3 years?

Solution Compounding quarterly pays interest at the rate of

$$\frac{4\%}{4} = 1\% \text{ per quarter.}$$

Thus, the quarterly growth factor is $1 + 0.01 = 1.01$. At the beginning of the year the account balance is P. After one year the balance is

$$P \cdot \underbrace{\left(1 + \frac{0.04}{4}\right)^4}_{\substack{\text{4 quarters(1 year) of} \\ \text{1\% quarterly interest}}} = P \cdot (1.0406).$$

So after three years the balance is

$$P \cdot \left(1 + \frac{0.04}{4}\right)^4 \cdot \left(1 + \frac{0.04}{4}\right)^4 \cdot \left(1 + \frac{0.04}{4}\right)^4 = P \cdot \underbrace{\left(1 + \frac{0.04}{4}\right)^{4 \cdot 3}}_{\substack{\text{3 years of} \\ \text{1\% quarterly interest}}} = P \cdot (1.126825).$$

After three years the initial account balance P grows by a factor of 1.126825.

To summarize:

> If interest at an annual rate of r is compounded n times a year, then r/n times the current balance is added n times a year. Therefore, with an initial deposit of $\$P$, the balance t years later is
>
> $$B = P \cdot \left(1 + \frac{r}{n}\right)^{nt}.$$
>
> Note that r is the nominal rate; for example, $r = 0.05$ if the annual rate is 5%.

Exercises and Problems for Section 4.4

Exercises

1. An account pays interest at a nominal rate of 8% per year. Find the effective annual yield if interest is compounded

   (a)   Monthly   **(b)**   Weekly

   (c)   Daily

2. What is the effective annual yield if a deposit of $1000 grows to $3500 in 15 years?

3. An investment grows by 5% per year for 20 years. By what percent does it increase over the 20-year period?

4. An investment decreases by 50% over an 8-year period. At what effective annual percent rate does it decrease?

5. Suppose $1000 is deposited into an account paying interest at a nominal rate of 8% per year. Find the balance three years later if the interest is compounded

   (a)   Monthly   **(b)**   Weekly

   (c)   Daily

6. A bank pays interest at the nominal rate of 1.3% per year. What is the effective annual rate if compounding is:

   (a)   Annual   **(b)**   Monthly

In Exercises 7–10, what is the balance after 1 year if an account containing $500 earns the stated yearly nominal interest, compounded

   (a)   Annually   **(b)**   Weekly (52 weeks per year)

   (c)   Every minute (525,600 per year)

7. 1%   **8.** 3%   **9.** 5%   **10.** 8%

In Exercises 11–14, what are the nominal and effective annual rates for an account paying the stated annual interest, compounded

   (a)   Annually?   **(b)**   Quarterly?

   (c)   Daily?

11. 1%   **12.** 100%   **13.** 3%   **14.** 6%

Problems

15. An investment grows by 3% per year for 10 years. By what percent does it increase over the 10-year period?

16. An investment grows by 30% over a 5-year period. What is its effective annual percent growth rate?

17. An investment decreases by 60% over a 12-year period. At what effective annual percent rate does it decrease?

18. If you need $25,000 six years from now, what is the minimum amount of money you need to deposit into a bank account that pays 5% annual interest, compounded:

   (a)   Annually   **(b)**   Monthly   **(c)**   Daily

   (d)   Your answers get smaller as the number of times of compounding increases. Why is this so?

19. A sum of $850 is invested for 10 years and the interest is compounded quarterly. There is $1000 in the account at the end of 10 years. What is the nominal annual rate?

20. If the balance, M, at time t in years, of a bank account that compounds its interest payments monthly is given by

$$M = M_0(1.07763)^t,$$

   (a)   What is the effective annual rate for this account?

   (b)   What is the nominal annual rate?

21. Suppose $300 was deposited into one of five bank accounts and t is time in years. For each verbal description (i)–(v), state which formulas (a)–(e) could represent it.

   (a) $B = 300(1.2)^t$ **(b)** $B = 300(1.12)^t$

   (c) $B = 300(1.06)^{2t}$ **(d)** $B = 300(1.06)^{t/2}$

   (e) $B = 300(1.03)^{4t}$

   (i) This investment earned 12% annually, compounded annually.

   (ii) This investment earned, on average, more than 1% each month.

   (iii) This investment earned 12% annually, compounded semi-annually.

   (iv) This investment earned, on average, less than 3% each quarter.

   (v) This investment earned, on average, more than 6% every 6 months.

22. Without making any calculations, briefly describe in words what the following formulas tell you about the value of the investments they describe. Be specific. Note that units are in dollars and years.

   (a) $V = 1500(1.077)^t$

   (b) $V = 9500(0.945)^t$

   (c) $V = 1000 \cdot 3^{t/5}$

   (d) $V = 500 \left(1 + \frac{0.04}{12}\right)^{12t}$

4.5 THE NUMBER e

An irrational number, introduced by Euler[17] in 1727, is so important that it is given a special name, e. Its value is approximately $e \approx 2.71828\ldots$. It is often used for the base, b, of the exponential function. Base e is called the *natural base*. This may seem mysterious, as what could possibly be natural about using an irrational base such as e? The answer is that the formulas of calculus are much simpler if e is used as the base for exponentials. Some of the remarkable properties of the number e are introduced in Problems 52–53 on page 167. Since $2 < e < 3$, the graph of $Q = e^t$ lies between the graphs of $Q = 3^t$ and $Q = 2^t$. See Figure 4.29.

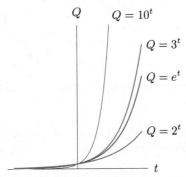

Figure 4.29: Graphs of exponential functions with various bases

Exponential Functions with Base e

Since any positive base b can be written as a power of e:

$$b = e^k,$$

any exponential function $Q = ab^t$ can be rewritten in terms of e:

$$Q = ab^t = a\left(e^k\right)^t = ae^{kt}.$$

If $b > 1$, then k is positive; if $0 < b < 1$, then k is negative. The constant k is called the *continuous growth rate*. In general:

> For the exponential function $Q = ab^t$, the **continuous growth rate**, k, is given by solving $e^k = b$. Then
> $$Q = ae^{kt}.$$
>
> If a is positive,
> - If $k > 0$, then Q is increasing.
> - If $k < 0$, then Q is decreasing.

The value of the continuous growth rate, k, may be given as a decimal or a percent. If t is in years, for example, then the units of k are given per year; if t is in minutes, then k is given per minute.

Example 1 Give the continuous growth rate of each of the following functions and graph each function:

$$P = 5e^{0.2t}, \qquad Q = 5e^{0.3t}, \qquad \text{and} \quad R = 5e^{-0.2t}.$$

[17]Leonhard Euler (1707-1783), a Swiss mathematician, introduced e, $f(x)$ notation, π, and i (for $\sqrt{-1}$).

Solution   The function $P = 5e^{0.2t}$ has a continuous growth rate of 20%, and $Q = 5e^{0.3t}$ has a continuous 30% growth rate. The function $R = 5e^{-0.2t}$ has a continuous growth rate of -20%. The negative sign in the exponent tells us that R is decreasing instead of increasing.

Because $a = 5$ in all three formulas, all three functions cross the vertical axis at 5. Note that the graphs of these functions in Figure 4.30 have the same shape as the exponential functions in Section 4.3. They are concave up and have horizontal asymptotes of $y = 0$. (Note that $P \to 0$ and $Q \to 0$ as $t \to -\infty$, whereas $R \to 0$ as $t \to \infty$.)

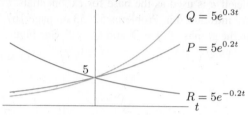

Figure 4.30: Exponential functions with different continuous growth rates

---

Example 2   A population increases from 7.3 million at a continuous rate of 2.2% per year. Write a formula for the population, and estimate graphically when the population reaches 10 million.

Solution   We express the formula in base e since the continuous growth rate is given. If P is the population (in millions) in year t, then

$$P = 7.3e^{0.022t}.$$

See Figure 4.31. We see that $P = 10$ when $t \approx 14.3$. Thus, it takes about 14.3 years for the population to reach 10 million.

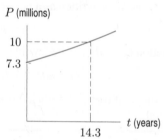

Figure 4.31: Estimating when the
population reaches 10 million

Example 3   Caffeine leaves the body at a continuous rate of 17% per hour. How much caffeine is left in the body 8 hours after drinking a cup of coffee containing 100 mg of caffeine?

Solution   If A is the amount of caffeine in the body t hours after drinking the coffee, then

$$A = 100e^{-0.17t}.$$

Note that the continuous growth rate is -17% since A is decreasing. After 8 hours, we have $A = 100e^{-0.17(8)} = 25.67$ mg.

The Difference Between Annual and Continuous Growth Rates

If $P = P_0(1.07)^t$, with t in years, we say that P is growing at an *annual* rate of 7%. If $P = P_0e^{0.07t}$, with t in years, we say that P is growing at a *continuous* rate of 7% per year. Since

$e^{0.07} = 1.0725\ldots$, we can rewrite $P_0 e^{0.07t} = P_0(1.0725)^t$. In other words, a 7% continuous rate and a 7.25% annual rate generate the same increases in P. We say the two rates are equivalent.

We can check that $e^{0.0677} = 1.07\ldots$, so a 7% annual growth rate is equivalent to a 6.77% continuous growth rate. The continuous growth rate is always smaller than the equivalent annual rate.

The bank account example at the start of the previous section reminds us why a quantity growing at continuous rate of 7% per year increases faster than a quantity growing at an annual rate of 7%: In the continuous case, the interest earns more interest.

Connection: The Number e and Compound Interest

The number e has a surprising relationship with compound interest when the compounding period is made smaller and smaller.

If \$1.00 is invested in a bank account that pays 100% interest once a year, then, assuming no other deposits or withdrawals, after one year we have

$$\$1.00(1 + 100\%) = \$2.00.$$

Now we decrease the compounding period. Suppose \$1.00 is invested in a bank account that pays 100% nominal interest compounded n times a year; then

$$\text{Balance after one year} = \$1.00 \left(1 + \frac{100\%}{n}\right)^n$$

As the frequency of compounding increases, the balance increases, because the interest earns more. How large can the balance grow? Table 4.13 shows the balance after one year as the interest is calculated more and more frequently. It appears that the balance approaches $e = 2.71828182\ldots$.

Assuming that the initial balance of \$1 is growing at a continuous rate of 100%, the balance after one year would be $1 \cdot e^1 = e$ dollars, so the surprising relationship arises from the fact that by increasing the compounding frequency we get the effect of continuous growth that we discussed earlier.

Table 4.13   *Balance after 1 year, 100% nominal interest, various compounding frequencies*

Frequency	Approximate balance
1 (annually)	\$2.00
2 (semi-annually)	\$2.25
4 (quarterly)	\$2.441406
12 (monthly)	\$2.613035
365 (daily)	\$2.714567
8760 (hourly)	\$2.718127
525,600 (each minute)	\$2.718279
31,536,000 (each second)	\$2.718282

In Example 2 of Section 4.4 we calculated the effective interest rates for two accounts with a 6% per year nominal interest rate, but different compounding periods. We see that the account with more frequent compounding earns a higher effective rate, though the increase is small. Compounding more and more frequently—every minute or every second or many times per second—increases the effective rate still further. However, there is again a limit to how much an account can earn by increasing the frequency of compounding.

Table 4.14 *Effect of increasing the frequency of compounding, 6% nominal interest*

Compounding frequency	Annual growth factor	Effective annual rate
Annually	1.0600000	6%
Monthly	1.0616778	6.16778%
Daily	1.0618313	6.18313%
Hourly	1.0618363	6.18363%
$\vdots$	$\vdots$	$\vdots$
Continuously	$e^{0.06} \approx 1.0618365$	6.18365%

Table 4.14 shows several compounding periods with their annual growth factors and effective annual rates. As the compounding periods become shorter, we discover that the growth factor approaches $e^{0.06}$. Using a calculator, we check that the final value for the annual growth factors in Table 4.14 is given by

$$e^{0.06} \approx 1.0618365,$$

If an account with a 6% nominal interest rate per year delivers an annual growth factor of $e^{0.06}$, we say that the interest has been *compounded continuously*. In general:

If interest on an initial deposit of $\$P$ is *compounded continuously* at a nominal rate of r per year, the balance t years later can be calculated using the formula

$$B = Pe^{rt}.$$

For example, if the nominal rate is 6%, then $r = 0.06$.

It is important to realize that the functions $B = Pe^{0.06t}$ and $B = P(1.0618365)^t$ both give the balance in a bank account growing at a continuous rate of 6% per year. These formulas both represent the *same* exponential function—they just describe it in different ways.[18]

Example 4   In November 2005, the Wells Fargo Bank offered interest at a 2.323% continuous yearly rate.[19] Find the effective annual rate.

Solution   Since $e^{0.02323} = 1.0235$, the effective annual rate is 2.35%. As expected, the effective annual rate is larger than the continuous yearly rate.

Example 5   Which is better: An account that pays 8% annual interest compounded quarterly or an account that pays 7.95% annual interest compounded continuously?

---

[18]Actually, this is not precisely true, because we rounded off when we found $b = 1.0618365$. However, we can find b to as many digits as we want, and to this extent the two formulas are the same.

[19]http://money.cnn.com/2005/11/30/debt/informa_rate, accessed November 30, 2005.

Solution   The account that pays 8% interest compounded quarterly pays 2% interest 4 times a year. Thus, in one year the balance is

$$P(1.02)^4 \approx P(1.08243),$$

which means the effective annual rate is 8.243%.

The account that pays 7.95% interest compounded continuously has a year-end balance of

$$Pe^{0.0795} \approx P(1.08275),$$

so the effective annual rate is 8.275%. Thus, 7.95% compounded continuously pays more than 8% compounded quarterly.

Exercises and Problems for Section 4.5

Skill Refresher

In Exercises S1–S4, using a calculator approximate to 3 decimal places.

S1. $e^{0.07}$ **S2.** $10e^{-0.14}$ **S3.** $\dfrac{2}{\sqrt[3]{e}}$ **S4.** e^{3e}

In Exercises S5–S8, evaluate the functions for $t = 0$ and $t = 4$.

S5. $f(t) = 2.3e^{0.3t}$

S6. $g(t) = 4.2e^{-0.12t}$

S7. $h(t) = 153 + 8.6e^{0.43t}$

S8. $k(t) = 289 - 4.7e^{-0.0018t}$

In Exercises S9–S15, write the function in the form $f(t) = ae^{kt}$.

S9. $f(t) = \left(3e^{0.04t}\right)^3$ **S10.** $g(z) = 5e^{7z} \cdot e^{4z} \cdot 3e^z$

S11. $Q(t) = e^{7-3t}$ **S12.** $Q(t) = \sqrt{e^{3+6t}}$

S13. $m(x) = \dfrac{7e^{0.2x}}{\sqrt{3e^x}}$ **S14.** $P(t) = \left(2\sqrt[3]{e^{5t}}\right)^4$

S15. $H(r) = \dfrac{\left(e^{0.4r}\right)^2}{6e^{0.15r}}$

Exercises

1. Without a calculator, match the functions $y = e^x$, $y = 2e^x$, and $y = 3e^x$ to the graphs in Figure 4.32.

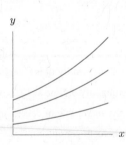

Figure 4.32

2. Without a calculator, match the functions $y = 2^x$, $y = 3^x$, and $y = e^x$ with the graphs in Figure 4.33.

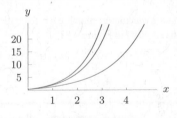

Figure 4.33

3. Without a calculator, match the functions (a)–(d) with the graphs (I)–(IV) in Figure 4.34.

   (a) $e^{0.25t}$ **(b)** $(1.25)^t$ **(c)** $(1.2)^t$ **(d)** $e^{0.3t}$

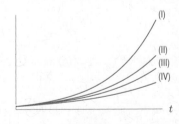

Figure 4.34

4. Without graphing on a calculator, match the functions (a)–(d) with the graphs (I)–(IV) in Figure 4.35.

   (a) 1.5^x **(b)** $e^{0.45x}$ **(c)** $e^{0.47x}$ **(d)** $e^{0.5x}$

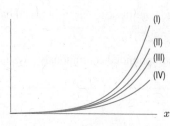

Figure 4.35

5. Without a calculator, match the functions $y = e^x$, $y = e^{-x}$, and $y = -e^x$ to the graphs in Figure 4.36.

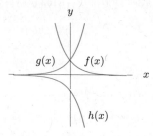

Figure 4.36

6. Without a calculator, match each formula to one of the graphs (I)–(IV) in Figure 4.37.

   (a) $e^{-0.01t}$ **(b)** $e^{0.05t}$ **(c)** $e^{-0.10t}$ **(d)** $e^{0.20t}$

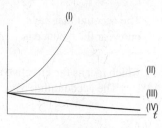

Figure 4.37

7. Without a calculator, match the functions (a)–(d) with the graphs (I)–(IV) in Figure 4.38.

   (a) $y = e^x$ **(b)** $y = e^{-x}$

   (c) $y = e^{-2x}$ **(d)** $y = e^{-3x}$

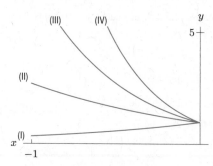

Figure 4.38

Problems

8. Without a calculator, arrange the following quantities in ascending order:

   (a) $3^{2.2}$, $e^{2.2}$, $(\sqrt{2})^{2.2}$
   (b) $3^{-2.2}$, $e^{-2.2}$

In Problems 9–12, find the limits.

9. $\lim\limits_{x \to \infty} e^{-3x}$

10. $\lim\limits_{t \to -\infty} 5e^{0.07t}$

11. $\lim\limits_{t \to \infty} (2 - 3e^{-0.2t})$

12. $\lim\limits_{t \to -\infty} 2e^{-0.1t+6}$

13. If $\lim_{t \to \infty} ae^{kt} = \infty$, what can you say about the values of a and k?

In Problems 14–19, a quantity Q is changing over time t.

   (a) What is the quantity at time $t = 0$?

   (b) Is the quantity increasing or decreasing over time?

   (c) What is the percent per unit time growth or decay rate?

   (d) Is the growth rate continuous?

14. $Q = 25e^{0.032t}$ **15.** $Q = 2.7(0.12)^t$

16. $Q = 158(1.137)^t$ **17.** $Q = 0.01e^{-0.2t}$

18. $Q = 50e^{1.05t}$ **19.** $Q = 2^t$

In Problems 20–22, an initial quantity Q_0 and a growth rate are given. Give a formula for quantity Q as a function of time t, and find the value of the quantity at $t = 10$, if we assume that the growth rate is:

(a) Not continuous   **(b)** Continuous

20. $Q_0 = 100$;   growth rate of 5% per unit time

21. $Q_0 = 8$;   growth rate of 12% per unit time

22. $Q_0 = 500$;   decay rate of -7% per unit time

23. A population of 3.2 million grows at a constant percentage rate.

    (a) What is the population one century later if there is:

       (i) An annual growth rate of 2%

       (ii) A continuous growth rate of 2% per year

    (b) Explain how you can tell which of the answers would be larger before doing the calculations.

24. The following formulas each describe the size of an animal population, P, in t years since the start of the study. Describe the growth of each population in words.

    (a) $P = 200(1.028)^t$ **(b)** $P = 50e^{-0.17t}$

    (c) $P = 1000(0.89)^t$ **(d)** $P = 600e^{0.20t}$

    (e) $P = 2000 - 300t$ **(f)** $P = 600 + 50t$

25. A town has population 3000 people at year $t = 0$. Write a formula for the population, P, in year t if the town

    (a) Grows by 200 people per year.

    (b) Grows by 6% per year.

    (c) Grows at a continuous rate of 6% per year.

    (d) Shrinks by 50 people per year.

    (e) Shrinks by 4% per year.

    (f) Shrinks at a continuous rate of 4% per year.

26. A population is 25,000 in year $t = 0$ and grows at a continuous rate of 7.5% per year.

    (a) Find a formula for $P(t)$, the population in year t.

    (b) By what percent does the population increase each year? Why is this more than 7.5%?

27. A population grows from its initial level of 22,000 at a continuous growth rate of 7.1% per year.

    (a) Find a formula for $P(t)$, the population in year t.

    (b) By what percent does the population increase each year?

28. An investment of $7000 earns interest at a continuous annual rate of 5.2%. What is the investment's value in 7 years?

29. Without making any calculations, describe in words what the following formulas tell you about the value of three different investments. Be specific. Note that units are in dollars and years.

    (a) $V = 1000e^{0.115t}$ **(b)** $V = 1000 \cdot 2^{t/6}$

    (c) $V = 1000(1.122)^t$

30. Calculate the amount of money in a bank account if $2000 is deposited for 15 years at an interest rate of

    (a) 5% annually

    (b) 5% continuously per year

31. At time t in years, the value, V, of an investment of $1000 is given by $V = 1000e^{0.02t}$. When is the investment worth $3000?

32. How long does it take an investment to double if it grows according to the formula $V = 537e^{0.015t}$? Assume t is in years.

33. From time $t = 0$, with t in years, a $1200 deposit in a bank account grows according to the formula

$$B = 1200e^{0.03t}.$$

    (a) What is the balance in the account at the end of 100 years?

    (b) When does the balance first go over $50,000?

34. The same amount of money is deposited into two different bank accounts paying the same nominal rate, one compounded annually and the other compounded continuously. Which curve in Figure 4.39 corresponds to which compounding method? What is the initial deposit?

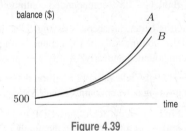

Figure 4.39

35. Find the effective annual yield and the continuous growth rate if $Q = 5500\,e^{0.19\,t}$.

36. If $5000 is deposited in an account paying a nominal interest rate of 4% per year, how much is in the account 10 years later if interest is compounded

    (a) Annually?

    (b) Continuously?

37. Find the effective annual rate if $1000 is deposited at 5% annual interest, compounded continuously.

38. An investment of $500 earns interest at a 6.75% continuous annual rate. Give a formula $V = ab^t$ for the investment's value in year t, and state the values of a, b, and the annual growth rate r.

39. A bank account pays 6% annual interest. As the number of compounding periods increases, the effective interest rate earned also rises.

    (a) Find the annual interest rate earned by the account if the interest is compounded:

        (i) Quarterly   (ii) Monthly
        (iii) Weekly   (iv) Daily

    (b) Evaluate $e^{0.06}$, where $e = 2.71828\ldots$ Explain what your result tells you about the bank account.

40. Three different investments are given.

    (a) Find the balance of each of the investments after a two-year period.

    (b) Rank them from best to worst in terms of rate of return. Explain your reasoning.

    • Investment A: $875 deposited at 13.5% per year compounded daily for 2 years.
    • Investment B: $1000 deposited at 6.7% per year compounded continuously for 2 years.
    • Investment C: $1050 deposited at 4.5% per year compounded monthly for 2 years.

41. Rank the following three bank deposit options from best to worst.

    • Bank A: 7% compounded daily
    • Bank B: 7.1% compounded monthly
    • Bank C: 7.05% compounded continuously

42. Which is better, an account paying 5.3% interest compounded continuously or an account paying 5.5% interest compounded annually? Justify your answer.

43. The GDP of Chile was 145.8 billion dollars in 2007 and was growing at a continuous rate of 5.1% per year.[20]

    (a) Find a formula for G, the GDP of Chile in billion dollars, as a function of t, the number of years since 2007.

    (b) By what percent does the GDP increase each year?

    (c) Use your answer to part (b) to write a formula for G as a function of t using the form $G = ab^t$.

    (d) Graph your answers to part (a) and part (c) on the same axes. Explain what you see.

44. Which is larger after 5 years: an investment of $1000 earning 5% per year compounded monthly or an investment of $1100 earning 4% per year compounded con-

tinuously? Which is larger after 10 years? Justify your answers.

45. One bank pays 5% interest compounded annually and another bank pays 5% interest compounded continuously. Given a deposit of $10,000, what is the difference in the balance between the two banks in 8 years?

46. An investment of $1000 earns 8% interest compounded continuously. An investment of $1500 earns 6% interest compounded annually. Figure 4.40 shows the balance of the two investments over time.

    (a) Which graph goes with which investment?

    (b) Use a graph of the two functions to estimate the time until the balances are equal.

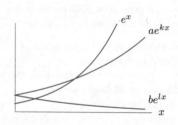

Figure 4.40

47. What can you say about the value of the constants a, k, b, l in Figure 4.41?

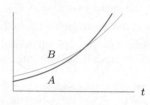

Figure 4.41

48. World poultry production was 94.7 million tons in the year 2009 and increasing at a continuous rate of 1.1% per year.[21] Assume that this growth rate continues.

    (a) Write an exponential formula for world poultry production, P, in million tons, as a function of the number of years, t, since 2009.

    (b) Use the formula to estimate world poultry production in the year 2015.

    (c) Use a graph to estimate the year in which world poultry production goes over 110 million tons.

---

[20]www.nationmaster.com, accessed February 2010.
[21]www.sourcejuice.com/1266927/2009/10/19/world-poultry-production-growth-but-decline-trade, accessed Jan., 2010.

49. A radioactive substance decays at a continuous rate of 14% per year, and 50 mg of the substance is present in the year 2009.

  (a) Write a formula for the amount present, A (in mg), t years after 2009.
  (b) How much will be present in the year 2019?
  (c) Estimate when the quantity drops below 5 mg.

50. The annual inflation rate, r, for a five-year period is given in Table 4.15.

  (a) By what total percent did prices rise between the start of 2000 and the end of 2004?
  (b) What is the average annual inflation rate for this time period?
  (c) At the beginning of 2000, a shower curtain costs $20. Make a prediction for the good's cost at the beginning of 2010, using the average inflation rate found in part (b).

Table 4.15

t	2000	2001	2002	2003	2004
r	3.4%	2.8%	1.6%	2.3%	2.7%

51. In the 1980s a northeastern bank experienced an unusual robbery. Each month an armored car delivered cash deposits from local branches to the main office, a trip requiring only one hour. One day, however, the delivery was six hours late. This delay turned out to be a scheme devised by an employee to defraud the bank. The armored car drivers had lent the money, a total of approximately $200,000,000, to arms merchants, who then used it as collateral against the purchase of illegal weapons. The interest charged for this loan was 20% per year compounded continuously. How much was the fee for the six-hour period?

52. This problem explores the value of $(1+1/n)^n$ for integer values of n as n gets large.

  (a) Use a calculator or computer to evaluate $(1+1/n)^n$, correct to seven decimal places, for $n = 1000$, 10,000, 100,000, and 1,000,000. Does $(1+1/n)^n$ appear to be an increasing or decreasing function of n?
  (b) The limit of the sequence of values in part (a) is $e = 2.718281828\ldots$. What power of 10 is needed to give a value of e correct to 6 decimal places?
  (c) What happens if you evaluate $(1+1/n)^n$ using much larger values of n? For example, try $n = 10^{16}$ on a calculator.

53. With more terms giving a better approximation, it can be shown that

$$e = 1 + \frac{1}{1} + \frac{1}{1 \cdot 2} + \frac{1}{1 \cdot 2 \cdot 3} + \frac{1}{1 \cdot 2 \cdot 3 \cdot 4} + \cdots.$$

  (a) Use a calculator to sum the five terms shown.
  (b) Find the sum of the first seven terms.
  (c) Compare your sums with the calculator's displayed value for e (which you can find by entering $e\hat{\ }1$) and state the number of correct digits in the five- and seven-term sum.
  (d) How many terms of the sum are needed in order to give a nine-decimal-digit approximation equal to the calculator's displayed value for e?

CHAPTER SUMMARY

- **Exponential Functions**
  Value of $f(t)$ changes at constant percent rate with respect to t.

- **General Formula for Exponential Functions**
  Exponential function: $f(t) = ab^t$, $b > 0$.
  f increasing for $b > 1$, decreasing for $0 < b < 1$.
      Growth factor: $b = 1 + r$.
      Growth rate: r, percent change as a decimal.

- **Comparing Linear and Exponential Functions**
  An increasing exponential function eventually overtakes any linear function.

- **Graphs of Exponential Functions**
  Concavity; asymptotes; effect of parameters a and b.
  Solving exponential equations graphically; finding an exponential function for data.

- **The Number e**
  Continuous growth: $f(t) = ae^{kt}$.
  f is increasing for $k > 0$, decreasing for $k < 0$.
  Continuous growth rate: k.

- **Compound Interest**
  For compounding n times per year, balance,
  $$B = P\left(1 + \frac{r}{n}\right)^{nt}.$$
  For continuous compounding, $B = Pe^{kt}$.
  Nominal rate, r or k, versus effective rate earned over one year.

- **Horizontal Asymptotes and Limits to Infinity**

REVIEW EXERCISES AND PROBLEMS FOR CHAPTER FOUR

Exercises

In Exercises 1–6, you start with 500 items. How many do you have after the following change?

1. 10% increase

2. 100% increase

3. 1% decrease

4. 42% decrease

5. 42% increase followed by 42% decrease

6. 42% decrease followed by 42% increase

7. Find a formula for $P = f(t)$, the size of a population that begins in year $t = 0$ with 2200 members and decreases at a 3.2% annual rate.

8. Without a calculator or computer, match each exponential formula to one of the graphs I–VI.

   (a) $10(1.2)^t$ **(b)** $10(1.5)^t$ **(c)** $20(1.2)^t$
   (d) $30(0.85)^t$ **(e)** $30(0.95)^t$ **(f)** $30(1.05)^t$

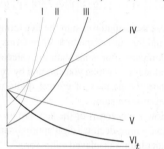

9. A quantity increases from 10 to 12. By what percent has it increased? Now suppose that it had increased from 100 to 102. What is the percent increase in this case?

10. Determine whether the function whose values are in Table 4.16 could be exponential.

Table 4.16

x	1	2	4	5	8	9
$f(x)$	4096	1024	64	16	0.25	0.0625

In Problems 11–14, could the function be linear or exponential or is it neither? Write possible formulas for the linear or exponential functions.

11.

r	1	3	7	15	31
$p(r)$	13	19	31	55	103

12.

x	6	9	12	18	24
$q(x)$	100	110	121	146.41	177.16

13.

x	10	12	15	16	18
$f(x)$	1	2	4	8	16

14.

t	1	2	3	4	5
$g(t)$	512	256	128	64	32

Problems

15. In 2010, the cost of a train ticket from Boston to New York was \$95.[22] Assume that the price rises by 7% per year. Make a table showing the price of tickets each year until 2014.

16. Radioactive gallium-67 decays by 1.48% every hour; there are 100 milligrams initially.

   (a) Find a formula for the amount of gallium-67 remaining after t hours.
   (b) How many milligrams are left after 24 hours? After 1 week?

17. A bank pays interest at the nominal rate of 4.2% per year. What is the effective annual rate if compounding is:

   (a) Annual   **(b)** Monthly   **(c)** Continuous

18. Explain the difference between linear and exponential growth. That is, without writing down any formulas, describe how linear and exponential functions progress differently from one value to the next.

In Problems 19–24, find formulas for the exponential functions satisfying the given conditions.

19. $h(0) = 3$ and $h(1) = 15$

20. $f(3) = -3/8$ and $f(-2) = -12$

---
[22]http://www.amtrak.com, accessed May 23, 2010.

21. $g(1/2) = 4$ and $g(1/4) = 2\sqrt{2}$

22. $g(0) = 5$ and $g(-2) = 10$

23. $g(1.7) = 6$ and $g(2.5) = 4$

24. $f(1) = 4$ and $f(3) = d$

25. Suppose $f(-3) = 5/8$ and $f(2) = 20$. Find a formula for f assuming it is:

    (a) Linear   **(b)** Exponential

For Problems 26–31, find formulas for the exponential functions.

26.

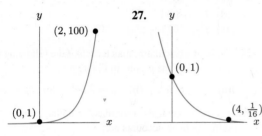

27.

28.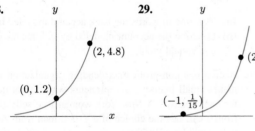

29.

30.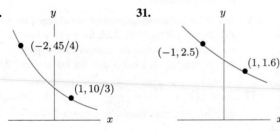

31.

32. Find possible formulas for the functions in Figure 4.42.

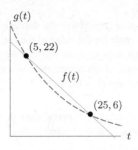

Figure 4.42

33. Let $P(t)$ be the population of a country, in millions, t years after 1990, with $P(7) = 3.21$ and $P(13) = 3.75$.

    (a) Find a formula for $P(t)$ assuming it is linear. Describe in words the country's annual population growth given this assumption.

    (b) Find a formula for $P(t)$ assuming it is exponential. Describe in words the country's annual population growth given this assumption.

34. A population has size 100 at time $t = 0$, with t in years.

    (a) If the population grows by 10 people per year, find a formula for the population, P, at time t.

    (b) If the population grows by 10% per year, find a formula for the population, P, at time t.

    (c) Graph both functions on the same axes.

Find the limits in Problems 35–40.

35. $\lim\limits_{x \to \infty} 257(0.93)^x$ **36.** $\lim\limits_{t \to \infty} 5.3e^{-0.12t}$

37. $\lim\limits_{x \to -\infty} (15 - 5e^{3x})$ **38.** $\lim\limits_{t \to -\infty} (21(1.2)^t + 5.1)$

39. $\lim\limits_{x \to \infty} (7.2 - 2e^{3x})$ **40.** $\lim\limits_{x \to -\infty} (5e^{-7x} + 1.5)$

41. In 1940, there were about 10 brown tree snakes per square mile on the island of Guam, and in 2002, there were about 20,000 per square mile.[23] Find an exponential formula for the number, N, of brown tree snakes per square mile on Guam t years after 1940. What was, on average, the annual percent increase in the population during this period?

42. A 2010 Lexus LS costs $64,680.[24] Assume that the car depreciates a total of 42% during its first 5 years.

    (a) Suppose the depreciation is exponential. Find a formula for the value of the car at time t.

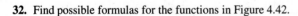

[23]*Science News*, Vol. 162, August 10, 2002, p. 85.
[24]http://www.lexus.com, accessed November, 2009.

(b) Suppose instead that the depreciation is linear. Find a formula for the value of the car at time t.

(c) If this were your car and you were trading it in after 4 years, which depreciation model would you prefer (exponential or linear)?

43. Table 4.17 gives the approximate number of cell phone subscribers, S, in the United States.[25]

(a) Explain how you know an exponential function fits the data. Find a formula for S in terms of t, the number of years since 2001.

(b) Interpret the growth rate in terms of cell phone subscribers.

(c) In 2008, there were 262.7 million subscribers. Does this fit the pattern?

Table 4.17

Year	2001	2002	2003	2004	2005	2006
Subscribers (m.)	128.4	140.8	158.7	182.1	207.9	233

44. Find the annual growth rates of a quantity which:

(a) Doubles in size every 7 years

(b) Triples in size every 11 years

(c) Grows by 3% per month

(d) Grows by 18% every 5 months

In Problems 45–48, graph $f(x)$, a function defined for all real numbers and satisfying the condition.

45. $f(x) \to 5$ as $x \to \infty$

46. $f(x) \to 3$ as $x \to \infty$ and $f(x) \to -2$ as $x \to -\infty$

47. $\lim_{x \to -\infty} f(x) = -4$

48. $\lim_{x \to -\infty} f(x) = 0$ and $\lim_{x \to \infty} f(x) = -\infty$

49. The functions $f(x) = \left(\frac{1}{2}\right)^x$ and $g(x) = 1/x$ are similar in that they both tend toward zero as x becomes large. Using a calculator, determine which function, f or g, approaches zero faster.

In Problems 50–51, graph the function to find horizontal asymptotes.

50. $f(x) = 8 - 2^x$

51. $f(x) = 3^{-x^2} + 2$

52. Without making any calculations, briefly describe the following investments, where t is in years. Be specific.

(a) $V = 2500e^{-0.0434t}$

(b) $V = 4000(1.005)^{12t}$

(c) $V = 8000 \cdot 2^{-t/14}$

(d) $V = 5000 + 250(t - 10)$

53. Without making any calculations, briefly describe in words what the following formulas tell you about the size of the animal populations they describe. Be specific. Note that t is in years.

(a) $P = 5200(1.118)^t$

(b) $P = 4600(1.01)^{12t}$

(c) $P = 3800 \left(\frac{1}{2}\right)^{t/12}$

(d) $P = 8000e^{0.0778t}$

(e) $P = 1675 - 25(t - 30)$

54. Without a calculator, match each of the following formulas to one of the graphs in Figure 4.6.

(a) $y = 8.3e^{-t}$ **(b)** $y = 2.5e^t$ **(c)** $y = -4e^{-t}$

55. If t is in years, the formulas for dollar balances of two different bank accounts are:

$$f(t) = 1100(1.05)^t \quad \text{and} \quad g(t) = 1500e^{0.05t}.$$

(a) Describe in words the bank account modeled by f.

(b) Describe the account modeled by g. State the effective annual yield.

56. Accion is a non-profit microlending organization which makes small loans to entrepreneurs who do not qualify for bank loans.[26] A New York woman who sells clothes from a cart has the choice of a $1000 loan from Accion to be repaid by $1150 a year later and a $1000 loan from a loan shark with an annual interest rate of 22%, compounded annually.

(a) What is the annual interest rate charged by Accion?

(b) To pay off the loan shark for a year's loan of $1000, how much would the woman have to pay?

(c) Which loan is a better deal for the woman? Why?

57. Write $p(x) = \dfrac{7e^{6x} \cdot \sqrt{e} \cdot (2e^x)^{-1}}{10e^{4x}}$ in the form $p(x) = ae^x$. All constants should be expressed exactly.

In Problems 58–59, write each function in standard form. Note that one of them is linear and one exponential.

58. $r(v) = vj^w - 4tj^w + kvj^w$

59. $s(w) = vj^w - 4tj^w + kvj^w$

---

[25]www.infoplease.com/ipa/A0933563.html, accessed December 22, 2009.
[26]http://www.accionusa.org/, accessed November, 2005.

Problems 60–61 concern ISO A- and B-series paper, commonly used in many countries. The width in millimeters (mm) of a sheet of A_n paper in this series is given by the formula[27]

$$f(n) = 1000 \cdot 2^{-\frac{1}{4} - \frac{n}{2}}.$$

The width $g(n)$ of a sheet of B_n paper is the geometric mean of the widths of A_n paper and the next larger size, A_{n-1} paper. Since the geometric mean of two quantities p and q is the square root of their product, this means

$$g(n) = \sqrt{f(n) \cdot f(n-1)}.$$

60. Evaluate $g(1)$. What does your answer tell you about B-series paper?

61. Show that g is an exponential function by writing it in standard form.

62. The figure gives graphs of two functions, f and g. Explain why not both of these functions can be exponential.

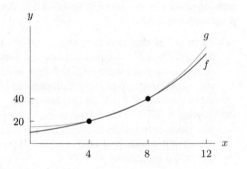

63. Write a paragraph that compares the function $f(x) = a^x$, where $a > 1$, and $g(x) = b^x$, where $0 < b < 1$. Include graphs in your answer.

Problems 64–67 use Figure 4.43, which shows $f(x) = ab^x$ and $g(x) = cd^x$ on three different scales. Their point of intersection is marked.

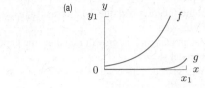
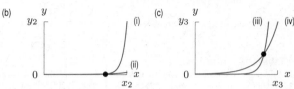

Figure 4.43

64. Which is larger, a or c?

65. Which is larger, b or d?

66. Rank in order from least to greatest: x_1, x_2, x_3.

67. Match f and g to the graphs labeled (i)–(iv) in (b) and (c).

68. On November 27, 1993, the *New York Times* reported that wildlife biologists have found a direct link between the increase in the human population in Florida and the decline of the local black bear population. From 1953 to 2009, the human population increased, on average, at a rate of 6% per year, while the black bear population decreased at a rate of 6% per year. In 1953 the black bear population was 11,000.

    (a) The 2009 human population of Florida was 16 million. What was the human population in 1953?

    (b) Find the black bear population for 2009.

    (c) Had this trend continued,[28] when would the black bear population have numbered less than 100?

69. **(a)** Using a computer or calculator, graph $f(x) = 2^x$.

    (b) Find the slope of the line tangent to f at $x = 0$ to an accuracy of two decimals. [Hint: Zoom in on the graph until it is indistinguishable from a line and estimate the slope using two points on the graph.]

    (c) Find the slope of the line tangent to $g(x) = 3^x$ at $x = 0$ to an accuracy of two decimals.

    (d) Find b (to two decimals) such that the line tangent to the function $h(x) = b^x$ at $x = 0$ has slope 1.

70. Sales of energy-efficient compact fluorescent lamps in China have been growing approximately exponentially. Table 4.18 shows the sales in millions.[29]

    (a) Use a calculator or computer to find the exponential regression function for sales, S (in millions), as a function of the number of years, t, since 1994.

---

[27]Actual paper sizes are rounded to the nearest mm, so this formula is only approximate. See http://www.cl.cam.ac.uk/~mgk25/iso-paper.html, accessed February 24, 2008.

[28]Since 1993, the black bear population has in fact remained stable: www.myfwc.com/bear, accessed January 5, 2006.

[29]S. Nadel and Hong, "Market Data on Efficient Lighting," Right Light 6 Conference, Session 8, May, 2005.

(b) Plot the function with the data. Does it appear to fit the data well?

(c) What annual percent growth rate does the exponential model show?

(d) If this growth rate continues, what sales are predicted in the year 2010?

Table 4.18

Year	1994	1996	1998	2000	2002	2003
Sales (millions)	20	30	60	125	295	440

Find possible formulas for the functions in Problems 71–73.

71. V gives the value of an account that begins in year $t = 0$ with \$12,000 and earns 4.2% annual interest, compounded continuously.

72. The exponential function $p(t)$ given that $p(20) = 300$ and $p(50) = 40$.

73. The linear function $q(x)$ whose graph intersects the graph of $y = 5000e^{-x/40}$ at $x = 50$ and $x = 150$.

74. An investment worth $V = \$2500$ in year $t = 0$ earns 4.2% annual interest, compounded continuously. Find a formula for V in terms of t.

75. A population is represented by $P = 12,000e^{-0.122t}$. Give the values of a, k, b, and r, where $P = ae^{kt} = ab^t$. What do these values tell you about the population?

76. This problem uses a calculator or computer to explore graphically the value of $(1 + 1/x)^x$ as x gets large.

(a) Graph $y = (1 + 1/x)^x$ for $1 \leq x \leq 10$.

(b) Are the values of y in part (a) increasing or decreasing?

(c) Do the values of y in part (a) appear to approach a limiting value?

(d) Graph $y = (1 + 1/x)^x$, for $1 \leq x \leq 100$, and then for $1 \leq x \leq 1000$. Do the y values appear to approach a limiting value? If so, approximately what is it?

(e) Graph $y = (1 + 1/x)^x$ and $y = e$ on the same axes, for $1 \leq x \leq 10,000$. What does the graph suggest?

(f) By checking $x = 10,000$, $x = 20,000$, and so on, decide how large (as a multiple of 10,000) x should be to give a value of e correct to 4 decimal places.

77. Hong Kong shifted from British to Chinese rule in 1997. Figure 4.44 shows[30] the number of people who emigrated from Hong Kong during each of the years from 1980 to 1992.

(a) Find an exponential function that approximates the data.

(b) What does the model predict about the number of emigrants in 1997?

(c) Briefly explain why this model is or is not useful to predict emigration in the year 2010.

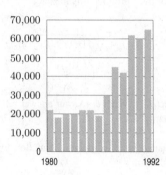

Figure 4.44

78. Before the AIDS epidemic, Botswana[31] had a rapidly growing population, as shown in Table 4.19. In 2005, the population started falling.

(a) Fit an exponential growth model, $P = ab^t$, to this data set, where P is the population in millions and t measures the years since 1975 in 5-year intervals— so $t = 1$ corresponds to 1980. Estimate a and b. Plot the data set and $P = ab^t$ on the same graph.

(b) Starting from 1975, how long does it take for the population of Botswana to double? When is the population of Botswana projected to exceed 214 million, the 1975 population of the US?

Table 4.19

Year	1975	1980	1985	1990
Population (millions)	0.755	0.901	1.078	1.285

Problems 79–80 use Figure 4.45, where t_0 is the t-coordinate of the point of intersection of the graphs. Describe what happens to t_0 if the following changes are made, assuming the other quantities remain the same.

[30]Adapted from the *New York Times*, July 5, 1995.

[31]N. Keyfitz, *World Population Growth and Aging* (Chicago: University of Chicago Press), 1990.

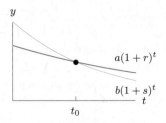

$$a(1+r)^t$$

$$b(1+s)^t$$

Figure 4.45

79. b is decreased

80. r is increased

81. It is a well-documented fact that the earning power of men is higher than that of women.[32] Table 4.20 gives the median income of year-round full-time workers in the US in dollars.

 (a) Plot the data and connect the points.

 (b) Let t be the year. Construct two functions of the form $W(t) = ae^{b(t-1950)}$, one each for the men's and women's earning power data.

 (c) Graph the two functions from 1950 to 2000 and again from 2000 to 2080.

 (d) Do the graphs in part (c) predict women's salaries will catch up with men's? If so, when?

 (e) Comment on your predictions in part (d).

Table 4.20

Year	1950	1960	1970	1980	1990	2000
Female	953	1261	2237	4920	10,070	16,063
Male	2570	4080	6670	12,530	20,293	28,343

82. According to a letter to the *New York Times* on April 10, 1993, "... the probability of [a driver's] involvement in a single-car accident increases exponentially with increasing levels of blood alcohol." The letter goes on to state that when a driver's blood-alcohol content (BAC) is 0.15, the risk of such an accident is about 25 times greater than for a nondrinker.

 (a) Let p_0 be a nondrinker's probability of being involved in a single-car accident. Let $f(x)$ be the probability of an accident for a driver whose blood alcohol level is x. Find a formula for $f(x)$. (This only makes sense for some values of x.)

 (b) At the time of the letter, the legal definition of intoxication was a BAC of 0.1 or higher. According to your formula for $f(x)$, how many times more likely to be involved in a single-car accident was a driver at the legal limit than a nondrinker?

 (c) Suppose that new legislation is proposed to change the definition of legal intoxication. The new definition states that a person is legally intoxicated when their likelihood of involvement in a single-car accident is three times that of a non-drinker. To what BAC would the new definition of legal intoxication correspond?

Pure water is not perfectly clear—it has a bluish cast—because it absorbs light differently at different wavelengths. The table gives values of the *absorption coefficient* $\mu(\lambda)$, in units of cm^{-1}, as a function of the wavelength λ in nanometers or nm.[33] If light of wavelength λ nanometers (nm) travels through l cm of water, the percent transmitted (without being absorbed) is given by

$$T_\lambda(l) = e^{-\mu(\lambda)\cdot l}.$$

Note that here, T_λ is the name of the function. Answer Problems 83–84.

color	λ	$\mu(\lambda)$	color	λ	$\mu(\lambda)$
violet	400	0.000066	yellow	570	0.000695
indigo	445	0.000075	orange	590	0.001351
blue	475	0.000114	red	650	0.003400
green	510	0.000325	—	—	—

83. What percent of red light will be transmitted after passing through 200 cm of water?

84. What percent of blue light will be transmitted over the same distance?

---

[32] *The World Almanac and Book of Facts 2006*, p. 84.

[33] Note that aside from absorption, optical scattering also plays a role. See http://omlc.ogi.edu/spectra/water/data/pope97.dat, http://eosweb.larc.nasa.gov/EDDOCS/Wavelengths_for_Colors.html, and http://en.wikipedia.org/wiki/Color_of_water, accessed February 29, 2008.

CHECK YOUR UNDERSTANDING

Are the statements in Problems 1–32 true or false? Give an explanation for your answer.

1. Exponential functions are functions that increase or decrease at a constant percent rate.

2. The independent variable in an exponential function is always found in the exponent.

3. If $y = 40(1.05)^t$ then y is an exponential function of t.

4. The following table shows a function that could be exponential.

x	1	2	4	5	6
y	1	2	4	7	11

5. If your salary, S, grows by 4% each year, then $S = S_0(0.04)^t$ where t is in years.

6. If $f(t) = 4(2)^t$ then $f(2) = 64$.

7. If $f(t) = 3(\frac{2}{5})^t$ then f is a decreasing function.

8. If $Q = f(t) = 1000(0.5)^t$ then when $Q = 125, t = 3$.

9. If $Q = f(t) = ab^t$ then a is the initial value of Q.

10. If we are given two data points, we can find a linear function and an exponential function that go through these points.

11. A population that has 1000 members and decreases at 10% per year can be modeled as $P = 1000(0.10)^t$.

12. A positive increasing exponential function always becomes larger than any increasing linear function in the long run.

13. A possible formula for an exponential function that passes through the point $(0, 1)$ and the point $(2, 10)$ is $y = 4.5t + 1$.

14. If a population increases by 50% each year, then in two years it increases by 100%.

15. In the formula $Q = ab^t$, the value of a tells us where the graph crosses the Q-axis.

16. In the formula $Q = ab^t$, if $a > 1$, the graph always rises as we read from left to right.

17. The symbol e represents a constant whose value is approximately 2.71828.

18. If $f(x) \to k$ as $x \to \infty$ we say that the line $y = k$ is a horizontal asymptote.

19. Exponential graphs are always concave up.

20. If there are 110 grams of a substance initially and its decay rate is 3% per minute, then the amount after t minutes is $Q = 110(0.03)^t$ grams.

21. If a population had 200 members at time zero and was growing at 4% per year, then the population size after t years can be expressed as $P = 200(1.04)^t$.

22. If $P = 5e^{0.2t}$, we say the continuous growth rate of the function is 2%.

23. If $P = 4e^{-0.90t}$, we say the continuous growth rate of the function is 10%.

24. If $Q = 3e^{0.2t}$, then when $t = 5, Q = 3$.

25. If $Q = Q_0 e^{kt}$, with Q_0 positive and k negative, then Q is decreasing.

26. If an investment earns 5% compounded monthly, its effective rate will be more than 5%.

27. If a \$500 investment earns 6% per year, compounded quarterly, we can find the balance after three years by evaluating the formula $B = 500(1 + \frac{6}{4})^{3 \cdot 4}$.

28. If interest on a \$2000 investment is compounded continuously at 3% per year, the balance after five years is found by evaluating the formula $B = 2000e^{(0.03)(5)}$.

29. Investing \$10,000 for 20 years at 5% earns more if interest is compounded quarterly than if it is compounded annually.

30. Investing \$P for T years always earns more if interest is compounded continuously than if it is compounded annually.

31. There is no limit to the amount a twenty-year \$10,000 investment at 5% interest can earn if the number of times the interest is compounded becomes greater and greater.

32. If you put \$1000 into an account that earns 5.5% compounded continuously, then it takes about 18 years for the investment to grow to \$2000.

SKILLS REFRESHER FOR CHAPTER 4: EXPONENTS

We list the definition and properties that are used to manipulate exponents.

Definition of Zero, Negative, and Fractional Exponents

If m and n are positive integers:[34]

- $a^0 = 1$
- $a^{-n} = \dfrac{1}{a^n}$
- $a^{1/n} = \sqrt[n]{a}$, the nth root of a
- $a^{m/n} = \sqrt[n]{a^m} = \left(\sqrt[n]{a}\right)^m$

Properties of Exponents

- $a^m \cdot a^n = a^{m+n}$ For example, $2^4 \cdot 2^3 = (2 \cdot 2 \cdot 2 \cdot 2) \cdot (2 \cdot 2 \cdot 2) = 2^7$.
- $\dfrac{a^m}{a^n} = a^{m-n}, a \neq 0$ For example, $\dfrac{2^4}{2^3} = \dfrac{2 \cdot 2 \cdot 2 \cdot 2}{2 \cdot 2 \cdot 2} = 2^1$.
- $(a^m)^n = a^{mn}$ For example, $(2^3)^2 = 2^3 \cdot 2^3 = 2^6$.
- $(ab)^n = a^n b^n$
- $\left(\dfrac{a}{b}\right)^n = \dfrac{a^n}{b^n}, \quad b \neq 0$

Be aware of the following notational conventions:

$$ab^n = a(b^n), \qquad \text{but } ab^n \neq (ab)^n,$$
$$-b^n = -(b^n), \qquad \text{but } -b^n \neq (-b)^n,$$
$$-ab^n = (-a)(b^n).$$

For example, $-2^4 = -(2^4) = -16$, but $(-2)^4 = (-2)(-2)(-2)(-2) = +16$. Also, be sure to realize that for $n \neq 1$,

$$(a+b)^n \neq a^n + b^n \qquad \text{Power of a sum} \neq \text{Sum of powers.}$$

Example 1   Evaluate without a calculator:

(a) $(27)^{2/3}$ (b) $(4)^{-3/2}$ (c) $8^{1/3} - 1^{1/3}$

Solution   (a) We have $(27)^{2/3} = \sqrt[3]{27^2} = \sqrt[3]{729} = 9$, or, equivalently, $(27)^{2/3} = \left(27^{1/3}\right)^2 = \left(\sqrt[3]{27}\right)^2 = 3^2 = 9$.

           (b) We have $(4)^{-3/2} = (2)^{-3} = \dfrac{1}{2^3} = \dfrac{1}{8}$.

           (c) We have $8^{1/3} - 1^{1/3} = 2 - 1 = 1$.

---

[34]We assume that the base is restricted to the values for which the power is defined.

Example 2   Use the rules of exponents to simplify the following:

(a) $\dfrac{100x^2y^4}{5x^3y^2}$ (b) $\dfrac{y^4(x^3y^{-2})^2}{2x^{-1}}$ (c) $\sqrt[3]{-8x^6}$ (d) $\left(\dfrac{M^{1/5}}{3N^{-1/2}}\right)^2$

Solution   (a) We have

$$\frac{100x^2y^4}{5x^3y^2} = 20(x^{2-3})(y^{4-2}) = 20x^{-1}y^2 = \frac{20y^2}{x}.$$

(b) We have

$$\frac{y^4\left(x^3y^{-2}\right)^2}{2x^{-1}} = \frac{y^4x^6y^{-4}}{2x^{-1}} = \frac{y^{(4-4)}x^{(6-(-1))}}{2} = \frac{y^0x^7}{2} = \frac{x^7}{2}.$$

(c) We have

$$\sqrt[3]{-8x^6} = \sqrt[3]{-8} \cdot \sqrt[3]{x^6} = -2x^2.$$

(d) We have

$$\left(\frac{M^{1/5}}{3N^{-1/2}}\right)^2 = \frac{\left(M^{1/5}\right)^2}{\left(3N^{-1/2}\right)^2} = \frac{M^{2/5}}{3^2N^{-1}} = \frac{M^{2/5}N}{9}.$$

Example 3   Solve for x:

(a) $\dfrac{10x^7}{4x^2} = 37$ (b) $\dfrac{x^2}{3x^5} = 10$ (c) $\sqrt{9x^5} = 10$

Solution   (a) We have

$$\frac{10x^7}{4x^2} = 37$$
$$2.5x^5 = 37$$
$$x^5 = 14.8$$
$$x = (14.8)^{1/5} = 1.714.$$

(b) We have

$$\frac{x^2}{3x^5} = 10$$
$$\frac{1}{3}x^{-3} = 10$$
$$\frac{1}{x^3} = 30$$
$$x^3 = \frac{1}{30}$$
$$x = \left(\frac{1}{30}\right)^{1/3} = 0.322.$$

(c) We have

$$\sqrt{9x^5} = 10$$
$$3x^{5/2} = 10$$
$$x^{5/2} = \frac{10}{3}$$
$$x = \left(\frac{10}{3}\right)^{2/5} = 1.619.$$

Exercises to Skills for Chapter 4

For Exercises 1–33, evaluate without a calculator.

1. $(-5)^2$

2. 11^2

3. 10^4

4. $(-1)^{13}$

5. $\dfrac{5^3}{5^2}$

6. $\dfrac{10^8}{10^5}$

7. $\dfrac{6^4}{6^4}$

8. $\sqrt{4}$

9. $\sqrt{4^2}$

10. $\sqrt{4^4}$

11. $\sqrt{(-4)^2}$

12. $\dfrac{1}{7^{-2}}$

13. $\dfrac{2^7}{2^3}$

14. $(-1)^{445}$

15. -11^2

16. $\left(5^0\right)^3$

17. $2.1\left(10^3\right)$

18. $16^{1/2}$

19. $16^{1/4}$

20. $16^{3/4}$

21. $16^{5/4}$

22. $16^{5/2}$

23. $100^{5/2}$

24. $\sqrt{(-4)^2}$

25. $(-1)^3\sqrt{36}$

26. $(0.04)^{1/2}$

27. $(-8)^{2/3}$

28. 3^{-1}

29. $3^{-3/2}$

30. 25^{-1}

31. 25^{-2}

32. $(1/27)^{-1/3}$

33. $(0.125)^{1/3}$

Simplify the expressions in Exercises 34–55 and leave without radicals if possible. Assume all variables are positive.

34. $\sqrt{x^4}$

35. $\sqrt{y^8}$

36. $\sqrt{w^8 z^4}$

37. $\sqrt{x^5 y^4}$

38. $\sqrt{49 w^9}$

39. $\sqrt{25 x^3 z^4}$

40. $\sqrt{r^2}$

41. $\sqrt{r^3}$

42. $\sqrt{r^4}$

43. $\sqrt{64 s^7}$

44. $\sqrt{50 x^4 y^6}$

45. $\sqrt{48 u^{10} v^{12} y^5}$

46. $\sqrt{6 s^2 t^3 v^5}\sqrt{6 s t^5 v^3}$

47. $\left(S\sqrt{16 x t^2}\right)^2$

48. $\sqrt{e^{2x}}$

49. $(3AB)^{-1}\left(A^2 B^{-1}\right)^2$

50. $e^{kt}\cdot e^3\cdot e$

51. $\sqrt{M+2}(2+M)^{3/2}$

52. $\left(y^{-2} e^y\right)^2$

53. $\dfrac{a^{n+1} 3^{n+1}}{a^n 3^n}$

54. $\left(a^{-1}+b^{-1}\right)^{-1}$

55. $\left(\dfrac{35(2b+1)^9}{7(2b+1)^{-1}}\right)^2$ (Do not expand $(2b+1)^9$.)

If possible, evaluate the quantities in Exercises 56–64. Check your answers with a calculator.

56. $(-32)^{3/5}$

57. $-32^{3/5}$

58. $-625^{3/4}$

59. $(-625)^{3/4}$

60. $(-1728)^{4/3}$

61. $64^{-3/2}$

62. $-64^{3/2}$

63. $(-64)^{3/2}$

64. $81^{5/4}$

In Exercises 65–66, solve for x.

65. $7x^4 = 20x^2$

66. $2(x+2)^3 = 100$

In Exercises 67–68, use algebra to find the point of intersection.

67.

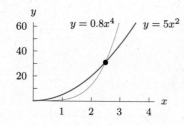

68.

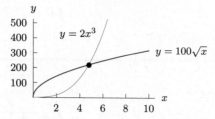

Are the statements in Exercises 69–74 true or false?

69. $x^2 y^5 = (xy)^{10}$

70. $5u^2 + 5u^3 = 10u^5$

71. $(3r)^2 9s^2 = 81r^2 s^2$

72. $\sqrt[3]{-64b^3 c^6} = -4bc^2$

73. $-4w^2 - 3w^3 = -w^2(4 + 3w)$

74. $(u + v)^{-1} = \dfrac{1}{u} + \dfrac{1}{v}$

Solve the equations in Exercises 75–76 in terms of r and s, given that

$$2^r = 5 \quad \text{and} \quad 2^s = 7.$$

75. $2^x = 35.$

76. $2^x = 140.$

Let $2^a = 5$ and $2^b = 7$. Using exponent rules, solve the equations in Exercises 77–82 in terms of a and b.

77. $5^x = 32$

78. $7^x = \dfrac{1}{8}$

79. $25^x = 64$

80. $14^x = 16$

81. $5^x = 7$

82. $0.4^x = 49$

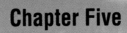

Chapter Five

LOGARITHMIC FUNCTIONS

Contents

5.1 LOGARITHMS AND THEIR PROPERTIES

What Is a Logarithm?

Suppose that a population grows according to the formula $P = 10^t$, where P is the colony size at time t, in hours. When will the population be 2500? We want to solve the following equation for t:

$$10^t = 2500.$$

In Section 4.2, we used a graphical method to approximate t. This time, we introduce a function that returns precisely the exponent of 10 we need.

Since $10^3 = 1000$ and $10^4 = 10,000$, and $1000 < 2500 < 10,000$, the exponent we are looking for is between 3 and 4. But how do we find the exponent exactly?

To answer this question, we define the *common logarithm function*, or simply the *log function*, written $\log_{10} x$, or $\log x$, as follows.

If x is a positive number,

$$\log x \text{ is the exponent of 10 that gives } x.$$

In other words, if

$$y = \log x \qquad \text{then} \qquad 10^y = x.$$

For example, $\log 100 = 2$, because 2 is the exponent of 10 that gives 100, or $10^2 = 100$.

To solve the equation $10^t = 2500$, we must find the power of 10 that gives 2500. Using the log button on a calculator, we can approximate this exponent. We find

$$\log 2500 \approx 3.398, \quad \text{which means that} \quad 10^{3.398} \approx 2500.$$

As predicted, this exponent is between 3 and 4. The precise exponent is $\log 2500$; the approximate value is 3.398. Thus, it takes roughly 3.4 hours for the population to reach 2500.

Example 1   Rewrite the following statements using exponents instead of logs.

(a) $\log 100 = 2$ (b) $\log 0.01 = -2$ (c) $\log 30 = 1.477$

Solution   For each statement, we use the fact that if $y = \log x$ then $10^y = x$.

(a) $2 = \log 100$ means that $10^2 = 100$.

(b) $-2 = \log 0.01$ means that $10^{-2} = 0.01$.

(c) $1.477 = \log 30$ means that $10^{1.477} = 30$. (Actually, this is only an approximation. Using a calculator, we see that $10^{1.477} = 29.9916\ldots$ and that $\log 30 = 1.47712125\ldots$.)

Example 2   Rewrite the following statements using logs instead of exponents.

(a) $10^5 = 100,000$ (b) $10^{-4} = 0.0001$ (c) $10^{0.8} = 6.3096.$

Solution   For each statement, we use the fact that if $10^y = x$, then $y = \log x$.

(a) $10^5 = 100,000$ means that $\log 100,000 = 5$.

(b) $10^{-4} = 0.0001$ means that $\log 0.0001 = -4$.

(c) $10^{0.8} = 6.3096$ means that $\log 6.3096 = 0.8$. (This, too, is only an approximation because $10^{0.8}$ actually equals $6.30957344 \ldots$.)

Logarithms Are Exponents

Note that logarithms are just exponents! Thinking in terms of exponents is often a good way to answer a logarithm problem.

Example 3   Without a calculator, evaluate the following, if possible:

(a) $\log 1$ (b) $\log 10$ (c) $\log 1,000,000$

(d) $\log 0.001$ (e) $\log \dfrac{1}{\sqrt{10}}$ (f) $\log(-100)$

Solution   (a) We have $\log 1 = 0$, since $10^0 = 1$.

(b) We have $\log 10 = 1$, since $10^1 = 10$.

(c) Since $1,000,000 = 10^6$, the exponent of 10 that gives $1,000,000$ is 6. Thus, $\log 1,000,000 = 6$.

(d) Since $0.001 = 10^{-3}$, the exponent of 10 that gives 0.001 is -3. Thus, $\log 0.001 = -3$.

(e) Since $1/\sqrt{10} = 10^{-1/2}$, the exponent of 10 that gives $1/\sqrt{10}$ is $-\frac{1}{2}$. Thus $\log(1/\sqrt{10}) = -\frac{1}{2}$.

(f) Since 10 to any power is positive, -100 cannot be written as a power of 10. Thus, $\log(-100)$ is undefined.

Logarithmic and Exponential Functions Are Inverses

The operation of taking a logarithm "undoes" the exponential function; the logarithm and the exponential are inverse functions. For example, $\log(10^6) = 6$ and $10^{\log 6} = 6$. In particular,

> For any N,
> $$\log(10^N) = N$$
> and for $N > 0$,
> $$10^{\log N} = N.$$

Example 4   Evaluate without a calculator: (a) $\log \left(10^{8.5}\right)$ (b) $10^{\log 2.7}$ (c) $10^{\log(x+3)}$

Solution   Using $\log(10^N) = N$ and $10^{\log N} = N$, we have:

(a) $\log \left(10^{8.5}\right) = 8.5$ (b) $10^{\log 2.7} = 2.7$ (c) $10^{\log(x+3)} = x + 3$

You can check the first two results on a calculator.

Properties of Logarithms

In Chapter 4, we saw how to solve exponential equations such as $100 \cdot 2^t = 337,000,000$, graphically. To use logarithms to solve these equations, we use the properties of logarithms, which are justified on page 184.

Properties of the Common Logarithm

- By definition, $y = \log x$ means $10^y = x$.
- In particular,

$$\log 1 = 0 \quad \text{and} \quad \log 10 = 1.$$

- The functions 10^x and $\log x$ are inverses, so they "undo" each other:

$$\log(10^x) = x \qquad \text{for all } x,$$
$$10^{\log x} = x \qquad \text{for } x > 0.$$

- For a and b both positive and any value of t,

$$\log(ab) = \log a + \log b$$

$$\log\left(\frac{a}{b}\right) = \log a - \log b$$

$$\log(b^t) = t \cdot \log b.$$

We can now use logarithms to solve the equation that we solved graphically in Section 4.2.

Example 5   Solve $100 \cdot 2^t = 337,000,000$ for t.

Solution   Dividing both sides of the equation by 100 gives

$$2^t = 3,370,000.$$

Taking logs of both sides gives

$$\log\left(2^t\right) = \log(3,370,000).$$

Since $\log(2^t) = t \cdot \log 2$, we have

$$t \log 2 = \log(3,370,000),$$

so, solving for t, we have

$$t = \frac{\log(3,370,000)}{\log 2} = 21.684.$$

In Example 2 on page 151, we found the graphical approximation of between 21 and 22 days as the time for the Yonkers fine to exceed the city's annual budget.

The Natural Logarithm

When e is used as the base for exponential functions, computations are easier with the use of another logarithm function, called log base e. The log base e is used so frequently that it has its own notation: $\ln x$, read as the *natural log of x*. We make the following definition:

For $x > 0$,

$$\ln x \text{ is the power of } e \text{ that gives } x$$

or, in symbols,

$$\ln x = y \quad \text{means} \quad e^y = x,$$

and y is called the **natural logarithm** of x.

Just as the functions 10^x and $\log x$ are inverses, so are e^x and $\ln x$. The function $\ln x$ has similar properties to the common log function:

Properties of the Natural Logarithm
- By definition, $y = \ln x$ means $x = e^y$.
- In particular,

$$\ln 1 = 0 \quad \text{and} \quad \ln e = 1.$$

- The functions e^x and $\ln x$ are inverses, so they "undo" each other:

$$\ln(e^x) = x \qquad \text{for all } x$$
$$e^{\ln x} = x \qquad \text{for } x > 0.$$

- For a and b both positive and any value of t,

$$\ln(ab) = \ln a + \ln b$$
$$\ln\left(\frac{a}{b}\right) = \ln a - \ln b$$
$$\ln(b^t) = t \cdot \ln b.$$

Example 6   Solve for x:
(a) $5e^{2x} = 50$
(b) $3^x = 100$.

Solution   (a) We first divide both sides by 5 to obtain

$$e^{2x} = 10.$$

Taking the natural log of both sides, we have

$$\ln(e^{2x}) = \ln 10$$
$$2x = \ln 10$$
$$x = \frac{\ln 10}{2} \approx 1.151.$$

(b) Taking natural logs of both sides,

$$\ln(3^x) = \ln 100$$
$$x \ln 3 = \ln 100$$
$$x = \frac{\ln 100}{\ln 3} \approx 4.192.$$

For more practice with logarithms, see the Skills Review on page 219.

Misconceptions and Calculator Errors Involving Logs

It is important to know how to use the properties of logarithms. It is equally important to recognize statements that are *not* true. Beware of the following:

- $\log(a + b)$ is not the same as $\log a + \log b$
- $\log(a - b)$ is not the same as $\log a - \log b$
- $\log(ab)$ is not the same as $(\log a)(\log b)$
- $\log\left(\dfrac{a}{b}\right)$ is not the same as $\dfrac{\log a}{\log b}$
- $\log\left(\dfrac{1}{a}\right)$ is not the same as $\dfrac{1}{\log a}$.

There are no formulas to simplify either $\log(a+b)$ or $\log(a-b)$. Also the expression $\log 5x^2$ is not the same as $2 \cdot \log 5x$, because the exponent, 2, applies only to the x and not to the 5. However, it is correct to write

$$\log 5x^2 = \log 5 + \log x^2 = \log 5 + 2 \log x.$$

Using a calculator to evaluate expressions like $\log(\frac{17}{3})$ requires care. On some calculators, entering log 17/3 gives 0.410, which is incorrect. This is because the calculator assumes that you mean $(\log 17)/3$, which is not the same as $\log(17/3)$. Notice also that

$$\frac{\log 17}{\log 3} \approx \frac{1.230}{0.477} \approx 2.579,$$

which is not the same as either $(\log 17)/3$ or $\log(17/3)$. Thus, the following expressions are all different:

$$\log \frac{17}{3} \approx 0.753, \qquad \frac{\log 17}{3} \approx 0.410, \qquad \text{and} \qquad \frac{\log 17}{\log 3} \approx 2.579.$$

Justification of $\log(a \cdot b) = \log a + \log b$ and $\log(a/b) = \log a - \log b$

If a and b are both positive, we can write $a = 10^m$ and $b = 10^n$, so $\log a = m$ and $\log b = n$. Then, the product $a \cdot b$ can be written

$$a \cdot b = 10^m \cdot 10^n = 10^{m+n}.$$

Therefore $m + n$ is the power of 10 needed to give $a \cdot b$, so

$$\log(a \cdot b) = m + n,$$

which gives

$$\log(a \cdot b) = \log a + \log b.$$

Similarly, the quotient a/b can be written as

$$\frac{a}{b} = \frac{10^m}{10^n} = 10^{m-n}.$$

Therefore $m - n$ is the power of 10 needed to give a/b, so

$$\log\left(\frac{a}{b}\right) = m - n,$$

and thus

$$\boxed{\log\left(\frac{a}{b}\right) = \log a - \log b.}$$

Justification of $\log(b^t) = t \cdot \log b$

Suppose that b is positive, so we can write $b = 10^k$ for some value of k. Then

$$b^t = (10^k)^t.$$

We have rewritten the expression b^t so that the base is a power of 10. Using a property of exponents, we can write $(10^k)^t$ as 10^{kt}, so

$$b^t = (10^k)^t = 10^{kt}.$$

Therefore kt is the power of 10 which gives b^t, so

$$\log(b^t) = kt.$$

But since $b = 10^k$, we know $k = \log b$. This means

$$\log(b^t) = (\log b)t = t \cdot \log b.$$

Thus, for $b > 0$ we have

$$\boxed{\log\left(b^t\right) = t \cdot \log b.}$$

Exercises and Problems for Section 5.1

Skill Refresher

Without using logs or a calculator, solve the equations in Exercises S1–S10 if possible.

S1. $10^x = 1{,}000{,}000$

S2. $10^t = 0.01$

S3. $e^z = \sqrt{e^3}$

S4. $10^x = 1$

S5. $e^w = 0$

S6. $e^{3x} = \dfrac{1}{e^5}$

S7. $\sqrt{e^{9t}} = e^7$

S8. $10^{-x} = -1{,}000$

S9. $10^{2t} = \sqrt[4]{0.1}$

S10. $e^{3x} = \sqrt[3]{e^5}$

Exercises

Rewrite the statements in Exercises 1–6 using exponents instead of logs.

1. $\log 19 = 1.279$

2. $\log 4 = 0.602$

3. $\ln 26 = 3.258$

4. $\ln(0.646) = -0.437$

5. $\log P = t$

6. $\ln q = z$

Rewrite the statements in Exercises 7–10 using logs.

7. $10^8 = 100{,}000{,}000$

8. $e^{-4} = 0.0183$

9. $10^v = \alpha$

10. $e^a = b$

11. Evaluate without a calculator.

(a) $\log 1000$ (b) $\log \sqrt{1000}$ (c) $\log (10^0)$

(d) $\log \sqrt{10}$ (e) $\log (10^5)$ (f) $\log (10^2)$

(g) $\log \left(\dfrac{1}{\sqrt{10}}\right)$ (h) $10^{\log 100}$ (i) $10^{\log 1}$

(j) $10^{\log (0.01)}$

12. Evaluate without a calculator.

(a) $\ln 1$ (b) $\ln e^0$ (c) $\ln e^5$

(d) $\ln \sqrt{e}$ (e) $e^{\ln 2}$ (f) $\ln \left(\dfrac{1}{\sqrt{e}}\right)$

Solve the equations in Exercises 13–18 using logs.

13. $2^x = 11$

14. $(1.45)^x = 25$

15. $e^{0.12x} = 100$

16. $10 = 22(0.87)^q$

17. $48 = 17(2.3)^w$

18. $2/7 = (0.6)^{2t}$

Problems

19. Express the following in terms of x without logs.

    (a) $\log 100^x$ **(b)** $1000^{\log x}$ **(c)** $\log 0.001^x$

20. Express the following in terms of x without natural logs.

    (a) $\ln e^{2x}$ **(b)** $e^{\ln(3x+2)}$

    (c) $\ln\left(\dfrac{1}{e^{5x}}\right)$ **(d)** $\ln\sqrt{e^x}$

21. Evaluate the following pairs of expressions without using a calculator. What do you notice?

    (a) $\log(10 \cdot 100)$ and $\log 10 + \log 100$
    (b) $\log(100 \cdot 1000)$ and $\log 100 + \log 1000$
    (c) $\log\left(\dfrac{10}{100}\right)$ and $\log 10 - \log 100$
    (d) $\log\left(\dfrac{100}{1000}\right)$ and $\log 100 - \log 1000$
    (e) $\log(10^2)$ and $2\log 10$
    (f) $\log(10^3)$ and $3\log 10$

22. **(a)** Write the general formulas reflected in what you observed in Problem 21.

    (b) Apply these formulas to rewrite $\log\left(\dfrac{AB}{C}\right)^p$ at least two different ways.

23. True or false?

    (a) $\log AB = \log A + \log B$
    (b) $\dfrac{\log A}{\log B} = \log A - B$
    (c) $\log A \log B = \log A + \log B$
    (d) $p \cdot \log A = \log A^p$
    (e) $\log \sqrt{x} = \frac{1}{2}\log x$
    (f) $\sqrt{\log x} = \log(x^{1/2})$

Use properties of logarithms to solve for x in Problems 24–29. Assume a, b, M, and N are constants.

24. $\log(3 \cdot 2^x) = 8$

25. $\ln(25(1.05)^x) = 6$

26. $\ln(ab^x) = M$

27. $\log(MN^x) = a$

28. $\ln(3x^2) = 8$

29. $\log(5x^3) = 2$

30. A graph of $P = 25(1.075)^t$ is given in Figure 5.1.

    (a) What is the initial value of P (when $t = 0$)? What is the percent growth rate?
    (b) Use the graph to estimate the value of t when $P = 100$.

(c) Use logs to find the exact value of t when $P = 100$.

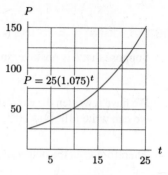

$P = 25(1.075)^t$

Figure 5.1

31. A graph of $Q = 10e^{-0.15t}$ is given in Figure 5.2.

    (a) What is the initial value of Q (when $t = 0$)? What is the continuous percent decay rate?
    (b) Use the graph to estimate the value of t when $Q = 2$.
    (c) Use logs to find the exact value of t when $Q = 2$.

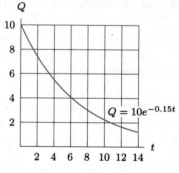

$Q = 10e^{-0.15t}$

Figure 5.2

32. Let $u = \log 2$ and $v = \log 3$. Evaluate the following expressions in terms of u and/or v. For example, $\log 9 = \log(3^2) = 2\log 3 = 2v$.

    (a) $\log 6$ **(b)** $\log 0.08$ **(c)** $\log \sqrt{\frac{3}{2}}$ **(d)** $\log 5$

33. Without using a calculator, write the following quantities in terms of $\log 15$ and/or $\log 5$.

    (a) $\log 3$ **(b)** $\log 25$ **(c)** $\log 75$

34. Find a possible formula for the exponential function S in Figure 5.3, if $R(x) = 5.1403(1.1169)^x$.

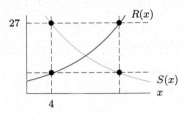

Figure 5.3

In Problems 35–51, solve the equations exactly for x or t.

35. $91 = 46(1.1)^x$

36. $84(0.74)^t = 38$

37. $e^{0.044t} = 6$

38. $200 \cdot 2^{t/5} = 355.$

39. $e^{x+4} = 10$

40. $e^{x+5} = 7 \cdot 2^x$

41. $0.4(\frac{1}{3})^{3x} = 7 \cdot 2^{-x}$

42. $\log_3 3^{5x+1} = 2$

43. $400e^{0.1x} = 500e^{0.08x}$

44. $6000 \left(\frac{1}{2}\right)^{t/15} = 1000$

45. $e^{x+4} = 10$

46. $ab^x = c$

47. $Pe^{kx} = Q$

48. $58e^{4t+1} = 30$

49. $\log(2x + 5) \cdot \log(9x^2) = 0$

50. $\log(1 - x) - \log(1 + x) = 2$

51. $\log(2x + 5) \cdot \log(9x^2) = 0$

52. Solve each of the following equations exactly for x.

   (a) $e^{2x} + e^{2x} = 1$ **(b)** $2e^{3x} + e^{3x} = b$

53. If we square a positive quantity n, we double its log: $\log(n^2) = 2 \log n$. Briefly describe what happens to the log when we double a positive quantity n.

54. Consider the exponential function $Q = r \cdot s^t$. Letting $q = \ln Q$, show that q is a linear function of t by writing it in the form $q = b + mt$. State the values of m and b.

55. The *arithmetic mean* of two numbers is half their sum, and the *geometric mean* is the square root of their product. Using log properties, show how we can think of the log of the geometric mean of v and w as the arithmetic mean of two related numbers, p and q.

56. Because they are so large, it is impossible to compare directly the two numbers[1]

$$A = 2^{2^{2^{83}}} \quad \text{and} \quad B = 3^{3^{3^{52}}}.$$

Instead, first simplify $\ln(\ln A)$ and $\ln(\ln B)$, and then use a calculator to determine which is larger, A or B.

57. Both of these numbers are slightly larger than 1:

$$A = 5^{3^{-47}} \quad \text{and} \quad B = 7^{5^{-32}}.$$

Which is larger? Explain your reasoning.

5.2 LOGARITHMS AND EXPONENTIAL MODELS

The log function is often useful when answering questions about exponential models. Logarithms "undo" exponentials—because the log is the inverse of the exponential function—so logs are used to solve many exponential equations.

Example 1   In Example 3 on page 151 we solved the equation $200(0.886^t) = 25$ graphically, where t is in thousands of years. We found that a 200 microgram sample of carbon-14 decays to 25 micrograms in approximately 17,200 years. Now solve $200(0.886)^t = 25$ using logarithms.

Solution   First, isolate the power on one side of the equation

$$200(0.886^t) = 25$$
$$0.886^t = 0.125.$$

---

[1] Adapted from Robert P. Munafo's website on large numbers. These numbers are given as examples of Class-4 numbers. A Class-3 number is too large to be evaluated exactly on a computer; a Class-4 number is one whose *logarithm* is too large to be evaluated exactly. See http://www.mrob.com/pub/index.html, accessed April 7, 2008.

Take the log of both sides, and use the fact that $\log(0.886^t) = t \log 0.886$. Then

$$\log(0.886^t) = \log 0.125$$
$$t \log 0.886 = \log 0.125,$$

so

$$t = \frac{\log 0.125}{\log 0.886} \approx 17.180 \text{ thousand years.}$$

This answer is close to the value we found from the graph, 17,200.

Example 2   The US population, P, in millions, is currently growing according to the formula[2]

$$P = 299e^{0.009t},$$

where t is in years since 2006. When is the population predicted to reach 350 million?

Solution   We want to solve the following equation for t:

$$299e^{0.009t} = 350.$$

Dividing by 299 gives

$$e^{0.009t} = \frac{350}{299},$$

so $0.009t$ is the power of e which gives $350/299$. Thus, by the definition of the natural log,

$$0.009t = \ln\left(\frac{350}{299}\right).$$

Solving for t and evaluating $\ln(350/299)$ on a calculator gives

$$t = \frac{\ln(350/299)}{0.009} = 17.5 \text{ years.}$$

The US population is predicted to reach 350 million during the year 2024.

Example 3   The population of City A begins with 50,000 people and grows at 3.5% per year. The population of City B begins with a larger population of 250,000 people but grows at the slower rate of 1.6% per year. Assuming that these growth rates hold constant, will the population of City A ever catch up to the population of City B? If so, when?

Solution   If t is time measured in years and P_A and P_B are the populations of these two cities, then

$$P_A = 50{,}000(1.035)^t \quad \text{and} \quad P_B = 250{,}000(1.016)^t.$$

We want to solve the equation

$$50{,}000(1.035)^t = 250{,}000(1.016)^t.$$

We first get the exponential terms together by dividing both sides of the equation by $50{,}000(1.016)^t$:

$$\frac{(1.035)^t}{(1.016)^t} = \frac{250{,}000}{50{,}000} = 5.$$

Since $\dfrac{a^t}{b^t} = \left(\dfrac{a}{b}\right)^t$, this gives

$$\left(\frac{1.035}{1.016}\right)^t = 5.$$

---

[2]Based on data from www.census.gov and www.cia.gov/cia/publications/factbook, accessed July 31, 2006.

Taking logs of both sides and using $\log b^t = t \log b$, we have

$$\log \left(\frac{1.035}{1.016} \right)^t = \log 5$$

$$t \log \left(\frac{1.035}{1.016} \right) = \log 5$$

$$t = \frac{\log 5}{\log(1.035/1.016)} \approx 86.865.$$

Thus, the cities' populations will be equal in just under 87 years. To check this, notice that when $t = 86.865$,

$$P_A = 50{,}000(1.035)^{86.865} = 992{,}575$$

and

$$P_B = 250{,}000(1.016)^{86.865} = 992{,}572.$$

The answers are not exactly equal because we rounded off the value of t. Rounding can introduce significant errors, especially when logs and exponentials are involved. Using $t = 86.86480867$, the computed values of P_A and P_B agree to three decimal places.

Doubling Time

Eventually, any exponentially growing quantity doubles, or increases by 100%. Since its percent growth rate is constant, the time it takes for the quantity to grow by 100% is also a constant. This time period is called the *doubling time*.

Example 4   (a) Find the time needed for the turtle population described by the function $P = 175(1.145)^t$ to double its initial size.

(b) How long does this population take to quadruple its initial size? To increase by a factor of 8?

Solution   (a) The initial size is 175 turtles; doubling this gives 350 turtles. We need to solve the following equation for t:

$$175(1.145)^t = 350$$

$$1.145^t = 2$$

$$\log \left(1.145^t \right) = \log 2$$

$$t \cdot \log 1.145 = \log 2$$

$$t = \frac{\log 2}{\log 1.145} \approx 5.119 \text{ years.}$$

We check this by noting that

$$175(1.145)^{5.119} = 350,$$

which is double the initial population. In fact, at any time it takes the turtle population about 5.119 years to double in size.

(b) Since the population function is exponential, it increases by 100% every 5.119 years. Thus it doubles its initial size in the first 5.119 years, quadruples its initial size in two 5.119 year periods, or 10.238 years, and increases by a factor of 8 in three 5.119 year periods, or 15.357 years. We check this by noting that

$$175(1.145)^{10.238} = 700,$$

or 4 times the initial size, and that

$$175(1.145)^{15.357} = 1400,$$

or 8 times the initial size.

Example 5   A population doubles in size every 20 years. What is its continuous growth rate?

Solution   We are not given the initial size of the population, but we can solve this problem without that information. Let the symbol P_0 represent the initial size of the population. We have $P = P_0 e^{kt}$. After 20 years, $P = 2P_0$, and so

$$P_0 e^{k \cdot 20} = 2P_0$$
$$e^{20k} = 2$$
$$20k = \ln 2 \qquad \text{Taking ln of both sides}$$
$$k = \frac{\ln 2}{20} \approx 0.03466.$$

Thus, the population grows at the continuous rate of 3.466% per year.

Example 6   Interest rates in Brazil have fluctuated widely since 1995: investments in Brazil in different years were expected to double in value at wildly different rates.[3] The Brazilian currency is the real.

(a) An investment purchased in May 1995 has a value, V, in reals, t years later, given by

$$V = 100{,}000 \cdot 2^t.$$

　　(i) How much was the investment worth in May 1996? 1997? 1998?
　　(ii) What is the doubling time?

(b) An investment purchased in January 2009 is expected to have value, Z, in reals, t years later, given by

$$Z = 100{,}000 \cdot 2^{t/6}.$$

　　(i) How much is it expected to be worth in January 2015? 2021?
　　(ii) What is the doubling time?

(c) Suppose an investment's value t years after 2011 is predicted to be $100{,}000 \cdot 2^{t/n}$.

　　(i) How much is the investment expected to be worth after n years?
　　(ii) What is its doubling time?

Solution   (a)　(i) May 1996 is one year after the investment began, so $t = 1$, and

$$V = 100{,}000 \cdot 2^1 = 200{,}000.$$

　　　　May 1997 is two years after the investment began, so $t = 2$, and

$$V = 100{,}000 \cdot 2^2 = 400{,}000.$$

　　　　May 1998 is three years after the investment began, so $t = 3$, and

$$V = 100{,}000 \cdot 2^3 = 800{,}000.$$

　　(ii) The value of the investment, which started at 100,000 reals, doubles each year, so the doubling time is 1 year. Since the formula is

$$V = 100{,}000 \cdot 2^t = 100{,}000(1 + 1)^t,$$

　　　　the growth rate is $1 = 100\%$ per year.

---

[3] www.latin-focus.com/latinfocus/countries/brazil/brainter.htm, accessed January 10, 2010.

(b) (i) January 2015 is six years after the investment begins, so $t = 6$, and $t/6 = 1$, giving

$$Z = 100{,}000 \cdot 2^1 = 200{,}000.$$

January 2021 is twelve years after the investment begins, so $t = 12$, and $t/6 = 2$, giving

$$Z = 100{,}000 \cdot 2^2 = 400{,}000.$$

   (ii) Note that the value of the investment doubles every 6 years, so the doubling time is 6 years. Since $Z = 100{,}000 \cdot 2^{t/6}$, when $t = 6$, the growth factor is $2^{6/6} = 2$, as expected.

(c) (i) After n years, the investment is worth $100{,}000 \cdot 2^{n/n} = 100{,}000 \cdot 2^1 = 200{,}000$.

   (ii) We see that the value of the investment doubles after the first n years, so the doubling time is n years. Algebraically, we see that when $t = n$, the growth factor becomes

$$2^{t/n} = 2^{n/n} = 2^1 = 2,$$

so we see that the investment doubles in n years.

Half-Life

Just as an exponentially growing quantity doubles in a fixed amount of time, an exponentially decaying quantity decreases by a factor of 2 in a fixed amount of time, called the *half-life* of the quantity.

Example 7   Carbon-14 decays radioactively at a constant annual rate of 0.0121%. Show that the half-life of carbon-14 is about 5728 years.

Solution   We are not given an initial amount of carbon-14, but we can solve this problem without that information. Let the symbol Q_0 represent the initial quantity of carbon-14 present. The growth rate is -0.000121 because carbon-14 is decaying. So the growth factor is $b = 1 - 0.000121 = 0.999879$. Thus, after t years the amount left will be

$$Q = Q_0(0.999879)^t.$$

We want to find how long it takes for the quantity to drop to half its initial level. Thus, we need to solve for t in the equation

$$\frac{1}{2}Q_0 = Q_0(0.999879)^t.$$

Dividing each side by Q_0, we have

$$\frac{1}{2} = 0.999879^t.$$

Taking logs

$$\log \frac{1}{2} = \log\left(0.999879^t\right)$$
$$\log 0.5 = t \cdot \log 0.999879$$
$$t = \frac{\log 0.5}{\log 0.999879} \approx 5728.143.$$

Thus, no matter how much carbon-14 there is initially, after about 5728 years, half will remain.

Similarly, we can determine the growth rate given the half-life or doubling time.

Example 8   The quantity, Q, of a substance decays according to the formula $Q = Q_0 e^{-kt}$, where t is in minutes. The half-life of the substance is 11 minutes. What is the value of k?

Solution   We know that after 11 minutes, $Q = \frac{1}{2}Q_0$. Thus, solving for k, we get

$$Q_0 e^{-k \cdot 11} = \frac{1}{2}Q_0$$

$$e^{-11k} = \frac{1}{2}$$

$$-11k = \ln\frac{1}{2}$$

$$k = \frac{\ln(1/2)}{-11} \approx 0.06301,$$

so $k = 0.063$ per minute. This substance decays at the continuous rate of 6.301% per minute.

Converting Between $Q = ab^t$ and $Q = ae^{kt}$

Any exponential function can be written in either of the two forms:

$$Q = ab^t \qquad \text{or} \qquad Q = ae^{kt}.$$

If $b = e^k$, so $k = \ln b$, the two formulas represent the same function.

Example 9   Convert the exponential function $P = 175(1.145)^t$ to the form $P = ae^{kt}$.

Solution   Since the new formula represents the same function, we want $P = 175$ when $t = 0$. Thus, substituting $t = 0$ gives $175 = ae^{k(0)} = a$, so $a = 175$. The parameter a in both functions represents the initial population. For all t,

$$175(1.145)^t = 175(e^k)^t,$$

so we must find k such that

$$e^k = 1.145.$$

Therefore k is the power of e that gives 1.145. By the definition of ln, we have

$$k = \ln 1.145 \approx 0.1354.$$

Therefore,

$$P = 175e^{0.1354t}.$$

Example 10   Convert the formula $Q = 7e^{0.3t}$ to the form $Q = ab^t$.

Solution   Using the properties of exponents,

$$Q = 7e^{0.3t} = 7(e^{0.3})^t.$$

Using a calculator, we find $e^{0.3} \approx 1.3499$, so

$$Q = 7(1.3499)^t.$$

Example 11   Assuming t is in years, find the continuous and annual percent growth rates in Examples 9 and 10.

Solution   In Example 9, the annual percent growth rate is 14.5% and the continuous percent growth rate per year is 13.54%. In Example 10, the continuous percent growth rate is 30% and the annual percent growth rate is 34.99%.

Example 12   Find the continuous percent growth rate of $Q = 200(0.886)^t$, where t is in thousands of years.

Solution   Since this function describes exponential decay, we expect a negative value for k. We want

$$e^k = 0.886.$$

Solving for k gives

$$k = \ln(0.886) = -0.12104.$$

So we have $Q = 200e^{-0.12104t}$ and the continuous growth rate is -12.104% per thousand years.

Exponential Growth Problems That Cannot Be Solved by Logarithms

Some equations with the variable in the exponent cannot be solved using logarithms.

Example 13   With t in years, the population of a country (in millions) is given by $P = 2(1.02)^t$, while the food supply (in millions of people that can be fed) is given by $N = 4 + 0.5t$. Determine the year in which the country first experiences food shortages.

Solution   The country starts to experience shortages when the population equals the number of people that can be fed—that is, when $P = N$. We attempt to solve the equation $P = N$ by using logs:

$$2(1.02)^t = 4 + 0.5t$$
$$1.02^t = 2 + 0.25t \qquad \text{Dividing by 2}$$
$$\log 1.02^t = \log(2 + 0.25t)$$
$$t \log 1.02 = \log(2 + 0.25t).$$

Unfortunately, we cannot isolate t, so, this equation cannot be solved using logs. However, we can approximate the solution of the original equation numerically or graphically, as shown in Figure 5.4. The two functions, P and N, are equal when $t \approx 199.381$. Thus, it will be almost 200 years before shortages occur.

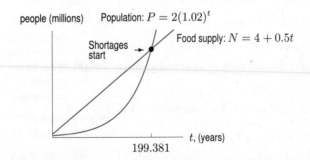

Figure 5.4: Finding the intersection of linear and exponential graphs

Exercises and Problems for Section 5.2

Skill Refresher

For Exercises S1–S4, simplify the expression if possible.

S1. $10^{-\log 5x}$

S2. $e^{-3\ln t}$

S3. $t \ln e^{t/2}$

S4. $10^{2+\log x}$

In Exercises S5–S10, solve for x.

S5. $4^x = 9$

S6. $e^x = 8$

S7. $2e^x = 13$

S8. $e^{7x} = 5e^{3x}$

S9. $\log(2x + 7) = 2$

S10. $\log(2x) = \log(x + 10)$

Exercises

For Exercises 1–2, write the exponential function in the form $y = ab^t$. Find b accurate to four decimal places. If t is measured in years, give the percent annual growth or decay rate and the continuous percent growth or decay rate per year.

1. $y = 25e^{0.053t}$

2. $y = 100e^{-0.07t}$

For Exercises 3–4, write the exponential function in the form $y = ae^{kt}$. Find k accurate to four decimal places. If t is measured in years, give the percent annual growth rate and the continuous percent growth rate per year.

3. $y = 6000(0.85)^t$

4. $y = 5(1.12)^t$

In Exercises 5–8, convert to the form $Q = ab^t$.

5. $Q = 4e^{7t}$

6. $Q = 0.3e^{0.7t}$

7. $Q = \dfrac{14}{5}e^{0.03t}$

8. $Q = e^{-0.02t}$

In Exercises 9–12, convert to the form $Q = ae^{kt}$.

9. $Q = 12(0.9)^t$

10. $Q = 16(0.487)^t$

11. $Q = 14(0.862)^{1.4t}$

12. $Q = 721(0.98)^{0.7t}$

In Exercises 13–20, give the starting value a, the growth rate r, and the continuous growth rate k.

13. $Q = 230(1.182)^t$

14. $Q = 0.181\left(e^{0.775}\right)^t$

15. $Q = 0.81(2)^t$

16. $Q = 5 \cdot 2^{t/8}$

17. $Q = 12.1 \cdot 10^{-0.11t}$

18. $Q = 40e^{(t-5)/12}$

19. $Q = 2e^{(1-3t/4)}$

20. $Q = 2^{-(t-5)/3}$

Problems

Find the doubling time in Exercises 21–24.

21. A population growing according to $P = P_0e^{0.2t}$.

22. A city is growing by 26% per year.

23. A bank account is growing by 2.7% per year.

24. A company's profits are increasing by an annual growth factor of 1.12.

Find the half-lives of the substances in Exercises 25–27.

25. Tritium, which decays at a rate of 5.471% per year.

26. Einsteinium-253, which decays at a rate of 3.406% per day.

27. A radioactive substance that decays at a continuous rate of 11% per minute.

28. You place $800 in an account that earns 4% annual interest, compounded annually. How long will it be until you have $2000?

29. (a) What annual interest rate, compounded continuously, is equivalent to an annual rate of 8%, compounded annually?

  (b) What annual interest rate, compounded annually, is equivalent to an annual rate of 6%, compounded continuously?

30. A population grows from 11000 to 13000 in three years. Assuming the growth is exponential, find the:

  (a) Annual growth rate   **(b)** Continuous growth rate

  (c) Why are your answers to parts (a) and (b) different?

31. A $5000 investment earns 7.2% annual interest, and an $8000 investment earns 5.4%, both compounded annually. How long will it take for the smaller investment to catch up to the larger one?

32. A \$9000 investment earns 5.6% annual interest, and a \$4000 investment earns 8.3%, both compounded continuously. When will the smaller catch up to the larger?

33. A population doubles in size every 15 years. Assuming exponential growth, find the

 (a) Annual growth rate   (b) Continuous growth rate

34. A population increases from 5.2 million at an annual rate of 3.1%. Find the continuous growth rate.

35. The half-life of nicotine in the body is 2 hours. What is the continuous decay rate?

36. If 17% of a radioactive substance decays in 5 hours, what is the half-life of the substance?

37. Total power generated by wind worldwide doubles every 3 years.[4] In 2008, world wind-energy generating capacity was about 90 thousand megawatts. Find the continuous growth rate and give a formula for wind generating capacity W (in thousand megawatts) as a function of t, number of years since 2008.

38. Sketch the exponential function $y = u(t)$ given that it has a starting value of 0.8 and a doubling time of 12 years. Label the axes and indicate the scale.

39. A town has 5000 people in year $t = 0$. Calculate how long it takes for the population P to double once, twice, and three times, assuming that the town grows at a constant rate of

 (a) 500 people per year.
 (b) 5% per year.

40. (a) Estimate the doubling time of the exponential function shown in Figure 5.5.
 (b) Use the doubling time to find the continuous percent growth rate and give a formula for the function.

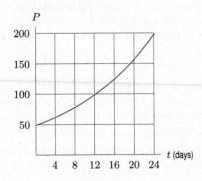

Figure 5.5

[4]World Wind Energy Report 2008.

41. (a) The quantity of caffeine in the body after drinking a cup of coffee is shown in Figure 5.6. Estimate the half-life of caffeine.
 (b) Use the half-life to find the continuous percent decay rate and give a formula for Q as function of t.

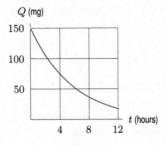

Figure 5.6

42. The temperature, H, in °F, of a cup of coffee t hours after it is set out to cool is given by the equation:

$$H = 70 + 120(1/4)^t.$$

 (a) What is the coffee's temperature initially (that is, at time $t = 0$)? After 1 hour? 2 hours?
 (b) How long does it take the coffee to cool down to 90°F? 75°F?

43. Use algebra to show that the time it takes for a quantity growing exponentially to double is independent of the starting quantity and the time. To do this, let d represent the time it takes for P to double. Show that if P becomes $2P$ at time $t + d$, then d depends only on the growth factor b, but not on the starting quantity a and time t. (Assume $P \neq 0$.)

44. Prices climb at a constant 3% annual rate.

 (a) By what percent will prices have climbed after 5 years?
 (b) How long will it take for prices to climb 25%?

45. The growth of an animal population, P, is described by the function $P = 300 \cdot 2^{t/20}$.

 (a) How large is this population in year $t = 0$? $t = 20$?
 (b) When does this population reach 1000?

46. Find values for a, b, k, s where

$$f(t) = ab^t = ae^{kt} = a \cdot 2^{t/s},$$

given that $f(-20) = 5$ and $f(40) = 30$.

47. (a) Find the time required for an investment to triple in value if it earns 4% annual interest, compounded continuously.
   (b) Now find the time required assuming that the interest is compounded annually.

48. The world's population is aging. The approximate world population age 80 or older[5] is given in Table 5.1.

   (a) Find a formula for P, the number of people in the world age 80 or older, in millions, as a function of time, t, in years since 2005. Use the form $P = ab^t$. What is the annual percent rate of increase?
   (b) Convert to the form $P = ae^{kt}$. What is the continuous percent increase per year?
   (c) Find the doubling time.

Table 5.1

t (year)	2005	2006	2007	2008	2009
P (millions)	89.144	92.175	95.309	98.550	101.901

49. Technetium-99m is a radioactive substance used to diagnose brain diseases. Its half-life is approximately 6 hours. Initially you have 200 mg of technetium-99m.

   (a) Write an equation that gives the amount of technetium-99m remaining after t hours.
   (b) Determine the number of hours needed for your sample to decay to 120 mg.
   (c) Determine the concavity of the graph that models the half-life of technetium-99m using average rates of change over intervals of length 2 between $t = 0$ and $t = 6$.

50. The US census projects the population of the state of Washington using the function $N(t) = 5.4e^{0.013t}$, where $N(t)$ is in millions and t is in years since 1995.

   (a) What is the population's continuous growth rate?
   (b) What is the population of Washington in year $t = 0$?
   (c) How many years is it before the population triples?
   (d) In what year does this model indicate a population of only one person? Is this reasonable or unreasonable?

51. In 1991, the body of a man was found in melting snow in the Alps of Northern Italy. An examination of the tissue sample revealed that 46% of the carbon-14 present in his body at the time of his death had decayed. The half-life of carbon-14 is approximately 5728 years. How long ago did this man die?

52. A manager at Saks Fifth Avenue wants to estimate the number of customers to expect on the last shopping day before Christmas. She collects data from three previous years, and determines that the crowds follow the same

general pattern. When the store opens at 10 am, 500 people enter, and the total number in the store doubles every 40 minutes. When the number of people in the store reaches 10,000, security guards need to be stationed at the entrances to control the crowds. At what time should the guards be commissioned?

53. Figure 5.7 shows the graphs of the exponential functions f and g, and the linear function, h.

   (a) Find formulas for f, g, and h.
   (b) Find the exact value(s) of x such that $f(x) = g(x)$.
   (c) Estimate the value(s) of x such that $f(x) = h(x)$.

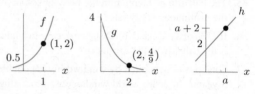

Figure 5.7

Problems 54–55 involve the Rule of 70, which gives quick estimates of the doubling time of an exponentially growing quantity. If $r\%$ is the annual growth rate of the quantity, then the Rule of 70 says

$$\text{Doubling time in years} \approx \frac{70}{r}.$$

54. Use the Rule of 70 to estimate how long it takes a $1000 investment to double if it grows at the following annual rates: 1%, 2%, 5%, 7%, 10%. Compare with the actual doubling times.

55. Using natural logs, solve for the doubling time for $Q = ae^{kt}$. Use your result to explain why the Rule of 70 works.

56. A person's blood alcohol content (BAC) is a measure of how much alcohol is in the blood stream. When a person stops drinking, the BAC declines over time as the alcohol is metabolized. The BAC, Q, of a person t minutes after the he stops drinking is given by

$$Q = Q_0e^{-t/\tau},$$

where Q_0 is the person's initial BAC and τ is known as the *elimination time*. How long does it take for a person's BAC to drop from 0.10 to 0.04 if the elimination time is 2.5 hours?

57. The size of a population, P, of toads t years after it is introduced into a wetland is given by

$$P = \frac{1000}{1 + 49(1/2)^t}.$$

   (a) How many toads are there in year $t = 0$? $t = 5$? $t = 10$?

---
[5]UN Department of Economic and Social Affairs, 2009.

(b) How long does it take for the toad population to reach 500? 750?

(c) What is the maximum number of toads that the wetland can support?

58. Write the exponential function $y = ab^t$ in the form

$$y = e^{k(t - t_0)}.$$

Give k and t_0 in terms of a and b.

59. *Gompertz functions* can be used to model population growth.[6] Solve $f(t) = 3$ for t for the particular Gompertz function

$$f(t) = 6e^{-0.5e^{-0.1t}}.$$

60. (a) Rewrite the equation $23 (1.36)^t = 85$ in the form $e^{k + rt} = e^s$. State the values of the constants $k, r,$ and s.

(b) Solve the original equation in terms of $k, r,$ and s, then give a numerical approximation.

61. (a) Rewrite the equation $1.12^t = 6.3$ in the form $10^{vt} = 10^w$. State the values of the constants v and w.

(b) Solve the original equation in terms of v and w, then give a numerical approximation.

5.3 THE LOGARITHMIC FUNCTION

The Graph, Domain, and Range of the Common Logarithm

In Section 5.1 we defined the log function (to base 10) for all positive numbers. In other words,

Domain of $\log x$ is all positive numbers.

By considering its graph in Figure 5.8, we determine the range of $y = \log x$. The log graph crosses the x-axis at $x = 1$, because $\log 1 = \log(10^0) = 0$. The graph climbs to $y = 1$ at $x = 10$, because $\log 10 = \log(10^1) = 1$. In order for the log graph to climb to $y = 2$, the value of x must reach 100, or 10^2, and in order for it to climb to $y = 3$, the value of x must be 10^3, or 1000. To reach the modest height of $y = 20$ requires x to equal 10^{20}, or 100 billion billion! The log function increases so slowly that it often serves as a benchmark for other slow-growing functions. Nonetheless, the graph of $y = \log x$ eventually climbs to any value we choose.

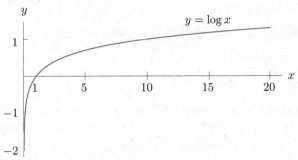

Figure 5.8: The log function grows very rapidly for $0 < x < 1$ and very slowly for $x > 1$. It has a vertical asymptote at $x = 0$ but never touches the y-axis

Although x cannot equal zero in the log function, we can choose $x > 0$ to be as small as we like. As x decreases toward zero, the values of $\log x$ get large and negative. For example,

$$\log 0.1 = \log 10^{-1} = -1,$$
$$\log 0.01 = \log 10^{-2} = -2,$$
$$\vdots \qquad \qquad \vdots$$
$$\log 0.0000001 = \log 10^{-7} = -7,$$

[6] See http://en.wikipedia.org/wiki/Gompertz_curve, accessed April 13, 2008.

and so on. So small positive values of x give exceedingly large negative values of y. The graph has a vertical asymptote at $x = 0$ and

$$\text{Range of } \log x \text{ is all real numbers.}$$

The log function is increasing and its graph is concave down, since its rate of change is decreasing.

Graphs of the Inverse Functions $y = \log x$ and $y = 10^x$

The fact that $y = \log x$ and $y = 10^x$ are inverses means that their graphs are related. Looking at Tables 5.2 and 5.3, we see that the point $(0.01, -2)$ is on the graph of $y = \log x$ and the point $(-2, 0.01)$ is on the graph of $y = 10^x$. In general, if the point (a, b) is on the graph of $y = \log x$, the point (b, a) is on the graph of $y = 10^x$. Thus, the graph of $y = \log x$ is the graph of $y = 10^x$ with x- and y-axes interchanged. If the x- and y-axes have the same scale, this is equivalent to reflecting the graph of $y = 10^x$ across the diagonal line $y = x$. See Figure 5.9.

Table 5.2   *Log function*

x	$y = \log x$
0.01	-2
0.1	-1
1	0
10	1
100	2
1000	3

Table 5.3   *Exponential function*

x	$y = 10^x$
-2	0.01
-1	0.1
0	1
1	10
2	100
3	1000

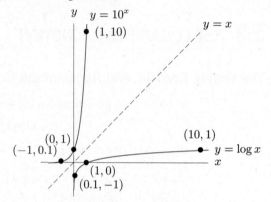

Figure 5.9: The functions $y = \log x$ and $y = 10^x$ are inverses of one another

Graph of Natural Logarithm

In addition to similar algebraic properties, the natural log and the common log have similar graphs.

Example 1   Graph $y = \ln x$ for $0 < x < 10$.

Solution   Values of $\ln x$ are in Table 5.4. Like the common log, the natural log is only defined for $x > 0$ and has a vertical asymptote at $x = 0$. The graph is slowly increasing and concave down.

Table 5.4   *Values of $\ln x$ (rounded)*

x	$\ln x$
0	Undefined
1	0
2	0.7
e	1
3	1.1
4	1.4
$\vdots$	$\vdots$

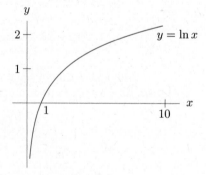

Figure 5.10: Graph of the natural logarithm

The functions $y = \ln x$ and $y = e^x$ are inverses. If the scales on the axes are the same, their graphs are reflections of one another across the line $y = x$. See Figure 5.11. For example, the vertical asymptote of the logarithm is the reflection of the horizontal asymptote of the exponential. On page 201, we see how to write asymptotes in limit notation.

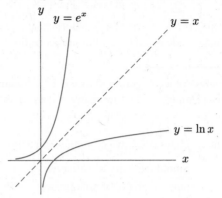

Figure 5.11: The functions $y = \ln x$ and $y = e^x$ are inverses of one another

Chemical Acidity

Logarithms are useful in measuring quantities whose magnitudes vary widely, such as acidity (pH), sound (decibels), and earthquakes (the Richter scale). In chemistry, the acidity of a liquid is expressed using pH. The acidity depends on the hydrogen ion concentration in the liquid (in moles per liter); this concentration is written [H$^+$]. The greater the hydrogen ion concentration, the more acidic the solution. The pH is defined as:

$$\text{pH} = -\log[\text{H}^+].$$

Example 2   The hydrogen ion concentration of seawater is $[\text{H}^+] = 1.1 \cdot 10^{-8}$. Estimate the pH of seawater. Then check your answer with a calculator.

Solution   We want to estimate $\text{pH} = -\log(1.1 \cdot 10^{-8})$. Since $1.1 \cdot 10^{-8} \approx 10^{-8}$ and $\log 10^{-8} = -8$, we know that

$$\text{pH} = -\log(1.1 \cdot 10^{-8}) \approx -(-8) = 8.$$

Using a calculator, we have

$$\text{pH} = -\log(1.1 \cdot 10^{-8}) = 7.959.$$

Example 3   A vinegar solution has a pH of 3. Determine the hydrogen ion concentration.

Solution   Since $3 = -\log[\text{H}^+]$, we have $-3 = \log[\text{H}^+]$. This means that $10^{-3} = [\text{H}^+]$. So the hydrogen ion concentration is 10^{-3} moles per liter.

Logarithms and Orders of Magnitude

We often compare sizes or quantities by computing their ratios. If A is twice as tall as B, then

$$\frac{\text{Height of } A}{\text{Height of } B} = 2.$$

If one object is 10 times heavier than another, we say it is an *order of magnitude* heavier. If one quantity is two factors of 10 greater than another, we say it is two orders of magnitude greater, and so on. For example, the value of a dollar is two orders of magnitude greater than the value of a penny, because we have

$$\frac{\$1}{\$0.01} = 100 = 10^2.$$

The order of magnitude is the logarithm of their ratio.

Example 4   The sound intensity of a refrigerator motor is 10^{-11} watts/cm^2. A typical school cafeteria has sound intensity of 10^{-8} watts/cm^2. How many orders of magnitude more intense is the sound of the cafeteria?

Solution   To compare the two intensities, we compute their ratio:

$$\frac{\text{Sound intensity of cafeteria}}{\text{Sound intensity of refrigerator}} = \frac{10^{-8}}{10^{-11}} = 10^{-8-(-11)} = 10^3.$$

Thus, the sound intensity of the cafeteria is 1000 times greater than the sound intensity of the refrigerator. The log of this ratio is 3. We say that the sound intensity of the cafeteria is three orders of magnitude greater than the sound intensity of the refrigerator.

Decibels

The intensity of audible sound varies over an enormous range. The range is so enormous that we consider the logarithm of the sound intensity. This is the idea behind the *decibel* (abbreviated dB). To measure a sound in decibels, the sound's intensity, I, is compared to the intensity of a standard benchmark sound, I_0. The intensity of I_0 is defined to be 10^{-16} watts/cm^2, roughly the lowest intensity audible to humans. The comparison between a sound intensity I and the benchmark sound intensity I_0 is made as follows:

$$\text{Noise level in decibels} = 10 \cdot \log\left(\frac{I}{I_0}\right).$$

For instance, let's find the decibel rating of the refrigerator in Example 4. First, we find how many orders of magnitude more intense the refrigerator sound is than the benchmark sound:

$$\frac{I}{I_0} = \frac{\text{Sound intensity of refrigerator}}{\text{Benchmark sound intensity}} = \frac{10^{-11}}{10^{-16}} = 10^5.$$

Thus, the refrigerator's intensity is 5 orders of magnitude more than I_0, the benchmark intensity. We have

$$\text{Decibel rating of refrigerator} = 10 \cdot \underbrace{\text{Number of orders of magnitude}}_{5} = 50 \text{ dB}.$$

Note that 5, the number of orders of magnitude, is the log of the ratio I/I_0. We use the log function because it "counts" the number of powers of 10. Thus if N is the decibel rating, then

$$N = 10\log\left(\frac{I}{I_0}\right).$$

Example 5   (a) If a sound doubles in intensity, by how many units does its decibel rating increase?

(b) Loud music can measure 110 dB whereas normal conversation measures 50 dB. How many times more intense is loud music than normal conversation?

Solution   (a) Let I be the sound's intensity before it doubles. Once doubled, the new intensity is $2I$. The decibel rating of the original sound is $10 \log(I/I_0)$, and the decibel rating of the new sound is $10 \log(2I/I_0)$. The difference in decibel ratings is given by

$$\text{Difference in decibel ratings} = 10 \log\left(\frac{2I}{I_0}\right) - 10 \log\left(\frac{I}{I_0}\right)$$

$$= 10\left(\log\left(\frac{2I}{I_0}\right) - \log\left(\frac{I}{I_0}\right)\right) \qquad \text{Factoring out 10}$$

$$= 10 \cdot \log\left(\frac{2I/I_0}{I/I_0}\right) \qquad \text{Using the property } \log a - \log b = \log(a/b)$$

$$= 10 \cdot \log 2 \qquad \text{Canceling } I/I_0$$

$$\approx 3.010 \text{ dB.} \qquad \text{Because } \log 2 \approx 0.3$$

Thus, if the sound intensity is doubled, the decibel rating goes up by approximately 3 dB.

(b) If I_M is the sound intensity of loud music, then

$$10 \log\left(\frac{I_M}{I_0}\right) = 110 \text{ dB.}$$

Similarly, if I_C is the sound intensity of conversation, then

$$10 \log\left(\frac{I_C}{I_0}\right) = 50 \text{ dB.}$$

Computing the difference of the decibel ratings gives

$$10 \log\left(\frac{I_M}{I_0}\right) - 10 \log\left(\frac{I_C}{I_0}\right) = 60.$$

Dividing by 10 gives

$$\log\left(\frac{I_M}{I_0}\right) - \log\left(\frac{I_C}{I_0}\right) = 6$$

$$\log\left(\frac{I_M/I_0}{I_C/I_0}\right) = 6 \qquad \text{Using the property } \log b - \log a = \log(b/a)$$

$$\log\left(\frac{I_M}{I_C}\right) = 6 \qquad \text{Canceling } I_0$$

$$\frac{I_M}{I_C} = 10^6. \qquad \log x = 6 \text{ means that } x = 10^6$$

So $I_M = 10^6 I_C$, which means that loud music is 10^6 times, or one million times, as intense as normal conversation.

Asymptotes and Limit Notation

In Section 4.3 we saw that the graph of an exponential function has a horizontal asymptote. In Figure 5.9 on page 198, we see that $y = 10^x$ has horizontal asymptote $y = 0$, because

$$\text{as } x \to -\infty, \quad 10^x \to 0.$$

Correspondingly, as x gets closer to zero, $y = \log x$ takes on larger and larger negative values. We write

$$\text{as } x \to 0^+, \qquad \log x \to -\infty.$$

The notation $x \to 0^+$ is read "x approaches zero from the right" and means that we are choosing smaller and smaller positive values of x—that is, we are sliding toward $x = 0$ through small positive values. We say the graph of the log function $y = \log x$ has a *vertical asymptote* of $x = 0$.

To describe vertical asymptotes in general, we use the notation

$$x \to a^+$$

to mean that x slides toward a from the right (that is, through values larger than a) and

$$x \to a^-$$

to mean that x slides toward a from the left (that is, through values smaller than a).

If $f(x) \to \infty$ as $x \to a^+$, we say the *limit* of $f(x)$ as x approaches a from the right is infinity,[7] and write

$$\lim_{x \to a^+} f(x) = \infty.$$

If $f(x) \to \infty$ as $x \to a^-$, we write

$$\lim_{x \to a^-} f(x) = \infty.$$

If both $\lim_{x \to a^+} f(x) = \infty$ and $\lim_{x \to a^-} f(x) = \infty$, we say the limit of $f(x)$ as x approaches a is infinity, and write

$$\lim_{x \to a} f(x) = \infty.$$

Similarly, we can write

$$\lim_{x \to a^+} f(x) = -\infty \quad \text{or} \quad \lim_{x \to a^-} f(x) = -\infty \quad \text{or} \quad \lim_{x \to a} f(x) = -\infty.$$

We summarize the information about both horizontal and vertical asymptotes:

Let $y = f(x)$ be a function and let a be a finite number.
- The graph of f has a **horizontal asymptote** of $y = a$ if

$$\lim_{x \to \infty} f(x) = a \qquad \text{or} \qquad \lim_{x \to -\infty} f(x) = a \qquad \text{or both.}$$

- The graph of f has a **vertical asymptote** of $x = a$ if

$$\lim_{x \to a^+} f(x) = \infty \quad \text{or} \quad \lim_{x \to a^+} f(x) = -\infty \quad \text{or} \quad \lim_{x \to a^-} f(x) = \infty \quad \text{or} \quad \lim_{x \to a^-} f(x) = -\infty.$$

Notice that the process of finding a vertical asymptote is different from the process for finding a horizontal asymptote. Vertical asymptotes occur where the function values grow larger and larger, either positively or negatively, as x approaches a finite value (i.e. where $f(x) \to \infty$ or $f(x) \to -\infty$ as $x \to a$). Horizontal asymptotes are determined by whether the function values approach a finite number as x takes on large positive or large negative values (i.e., as $x \to \infty$ or $x \to -\infty$).

Exercises and Problems for Section 5.3

Skill Refresher

For Exercises S1–S2, evaluate without a calculator.

S1. $\log 0.0001$

S2. $\dfrac{\log 100^6}{\log 100^2}$

---

[7]Some authors say that these limits do not exist.

For Exercises S3–S4, rewrite the exponential equation in equivalent logarithmic form.

S3. $10^5 = 100{,}000$

S4. $e^2 = 7.389$

For Exercises S5–S6, rewrite the logarithmic equation in equivalent exponential form.

S5. $-\ln x = 12$

S6. $\log(x+3) = 2$

For Exercises S7–S8, if possible, write the expression using sums and/or differences of logarithmic expressions that do not contain the logarithms of products, quotients or powers.

S7. $\ln(x(7-x)^3)$

S8. $\ln\left(\dfrac{xy^2}{z}\right)$

For Exercises S9–S10, rewrite the expression as a single logarithm.

S9. $\ln x^3 + \ln x^2$

S10. $\frac{1}{3}\log 8 - \frac{1}{2}\log 25$

Exercises

1. What is the equation of the asymptote of the graph of $y = 10^x$? Of the graph of $y = 2^x$? Of the graph of $y = \log x$?

2. What is the equation for the asymptote of the graph of $y = e^x$? Of the graph of $y = e^{-x}$? Of the graph of $y = \ln x$?

3. Without a calculator, match the functions $y = 10^x$, $y = e^x$, $y = \log x$, $y = \ln x$ with the graphs in Figure 5.12.

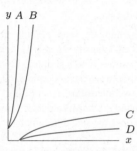

Figure 5.12

4. Without a calculator, match the functions $y = 2^x$, $y = e^{-x}$, $y = 3^x$, $y = \ln x$, $y = \log x$ with the graphs in Figure 5.13.

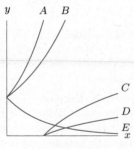

Figure 5.13

Graph the functions in Problems 5–8. Label all asymptotes and intercepts.

5. $y = 2 \cdot 3^x + 1$

6. $y = -e^{-x}$

7. $y = \log(x-4)$

8. $y = \ln(x+1)$

In Problems 9–10, graph the function. Identify any vertical asymptotes. State the domain of the function.

9. $y = 2\ln(x-3)$

10. $y = 1 - \ln(2-x)$

11. What is the value (if any) of the following?
(a) 10^{-x} as $x \to \infty$ (b) $\log x$ as $x \to 0^+$

12. What is the value (if any) of the following?
(a) e^x as $x \to -\infty$ (b) $\ln x$ as $x \to 0^+$

13. Find (a) $\displaystyle\lim_{x \to 0^+} \log x$ (b) $\displaystyle\lim_{x \to 0^-} \ln(-x)$

In Exercises 14–18, find the hydrogen ion concentration, $[H^+]$, for the substances.[8] [Hint: $\text{pH} = -\log[H^+]$.]

14. Lye, with a pH of 13.

15. Battery acid, with a pH of 1.

16. Baking soda, with a pH of 8.3.

17. Tomatoes, with a pH of 4.5.

18. Hydrochloric acid, with a pH of 0.

---

[8]Data from www.miamisci.org/ph/hhoh.html, accessed November, 2001.

Problems

19. Immediately following the gold medal performance of the US women's gymnastic team in the 1996 Olympic Games, an NBC commentator, John Tesh, said of one team member: "Her confidence and performance have grown logarithmically." He clearly thought this was an enormous compliment. Is it a compliment? Is it realistic?

20. Match the statements (a)–(d) with the functions (I)–(IV).

(a) $\lim_{x \to 0^+} f(x) = -\infty$　**(b)** $\lim_{x \to 0^-} f(x) = 0$

(c) $\lim_{x \to \infty} f(x) = \infty$　**(d)** $\lim_{x \to -\infty} f(x) = 0$

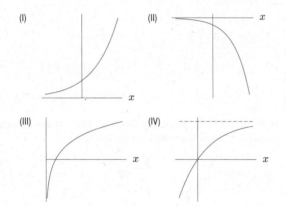

21. Match the graphs (a)–(c) to one of the functions $r(x)$, $s(x)$, $t(x)$ whose values are in the tables.

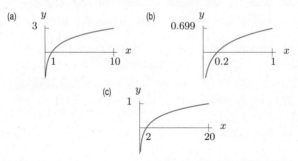

x	2	4	10
$r(x)$	1	1.301	1.699

x	0.5	5	10
$s(x)$	−0.060	0.379	0.699

x	0.1	2	100
$t(x)$	−3	0.903	6

In Problems 22–26, sound in decibels is measured by comparing the sound intensity, I, to a benchmark sound I_0 with intensity 10^{-16} watts/cm^2. Then,

$$\text{Noise level in decibels} = 10\log(I/I_0).$$

22. The noise level of a whisper is 30 dB. Compute the sound intensity of a whisper.

23. Death of hearing tissue begins to occur at a noise level of 180 dB. Compute the sound's intensity at this noise level.

24. Denver Broncos fans recently broke the world record for "loudest roar" at a sports event.[9] A crowd of 76,000 fans reached a noise level of 128.7 dB. The previous world record of 125.4 dB was held by soccer fans in Dublin, Ireland. How many times more intense was the roar of the crowd of Denver Broncos fans than the roar of the soccer fans in Ireland?

25. Sound A measures 30 decibels and sound B is 5 times as loud as sound A. What is the decibel rating of sound B to the nearest integer?

26. (a) Let D_1 and D_2 represent the decibel ratings of sounds of intensity I_1 and I_2, respectively. Using log properties, find a simplified formula for the difference between the two ratings, $D_2 - D_1$, in terms of the two intensities, I_1 and I_2.
   (b) If a sound's intensity doubles, how many decibels louder does the sound become?

Problems 27–30 use the *Richter scale* for the strength of an earthquake. The strength, W, of the seismic waves of an earthquake are compared to the strength, W_0, of the seismic waves of a standard earthquake. The Richter scale rating, M, is

$$M = \log\left(\frac{W}{W_0}\right).$$

27. In 2008 the Sichuan earthquake in China had a Richter-scale rating of 7.9. How many times more powerful were the seismic waves of the Sichuan earthquake than standard seismic waves?

28. In 1986 the worst nuclear power plant accident in history occurred in Chernobyl, Ukraine. The explosion resulted in seismic waves with a Richter scale rating of 3.5. How many times stronger were the seismic waves of the Chernobyl disaster than standard seismic waves?

---

[9] See http://www.encyclopedia.com/doc/1G1-65629077.html, accessed January 8, 2010.

29. Let M_1 and M_2 be the magnitude of two earthquakes whose seismic waves are of sizes W_1 and W_2, respectively. Using log properties, find a simplified formula for the difference $M_2 - M_1$ in terms of W_1 and W_2.

30. The 1989 earthquake in California had a rating of 7.1 on the Richter scale. How many times larger than the California earthquake were the seismic waves in the March 2005 earthquake off the coast of Sumatra, which measured 8.7 on the Richter scale? Give your answer to the nearest integer.

31. (a) Using the definition of pH on page 199, find the concentrations of hydrogen ions in solutions with

    (i) pH $= 2$ (ii) pH $= 4$ (iii) pH $= 7$

  (b) A high concentration of hydrogen ions corresponds to an acidic solution. From your answer to part (a), decide if solutions with high pHs are more or less acidic than solutions with low pHs.

32. (a) A 12-oz cup of coffee contains about $2.41 \cdot 10^{18}$ hydrogen ions. What is the concentration (moles/liter) of hydrogen ions in a 12-oz cup of coffee? [Hint: One liter equals 30.3 oz. One mole of hydrogen ions equals $6.02 \cdot 10^{23}$ hydrogen ions.]

  (b) Based on your answer to part (a) and the formula for pH, what is the pH of a 12-oz cup of coffee?

33. (a) The pH of lemon juice is about 2.3. What is the concentration of hydrogen ions in lemon juice?

  (b) A person squeezes 2 oz of lemon juice into a cup. Based on your answer to part (a), how many hydrogen ions does this juice contain?

In Problems 34–39, find possible formulas for the functions using logs or exponentials.

34.
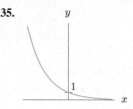

35.
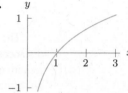

36.
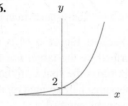

37.
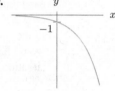

38.
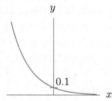

39.

40. Give the domain of $y = \dfrac{1}{2 - \sqrt{7 - e^{2t}}}$.

5.4 LOGARITHMIC SCALES

The Solar System and Beyond

Table 5.5 gives the distance from the sun to a number of different astronomical objects. The planet Mercury is 58,000,000 km from the sun, the earth is 149,000,000 km from the sun, and Pluto is 5,900,000,000 km, or almost 6 billion kilometers from the sun. The table also gives the distance to Proxima Centauri, the star closest to the sun, and to the Andromeda Galaxy, the spiral galaxy closest to our own galaxy, the Milky Way.

Table 5.5 *Distance from the sun to various astronomical objects*

Object	Distance (million km)		
Mercury	58	Saturn	1426
Venus	108	Uranus	2869
Earth	149	Neptune	4495
Mars	228	Pluto	5900
Jupiter	778	Proxima Centauri	$4.1 \cdot 10^7$
		Andromeda Galaxy	$2.4 \cdot 10^{13}$

Linear Scales

We can represent the information in Table 5.5 graphically in order to get a better feel for the distances involved. Figure 5.14 shows the distance from the sun to the first five planets on a *linear scale*, which means that the evenly spaced units shown in the figure represent equal distances. In this case, each unit represents 100 million kilometers.

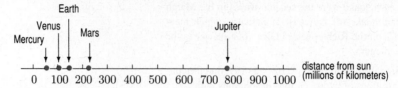

Figure 5.14: The distance from the sun of the first five planets (in millions of kilometers)

The drawback of Figure 5.14 is that the scale is too small to show all of the astronomical distances described by the table. For example, to show the distance to Pluto on this scale would require over six times the space on the page. Even worse, assuming that each 100 million km unit on the scale measures half an inch on the printed page, we would need 3 miles of paper to show the distance to Proxima Centauri!

You might conclude that we could fix this problem by choosing a larger scale. In Figure 5.15 each unit on the scale is 1 billion kilometers. Notice that all five planets shown by Figure 5.14 are crowded into the first unit of Figure 5.15; even so, the distance to Pluto barely fits. The distances to the other objects certainly don't fit. For instance, to show the Andromeda Galaxy, Figure 5.15 would have to be almost 200,000 miles long. Choosing an even larger scale will not improve the situation.

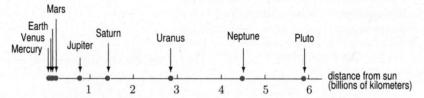

Figure 5.15: The distance to all nine planets (in billions of kilometers)

Logarithmic Scales

We conclude that the data in Table 5.5 cannot easily be represented on a linear scale. If the scale is too small, the more distant objects do not fit; if the scale is too large, the less distant objects are indistinguishable. The problem is not that the numbers are too big or too small; the problem is that the numbers vary too greatly in size.

We consider a different type of scale on which equal distances are not evenly spaced. All the objects from Table 5.5 are represented in Figure 5.16. The nine planets are still cramped, but it is possible to tell them apart. Each tick mark on the scale in Figure 5.16 represents a distance ten times larger than the one before it. This kind of scale is called *logarithmic*.

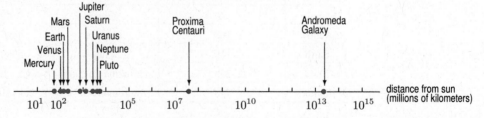

Figure 5.16: The distance from the sun (in millions of kilometers)

How Do We Plot Data on a Logarithmic Scale?

A logarithmic scale is marked with increasing powers of 10: 10^1, 10^2, 10^3, and so on. Notice that even though the distances in Figure 5.16 are not evenly spaced, the exponents are evenly spaced. Therefore the distances in Figure 5.16 are spaced according to their logarithms.

In order to plot Mercury's distance from the sun, 58 million kilometers, we use the fact that

$$10 < 58 < 100,$$

so Mercury's distance is between 10^1 and 10^2, as shown in Figure 5.16. To plot Mercury's distance more precisely, calculate $\log 58 = 1.763$, so $10^{1.763} = 58$, and use 1.763 to represent Mercury's position. See Figure 5.17.

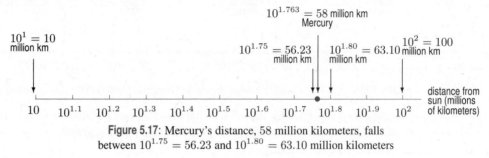

Figure 5.17: Mercury's distance, 58 million kilometers, falls between $10^{1.75} = 56.23$ and $10^{1.80} = 63.10$ million kilometers

---

Example 1   Where should Saturn be on the logarithmic scale? What about the Andromeda Galaxy?

Solution   Saturn's distance is 1426 million kilometers, so we want the exponent of 10 that gives 1426, which is

$$\log 1426 \approx 3.154119526.$$

Thus $10^{3.154} \approx 1426$, so we use 3.154 to indicate Saturn's distance.

Similarly, the distance to the Andromeda Galaxy is $2.4 \cdot 10^{13}$ million kilometers, and since

$$\log(2.4 \cdot 10^{13}) \approx 13.38,$$

we use 13.38 to represent the galaxy's distance. See Figure 5.18.

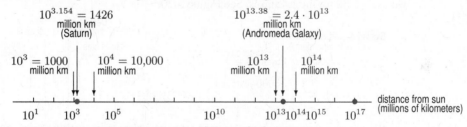

Figure 5.18: Saturn's distance is $10^{3.154}$ and the Andromeda Galaxy's distance is $10^{13.38}$

Logs of Small Numbers

The history of the world, like the distance to the stars and planets, involves numbers of vastly different sizes. Table 5.6 gives the ages of certain events[10] and the logarithms of their ages. The logarithms have been used to plot the events in Figure 5.19.

---

[10]*CRC Handbook*, 75th ed., sec. 14-8.

Table 5.6 *Ages of various events in earth's history and logarithms of the ages*

Event	Age (millions of years)	log (age)	Event	Age (millions of years)	log (age)
Man emerges	1	0	Rise of dinosaurs	245	2.39
Ape-man fossils	5	0.70	Vertebrates appear	570	2.76
Rise of cats, dogs, pigs	37	1.57	First plants	2500	3.40
Demise of dinosaurs	67	1.83	Earth forms	4450	3.65

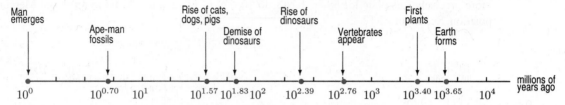

Figure 5.19: Logarithmic scale showing the ages of various events (in millions of years ago)

The events described by Table 5.6 all happened at least 1 million years ago. How do we indicate events which occurred less than 1 million years ago on the log scale?

Example 2   Where should the building of the pyramids be indicated on the log scale?

Solution   The pyramids were built about 5000 years ago, or

$$\frac{5000}{1,000,000} = 0.005 \text{ million years ago.}$$

Notice that 0.005 is between 0.001 and 0.01, that is,

$$10^{-3} < 0.005 < 10^{-2}.$$

Since

$$\log 0.005 \approx -2.30,$$

we use -2.30 for the pyramids. See Figure 5.20.

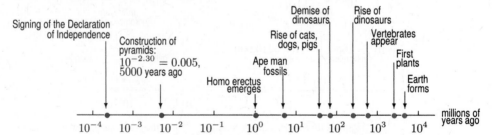

Figure 5.20: Logarithmic scale showing the ages of various events. Note that events that are less than 1 million years old are indicated by negative exponents

Another Way to Label a Log Scale

In Figures 5.19 and 5.20, the log scale has been labeled so that exponents are evenly spaced. Another way to label a log scale is with the values themselves instead of the exponents. This has been done in Figure 5.21.

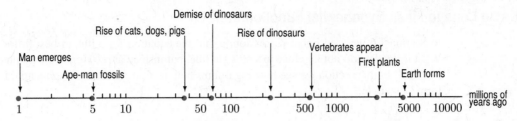

Figure 5.21: Axis labeled using actual values, not logs

Notice the characteristic way that the labels and tick marks "pile up" on each interval. The even spacing between exponents on log scales leads to uneven spacing in values. Although the values 10, 20, 30, 40, and 50 are evenly spaced, their corresponding exponents are not: $\log 10 = 1$, $\log 20 = 1.30$, $\log 30 = 1.48$, $\log 40 = 1.60$, and $\log 50 = 1.70$. Therefore, when we label an axis according to values on a scale that is spaced according to exponents, the labels get bunched up.

Log-Log Scales

Table 5.7 shows the average metabolic rate in kilocalories per day (kcal/day) for animals of different weights.[11] (A kilocalorie is the same as a standard nutritional calorie.) For instance, a 1-lb rat consumes about 35 kcal/day, whereas a 1750-lb horse consumes almost 9500 kcal/day.

Table 5.7   *The metabolic rate (in kcal/day) for animals of different weights*

Animal	Weight (lbs)	Rate (kcal/day)
Rat	1	35
Cat	8	166
Human	150	2000
Horse	1750	9470

It is not practical to plot these data on an ordinary set of axes. The values span too broad a range. However, we can plot the data using log scales for both the horizontal (weight) axis and the vertical (rate) axis. See Figure 5.22. Figure 5.23 shows a close-up view of the data point for cats to make it easier to see how the labels work. Once again, notice the characteristic piling up of labels and gridlines. This happens for the same reason as in Figure 5.21.

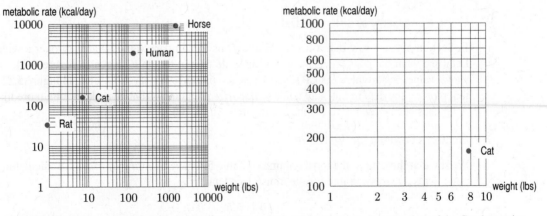

Figure 5.22: Metabolic rate (in kcal/hr) plotted against body weight   Figure 5.23: A close-up view of the Cat data point

[11] *The New York Times*, January 11, 1999.

Using Logs to Fit an Exponential Function to Data

In Section 1.6 we used linear regression to find the equation for a line of best fit for a set of data. What if the data do not lie close to a straight line, but instead approximate the graph of some other function? In this section we see how logarithms help us fit data with an exponential function of the form $Q = a \cdot b^t$.

Sales of Compact Discs

Table 5.8 shows the fall in the sales of vinyl long-playing records (LPs) and the rise of compact discs (CDs) during for the years 1982 through 1993.[12]

Table 5.8 *CD and LP sales*

t, years since 1982	c, CDs (millions)	l, LPs (millions)
0	0	244
1	0.8	210
2	5.8	205
3	23	167
4	53	125
5	102	107
6	150	72
7	207	35
8	287	12
9	333	4.8
10	408	2.3
11	495	1.2

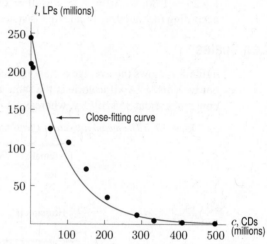

Figure 5.24: The number of LPs sold, l, as a function of number of CDs sold, c

From Table 5.8, we see that as CD sales rose dramatically during the 1980s and early 1990s, LP sales declined equally dramatically. Figure 5.24 shows the number of LPs sold in a given year as a function of the number of CDs sold that year.

Using a Log Scale to Linearize Data

In Section 5.4, we saw that a log scale allows us to compare values that vary over a wide range. Let's see what happens when we use a log scale to plot the data shown in Figure 5.24. Table 5.9 shows values $\log l$, where l is LP sales. These are plotted against c, CD sales, in Figure 5.25. Notice that plotting the data in this way tends to *linearize* the graph—that is, make it look more like a line. A line has been drawn in to emphasize the trend in the data.

Finding a Formula for the Curve

We say that the data in the third column of Table 5.9 have been *transformed*. A calculator or computer gives a regression line for the transformed data:[13]

$$y = 5.52 - 0.011c.$$

---

[12]Data from Recording Industry Association of America, Inc., 1998.

[13]The values obtained by a computer or another calculator may vary slightly from the ones given.

Table 5.9   *Values of* $y = \ln l$ *and* c.

c, CDs	l, LPs	$y = \ln l$
0	244	5.50
0.8	210	5.35
5.8	205	5.32
23	167	5.12
53	125	4.83
102	107	4.67
150	72	4.28
207	35	3.56
287	12	2.48
333	4.8	1.57
408	2.3	0.83
495	1.2	0.18

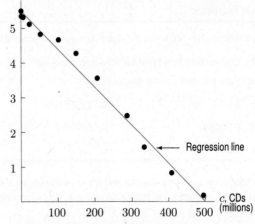

Figure 5.25: The y-axis of this graph gives the natural log of LP sales

Notice that this equation gives y in terms of c. To transform the equation back to our original variables, l and c, we substitute $\ln l$ for y, giving

$$\ln l = 5.52 - 0.011c.$$

We solve for l by raising e to both sides:

$$e^{\ln l} = e^{5.52 - 0.011c}$$
$$= (e^{5.52})(e^{-0.011c}). \qquad \text{Using an exponent rule}$$

Since $e^{\ln l} = l$ and $e^{5.52} \approx 250$, we have

$$l = 250e^{-0.011c}.$$

This is the equation of the curve in Figure 5.24.

Fitting an Exponential Function to Data

In general, to fit an exponential formula, $N = ae^{kt}$, to a set of data of the form (t, N), we use three steps. First, we transform the data by taking the natural log of both sides and making the substitution $y = \ln N$. This leads to the equation

$$y = \ln N = \ln\left(ae^{kt}\right)$$
$$= \ln a + \ln e^{kt}$$
$$= \ln a + kt.$$

Setting $b = \ln a$ gives a linear equation with k as the slope and b as the y-intercept:

$$y = b + kt.$$

Secondly, we can now use linear regression on the variables t and y. (Remember that $y = \ln N$.) Finally, as step three, we transform the linear regression equation back into our original variables by substituting $\ln N$ for y and solving for N.

Exercises and Problems for Section 5.4

Skill Refresher

In Exercises S1–S6, write the numbers in scientific notation.

S1. One million four hundred fifty-five thousand

S2. Four hundred twenty three billion

S3. 64.7×10^3 **S4.** 12,310,000

S5. 0.00036   **S6.** 0.00471

In Exercises S7–S10, without a calculator, determine between which two powers of ten the following numbers lie.

S7. 12,500   **S8.** 0.000881

S9. $\frac{1}{3}$ **S10.** $3,850 \cdot 10^8$

Exercises

In Exercises 1–4, you wish to graph the quantities on a standard piece of paper. On which should you use a logarithmic scale? On which a linear scale? Why?

1. The wealth of 20 different people, one of whom is a multi-billionaire.

2. The number of diamonds owned by 20 people, one of whom is a multi-billionaire.

3. The number of meals per week eaten in restaurants for a random sample of 20 people worldwide.

4. The number of tuberculosis bacteria in 20 different people, some never exposed to the disease, some slightly exposed, some with mild cases, and some dying of it.

5. (a) Use a calculator to fill in the following tables (round to 4 decimal digits).

n	1	2	3	4	5	6	7	8	9
$\log n$									

n	10	20	30	40	50	60	70	80	90
$\log n$									

(b) Using the results of part (a), plot the integer points 2 through 9 and the multiples of 10 from 20 to 90 on the log scaled axis shown in Figure 5.26.

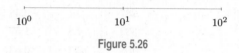

Figure 5.26

For the tables in Exercises 6–8,

(a) Use linear regression to find a linear function $y = b + mx$ that fits the data. Record the correlation coefficient.

(b) Use linear regression on the values x and $\ln y$ to fit a function of the form $\ln y = b + mx$. Record the correlation coefficient. Convert to an exponential function $y = ae^{kx}$.

(c) Compare the correlation coefficients. Graph the data and the two functions to assess which function fits best.

6.

x	y
30	70
85	120
122	145
157	175
255	250
312	300

7.

x	y
8	23
17	150
23	496
26	860
32	2720
37	8051

8.

x	y
3.2	35
4.7	100
5.1	100
5.5	150
6.8	200
7.6	300

Problems

9. The signing of the Declaration of Independence is marked on the log scale in Figure 5.20 on page 208. To two decimal places, what is its position?

10. (a) Draw a line segment about 5 inches long. On it, choose an appropriate linear scale and mark points that represent the integral powers of two from zero to the sixth power. What is true about the location of the points as the exponents get larger?

(b) Draw a second line segment. Repeat the process in (a) but this time use a logarithmic scale so that the units are now powers of ten. What do you notice about the location of these points?

11. Figure 5.27 shows the prices of seven different items, with the scale markings representing the logarithm of the price in dollars. Give the approximate price of each item, and explain why a log scale was necessary.

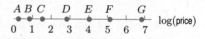

Figure 5.27

12. Microfinance refers to financial services, such as loans, offered to people with very low incomes. Table 5.10 shows the number of microborrowers in 2006.[14]

(a) Plot the data (in millions of borrowers) on a linear scale.

(b) Plot the data on a logarithmic scale.

(c) Which scale is more appropriate? Why?

Table 5.10

Region	Borrowers (millions)
A: Africa	8.4
B: Asia	112.7
C: Eastern Europe and Central Asia	3.4
D: Latin America and the Caribbean	6.8
E: Middle East and North Africa	1.7
F: North America and Western Europe	0.05

13. The usual distances for track (running) events are 100 meters, 200 meters, 400 meters, 800 meters, 1500 meters, 3000 meters, 5000 meters, and 10,000 meters.

(a) Plot the length of each track event on a linear scale.

(b) Plot the length of each track event on a logarithmic scale.

(c) Which scale, (a) or (b), is more useful to the runner?

(d) On each figure identify the point corresponding to 50 meters.

14. Table 5.11 shows the numbers of deaths in 2006 due to various causes in the US.[15]

(a) Explain why a log scale is necessary to plot the data from Table 5.11.

(b) Find the log of each value given.

(c) Plot the data using a log scale. Label each point with the related cause.

Table 5.11

Cause	Deaths
Scarlet fever	2
Whooping cough	9
Asthma	3613
HIV	12,113
Kidney diseases	46,095
Accidents	121,599
Malignant neoplasms	559,888
Cardiovascular disease	823,746
All causes	2,426,264

15. Table 5.12 shows the dollar value of some items in 2004. Plot and label these values on a log scale.

Table 5.12

Item	Dollar value	Item	Dollar value
Pack of gum	0.50	New house	264,400
Movie ticket	9.00	Lottery winnings	100 million
New computer	1200	Bill Gates' worth	46.6 bn
Year at college	27,500	National debt	7,500 bn
Luxury car	60,400	US GDP	11,700 bn

16. Table 5.13 shows the sizes of various organisms. Plot and label these values on a log scale.

Table 5.13

Animal	Size (cm)	Animal	Size (cm)
Virus	0.0000005	Domestic cat	60
Bacterium	0.0002	Wolf (with tail)	200
Human cell	0.002	Thresher shark	600
Ant	0.8	Giant squid	2200
Hummingbird	12	Sequoia	7500

17. (a) Plot the data in Table 5.14.

(b) What kind of function might the data from part (a) represent?

(c) Now plot $\log y$ versus x instead of y versus x. What do you notice?

Table 5.14

x	0.2	1.3	2.1	2.8	3.4	4.5
y	5.7	12.3	21.4	34.8	52.8	113.1

18. (a) Complete the Table 5.15 with values of $y = 3^x$.

(b) Complete Table 5.16 with values for $y = \log(3^x)$. What kind of function is this?

(c) Complete tables for $f(x) = 2 \cdot 5^x$ and $g(x) = \log(2 \cdot 5^x)$. What kinds of functions are these?

(d) What seems to be true about a function which is the logarithm of an exponential function? Is this true in general?

Table 5.15

x	0	1	2	3	4	5
$y = 3^x$						

Table 5.16

x	0	1	2	3	4	5
$y = \log(3^x)$						

---

[14]Based on data in Daley-Harris, *State of the Microsummit Campaign Report 2007*, p. 22.
[15]www.cdc.gov/nchs/data/nvsr/nvsr58/nvsr58_01.pdf, accessed May 30, 2010.

19. Repeat part (b) and (c) of Problem 18 using the natural log function. Is your answer to part (d) the same?

20. Table 5.17 shows newspapers' share of the expenditure of national advertisers. Using the method of Problem 22, fit an exponential function of the form $y = ae^{kx}$ to the data, where y is percent share and x is the number of years since 1950.

Table 5.17   *Newspapers' share of advertising*

	1950	1960	1970	1980	1990	1992
x	0	10	20	30	40	42
y	16.0	10.8	8.0	6.7	5.8	5.0

21. To study how recognition memory decreases with time, the following experiment was conducted. The subject read a list of 20 words slowly aloud, and later, at different time intervals, was shown a list of 40 words containing the 20 words that he or she had read. The percentage, P, of words recognized was recorded as a function of t, the time elapsed in minutes. Table 5.18 shows the averages for 5 different subjects.[16] This is modeled by $P = a \ln t + b$.

(a) Find $\ln t$ for each value of t, and then use regression on a calculator or computer to estimate a and b.

(b) Graph the data points and regression line on a coordinate system of P against $\ln t$.

(c) When does this model predict that the subjects will recognize no words? All words?

(d) Graph the data points and curve $P = a \ln t + b$ on a coordinate system with P against t, with $0 \le t \le 10,500$.

Table 5.18   *Percentage of words recognized*

t, min	5	15	30	60	120	240
$P\%$	73.0	61.7	58.3	55.7	50.3	46.7
t, min	480	720	1440	2880	5760	10,080
$P\%$	40.3	38.3	29.0	24.0	18.7	10.3

22. Table 5.19 shows the value, y, of US imports from China with x in years since 2002.

(a) Find a formula for a linear function $y = b + mx$ that approximates the data.

(b) Find $\ln y$ for each y value, and use the x and $\ln y$ values to find a formula for a linear function $\ln y = b + mx$ that approximates the data.

(c) Use the equation in part (b) to find an exponential function of the form $y = ae^{kx}$ that fits the data.

Table 5.19   *Value of US imports from China in millions of dollars*

	2002	2003	2004	2005	2006	2007	2008
x	0	1	2	3	4	5	6
y	125,193	152,436	196,682	243,470	287,774	321,443	337,7

23. Table 5.20 gives the length ℓ (in cm) and weight w (in gm) of 16 different fish known as threadfin bream (*Nemipterus marginatus*) found in the South China Sea.[17]

(a) Let $W = \ln w$ and $L = \ln \ell$. For these sixteen data points, plot W on the vertical axis and L on the horizontal axis. Describe the resulting scatterplot.

(b) Fitting a line to the scatterplot you drew in part (a), find a possible formula for W in terms of L.

(c) Based on your formula for part (b), find a possible formula for w in terms of ℓ.

(d) Comment on your formula, keeping in mind what you know about units as well the typical relationship between weight, volume, and length.

Table 5.20   *Length and weight of fish*

Type	1	2	3	4	5	6	7	8
ℓ	8.1	9.1	10.2	11.9	12.2	13.8	14.8	15.7
w	6.3	9.6	11.6	18.5	26.2	36.1	40.1	47.3
Type	9	10	11	12	13	14	15	16
ℓ	16.6	17.7	18.7	19.0	20.6	21.9	22.9	23.5
w	65.6	69.4	76.4	82.5	106.6	119.8	169.2	173.3

24. A light, flashing regularly, consists of cycles, each cycle having a dark phase and a light phase. The frequency of this light is measured in cycles per second. As the frequency is increased, the eye initially perceives a series of flashes of light, then a coarse flicker, a fine flicker, and ultimately a steady light. The frequency at which the flickering disappears is called the fusion frequency.[18] Table 5.21 shows the results of an experiment[19] in which the fusion frequency F was measured as a function of the light intensity I. It is modeled by $F = a \ln I + b$.

(a) Find $\ln I$ for each value of I, and then use linear regression on a calculator or computer to estimate a and b in the equation $F = a \ln I + b$.

(b) Plot F against $\ln I$, showing the data points and the line.

---

[16]Adapted from D. Lewis, *Quantitative Methods in Psychology* (New York: McGraw-Hill, 1960).

[17]Data taken from *Introduction to Tropical Fish Stock Assessment* by Per Sparre, Danish Institute for Fisheries Research, and Siebren C. Venema, FAO Fisheries Department, available at http://www.fao.org/docrep/W5449E/w5449e00.htm. This source cites the following original reference: Pauly, D., 1983. Some simple methods for the assessment of tropical fish stocks.

[18]R. S. Woodworth, *Experimental Psychology* (New York: Holt and Company, 1948).

[19]D. Lewis, *Quantitative Methods in Psychology* (New York: McGraw-Hill, 1960).

(c) Plot F against I, showing the data points and the curve and give its equation.

(d) The units of I are arbitrary, that is, not given. If the units of I were changed, which of the constants a and b would be affected, and in what way?

Table 5.21   *Fusion frequency, F, as a function of the light intensity, I*

I	0.8	1.9	4.4	10.0	21.4	48.4	92.5	218.7	437.3	980.0
F	8.0	12.1	15.2	18.5	21.7	25.3	28.3	31.9	35.2	38.2

CHAPTER SUMMARY

- **Logarithms**
  Common log: $y = \log x$ means $10^y = x$.
  $\log 10 = 1, \log 1 = 0$.
  Natural log: $y = \ln x$ means $e^y = x$.
  $\ln e = 1, \ln 1 = 0$.

- **Properties of Logs**

$$\log(ab) = \log a + \log b \qquad \ln(ab) = \ln a + \ln b.$$
$$\log(a/b) = \log a - \log b \qquad \ln(a/b) = \ln a - \ln b.$$
$$\log(b^t) = t \log b \qquad \ln(b^t) = t \ln b.$$
$$\log(10^x) = 10^{\log x} = x \qquad \ln(e^x) = e^{\ln x} = x.$$

- **Converting Between Base b and Base e**
  If $Q = ab^t$ and $Q = ae^{kt}$, then $k = \ln b$.

- **Solving Equations Using Logs**
  Solve equations such as $ab^t = c$ and $ae^{kt} = c$ using logs.
  Not all exponential equations can be solved with logs, e.g. $2^t = 3 + t$.

- **Logarithmic Functions**
  Graph; domain; range; concavity; asymptotes.

- **Applications of Logarithms**
  Doubling time; half life;
  Chemical acidity; orders of magnitude; decibels.

- **Logarithmic Scales**
  Plotting data; log-log scales. Linearizing data and fitting curves to data using logs.

- **Limits and Limits from the Right and from the Left**

REVIEW EXERCISES AND PROBLEMS FOR CHAPTER FIVE

Exercises

In Exercises 1–2, convert to the form $Q = ab^t$.

1. $Q = 7e^{-10t}$ **2.** $Q = 5e^t$

In Exercises 3–6, convert to the form $Q = ae^{kt}$.

3. $Q = 4 \cdot 7^t$ **4.** $Q = 2 \cdot 3^t$
5. $Q = 4 \cdot 8^{1.3t}$ **6.** $Q = 973 \cdot 6^{2.1t}$

Solve the equations in Exercises 7–22 exactly if possible.

7. $1.04^t = 3$ **8.** $e^{0.15t} = 25$
9. $3(1.081)^t = 14$ **10.** $40e^{-0.2t} = 12$
11. $5(1.014)^{3t} = 12$ **12.** $5(1.15)^t = 8(1.07)^t$
13. $5(1.031)^x = 8$ **14.** $4(1.171)^x = 7(1.088)^x$
15. $3 \log(2x + 6) = 6$ **16.** $1.7(2.1)^{3x} = 2(4.5)^x$
17. $3^{4 \log x} = 5$ **18.** $100^{2x+3} = \sqrt[3]{10{,}000}$
19. $13e^{0.081t} = 25e^{0.032t}$ **20.** $87e^{0.066t} = 3t + 7$

21. $\dfrac{\log x^2 + \log x^3}{\log(100x)} = 3$

22. $\log x + \log(x - 1) = \log 2$

In Exercises 23–25, simplify fully.

23. $\log\left(100^{x+1}\right)$ **24.** $\ln\left(e \cdot e^{2+M}\right)$

25. $\ln(A + B) - \ln(A^{-1} + B^{-1})$

In Exercises 26–31, state the domain of the function and identify any vertical asymptote of its graph. You need not graph the function.

26. $y = \ln(x + 8)$ **27.** $y = \log(x - 20)$
28. $y = \log(12 - x)$ **29.** $y = \ln(300 - x)$
30. $y = \ln\left(x - e^2\right)$ **31.** $y = \log(x + 15)$

In Exercises 32–37, say where you would mark the given animal lifespan on an inch scale, where 0 inches represents $10^0 = 1$ year and 5 inches represents $10^5 = 100,000$ years. Give your answer to the nearest tenth of an inch.[20]

32. A colony of quaking aspen in Utah is estimated to be 80,000 years old.

33. A bristlecone pine in California named Methuselah is es-

timated by ring count to be 4838 years old.

34. A specimen of antarctic sponge is estimated to be 1550 years old.

35. The Puget Sound saltwater clam called a geoduck can live for 160 years.

36. The oldest recorded dog lived 29 years.

37. The common house mouse can live 4 years in captivity.

Problems

38. Suppose that $x = \log A$ and that $y = \log B$. Write the following expressions in terms of x and y.

(a) $\log(AB)$
(b) $\log(A^3 \cdot \sqrt{B})$
(c) $\log(A - B)$
(d) $\dfrac{\log A}{\log B}$
(e) $\log \dfrac{A}{B}$
(f) AB

39. Let $p = \ln m$ and $q = \ln n$. Write the following expressions in terms of p and/or q without using logs.

(a) $\ln(nm^4)$
(b) $\ln\left(\dfrac{1}{n}\right)$
(c) $\dfrac{\ln m}{\ln n}$
(d) $\ln(n^3)$

40. Let $x = 10^U$ and $y = 10^V$. Write the following expressions in terms of U and/or V without using logs.

(a) $\log xy$
(b) $\log\left(\dfrac{x}{y}\right)$
(c) $\log x^3$
(d) $\log\left(\dfrac{1}{y}\right)$

41. Solve the following equations. Give approximate solutions if exact ones can't be found.

(a) $e^{x+3} = 8$
(b) $4(1.12^x) = 5$
(c) $e^{-0.13x} = 4$
(d) $\log(x - 5) = 2$
(e) $2\ln(3x) + 5 = 8$
(f) $\ln x - \ln(x-1) = 1/2$
(g) $e^x = 3x + 5$
(h) $3^x = x^3$
(i) $\ln x = -x^2$

42. Solve for x exactly.

(a) $\dfrac{3^x}{5^{x-1}} = 2^{x-1}$
(b) $-3 + e^{x+1} = 2 + e^{x-2}$
(c) $\ln(2x - 2) - \ln(x - 1) = \ln x$
(d) $9^x - 7 \cdot 3^x = -6$
(e) $\ln\left(\dfrac{e^{4x} + 3}{e}\right) = 1$
(f) $\dfrac{\ln(8x) - 2\ln(2x)}{\ln x} = 1$

In Problems 43–46, , the Richter scale ratings for two earthquakes are M_1 and M_2, with $M_2 > M_1$. If the earthquakes have seismic waves of sizes W_1 and W_2, respectively, then

$$M_2 - M_1 = \log\left(\frac{W_2}{W_1}\right).$$

How many times greater than the smaller one are the seismic waves for the larger one?

43. $M_1 = 4.2$ and $M_2 = 6.4$

44. $M_1 = 5.3$ and $M_2 = 5.8$

45. $M_1 = 4.4$ and $M_2 = 5.6$

46. $M_1 = 5.7$ and $M_2 = 8.1$

47. With t in years, the formulas for dollar balances of two bank accounts are:

$$f(t) = 1100(1.05)^t \quad \text{and} \quad g(t) = 1500e^{0.05t}.$$

(a) Describe in words the bank account modeled by f.
(b) Describe the account modeled by g. State the effective annual rate.
(c) What continuous interest rate has the same effective growth rate as f?

48. (a) Let $B = 5000(1.06)^t$ give the balance of a bank account after t years. If the formula for B is written $B = 5000e^{kt}$, estimate the value of k correct to four decimal places. What is the financial meaning of k?

(b) The balance of a bank account after t years is given by the formula $B = 7500e^{0.072t}$. If the formula for B is written $B = 7500b^t$, find b exactly, and give the value of b correct to four decimal places. What is the financial meaning of b?

49. The number of bacteria present in a culture after t hours is given by the formula $N = 1000e^{0.69t}$.

(a) How many bacteria will there be after $1/2$ hour?
(b) How long before there are 1,000,000 bacteria?
(c) What is the doubling time?

---

[20]From http://en.wikipedia.org/wiki/Maximum_life_span and http://en.wikipedia.org/wiki/List_of_long-living_organisms, accessed June, 2010.

50. In 2010, the population of the country Erehwon was 50 million people and increasing by 2.9% every year. The population of the country Ecalpon, on other hand, was 45 million people and increasing by 3.2% every year.

(a) For each country, write a formula expressing the population as a function of time t, where t is the number of years since 2010.

(b) Find the value(s) of t, if any, when the two countries have the same population.

(c) When is the population of Ecalpon double that of Erehwon?

51. The price $P(t) = 5(2)^{t/7}$ of a good is rising due to inflation, where t is time in years.

(a) What is the doubling time?

(b) What is the annual inflation rate?

52. Let $P = 15(1.04)^t$ give the population (in thousands) of a town, with t in years.

(a) Describe the population growth in words.

(b) If the formula for P is written $P = 15(b)^{12t}$, find b exactly. What is the meaning of b in the context of the population?

(c) If the formula for P is written $P = 15(2)^{t/c}$, find the value of c correct to 2 decimals. What is the meaning of c in this context?

In Problems 53–55, use $v(t) = 20e^{0.2t}$ and $w(t) = 12e^{0.22t}$.

53. Solve $v(t) = 30$ exactly.

54. Solve $3v(2t) = 2w(3t)$ exactly.

55. Find the doubling time of w.

56. A calculator confirms that $5 \approx 10^{0.7}$. Show how to use this fact to approximate the value of $\log 25$.

57. (a) What are the domain and range of $f(x) = 10^x$? What is the asymptote of $f(x) = 10^x$?

(b) What does your answer to part (a) tell you about the domain, range, and asymptotes of $g(x) = \log x$?

58. What is the domain of $y = \ln(x^2 - x - 6)$?

59. (a) Plot the data given by Table 5.22. What kind of function might fit this data well?

(b) Using the substitution $z = \ln x$, transform the data in Table 5.22, and compile your results into a new table. Plot the transformed data as $\ln x$ versus y.

(c) What kind of function gives a good fit to the plot you made in part (b)? Find a formula for y in terms of z that fits the data well.

(d) Using the formula from part (c), find a formula for y in terms of x that gives a good fit to the data in Table 5.22.

(e) What does your formula from part (d) tell you about x as a function of y (as opposed to y as a function of x)?

Table 5.22

x	0.21	0.55	1.31	3.22	5.15	12.48
y	-11	-2	6.5	16	20.5	29

60. Radioactive carbon-14 decays according to the function $Q(t) = Q_0 e^{-0.000121t}$ where t is time in years, $Q(t)$ is the quantity remaining at time t, and Q_0 is the amount of present at time $t = 0$. Estimate the age of a skull if 23% of the original quantity of carbon-14 remains.

61. Suppose 2 mg of a drug is injected into a person's bloodstream. As the drug is metabolized, the quantity diminishes at the continuous rate of 4% per hour.

(a) Find a formula for $Q(t)$, the quantity of the drug remaining in the body after t hours.

(b) By what percent does the drug level decrease during any given hour?

(c) The person must receive an additional 2 mg of the drug whenever its level has diminished to 0.25 mg. When must the person receive the second injection?

(d) When must the person receive the third injection?

62. A rubber ball is dropped onto a hard surface from a height of 6 feet, and it bounces up and down. At each bounce it rises to 90% of the height from which it fell.

(a) Find a formula for $h(n)$, the height reached by the ball on bounce n.

(b) How high will the ball bounce on the 12th bounce?

(c) How many bounces before the ball rises no higher than an inch?

63. Oil leaks from a tank. At hour $t = 0$ there are 250 gallons of oil in the tank. Each hour after that, 4% of the oil leaks out.

(a) What percent of the original 250 gallons has leaked out after 10 hours? Why is it less than $10 \cdot 4\% = 40\%$?

(b) If $Q(t) = Q_0 e^{kt}$ is the quantity of oil remaining after t hours, find the value of k. What does k tell you about the leaking oil?

64. Before the advent of computers, logarithms were calculated by hand. Various tricks were used to evaluate different logs. One such trick exploits the fact that $2^{10} \approx 1000$. (It actually equals 1024.) Using this fact and the log properties, show that

(a) $\log 2 \approx 0.3$ (b) $\log 7 \approx 0.85$

65. A googol is the number 1 followed by 100 zeros, or 10^{100}. A googolplex is the number 1 followed by a googol zeros, or 10^{googol}. Evaluate:

   (a) $\sqrt{\log(\text{googol})}$ **(b)** $\log \sqrt{\text{googol}}$

   (c) $\sqrt{\log(\text{googolplex})}$

66. Since $e = 2.718\ldots$ we know that $2 < e < 3$, which

means that $2^2 < e^2 < 3^2$. Without using a calculator, explain why

   (a) $1 < \ln 3 < 2$ **(b)** $1 < \ln 4 < 2$

67. Simplify the expression $\sqrt{1000^{\frac{1}{12} \cdot \log k}}$. Your answer should be exact and should not involve exponents or logs, though it may involve radicals.

CHECK YOUR UNDERSTANDING

Are the statements in Problems 1–37 true or false? Give an explanation for your answer.

1. The log of 2000 is less than 3.

2. The inverse of $y = \ln x$ is $y = e^x$.

3. If $2^x = 1024$ then $x = 10$.

4. If a quantity grew to 4 times its original amount in 8 hours then its doubling time is one-half hour.

5. If the function $y = ab^t$ is converted to the form $y = ae^{kt}$, k is always equal to $\ln b$.

6. If x is a positive number, $\log x$ is the exponent of 10 that gives x.

7. If $10^y = x$ then $\log x = y$.

8. The quantity 10^{-k} is a negative number when k is positive.

9. For any n, we have $\log(10^n) = n$.

10. If $n > 0$, then $10^{\log n} = n$.

11. If a and b are positive, $\log\left(\dfrac{a}{b}\right) = \dfrac{\log a}{\log b}$.

12. If a and b are positive, $\ln(a + b) = \ln a + \ln b$.

13. For any value a, $\log a = \ln a$.

14. For any value x, $\ln(e^{2x}) = 2x$.

15. The function $y = \log x$ has an asymptote at $y = 0$.

16. The graph of the function $y = \log x$ is concave down.

17. The reflected graph of $y = \log x$ across the line $y = x$ is the graph of $y = 10^x$.

18. If $y = \log \sqrt{x}$ then $y = \frac{1}{2}\log x$.

19. The function $y = \log(b^t)$ is always equal to $y = (\log b)^t$.

20. The values of $\ln e$ and $\log 10$ are both 1.

21. If $7.32 = e^t$ then $t = \dfrac{7.32}{e}$.

22. If $50(0.345)^t = 4$, then $t = \dfrac{\log(4/50)}{\log 0.345}$.

23. If $ab^t = n$, then $t = \dfrac{\log(n/a)}{\log b}$.

24. The doubling time of a quantity $Q = Q_0 e^{kt}$ is the time it takes for any t-value to double.

25. The half-life of a quantity is the time it takes for the quantity to be reduced by half.

26. If the half-life of a substance is 5 hours then there will be $\frac{1}{4}$ of the substance in 25 hours.

27. If $y = 6(3)^t$, then $y = 6e^{(\ln 3)t}$.

28. If a population doubles in size every 20 years, its annual continuous growth rate is 20%.

29. If $Q = Q_0 e^{kt}$, then $t = \dfrac{\ln(Q/Q_0)}{k}$.

30. Log scales provide a way to graph quantities that have vastly different magnitudes.

31. An elephant weighs about 8000 pounds. Its weight, plotted on a log scale, would be a little before 4.

32. A virus has a cell size of about 0.0000005 cm. On a log scale, its size would be plotted at about 7.

33. The closest star outside our solar system is about 26,395,630,000,000 miles away from Earth. This distance, plotted on a log scale, would occur a little after 26.

34. In a graph made using a log-log scale, consecutive powers of 10 are equally spaced on the horizontal axis and on the vertical axis.

35. One million and one billion differ by one order of magnitude.

36. After fitting a data set with both an exponential function, $y = Ae^{kx}$, and a power function, $y = Bx^n$, we must have $B = A$.

37. Given the points on a cubic curve, $(1, 1)$, $(2, 8)$, $(3, 27)$ and $(4, 64)$ it is not possible to fit an exponential function to this data.

SKILLS REFRESHER FOR CHAPTER 5: LOGARITHMS

We list the definitions and properties of the common and natural logarithms.

Properties of Logarithms If $M, N > 0$:

- Logarithm of a product: $\log MN = \log M + \log N$ $\ln MN = \ln M + \ln N$
- Logarithm of a quotient: $\log M/N = \log M - \log N$ $\ln M/N = \ln M - \ln N$
- Logarithm of a power: $\log M^P = P \log M$ $\ln M^P = P \ln M$
- Logarithm of 1: $\log 1 = 0$ $\ln 1 = 0$
- Logarithm of the base: $\log 10 = 1$ $\ln e = 1$

Be aware of the following two common errors,

$$\log(M + N) \neq (\log M)(\log N)$$

and

$$\log(M - N) \neq \frac{\log M}{\log N}.$$

Relationships Between Logarithms and Exponents

- $\log N = x$ if and only if $10^x = N$ $\ln N = x$ if and only if $e^x = N$
- $\log 10^x = x$ $\ln e^x = x$
- $10^{\log x} = x$, for $x > 0$ $e^{\ln x} = x$, for $x > 0$

Example 1   Evaluate without a calculator:

(a) $\log 10{,}000$ (b) $\ln 1$

Solution   (a) Common logarithms are powers of 10. The power of 10 needed to get 10,000 is 4, so $\log 10{,}000 = 4$.

(b) Natural logarithms are powers of e. The power of e needed to get 1 is zero, so $\ln 1 = 0$.

Example 2   Write the equation in exponential form:

(a) $\log x = -3$ (b) $\ln x = \sqrt{2}$

Solution   (a) By definition $\log x = -3$ means $10^{-3} = x$.

(b) By definition $\ln x = \sqrt{2}$ means $e^{\sqrt{2}} = x$.

Example 3   Write the equation in logarithmic form:

(a) $10^x = 1000$ (b) $10^{-2} = 0.01$ (c) $e^{-1} = 0.368$

Solution   (a) By definition $10^x = 1000$ means $\log 1000 = x$.

(b) By definition $10^{-2} = 0.01$ means $\log 0.01 = -2$.

(c) By definition $e^{-1} = 0.368$ means $\ln 0.368 = -1$.

Example 4   Write the expression using sums and/or differences of logarithmic expressions that do not contain the logarithms of products, quotients or powers.

(a) $\log(10x)$

(b) $\ln\left(\dfrac{e^2}{\sqrt{x}}\right)$

Solution   (a)

$$\log(10x) = \log 10 + \log x \quad \text{Logarithm of a product}$$
$$= 1 + \log x. \quad \text{Logarithm of the base}$$

(b)

$$\ln\left(\frac{e^2}{\sqrt{x}}\right) = \ln e^2 - \ln \sqrt{x} \quad \text{Logarithm of a quotient}$$
$$= \ln e^2 - \ln x^{1/2}$$
$$= 2\ln e - \frac{1}{2}\ln x \quad \text{Logarithm of a power}$$
$$= 2 \cdot 1 - \frac{1}{2}\ln x \quad \text{Logarithm of the base}$$
$$= 2 - \frac{1}{2}\ln x.$$

Example 5   Write the expression as a single logarithm.

(a) $\ln x - 2\ln y$

(b) $3\left(\log x + \frac{4}{3}\log y\right)$

Solution   (a)

$$\ln x - 2\ln y = \ln x - \ln y^2 \quad \text{Logarithm of a power}$$
$$= \ln\left(\frac{x}{y^2}\right). \quad \text{Logarithm of a quotient}$$

(b)

$$3\left(\log x + \frac{4}{3}\log y\right) = 3\log x + 4\log y$$
$$= \log x^3 + \log y^4 \quad \text{Logarithm of a power}$$
$$= \log(x^3 y^4). \quad \text{Logarithm of a product}$$

Example 6   Express in terms of x without logarithms.

(a) $e^{3\ln x}$

(b) $\log 10^{2x}$

Solution   (a)

$$e^{3\ln x} = e^{\ln x^3} \quad \text{Logarithm of a power}$$
$$= x^3. \quad \text{Logarithm of the base}$$

(b) $\log 10^{2x} = 2x.$ Logarithm of the base

Example 7   Solve the equation for x.

     (a) $12e^x = 5$ (b) $2^{-3x} = 17$

Solution   (a)

$$12e^x = 5$$
$$e^x = \frac{5}{12} \quad \text{Dividing by 12}$$
$$\ln e^x = \ln\left(\frac{5}{12}\right) \quad \text{Taking ln of both sides}$$
$$x = \ln\left(\frac{5}{12}\right). \quad \text{Logarithm of the base}$$

     (b)

$$2^{-3x} = 17$$
$$\log 2^{-3x} = \log 17 \quad \text{Taking logs of both sides}$$
$$-3x \log 2 = \log 17 \quad \text{Logarithm of a power}$$
$$-3x = \frac{\log 17}{\log 2} \quad \text{Dividing by log 2}$$
$$x = -\frac{\log 17}{3 \log 2}. \quad \text{Dividing by -3}$$

Example 8   Solve the equation for x.

     (a) $2(\log(2x + 50)) - 4 = 0$ (b) $\ln(x + 2) = 3$

Solution   (a)

$$2(\log(2x + 50)) - 4 = 0$$
$$2(\log(2x + 50)) = 4$$
$$\log(2x + 50) = 2$$
$$10^{\log(2x+50)} = 10^2 \quad \text{Converting to exponential form}$$
$$2x + 50 = 10^2$$
$$2x + 50 = 100$$
$$2x = 50$$
$$x = 25.$$

     (b)

$$\ln(x + 2) = 3$$
$$e^{\ln(x+2)} = e^3 \quad \text{Raise } e \text{ to each side}$$
$$x + 2 = e^3$$
$$x = e^3 - 2.$$

Exercises to Tools for Chapter 5

For Exercises 1–8, evaluate without a calculator.

1. $\log(\log 10)$

2. $\ln(\ln e)$

3. $2\ln e^4$

4. $\ln\left(\dfrac{1}{e^5}\right)$

5. $\dfrac{\log 1}{\log 10^5}$

6. $e^{\ln 3} - \ln e$

7. $\sqrt{\log 10{,}000}$

8. $10^{\log 7}$

For Exercises 9–12, rewrite the exponential equation in equivalent logarithmic form.

9. $10^{-4} = 0.0001$

10. $10^{0.477} = 3$

11. $e^{-2} = 0.135$

12. $e^{2x} = 7$

For Exercises 13–15, rewrite the logarithmic equation in equivalent exponential form.

13. $\log 0.01 = -2$

14. $\ln x = -1$

15. $\ln 4 = x^2$

For Exercises 16–24, if possible, write the expression using sums and/or differences of logarithmic expressions that do not contain the logarithms of products, quotients, or powers.

16. $\log 2x$

17. $\dfrac{\ln x}{2}$

18. $\log\left(\dfrac{x}{5}\right)$

19. $\log\left(\dfrac{x^2 + 1}{x^3}\right)$

20. $\ln\sqrt{\dfrac{x-1}{x+1}}$

21. $\log(x^2 + y^2)$

22. $\log(x^2 - y^2)$

23. $(\log x)(\log y)$

24. $\dfrac{\ln x^2}{\ln(x+2)}$

For Exercises 25–31, rewrite the expression as a single logarithm.

25. $\log 12 + \log x$

26. $\ln x^2 - \ln(x + 10)$

27. $\frac{1}{2}\log x + 4\log y$

28. $\log 3 + 2\log\sqrt{x}$

29. $3\left(\log(x+1) + \frac{2}{3}\log(x+4)\right)$

30. $\ln x + \ln\left(\dfrac{y}{2}(x+4)\right) + \ln z^{-1}$

31. $2\log(9 - x^2) - (\log(3 + x) + \log(3 - x))$

For Exercises 32–39, simplify the expression if possible.

32. $2\ln e^{\sqrt{x}}$

33. $\log(A^2 + B^2)$

34. $\log 10x - \log x$

35. $2\ln x^{-2} + \ln x^4$

36. $\ln\sqrt{x^2 + 16}$

37. $\log 100^{2z}$

38. $\dfrac{\ln e}{\ln e^2}$

39. $\ln\dfrac{1}{e^x + 1}$

For Exercises 40–45, solve for x using logarithms.

40. $12^x = 7$

41. $3 \cdot 5^x = 9$

42. $4 \cdot 13^{3x} = 17$

43. $e^{-5x} = 9$

44. $12^{5x} = 3 \cdot 15^{2x}$

45. $19^{6x} = 77 \cdot 7^{4x}$

In Exercises 46–49, solve for x.

46. $3\log(4x + 9) - 6 = 2$

47. $4\log(9x + 17) - 5 = 1$

48. $\ln(3x + 4) = 5$

49. $2\ln(6x - 1) + 5 = 7$

Chapter Six

TRANSFORMATIONS OF FUNCTIONS AND THEIR GRAPHS

Contents

6.1 VERTICAL AND HORIZONTAL SHIFTS

Suppose we shift the graph of a function vertically or horizontally, giving the graph of a new function. In this section we see the relationship between the formulas for the original function and the new function.

Vertical Shift: The Heating Schedule for an Office Building

We start with an example of a vertical shift in the context of the heating schedule for a building.

Example 1   To save money, an office building is kept warm only during business hours. Figure 6.1 shows the temperature, H, in °F, as a function of time, t, in hours after midnight. At midnight ($t = 0$), the building's temperature is 50°F. This temperature is maintained until 4 am. Then the building begins to warm up so that by 8 am the temperature is 70°F. At 4 pm the building begins to cool. By 8 pm, the temperature is again 50°F.

Suppose that the building's superintendent decides to keep the building 5°F warmer than before. Sketch a graph of the new function.

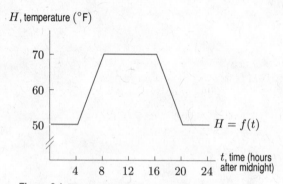

Figure 6.1: The heating schedule at an office building, $H = f(t)$

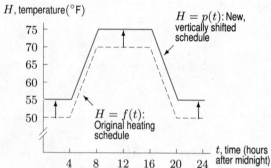

Figure 6.2: Graph of new heating schedule, $H = p(t)$, obtained by shifting original graph, $H = f(t)$, upward by 5 units

Solution   The graph of f, the heating schedule function of Figure 6.1, is shifted upward by 5 units. The new heating schedule, $H = p(t)$, is graphed in Figure 6.2. The building's overnight temperature is now 55°F instead of 50°F and its daytime temperature is 75°F instead of 70°F. The 5°F increase in temperature corresponds to the 5-unit vertical shift in the graph.

Example 2   What is the relationship between the formula for $f(t)$, the original heating schedule and $p(t)$, the new heating schedule?

Solution   The temperature under the new schedule, $p(t)$, is always 5°F warmer than the temperature under the old schedule, $f(t)$. Thus,

$$\text{New temperature at time } t = \text{Old temperature at time } t + 5.$$

Writing this algebraically:

$$\underbrace{p(t)}_{\substack{\text{New temperature} \\ \text{at time } t}} = \underbrace{f(t)}_{\substack{\text{Old temperature} \\ \text{at time } t}} + 5.$$

The relationship between the formulas for p and f is given by the equation $p(t) = f(t) + 5$.

We can get information from the relationship $p(t) = f(t) + 5$, although we do not have an explicit formula for f or p.

Suppose we need to know the temperature at 6 am under the schedule $p(t)$. The graph of $f(t)$ shows that under the old schedule $f(6) = 60$. Substituting $t = 6$ into the equation relating f and p gives $p(6)$:

$$p(6) = f(6) + 5 = 60 + 5 = 65.$$

Thus, at 6 am the temperature under the new schedule is 65°F.

Example 3   Find $r(t)$, the formula for the heating schedule if at each time the temperature is 2°F lower than the original temperature.

Solution   Since

$$\text{New temperature at time } t = \text{Old temperature at time } t - 2$$

we have

$$\underbrace{r(t)}_{\substack{\text{New temperature} \\ \text{at time } t}} = \underbrace{f(t)}_{\substack{\text{Old temperature} \\ \text{at time } t}} - 2.$$

The graph of $r(t)$ is the graph of f shifted down by 2 units.

Generalizing these observations to any function g:

> If $g(x)$ is a function and k is a positive constant, then the graph of
> - $y = g(x) + k$ is the graph of $y = g(x)$ shifted vertically upward by k units.
> - $y = g(x) - k$ is the graph of $y = g(x)$ shifted vertically downward by k units.

Horizontal Shift: The Heating Schedule

Example 4   The superintendent then changes the original heating schedule to start two hours earlier. The building now begins to warm at 2 am instead of 4 am, reaches 70°F at 6 am instead of 8 am, begins cooling off at 2 pm instead of 4 pm, and returns to 50°F at 6 pm instead of 8 pm. How are these changes reflected in the graph of the heating schedule?

Solution   Figure 6.3 gives a graph of $H = q(t)$, the new heating schedule, which is obtained by shifting the graph of the original heating schedule, $H = f(t)$, two units to the left.

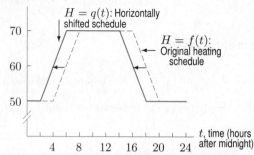

Figure 6.3: Graph of new heating schedule, $H = q(t)$, found by shifting, f, the original graph 2 units to the left

Notice that the upward shift in Example 1 results in a warmer temperature, whereas the leftward shift in Example 4 results in an earlier schedule.

Example 5   In Example 4 the heating schedule was changed to 2 hours earlier, shifting the graph horizontally 2 units to the left. Find a formula for q, this new schedule, in terms of f, the original schedule.

Solution   The old schedule always reaches a given temperature 2 hours after the new schedule. For example, at 4 am the temperature under the new schedule reaches 60°. The temperature under the old schedule reaches 60° at 6 am, 2 hours later. The temperature reaches 65° at 5 am under the new schedule, but not until 7 am, under the old schedule. In general, we see that

$$\begin{array}{ccc} \text{Temperature under new schedule} & = & \text{Temperature under old schedule} \\ \text{at time } t & & \text{at time } (t+2), \text{ two hours later.} \end{array}$$

Algebraically, we have

$$q(t) = f(t + 2).$$

This is a formula for q in terms of f.

Let's check the formula from Example 5 by using it to calculate $q(14)$, the temperature under the new schedule at 2 pm. The formula gives

$$q(14) = f(14 + 2) = f(16).$$

Figure 6.1 shows that $f(16) = 70$. Thus, $q(14) = 70$. This agrees with Figure 6.3.

Example 6   Suppose now the heating schedule is made 1 hour later than it was originally. Find the function $s(t)$ that describes this schedule.

Solution   The new schedule reaches a particular temperature 1 hour later than the original. For example, under the old schedule, the temperature reaches 60°F at 6 am, while it reaches 60°F at 7 am under the new schedule. Thus

$$\begin{array}{ccc} \text{Temperature under new schedule} & = & \text{Temperature under old schedule} \\ \text{at time } t & & \text{at time } (t-1), \text{ one hour earlier.} \end{array}$$

Thus, we have

$$s(t) = f(t - 1).$$

The graph of $s(t)$ is the graph of f shifted to the right by 1 unit.

Generalizing these observations to any function g:

> If $g(x)$ is a function and k is a positive constant, then the graph of
> - $y = g(x + k)$ is the graph of $y = g(x)$ shifted horizontally to the left by k units.
> - $y = g(x - k)$ is the graph of $y = g(x)$ shifted horizontally to the right by k units.

A vertical or horizontal shift of the graph of a function is called a *translation* because it does not change the shape of the graph, but simply translates it to another position in the plane. Shifts or translations are the simplest examples of *transformations* of a function. We will see others in later sections of Chapter 6.

Inside Versus Outside Changes

Since the horizontal shift in the heating schedule, $q(t) = f(t + 2)$, involves a change to the input value, it is called an *inside change* to f. Similarly the vertical shift, $p(t) = f(t) + 5$, is called an *outside change* because it involves changes to the output value.

Example 7   If $n = f(A)$ gives the number of gallons of paint needed to cover a house of area A ft^2, explain the meaning of the expressions $f(A + 10)$ and $f(A) + 10$ in the context of painting.

Solution   These two expressions are similar in that they both involve adding 10. However, for $f(A + 10)$, the 10 is added on the inside, so 10 is added to the area, A. Thus,

$$n = f(\underbrace{A + 10}_{\text{Area}}) = \begin{array}{c}\text{Amount of paint needed} \\ \text{to cover an area of } (A + 10) \text{ ft}^2\end{array} = \begin{array}{c}\text{Amount of paint needed to cover} \\ \text{an area 10 ft}^2 \text{ larger than } A.\end{array}$$

The expression $f(A) + 10$ represents an outside change. We are adding 10 to $f(A)$, which represents an amount of paint, not an area. We have

$$n = \underbrace{f(A)}_{\substack{\text{Amount} \\ \text{of paint}}} + 10 = \begin{array}{c}\text{Amount of paint needed} \\ \text{to cover region of area } A\end{array} + 10 \text{ gals} = \begin{array}{c}\text{10 gallons more paint than} \\ \text{amount needed to cover area } A.\end{array}$$

In $f(A + 10)$, we added 10 square feet on the inside of the function, which means that the area to be painted is now 10 ft^2 larger. In $f(A) + 10$, we added 10 gallons to the outside, which means that we have 10 more gallons of paint than we need.

Combining Horizontal and Vertical Shifts

We have seen how a function's formula changes when we shift its graph horizontally or vertically. What happens when we shift it both horizontally and vertically?

Example 8   Let r be the transformation of the heating schedule function, $H = f(t)$, given by

$$r(t) = f(t - 2) - 5.$$

(a) Sketch the graph of $H = r(t)$.

(b) Describe in words the heating schedule determined by r.

Solution   (a) To graph r, we break this transformation into two steps. First, we sketch a graph of $H = f(t - 2)$. This is an inside change to the function f and it results in the graph of f being shifted 2 units to the right. Next, we sketch a graph of $H = f(t - 2) - 5$. This graph can be found by shifting our sketch of $H = f(t - 2)$ down 5 units. The resulting graph is shown in Figure 6.4. The graph of r is the graph of f shifted 2 units to the right and 5 units down.

(b) The function r represents a schedule that is both 2 hours later and 5 degrees cooler than the original schedule.

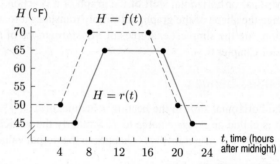

Figure 6.4: Graph of $r(t) = f(t - 2) - 5$ is graph of $H = f(t)$ shifted right by 2 and down by 5

We can use transformations to relate unfamiliar functions to functions we already know.

Example 9   A graph of $f(x) = x^2$ is in Figure 6.5. Define g by shifting the graph of f to the right 2 units and down 1 unit; see Figure 6.6. Find a formula for g in terms of f. Find a formula for g in terms of x.

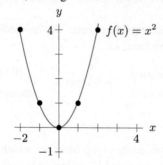

Figure 6.5: The graph of $f(x) = x^2$

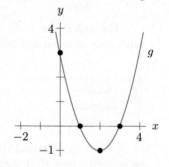

Figure 6.6: The graph of g, a transformation of f

Solution   The graph of g is the graph of f shifted to the right 2 units and down 1 unit, so a formula for g is $g(x) = f(x - 2) - 1$. Since $f(x) = x^2$, we have $f(x - 2) = (x - 2)^2$. Therefore,

$$g(x) = (x - 2)^2 - 1.$$

It is a good idea to check by graphing $g(x) = (x - 2)^2 - 1$ and comparing the graph with Figure 6.6.

Exercises and Problems for Section 6.1

Skill Refresher

In Exercises S1–S4, evaluate each function at $x = 4$.

S1. $f(x) = \sqrt{x}$

S2. $g(x) = \sqrt{x} + 6$

S3. $h(x) = \sqrt{x} - 3$

S4. $k(x) = \sqrt{x + 5}$

In Exercises S5–S8, solve for x.

S5. $e^x = 1$

S6. $e^{x-5} = 1$

S7. $e^{x+8} = 1$

S8. $e^x - 3 = 1$

S9. Describe shift(s) that can be applied to the graph of $f(x) = \ln x$ to obtain a graph of the following:

(a) $y = \ln(x - 4)$

(b) $y = \ln(x) - 7$

(c) $y = \ln(x + \sqrt{2})$

(d) $y = \ln(x - 3) + 5$

S10. Describe shift(s) that can be applied to the graph of $f(x) = \dfrac{1}{x}$ to obtain a graph of the following:

(a) $y = \dfrac{1}{x + 8}$

(b) $y = \dfrac{1}{x} + 3$

(c) $y = \dfrac{1}{x} - \dfrac{1}{5}$

(d) $y = \dfrac{1}{x - 2} - \ln 7$

Exercises

1. Using Table 6.1, complete the tables for g, h, k, m, where:

   (a) $g(x) = f(x - 1)$

   (b) $h(x) = f(x + 1)$

   (c) $k(x) = f(x) + 3$

   (d) $m(x) = f(x - 1) + 3$

   Explain how the graph of each function relates to the graph of $f(x)$.

   Table 6.1

x	-2	-1	0	1	2
$f(x)$	-3	0	2	1	-1

x	-1	0	1	2	3
$g(x)$					

x	-3	-2	-1	0	1
$h(x)$					

x	-2	-1	0	1	2
$k(x)$					

x	-1	0	1	2	3
$m(x)$					

2. Match the graphs in (a)–(f) with the formulas in (i)–(vi).

   (i) $y = |x|$

   (ii) $y = |x| - 1.2$

   (iii) $y = |x - 1.2|$

   (iv) $y = |x| + 2.5$

   (v) $y = |x + 3.4|$

   (vi) $y = |x - 3| + 2.7$

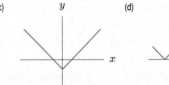

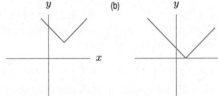

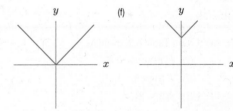

3. The graph of $f(x)$ contains the point $(3, -4)$. What point must be on the graph of

   (a) $f(x) + 5$?

   (b) $f(x + 5)$?

   (c) $f(x - 3) - 2$?

In Exercises 4–7, graph the transformations of $f(x)$ in Figure 6.7.

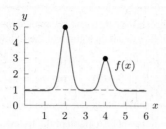

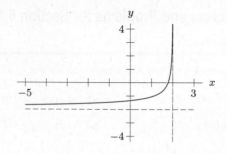

Figure 6.7

Write a formula and graph the transformations of $m(n) = \frac{1}{2}n^2$ in Exercises 13–20.

4. $y = f(x+2)$

5. $y = f(x) + 2$

6. $y = f(x-1) - 5$

7. $y = f(x+6) - 4$

13. $y = m(n) + 1$

14. $y = m(n+1)$

15. $y = m(n) - 3.7$

16. $y = m(n - 3.7)$

17. $y = m(n) + \sqrt{13}$

18. $y = m(n + 2\sqrt{2})$

8. Let $f(x) = 4^x$, $g(x) = 4^x + 2$, and $h(x) = 4^x - 3$. What is the relationship between the graph of $f(x)$ and the graphs of $h(x)$ and $g(x)$?

19. $y = m(n+3) + 7$

20. $y = m(n - 17) - 159$

9. Let $f(x) = \left(\frac{1}{3}\right)^x$, $g(x) = \left(\frac{1}{3}\right)^{x+4}$, and $h(x) = \left(\frac{1}{3}\right)^{x-2}$.
How do the graphs of $g(x)$ and $h(x)$ compare to the graph of $f(x)$?

Write a formula and graph the transformations of $k(w) = 3^w$ in Exercises 21–26.

10. The domain of the function $g(x)$ is $-2 < x < 7$. What is the domain of $g(x-2)$?

11. The range of the function $R(s)$ is $100 \le R(s) \le 200$. What is the range of $R(s) - 150$?

21. $y = k(w) - 3$

22. $y = k(w - 3)$

23. $y = k(w) + 1.8$

24. $y = k(w + \sqrt{5})$

25. $y = k(w + 2.1) - 1.3$

26. $y = k(w - 1.5) - 0.9$

12. The figure gives a graph of f. Sketch a graph of $y = f(x+3) + 3$. Label all important features.

Problems

27. (a) Using Table 6.2, evaluate

(i) $f(x)$ for $x = 6$.

(ii) $f(5) - 3$.

(iii) $f(5 - 3)$.

(iv) $g(x) + 6$ for $x = 2$.

(v) $g(x + 6)$ for $x = 2$.

(vi) $3g(x)$ for $x = 0$.

(vii) $f(3x)$ for $x = 2$.

(viii) $f(x) - f(2)$ for $x = 8$.

(ix) $g(x + 1) - g(x)$ for $x = 1$.

(b) Solve

(i) $g(x) = 6$.

(ii) $f(x) = 574$.

(iii) $g(x) = 281$.

(c) The values in the table were obtained using the formulas $f(x) = x^3 + x^2 + x - 10$ and $g(x) = 7x^2 - 8x - 6$. Use the table to find two solutions to the equation $x^3 + x^2 + x - 10 = 7x^2 - 8x - 6$.

Table 6.2

x	0	1	2	3	4	5	6	7	8	9
$f(x)$	-10	-7	4	29	74	145	248	389	574	809
$g(x)$	-6	-7	6	33	74	129	198	281	378	489

28. The graph of $y = m(r)$ is given in Figure 6.8. The graph of each function in parts (a) – (d) resulted from translations of $y = m(r)$. Give a formula for each of these functions in terms of m.

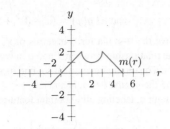

Figure 6.8

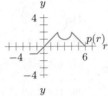
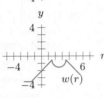
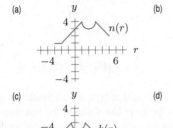
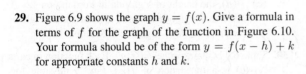

32. (a) Let $f(x) = \left(\dfrac{x}{2}\right)^3 + 2$. Calculate $f(-6)$.

    (b) Solve $f(x) = -6$.

    (c) Find points that correspond to parts (a) and (b) on the graph of $f(x)$ in Figure 6.11.

    (d) Calculate $f(4) - f(2)$. Draw a vertical line segment on the y-axis that illustrates this calculation.

    (e) If $a = -2$, compute $f(a + 4)$ and $f(a) + 4$.

    (f) In part (e), what x-value corresponds to $f(a + 4)$? To $f(a) + 4$?

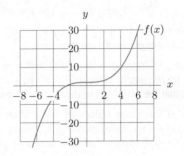

Figure 6.11

29. Figure 6.9 shows the graph $y = f(x)$. Give a formula in terms of f for the graph of the function in Figure 6.10. Your formula should be of the form $y = f(x - h) + k$ for appropriate constants h and k.

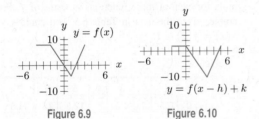

Figure 6.9   Figure 6.10

30. Judging from their graphs, find a formula for $g(x)$ in terms of $f(x)$.

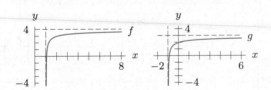

31. The graph of $g(x)$ contains the point $(-2, 5)$. Write a formula for a translation of g whose graph contains the point

  (a) $(-2, 8)$ (b) $(0, 5)$

33. The function $P(t)$ gives the number of people in a certain population in year t. Interpret in terms of population:

  (a) $P(t) + 100$ (b) $P(t + 100)$

In Problems 34–35, let $s(t)$ denote the average weight (in pounds) of a baby at age t months.

34. The weight, V, of a particular baby named Jonah is related to the average weight function $s(t)$ by the equation

$$V = s(t) + 2.$$

Find Jonah's weight at ages $t = 3$ and $t = 6$ months. What can you say about Jonah's weight in general?

35. The weight, W, of another baby named Ben is related to $s(t)$ by the equation

$$W = s(t + 4).$$

What can you say about Ben's weight at age $t = 3$ months? At $t = 6$ months? Assuming that babies increase in weight over the first year of life, decide if Ben is of average weight for his age, above average, or below average.

36. The function $g(x)$ is obtained by shifting the graph of $y = x^2$. If $g(3) = 16$, give a possible formula for g when

  (a) g is the result of applying only a horizontal shift to $y = x^2$.

  (b) g is the result of applying only a vertical shift to $y = x^2$.

  (c) g is the result of applying a horizontal shift right 2 units and an appropriate vertical shift of $y = x^2$.

37. Describe a series of shifts that translates the graph of $y = (x + 3)^3 - 1$ onto the graph of $y = x^3$.

38. Graph $f(x) = \ln(|x - 3|)$ and $g(x) = \ln(|x|)$. Find the vertical asymptotes of both functions.

39. Graph $y = \log x$, $y = \log(10x)$, and $y = \log(100x)$. How do the graphs compare? Use a property of logs to show that the graphs are vertical shifts of one another.

40. Table 6.3 contains values of $g(t)$. Each function in parts (a)–(e) is a translation of $g(t)$. Find a possible formula for each of these functions in terms of g.

Table 6.3

t	-1	-0.5	0	0.5	1
$g(t)$	0.5	0.8	1.0	0.9	0.6

(a)

t	-1	-0.5	0	0.5	1
$a(t)$	1.0	1.3	1.50	1.4	1.1

(b)

t	-1	-0.5	0	0.5	1
$b(t)$	1.0	0.9	0.6	0.1	-0.4

(c)

t	-1	-0.5	0	0.5	1
$c(t)$	0.7	0.6	0.3	-0.2	-0.7

(d)

t	-1	-0.5	0	$.5$	1
$d(t)$	0	0.5	0.8	1.0	0.9

(e)

t	-1	-0.5	0	0.5	1
$e(t)$	1.2	1.7	2.0	2.2	2.1

41. Graph $y = x^2 - 10x + 25$ and $y = x^2$. Use a shift transformation to explain the relationship between the two graphs.

42. Let $f(x) = x^2$ and let $g(x) = (x - 3)^2 + 2$.

  (a) Give the formula for g in terms of f, and describe the relationship between f and g in words.

  (b) Is g a quadratic function? If so, find its standard form and the parameters a, b, and c.

  (c) Graph g, labeling all important features.

In Problems 43–48, explain in words the effect of the transformation on the graph of $q(z)$. Assume a, b are positive constants.

43. $q(z) + 3$

44. $q(z) - a$

45. $q(z + 4)$

46. $q(z - a)$

47. $q(z + b) - a$

48. $q(z - 2b) + ab$

49. Let $S(d)$ give the height of high tide in Seattle on a specific day, d, of the year. Use shifts of the function $S(d)$ to find formulas for each of the following functions:

  (a) $T(d)$, the height of high tide in Tacoma on day d, given that high tide in Tacoma is always one foot higher than high tide in Seattle.

  (b) $P(d)$, the height of high tide in Portland on day d, given that high tide in Portland is the same height as the previous day's high tide in Seattle.

50. Table 6.4 contains values of $f(x)$. Each function in parts (a)–(c) is a translation of $f(x)$. Find a possible formula for each of these functions in terms of f. For example, given the data in Table 6.5, you could say that $k(x) = f(x) + 1$.

Table 6.4

x	0	1	2	3	4	5	6	7
$f(x)$	0	0.5	2	4.5	8	12.5	18	24.5

Table 6.5

x	0	1	2	3	4	5	6	7
$k(x)$	1	1.5	3	5.5	9	13.5	19	25.5

(a)

x	0	1	2	3	4	5	6	7
$h(x)$	-2	-1.5	0	2.5	6	10.5	16	22.5

(b)

x	0	1	2	3	4	5	6	7
$g(x)$	0.5	2	4.5	8	12.5	18	24.5	32

(c)

x	0	1	2	3	4	5	6	7
$i(x)$	-1.5	0	2.5	6	10.5	16	22.5	30

51. Tables 6.6 and 6.7 give values of functions v and w. Given that $w(x) = v(x - h) + k$, find the constants h and k.

Table 6.6

x	$v(x)$
-2	11
-1	17
0	20
1	17
2	11

Table 6.7

x	$w(x)$
3	4
4	10
5	13
6	10
7	4

52. For $t \geq 0$, let $H(t) = 68 + 93(0.91)^t$ give the temperature of a cup of coffee in degrees Fahrenheit t minutes after it is brought to class.

(a) Find formulas for $H(t + 15)$ and $H(t) + 15$.

(b) Graph $H(t)$, $H(t + 15)$, and $H(t) + 15$.

(c) Describe in practical terms a situation modeled by the function $H(t + 15)$. What about $H(t) + 15$?

(d) Which function, $H(t+15)$ or $H(t)+15$, approaches the same final temperature as the function $H(t)$? What is that temperature?

53. At a jazz club, the cost of an evening is based on a cover charge of \$20 plus a beverage charge of \$7 per drink.

(a) Find a formula for $t(x)$, the total cost for an evening in which x drinks are consumed.

(b) If the price of the cover charge is raised by \$5, express the new total cost function, $n(x)$, as a transformation of $t(x)$.

(c) The management increases the cover charge to \$30, leaves the price of a drink at \$7, but includes the first two drinks for free. For $x \geq 2$, express $p(x)$, the new total cost, as a transformation of $t(x)$.

54. A hot brick is removed from a kiln and set on the floor to cool. Let t be time in minutes after the brick was removed. The difference, $D(t)$, between the brick's temperature, initially $350°F$, and room temperature, $70°F$, decays exponentially over time at a rate of 3% per minute. The brick's temperature, $H(t)$, is a transformation of $D(t)$. Find a formula for $H(t)$. Compare the graphs of $D(t)$ and $H(t)$, paying attention to the asymptotes.

55. Let $T(d)$ give the average temperature in your hometown on the dth day of last year (so $d = 1$ is January 1, etc).

(a) Graph $T(d)$ for $1 \leq d \leq 365$.

(b) Give a possible value for each of the following: $T(6); T(100); T(215); T(371)$.

(c) What is the relationship between $T(d)$ and $T(d + 365)$? Explain.

(d) If you graph $w(d) = T(d + 365)$ on the same axes as $T(d)$, how would the two graphs compare?

(e) Do you think the function $T(d) + 365$ has any practical significance? Explain.

56. Let $f(t)$ be the odometer reading in miles on Joe's car at the start of day t after the car was built. On the morning of the 400th day of the car's life, when the odometer reads 3000 miles, Joe starts a long trip. Find formulas for the following functions.

(a) $h(t)$, the odometer reading at the start of day t of the trip.

(b) $k(t)$, the number of miles driven during the first t days of the trip.

57. Let $H(t)$ be the thermometer reading (Celsius) of a person t hours after onset of an illness. Normal body temperature is $37°C$. Find a formula for the fever, the number $f(t)$ of degrees greater than normal, after t hours.

58. Let $f(x) = e^x$ and $g(x) = 5e^x$. If $g(x) = f(x - h)$, find h.

6.2 REFLECTIONS AND SYMMETRY

In Section 6.1 we saw that a horizontal shift of the graph of a function results from a change to the input of the function (specifically, adding or subtracting a constant inside the function's parentheses). A vertical shift corresponds to an outside change.

In this section we consider the effect of reflecting a function's graph about the x or y-axis. A reflection about the x-axis corresponds to an outside change to the function's formula; a reflection about the y-axis corresponds to an inside change.

A Formula for a Reflection

Figure 6.12 shows the graph of a function $y = f(x)$ whose values are in Table 6.8. Note that we do not need an explicit formula for f.

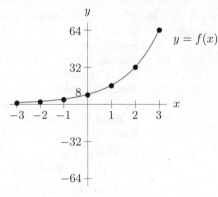

Figure 6.12: A graph of the function $y = f(x)$

Table 6.8   *Values of the function $y = f(x)$*

x	y
-3	1
-2	2
-1	4
0	8
1	16
2	32
3	64

Figure 6.13 shows a vertical reflection of the graph of f about the x-axis, giving the graph of $y = g(x)$. Figure 6.14 shows a horizontal reflection of the graph of f about the y-axis, giving $y = h(x)$. Figure 6.15 shows a horizontal reflection of the graph of f about the y-axis followed by a vertical reflection about the x-axis, giving $y = k(x)$.

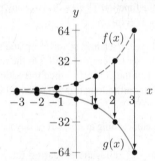

Figure 6.13: Reflection about x-axis: $y = g(x)$

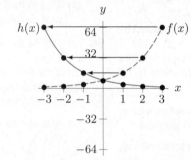

Figure 6.14: Reflection about y-axis: $y = h(x)$

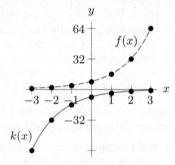

Figure 6.15: Reflection about y- and x-axes: $y = k(x)$

Example 1   Use the graphs in Figures 6.13 to 6.15 to find formulas in terms of f for

(a) $y = g(x)$ (b) $y = h(x)$ (c) $y = k(x)$.

Solution   (a) Figure 6.13 shows the graph of f reflected in the x-axis, giving the graph of $g(x)$. Values of $g(x)$ are in Table 6.9.

Table 6.9   *Values of the functions $g(x)$ and $f(x)$ from Figure 6.13*

x	-3	-2	-1	0	1	2	3
$g(x)$	-1	-2	-4	-8	-16	-32	-64
$f(x)$	1	2	4	8	16	32	64

Notice that under reflection in the x-axis,
The point $(2, 32)$ becomes $(2, -32)$,
The point $(3, 64)$ becomes $(3, -64)$, etc.
Thus, when a point is reflected vertically about the x-axis, the x-value stays fixed, while the y-value changes sign. That is, for a given x-value,

y-value of g is the negative of y-value of f.

Algebraically, this means

$$g(x) = -f(x).$$

(b) Figure 6.14 shows the graph of f reflected in the y-axis, giving the graph of $h(x)$. Values of $h(x)$ are in Table 6.10.

Table 6.10 *Values of the functions $h(x)$ and $f(x)$ from Figure 6.14*

x	-3	-2	-1	0	1	2	3
$h(x)$	64	32	16	8	4	2	1
$f(x)$	1	2	4	8	16	32	64

Notice that under reflection in the y-axis,

The point $(2, 32)$ becomes $(-2, 32)$,

The point $(3, 64)$ becomes $(-3, 64)$, etc.

Thus, when a point is reflected horizontally about the y-axis, the y-value remains fixed, while the x-value changes sign. This means

$$h(x) = f(-x).$$

(c) The graph of the function $y = k(x)$ results from a horizontal reflection of the graph of f about the y-axis, followed by a vertical reflection about the x-axis. Notice that a horizontal reflection corresponds to multiplying the inputs by -1 and a vertical reflection corresponds to multiplying the outputs by -1. Thus, we have

Vertical reflection across the x-axis

$$k(x) = -f(-x).$$

Horizontal reflection across the y-axis

Let's check a point. If $x = 1$, then the formula $k(x) = -f(-x)$ gives:

$$k(1) = -f(-1) = -4 \qquad \text{since } f(-1) = 4.$$

This result is consistent with the graph, since $(1, -4)$ is on the graph of $k(x)$.

For a function f:
- The graph of $y = -f(x)$ is a reflection of the graph of $y = f(x)$ about the x-axis.
- The graph of $y = f(-x)$ is a reflection of the graph of $y = f(x)$ about the y-axis.

Symmetry About the y-Axis

The graph of $p(x) = x^2$ in Figure 6.16 is *symmetric* about the y-axis. In other words, the part of the graph to the left of the y-axis is the mirror image of the part to the right of the y-axis. Reflecting the graph of $p(x)$ about the y-axis gives the graph of $p(x)$ again.

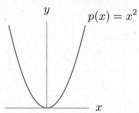

Figure 6.16: Reflecting the graph of $p(x) = x^2$ about the y-axis does not change its appearance

Symmetry about the y-axis is called *even symmetry*, because power functions with even exponents, such as $y = x^2$, $y = x^4$, $y = x^6$, ... have this property. Since $y = p(-x)$ is a reflection of the graph of p about the y-axis and $p(x)$ has even symmetry, we have

$$p(-x) = p(x).$$

Example 2   For $p(x) = x^2$, check that $p(-2) = p(2)$. Explain what this tells us about the graph of p.

Solution   Let $x = 2$. Then $p(2) = 2^2 = 4$, and $p(-2) = (-2)^2 = 4$, so $p(-2) = p(2)$. This means that the point $(2, 4)$ and its reflection about the y-axis, $(-2, 4)$, are both on the graph of $p(x)$.

Example 3   For the function $p(x) = x^2$, check algebraically that $p(-x) = p(x)$ for all x.

Solution   Substitute $-x$ into the formula for $p(x)$, giving

$$\begin{aligned} p(-x) &= (-x)^2 = (-x) \cdot (-x) \\ &= x^2 \\ &= p(x). \end{aligned}$$

Thus, $p(-x) = p(x)$.

In general,

> If f is a function, then f is called an **even function** if, for all values of x in the domain of f,
>
> $$f(-x) = f(x).$$
>
> The graph of f is symmetric about the y-axis.

Symmetry About the Origin

Figures 6.17 and 6.18 show the graph of $q(x) = x^3$. Reflecting the graph of q first about the y-axis and then about the x-axis (or vice-versa) gives the graph of q again. This kind of symmetry is called symmetry about the origin, or *odd symmetry*.

In Example 1, we saw that $y = -f(-x)$ is a reflection of the graph of $y = f(x)$ about both the y-axis and the x-axis. Since $q(x) = x^3$ is symmetric about the origin, q is the same function as this double reflection. That is,

$$q(x) = -q(-x), \quad \text{which means that} \quad q(-x) = -q(x).$$

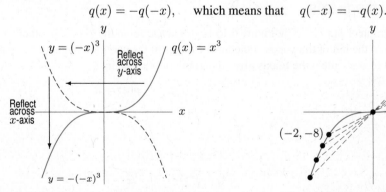
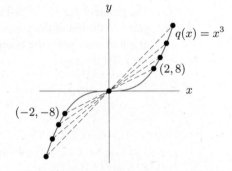

Figure 6.17: If the graph is reflected about the y-axis and then about the x-axis, it does not change

Figure 6.18: If every point on this graph is reflected about the origin, the graph is unchanged

Example 4   For $q(x) = x^3$, check that $q(-2) = -q(2)$. Explain what this tells us about the graph of q.

Solution   Let $x = 2$. Then $q(2) = 2^3 = 8$, and $q(-2) = (-2)^3 = -8$, so $q(-2) = -q(2)$. This means the point $(2, 8)$ and its reflection about the origin, $(-2, -8)$, are both on the graph of q.

Example 5   For the function $q(x) = x^3$, check algebraically that $q(-x) = -q(x)$ for all x.

Solution   We evaluate $q(-x)$, giving

$$q(-x) = (-x)^3 = (-x) \cdot (-x) \cdot (-x)$$
$$= -x^3$$
$$= -q(x).$$

Thus, $q(-x) = -q(x)$.

In general,

> If f is a function, then f is called an **odd function** if, for all values of x in the domain of f,
>
> $$f(-x) = -f(x).$$
>
> The graph of f is symmetric about the origin.

Example 6   Determine whether the following functions are symmetric about the y-axis, the origin, or neither.
(a) $f(x) = |x|$ (b) $g(x) = 1/x$ (c) $h(x) = -x^3 - 3x^2 + 2$

Solution   The graphs of the functions in Figures 6.19, 6.20, and 6.21 are helpful in identifying symmetry.

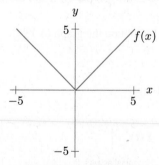

Figure 6.19: The graph of $f(x) = |x|$ appears to be symmetric about the y-axis

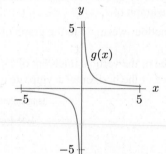

Figure 6.20: The graph of $g(x) = 1/x$ appears to be symmetric about the origin

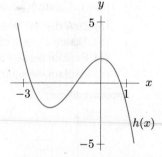

Figure 6.21: The graph of $h(x) = -x^3 - 3x^2 + 2$ is symmetric neither about the y-axis nor about the origin

From the graphs it appears that f is symmetric about the y-axis (even symmetry), g is symmetric about the origin (odd symmetry), and h has neither type of symmetry. However, to be sure, check algebraically.

If $f(-x) = f(x)$, then f has even symmetry. We check by substituting $-x$ in for x:

$$f(-x) = |-x|$$
$$= |x|$$
$$= f(x).$$

Thus, f does have even symmetry.

If $g(-x) = -g(x)$, then g is symmetric about the origin. We check by substituting $-x$ for x:

$$g(-x) = \frac{1}{-x}$$
$$= -\frac{1}{x}$$
$$= -g(x).$$

Thus, g is symmetric about the origin.

The graph of h does not exhibit odd or even symmetry. To confirm, look at an example, say $x = 1$:

$$h(1) = -1^3 - 3 \cdot 1^2 + 2 = -2.$$

Now substitute $x = -1$, giving

$$h(-1) = -(-1)^3 - 3 \cdot (-1)^2 + 2 = 0.$$

Thus $h(1) \neq h(-1)$, so the function is not symmetric about the y-axis. Also, $h(-1) \neq -h(1)$, so the function is not symmetric about the origin.

Combining Shifts and Reflections

We can combine the horizontal and vertical shifts from Section 6.1 with the horizontal and vertical reflections of this section to make more complex transformations of functions.

Example 7   When a yam is taken from a refrigerator at $0°C$ and put into an oven at $150°C$, the yam's temperature rises toward that of the oven.[1] Let $Y(t)$ be the temperature in $°C$ of the yam t minutes after it is put in the oven. Let $D(t) = 150 - Y(t)$ be the temperature difference between the oven and the yam at time t. Figure 6.22 shows a graph of $D(t)$.

(a) Describe the transformations we apply to the graph of $D(t)$ to obtain the graph of $Y(t)$.
(b) Sketch a graph of $Y(t)$.
(c) Explain the significance of the vertical intercept of Y.
(d) Explain the significance of the horizontal asymptote of Y.

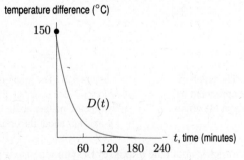

Figure 6.22: Temperature difference: Decreasing over time

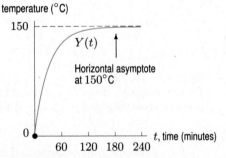

Figure 6.23: Temperature of the yam, $Y(t) = -D(t) + 150$

---

[1] In practice, refrigerators keep food slightly above $0°C$—at about 2-3$°C$—to prevent freezing.

Solution   (a) Writing $Y(t)$ in the form

$$Y(t) = \underbrace{-D(t)}_{\text{Reflect}} + \underbrace{150}_{\text{Shift}}$$

shows that the graph of Y is obtained by reflecting the graph of D about the t-axis and then shifting it vertically up 150 units.

(b) See Figure 6.23.

(c) The vertical intercept is $Y = 0$ because the temperature of the yam when it is first put into the oven is 0°C.

(d) The horizontal asymptote, $Y = 150$, represents the temperature of the oven. As the yam sits in the oven, its temperature approaches the temperature of the oven.

Exercises and Problems for Section 6.2

Skill Refresher

In Exercises S1–S4, evaluate each function at $x = 3$. Round your answer to 3 decimal places.

S1. $f(x) = e^x$ **S2.** $g(x) = -e^x$

S3. $h(x) = e^{-x}$ **S4.** $k(x) = -e^{-x}$

For each function in Exercises S5–S10, give a formula for the following expressions,

(a) $f(-x)$ (b) $-f(x)$

S5. $f(x) = 2x^2$ **S6.** $f(x) = \dfrac{1}{x}$

S7. $f(x) = 2x^3 - 3$ **S8.** $f(x) = 4x^3 + 9x$

S9. $f(x) = 3x^4 - 2x$ **S10.** $f(x) = \dfrac{3x^3}{x^2 - 1}$

Exercises

1. The graph of $y = f(x)$ contains the point $(2, -3)$. What point must lie on the reflected graph if the graph is reflected

(a)   About the y-axis?   (b)   About the x-axis?

2. The graph of $P = g(t)$ contains the point $(-1, -5)$.

(a) If the graph has even symmetry, which other point must lie on the graph?

(b) What point must lie on the graph of $-g(t)$?

3. The graph of $H(x)$ is symmetric about the origin. If $H(-3) = 7$, what is $H(3)$?

4. The range of $Q(x)$ is $-2 \le Q(x) \le 12$. What is the range of $-Q(x)$?

In Exercises 5–8, the function $Q(t)$ has domain $t > 0$ and range $-4 \le Q(t) \le 7$. Give the domain and range for the transformation of $Q(t)$.

5. $y = Q(-t)$ **6.** $y = -Q(t)$

7. $y = -Q(-t)$ **8.** $y = -Q(t - 4)$

9. If the graph of $y = e^x$ is reflected about the x-axis, what is the formula for the resulting graph? Check by graphing both functions together.

10. If the graph of $y = e^x$ is reflected about the y-axis, what is the formula for the resulting graph? Check by graphing both functions together.

11. Complete the following tables using $f(p) = p^2 + 2p - 3$, and $g(p) = f(-p)$, and $h(p) = -f(p)$. Graph the three functions. Explain how the graphs of g and h are related to the graph of f.

p	-3	-2	-1	0	1	2	3
$f(p)$							

p	-3	-2	-1	0	1	2	3
$g(p)$							

p	-3	-2	-1	0	1	2	3
$h(p)$							

12. Graph $y = f(x) = 4^x$ and $y = f(-x)$ on the same set of axes. How are these graphs related? Give an explicit formula for $y = f(-x)$.

13. Graph $y = g(x) = \left(\frac{1}{3}\right)^x$ and $y = -g(x)$ on the same set of axes. How are these graphs related? Give an explicit formula for $y = -g(x)$.

Give a formula and graph for each of the transformations of $m(n) = n^2 - 4n + 5$ in Exercises 14–17.

14. $y = m(-n)$

15. $y = -m(n)$

16. $y = -m(-n)$

17. $y = m(-n) + 3$

Give a formula and graph for each of the transformations of $k(w) = 3^w$ in Exercises 18–21.

18. $y = k(-w)$

19. $y = -k(w)$

20. $y = -k(-w)$

21. $y = -k(w - 2)$

In Exercises 22–25, show that the function is even, odd, or neither.

22. $f(x) = 7x^2 - 2x + 1$

23. $f(x) = 4x^7 - 3x^5$

24. $f(x) = 8x^6 + 12x^2$

25. $f(x) = x^5 + 3x^3 - 2$

Problems

26. (a) Graph the function obtained from $f(x) = x^3$ by first reflecting about the x-axis, then translating up two units. Write a formula for the resulting function.
   (b) Graph the function obtained from f by first translating up two units, then reflecting about the x-axis. Write a formula for the resulting function.
   (c) Are the functions in parts (a) and (b) the same?

27. (a) Graph the function obtained from $g(x) = 2^x$ by first reflecting about the y-axis, then translating down three units. Write a formula for the resulting function.
   (b) Graph the function obtained from g by first translating down three units, then reflecting about the y-axis. Write a formula for the resulting function.
   (c) Are the functions in parts (a) and (b) the same?

28. Using Figure 6.24, evaluate
   (a) $f(-x)$ for $x = -4$
   (b) $-f(x)$ for $x = -6$
   (c) $-f(-x)$ for $x = -4$
   (d) $-f(x + 2)$ for $x = 0$
   (e) $f(-x) + 4$ for $x = -6$

29. (a) If $g(x) = \sqrt[3]{x}$, find a formula for $g(-x)$.
   (b) Graph $y = g(x) = \sqrt[3]{x}$, $y = g(-x)$, and $y = -g(x)$ on the same axes.
   (c) Is $g(x) = \sqrt[3]{x}$ even, odd, or neither?

30. If the graph of a line $y = b + mx$ is reflected about the y-axis, what are the slope and intercepts of the resulting line?

31. Graph $y = \log(1/x)$ and $y = \log x$ on the same axes. How are the two graphs related? Use the properties of logarithms to explain the relationship algebraically.

32. Using Figure 6.25, graph the following transformations of f on separate axes.

   (a) $y = f(x) - 2$ **(b)** $y = f(x - 2)$
   (c) $y = -f(x)$ **(d)** $y = f(-x)$

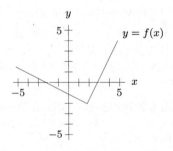

Figure 6.25

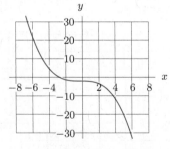

Figure 6.24

33. Using Figure 6.26, match the functions (i)-(v) with a graph (a)-(e).

(i) $y = f(-x)$ (ii) $y = -f(x)$

(iii) $y = f(-x) + 3$ (iv) $y = -f(x - 1)$

(v) $y = -f(-x)$

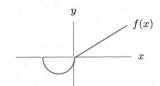

Figure 6.26

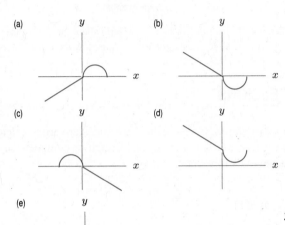

(a)   (b)

(c)   (d)

(e)

34. In Table 6.11, fill in as many y-values as you can if you know that f is

(a) An even function   (b) An odd function.

Table 6.11

x	-3	-2	-1	0	1	2	3
y	5		-4			-8	

35. Figure 6.27 shows the graph of a function f in the second quadrant. In each of the following cases, sketch $y = f(x)$, given that f is symmetric about

(a) The y-axis.   (b) The origin.   (c) The line $y = x$.

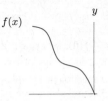

Figure 6.27

36. For each table, decide whether the function could be symmetric about the y-axis, about the origin, or neither.

(a)

x	-3	-2	-1	0	1	2	3
$f(x)$	6	1	-2	-3	-2	1	6

(b)

x	-3	-2	-1	0	1	2	3
$g(x)$	-8.1	-2.4	-0.3	0	0.3	2.4	8.1

(c)

x	-3	-2	-1	0	1	2	3
$f(x) + g(x)$	-2.1	-1.4	-2.3	-3	-1.7	3.4	14.1

(d)

x	-3	-2	-1	0	1	2	3
$f(x + 1)$	1	-2	-3	-2	1	6	13

37. Let $f(x)$ be an even function, and let $g(x)$ be an odd function. If possible, determine whether each function must be even or odd.

(a) $h(x) = f(x)g(x)$ (b) $k(x) = f(x) + g(x)$

(c) $m(x) = g(f(x))$

38. Let both $f(x)$ and $g(x)$ be odd functions. If possible, determine whether each function must be even or odd.

(a) $h(x) = f(x)g(x)$ (b) $k(x) = f(x) - g(x)$

(c) $m(x) = f(g(x))$

39. A function is called symmetric about the line $y = x$ if interchanging x and y gives the same graph. The simplest example is the function $y = x$. Graph another straight line that is symmetric about the line $y = x$ and give its equation.

40. Show that the graph of the function h is symmetric about the origin, given that

$$h(x) = \frac{1 + x^2}{x - x^3}.$$

41. Comment on the following justification that the function $f(x) = x^3 - x^2 + 1$ is an even function: Because $f(0) = 1 \neq -f(0)$, we know that $f(x)$ is not odd. If a function is not odd, it must be even.

42. Let $f(x)$ be a function that is always increasing and concave down. Determine whether each function is always increasing or always decreasing, and whether each function is always concave up or always concave down.

   (a) $f(-x)$ (b) $-f(x)$ (c) $-f(-x)$

43. Is it possible for an odd function whose domain is all real numbers to be strictly concave up?

44. Let $f(x) = b + mx$.

   (a) Can $f(x)$ be even? How?
   (b) Can $f(x)$ be odd? How?
   (c) Can $f(x)$ be both odd and even? How?

45. If f is an odd function and defined at $x = 0$, what is the value of $f(0)$? Explain how you can use this result to show that $c(x) = x + 1$ and $d(x) = 2^x$ are not odd.

46. In the first quadrant an even function is increasing and concave down. What can you say about the function's behavior in the second quadrant?

47. Show that the power function $f(x) = x^{1/3}$ is odd. Give a counterexample to the statement that all power functions of the form $f(x) = x^p$ are odd.

48. Graph $s(x) = 2^x + (\frac{1}{2})^x$, $c(x) = 2^x - (\frac{1}{2})^x$, and $n(x) = 2^x - (\frac{1}{2})^{x-1}$. State whether you think these functions are even, odd, or neither. Show that your statements are true using algebra. That is, prove or disprove statements such as $s(-x) = s(x)$.

49. There are functions that are *neither* even nor odd. Is there a function that is *both* even and odd?

50. Some functions are symmetric about the y-axis. Is it possible for a function to be symmetric about the x-axis?

6.3 VERTICAL STRETCHES AND COMPRESSIONS

We have studied translations and reflections of graphs. In this section, we consider vertical stretches and compressions of graphs. As with a vertical translation, a vertical stretch or compression of a function is represented by an outside change to its formula.

Vertical Stretch: An Amplifier

An amplifier takes a weak signal from a recording and transforms it into a stronger signal to power a set of speakers.

Figure 6.28 shows a graph of an audio signal (in volts) as a function of time, t, both before and after amplification. Notice that the wave crests of the amplified signal are 3 times as high as those of the original signal; similarly, the amplified wave troughs are 3 times deeper than the original wave troughs. The amplifier has boosted the strength of the signal by a factor of 3. If f is the original signal function and V is the amplified signal function, then

$$\underbrace{\text{Amplified signal strength at time } t}_{V(t)} = 3 \cdot \underbrace{\text{Original signal strength at time } t,}_{f(t)}$$

so we have

$$V(t) = 3 \cdot f(t).$$

This formula tells us that the values of the amplified signal are 3 times the values of the original signal. The graph of V is the graph of f stretched vertically by a factor of 3. As expected, a vertical stretch of the graph of $f(t)$ corresponds to an outside change in the formula.

Notice that the t-intercepts remain fixed under a vertical stretch, because the f-value of these points is 0, which is unchanged when multiplied by 3.

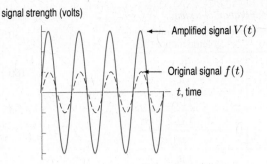

Figure 6.28: An amplifier transforms a weak signal into a signal 3 times as strong

Negative Stretch Factor

What happens if we multiply a function by a negative stretch factor? Figure 6.29 gives a graph of a function $y = f(x)$, together with a graph of $y = -2 \cdot f(x)$. The stretch factor is $k = -2$. We think of $y = -2f(x)$ as a combination of two separate transformations of $y = f(x)$. First, the graph is stretched by a factor of 2, then it is reflected across the x-axis.

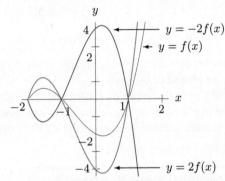

Figure 6.29: The graph of $y = -2f(x)$ is a vertically stretched version of the graph of $y = f(x)$ that has been reflected across the x-axis

Formula for Vertical Stretch or Compression

Generalizing the examples gives the following result:

If f is a function and k is a constant, then the graph of $y = k \cdot f(x)$ is the graph of $y = f(x)$
- Vertically stretched by a factor of k, if $k > 1$.
- Vertically compressed by a factor of k, if $0 < k < 1$.
- Vertically stretched or compressed by a factor $|k|$ and reflected across x-axis, if $k < 0$.

Example 1   A yam is placed in a 150°C oven. Table 6.12 gives values of $H = r(t)$, the yam's temperature t minutes after being placed in the oven. Figure 6.30 shows these data points joined by a curve.

(a) Describe the function r in words. What do the data tell you about the yam's temperature?
(b) Make a table of values for $q(t) = 1.5r(t)$. Graph the function q.
(c) How are the functions q and r related? Under what condition might q describe a yam's temperature?

Table 6.12   *Temperature of a yam*

t, time (min)	$r(t)$, temperature (°C)
0	0
10	75
20	113
30	131
40	141
50	145
60	148

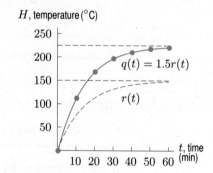

Figure 6.30: The temperature of a yam at time t

Solution

(a) The function r is increasing and concave down. The yam starts out at 0°C and warms up quickly at first. Later, the yam heats up more slowly. The temperature levels off at 150°C, the oven's temperature, represented by the horizontal asymptote.

(b) We calculate values of $q(t)$ from values of r. For example, Table 6.12 gives $r(0) = 0$ and $r(10) = 75$. Thus,

$$q(0) = 1.5r(0) = 1.5 \cdot 0 = 0,$$

$$q(10) = 1.5r(10) = 1.5(75) = 112.5 \text{ and so on.}$$

The values for $q(t)$ are 1.5 times as large as the corresponding values for $r(t)$. See Table 6.13. The data are plotted in Figure 6.31.

(c) The graph of q is the graph of r stretched vertically by a factor of $k = 1.5$. The horizontal asymptote of r was $H = 150$, so the horizontal asymptote of q is $H = 1.5 \cdot 150 = 225$. This suggests that the yam has been placed in a 225°C oven instead of a 150°C oven.

Table 6.13   *Values of $q(t) = 1.5r(t)$*

t, time (min)	$q(t)$, temperature (°C)
0	0
10	112.5
20	169.5
30	196.5
40	211.5
50	217.5
60	222

Figure 6.31: Graph of $q(t) = 1.5r(t)$

Stretch Factors and Average Rates of Change

Consider again the graph of the audio signal and its amplification in Figure 6.28. Notice that the amplified signal, V, is increasing on the same intervals as the original signal, f. Similarly, both functions decrease on the same intervals.

Stretching or compressing a function vertically does not change the intervals on which the function increases or decreases. However, the average rate of change of a function, visible in the steepness of the graph, is altered by a vertical stretch or compression.

Example 2   In Example 1, the function $H = r(t)$ gives the temperature (in °C) of a yam placed in a 150°C oven. The function $q(t) = 1.5r(t)$ gives the temperature of the yam placed in a 225°C oven. In both cases, the temperature starts at 0°C. After 10 minutes, $r(10) = 75°C$ and $q(10) = 112.5°C$.

(a) For each of the two yams, find the rate of change of temperature over ten-minute intervals from $t = 0$ to $t = 60$.

(b) For each ten-minute interval, what is the relationship between the two values you found in part (a) for the yams?

Solution   (a) For the yam with temperature $r(t)$, from $t = 0$ to $t = 10$, we have

$$\begin{matrix} \text{Average rate of change} \\ \text{of temperature, } r \end{matrix} = \frac{\Delta H}{\Delta t} = \frac{r(10) - r(0)}{10 - 0} = \frac{75 - 0}{10} = 7.5°\text{C/min.}$$

Thus, in the 150°C oven, the yam's temperature increased at an average rate of 7.5°C per minute. For the yam with temperature $q(t)$, from $t = 0$ to $t = 10$,

$$\begin{matrix} \text{Average rate of change} \\ \text{of temperature} \end{matrix} = \frac{\Delta H}{\Delta t} = \frac{112.5 - 0}{10} = 11.25°\text{C/min.}$$

Thus, in the 225°C oven, the yam's temperature increased at an average rate of 11.25°C per minute. Similar calculations for other time intervals give the values in Table 6.14.

(b) Notice that $11.25 = 1.5(7.5)$, and each rate of change in the 225°C oven is 1.5 times the corresponding rate of change in the 150°C oven. This reflects the fact that $q(t) = 1.5r(t)$.

Table 6.14   *The average rate of change of yams' temperatures, $r(t)$ and $q(t)$*

Time interval (min)	0 − 10	10 − 20	20 − 30	30 − 40	40 − 50	50 − 60
Average rate of change of r (°C/min)	7.5	3.8	1.8	1	0.4	0.3
Average rate of change of q (°C/min)	11.25	5.7	2.7	1.5	0.6	0.45

In the last example, multiplying a function by a factor of 1.5 had the effect of multiplying the function's average rate of change on each interval by the same factor. More generally, if $g(x) = k \cdot f(x)$, between $x = a$ and $x = b$,

$$\begin{matrix} \text{Average rate of change} \\ \text{of } y = g(x) \end{matrix} = \frac{\Delta y}{\Delta x} = \frac{g(b) - g(a)}{b - a} = \frac{k \cdot f(b) - k \cdot f(a)}{b - a}$$

$$= k \cdot \frac{f(b) - f(a)}{b - a} \quad \text{(factoring out } k\text{)}$$

$$= k \cdot \left(\begin{matrix} \text{Average rate of change} \\ \text{of } f \end{matrix} \right).$$

In general, we have the following result:

> If $g(x) = k \cdot f(x)$, then on any interval,
>
> Average rate of change of $g = k \cdot$ (Average rate of change of f).

Combining Stretches and Shifts

Stretches and shifts can be combined to give more general transformations of functions.

Example 3   The function $y = f(x)$ is graphed in Figure 6.32. Graph the function $g(x) = -\frac{1}{2}f(x+3) - 1$.

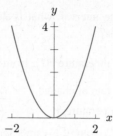

Figure 6.32: Graph of $y = f(x)$

Solution   To combine several transformations, always work from inside the parentheses outward as in Figure 6.33. The graphs corresponding to each step are shown in Figure 6.34. Note that we did not need a formula for f to graph g.

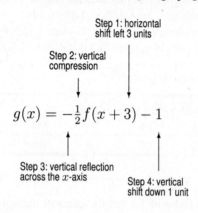

Figure 6.33

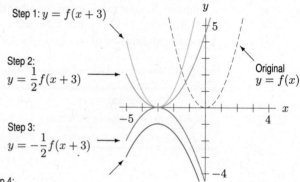

Figure 6.34: The graph of $y = f(x)$ transformed in four steps into $g(x) = -(1/2)f(x+3) - 1$

Exercises and Problems for Section 6.3

Skill Refresher

S1. If $f(x) = x^2$, evaluate each expression below at $x = 6$.

(a) $2f(x)$ (b) $-\frac{1}{2}f(x)$

(c) $5f(x) - 3$ (d) $\frac{1}{4}f(x - 1)$

S2. Evaluate each expression below at $x = -2$ if $g(x) = \frac{1}{x}$.

(a) $-4g(x)$ (b) $\frac{2}{3}g(x)$

(c) $2g(x + 5)$ (d) $-\frac{1}{5}g(-x)$

S3. Write a formula for each of the transformations of $f(x) = \sqrt{x}$ given below.

(a) $y = -\frac{1}{3}f(x)$ (b) $y = 5f(-x)$

(c) $y = 6f(x - 8)$ (d) $y = \frac{1}{4}f(2 - x)$

S4. Write a formula for each of the transformations of $p(x) = 3x^2 - 6$ given below.

(a) $y = 5p(x)$ (b) $y = -\frac{1}{3}p(-x)$

(c) $y = -2p(x + 3)$ (d) $y = \frac{5}{3}p(x - 1)$

Exercises

1. Let $y = f(x)$. Write a formula for the transformation that both increases the y-value by a factor of 10 and shifts the graph to the right by 2 units.

2. The graph of the function $g(x)$ contains the point $(5, \frac{1}{3})$. What point must be on the graph of $y = 3g(x + 1)$?

3. The range of the function $C(x)$ is $-1 \le C(x) \le 1$. What is the range of $0.25C(x)$?

Exercises 4–7 refer to functions obtained by applying a transformation to $P(n)$, whose domain is $-3 < n \le 8$ and range is $-6 \le P(n) < 12$. Find a possible formula for the function in terms of $P(n)$.

4. The domain of $Q(n)$ is $-3 < n \le 8$ and the range is $-2 \le Q(n) < 4$.

5. The domain of $R(n)$ is $-3 < n \le 8$ and the range is $-60 < R(n) \le 30$.

6. The domain of $S(n)$ is $-8 \le n < 3$ and the range is $2 \le S(n) < 20$.

7. The domain of $T(n)$ is $-10 < n \le 1$ and the range is $-1.5 \le T(n) < 3$.

In Exercises 8–11, graph and label $f(x)$, $4f(x)$, $-\frac{1}{2}f(x)$, and $-5f(x)$ on the same axes.

8. $f(x) = \sqrt{x}$

9. $f(x) = -x^2 + 7x$

10. $f(x) = e^x$

11. $f(x) = \ln x$

12. Using Table 6.15, make tables for the following transformations of f on an appropriate domain.

   (a) $\frac{1}{2}f(x)$ (b) $-2f(x + 1)$ (c) $f(x) + 5$
   (d) $f(x - 2)$ (e) $f(-x)$ (f) $-f(x)$

   Table 6.15

x	-3	-2	-1	0	1	2	3
$f(x)$	2	3	7	-1	-3	4	8

13. Using Table 6.16, create a table of values for

   (a) $f(-x)$ (b) $-f(x)$ (c) $3f(x)$

   (d) Which of these tables from parts (a), (b), and (c) represents an even function?

   Table 6.16

x	-4	-3	-2	-1	0	1	2	3	4
$f(x)$	13	6	1	-2	-3	-2	1	6	13

Without a calculator, graph the transformations in Exercises 14–19. Label at least three points.

14. $y = f(x + 3)$ if $f(x) = |x|$

15. $y = f(x) + 3$ if $f(x) = |x|$

16. $y = -g(x)$ if $g(x) = x^2$

17. $y = g(-x)$ if $g(x) = x^2$

18. $y = 3h(x)$ if $h(x) = 2^x$

19. $y = 0.5h(x)$ if $h(x) = 2^x$

20. Using Figure 6.35, match the functions (i)–(v) with a graph (a)–(i).

   (i) $y = 2f(x)$ (ii) $y = \frac{1}{3}f(x)$
   (iii) $y = -f(x + 1)$ (iv) $y = f(x + 2) + 1$
   (v) $y = f(-x)$

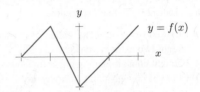

Figure 6.35

(a)

(b)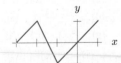

(c)

(d)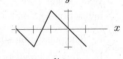

(e)

(f)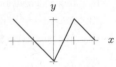

(g)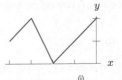

(h)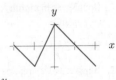

(i)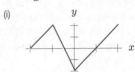

Problems

21. Describe the effect of the transformation $2f(x + 1)$ on the graph of $y = f(x)$.

22. The function $s(t)$ gives the distance (miles) in terms of time (hours). If the average rate of change of $s(t)$ on $0 \leq t \leq 4$ is 70 mph, what is the average rate of change of $\frac{1}{2}s(t)$ on this interval?

In Problems 23–27, let $f(t) = 1/(1+x^2)$. Graph the function given, labeling intercepts and asymptotes.

23. $y = f(t)$

24. $y = f(t - 3)$

25. $y = 0.5f(t)$

26. $y = -f(t)$

27. $y = f(t + 5) - 5$

28. The number of gallons of paint, $n = f(A)$, needed to cover a house is a function of the surface area, in ft^2. Match each story to one expression.

(a) I figured out how many gallons I needed and then bought two extra gallons just in case.

(b) I bought enough paint to cover my house twice.

(c) I bought enough paint to cover my house and my welcome sign, which measures 2 square feet.

(i) $2f(A)$ (ii) $f(A + 2)$ (iii) $f(A) + 2$

29. The US population in millions is $P(t)$ today and t is in years. Match each statement (I)–(IV) with one of the formulas (a)–(h).

I.   The population 10 years before today.

II. Today's population plus 10 million immigrants.

III. Ten percent of the population we have today.

IV. The population after 100,000 people have emigrated.

(a) $P(t) - 10$ (b) $P(t - 10)$ (c) $0.1P(t)$
(d) $P(t) + 10$ (e) $P(t + 10)$ (f) $P(t)/0.1$
(g) $P(t) + 0.1$ (h) $P(t) - 0.1$

30. Let $R = P(t)$ be the number of rabbits living in a national park in month t. What do the following expressions represent?

(a) $P(t + 1)$ (b) $2P(t)$

31. Suppose $C(t)$ represents the cost in Euros of the first t days of a business trip to France from the United States. Find a formula for $h(t)$, the cost in US dollars for the first t days. During the trip, 1 Euro was equivalent to 1.3 US dollars.

32. Suppose that $f(x)$ is the age in years of the ice x cm below the surface of a glacier in Antarctica. Find the age $g(x)$ for the same ice in centuries.

Graph the transformations of f in Problems 33–37 using Figure 6.36. Label the points corresponding to A and B.

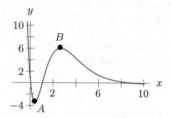

Figure 6.36

33. $y = f(x - 3)$

34. $y = f(x) - 3$

35. $y = f(-x)/3$

36. $y = -2f(x)$

37. Table 6.17 contains values of $f(x)$. Each function in parts (a)–(c) is obtained by applying a single transformation to $f(x)$. The transformation may be a stretch, compression, shift, or reflection. Find a possible formula for each of these functions in terms of f. For example, given the data in Table 6.18, we would say that $g(x) = 3f(x)$.

Table 6.17

x	-6	-4	-2	0	2	4	6
$f(x)$	12	4	-8	-14	-2	0	10

Table 6.18

x	-6	-4	-2	0	2	4	6
$g(x)$	36	12	-24	-42	-6	0	30

(a)

x	-6	-4	-2	0	2	4	6
$h(x)$	6	2	-4	-7	-1	0	5

(b)

x	-6	-4	-2	0	2	4	6
$k(x)$	10	0	-2	-14	-8	4	12

(c)

x	-6	-4	-2	0	2	4	6
$m(x)$	8	0	-12	-18	-6	-4	6

38. Using Figure 6.37, find formulas, in terms of f, for the horizontal and vertical shifts of the graph of f in parts (a)–(c). What is the equation of each asymptote?

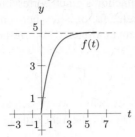

Figure 6.37

(a)

(b)

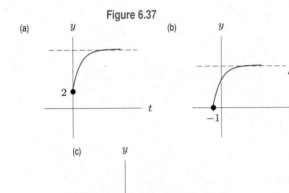

(c)

39. Using Figure 6.38, find formulas, in terms of f, for the transformations of f in parts (a)–(c).

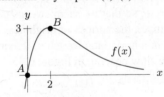

Figure 6.38

(a)

(b)

(c)

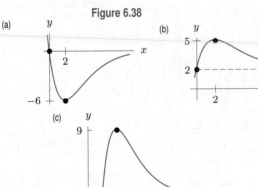

40. In Figure 6.39, the point b is labeled on the x-axis. On the y-axis, locate and label the output values:

(a) $f(b)$ (b) $-2f(b)$ (c) $-2f(-b)$

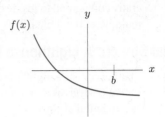

Figure 6.39

41. Figure 6.40 gives a graph of $y = f(x)$. Consider the transformations $y = \frac{1}{2}f(x)$ and $y = 2f(x)$. Which points on the graph of $y = f(x)$ stay fixed under these transformations? Compare the intervals on which all three functions are increasing and decreasing.

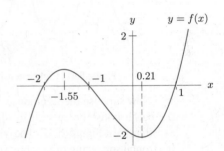

Figure 6.40

The average rate of change of $f(x)$ over the interval $a \leq x \leq b$ is 28, where a and b denote constants. In Problems 42–44 give the average rate of change over the interval $a \leq x \leq b$ for each transformation of $f(x)$.

42. $y = 3f(x)$ **43.** $y = -\frac{1}{4}f(x)$ **44.** $y = f(x) + 3$

6.4 HORIZONTAL STRETCHES AND COMPRESSIONS

In Section 6.3, we observed that a vertical stretch of a function's graph corresponds to an outside change in its formula, specifically, multiplication by a stretch factor. Since horizontal changes generally correspond to inside changes, we expect that a horizontal stretch will correspond to a constant multiple of the inputs. This turns out to be the case.

Horizontal Stretch: A Lighthouse Beacon

The beacon in a lighthouse turns once per minute, and its beam sweeps across a beach house. Figure 6.41 gives a graph of $L(t)$, the intensity, or brightness, of the light striking the beach house as a function of time.

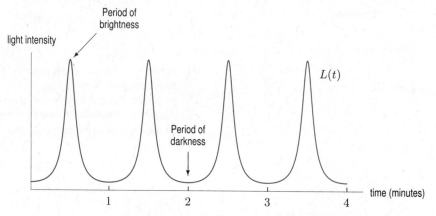

Figure 6.41: Light intensity or brightness, $L(t)$, as a function of time

Now suppose the lighthouse beacon turns twice as fast as before, so that its beam sweeps past the beach house twice instead of once each minute. The periods of brightness now occur twice as often. See Figure 6.42. The graph of $f(t)$, the intensity of light from this faster beacon, is a horizontal squeezing or compression of the original graph of $L(t)$.

If the lighthouse beacon turns at half its original rate, so that its beam sweeps past the beach house once every two minutes instead of once every minute, the periods of brightness occur half as often as originally. Slowing the beacon's speed results in a horizontal stretch of the original graph, illustrated by the graph of $s(t)$, the light intensity of the slow beacon, in Figure 6.43.

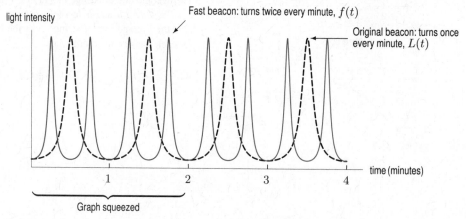

Figure 6.42: Comparing light intensity from the fast beacon, $f(t)$, to light intensity from the original beacon, $L(t)$

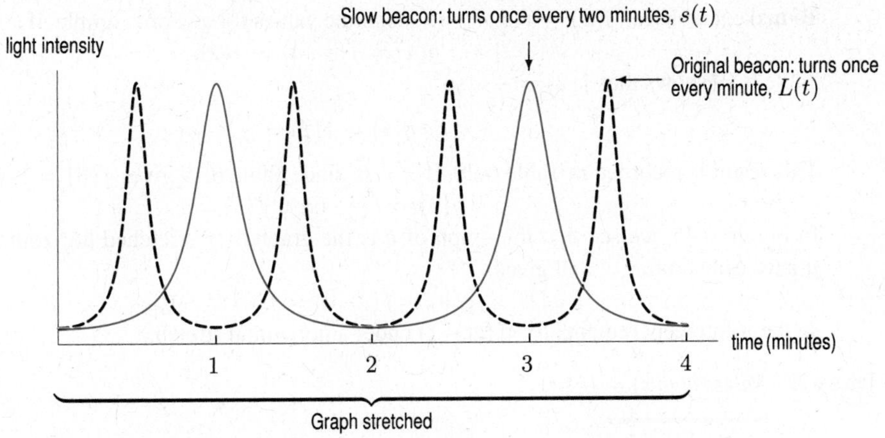

Slow beacon: turns once every two minutes, $s(t)$

light intensity

Original beacon: turns once every minute, $L(t)$

time (minutes)

Graph stretched

Figure 6.43: Comparing light intensity from the slow beacon, $s(t)$, to light intensity from the original beacon, $L(t)$

Formula for Horizontal Stretch or Compression

How are the formulas for the three light functions related? We expect that multiplying the function's input by a constant will horizontally stretch or compress its graph. The fast beacon corresponds to speeding up by a factor of 2, or multiplying the input by 2. Thus

$$f(t) = L(2t).$$

Similarly for the slow beacon, the input times are multiplied by $1/2$, so

$$s(t) = L(\tfrac{1}{2}t).$$

Generalizing the lighthouse example gives the following result:

If f is a function and k a positive constant, then the graph of $y = f(kx)$ is the graph of f
- Horizontally compressed by a factor of $1/k$ if $k > 1$,
- Horizontally stretched by a factor of $1/k$ if $k < 1$.

If $k < 0$, then the graph of $y = f(kx)$ also involves a horizontal reflection about the y-axis.

Example 1 Values of the function $f(x)$ are in Table 6.19 and its graph is in Figure 6.44. Make a table and a graph of the function $g(x) = f(\tfrac{1}{2}x)$.

Table 6.19 *Values of $f(x)$*

x	$f(x)$
-3	0
-2	2
-1	0
0	-1
1	0
2	-1
3	1

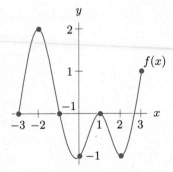

Figure 6.44

Solution   To make a table for $g(x) = f(\frac{1}{2}x)$, we substitute values for x. For example, if $x = 4$, then
$$g(4) = f(\tfrac{1}{2} \cdot 4) = f(2).$$
Table 6.19 shows that $f(2) = -1$, so

$$g(4) = f(2) = -1.$$

This result is recorded in Table 6.20. If $x = 6$, since Table 6.19 gives $f(3) = 1$, we have
$$g(6) = f(\tfrac{1}{2} \cdot 6) = f(3) = 1.$$
In Figure 6.45, we see that the graph of g is the graph of f stretched horizontally away from the y-axis. Substituting $x = 0$ gives

$$g(0) = f(\tfrac{1}{2} \cdot 0) = f(0) = -1,$$

so the y-intercept remains fixed (at -1) under a horizontal stretch.

Table 6.20   *Values of $g(x) = f(\frac{1}{2}x)$*

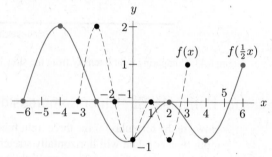

x	$g(x)$
-6	0
-4	2
-2	0
0	-1
2	0
4	-1
6	1

Figure 6.45: The graph of $g(x) = f(\frac{1}{2}x)$ is the graph of $y = f(x)$ stretched away from the y-axis by a factor of 2

Example 1 shows the effect of an inside multiple of $1/2$. We see that the graph of f is stretched by a factor of 2 horizontally from the y-axis. The next example shows the effect on the graph of an inside multiple of 2.

Example 2   Let $f(x)$ be the function in Example 1. Make a table and a graph for the function $h(x) = f(2x)$.

Solution   We use Table 6.19 and the formula $h(x) = f(2x)$ to evaluate $h(x)$ at several values of x. For example, if $x = 1$, then

$$h(1) = f(2 \cdot 1) = f(2).$$

Table 6.19 shows that $f(2) = -1$, so $h(1) = -1$. These values are recorded in Table 6.21. Similarly, substituting $x = 1.5$ gives

$$h(1.5) = f(2 \cdot 1.5) = f(3) = 1.$$

Table 6.21   *Values of $h(x) = f(2x)$*

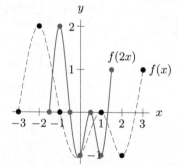

x	$h(x)$
-1.5	0
-1.0	2
-0.5	0
0.0	-1
0.5	0
1.0	-1
1.5	1

Figure 6.46: The graph of $h(x) = f(2x)$ is the graph of $y = f(x)$ compressed horizontally by a factor of $1/2$

Since $h(0) = f(2 \cdot 0) = f(0)$, the y-intercept remains fixed (at -1). In Figure 6.46 we see that the graph of h is the graph of f compressed by a factor of 1/2 horizontally toward the y-axis.

In Chapter 4, we used the function $P = 263e^{0.009t}$ to model the US population in millions. This function is a transformation of the exponential function $f(t) = e^t$, since we can write

$$P = 263e^{0.009t} = 263f(0.009t).$$

The US population is $f(t) = e^t$ stretched vertically by a factor of 263 and stretched horizontally by a factor of $1/0.009 \approx 111$.

Example 3   Match the functions $f(t) = e^t$, $g(t) = e^{0.5t}$, $h(t) = e^{0.8t}$, $j(t) = e^{2t}$ with the graphs in Figure 6.47.

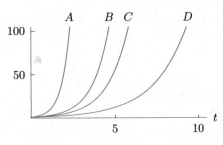

Figure 6.47

Solution   Since the function $j(t) = e^{2t}$ climbs fastest of the four and $g(t) = e^{0.5t}$ climbs slowest, graph A must be j and graph D must be g. Similarly, graph B is f and graph C is h.

Exercises and Problems for Section 6.4

Skill Refresher

In Exercises S1–S4, write a formula for each of the transformations of $f(x) = x^3 - 5$.

S1. $y = f(2x)$ **S2.** $y = 2f(x)$

S3. $y = f\left(-\frac{1}{3}x\right)$ **S4.** $y = \frac{1}{5}f(3x)$

In Exercises S5–S8, write a formula for each of the transformations of $Q(t) = 4e^{6t}$.

S5. $y = Q\left(\frac{1}{3}t\right)$ **S6.** $y = \frac{1}{3}Q(t)$

S7. $y = Q(2t) + 11$ **S8.** $y = 7Q(t - 3)$

Exercises

1. The point $(2, 3)$ lies on the graph of $g(x)$. What point must lie on the graph of $g(2x)$?

2. Describe the effect of the transformation $10f(\frac{1}{10}x)$ on the graph of $f(x)$.

3. Using Table 6.22, make a table of values for $f(\frac{1}{2}x)$ for an appropriate domain.

Table 6.22

x	-3	-2	-1	0	1	2	3
$f(x)$	2	3	7	-1	-3	4	8

4. Fill in all the blanks in Table 6.23 for which you have sufficient information.

Table 6.23

x	-3	-2	-1	0	1	2	3
$f(x)$	-4	-1	2	3	0	-3	-6
$f(\frac{1}{2}x)$							
$f(2x)$							

5. Graph $m(x) = e^x$, $n(x) = e^{2x}$, and $p(x) = 2e^x$ on the same axes and describe how the graphs of $n(x)$ and $p(x)$ compare with that of $m(x)$.

6. Graph $y = h(3x)$ if $h(x) = 2^x$.

In Exercises 7–9, graph and label $f(x)$, $f(\frac{1}{2}x)$, and $f(-3x)$ on the same axes between $x = -2$ and $x = 2$.

7. $f(x) = e^x + x^3 - 4x^2$

8. $f(x) = e^{x+7} + (x-4)^3 - (x+2)^2$

9. $f(x) = \ln(x^4 + 3x^2 + 4)$

10. Using Figure 6.48, match each function to a graph (if any) that represents it:

(i) $y = f(2x)$ (ii) $y = 2f(2x)$ (iii) $y = f(\frac{1}{2}x)$

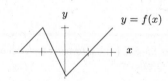

Figure 6.48

(a)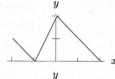
(b)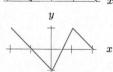
(c)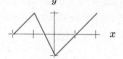
(d)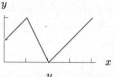
(e)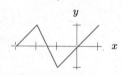
(f)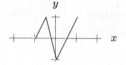
(g)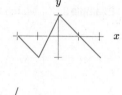
(h)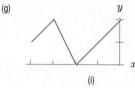
(i)

11. Using Figure 6.49, graph the following functions on separate sets of axes, together with the graph of the original function. Label any intercepts or special points.

(a) $y = f(3x)$ (b) $y = f(-2x)$ (c) $y = f(\frac{1}{2}x)$

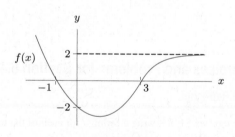

Figure 6.49

Problems

12. For the function $f(p)$ an input of 2 yields an output value of 4. What value of p would you use to have $f(3p) = 4$?

13. The domain of $l(x)$ is $-12 \le x \le 12$ and its range is $0 \le l(x) \le 3$. What are the domain and range of

(a) $l(2x)$?   (b) $l(\frac{1}{2}x)$?

14. The point (a, b) lies on the graph of $y = f(x)$. If the graph is stretched away from the y-axis by a factor of d (where $d > 1$), and then translated upward by c units, what are the new coordinates for the point?

In Problems 15–16, graph the transformation of f, the function in Figure 6.50.

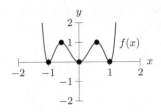

Figure 6.50

15. $y = -2f(x - 1)$ **16.** $y = f(x/2) - 1$

17. Let $T(d)$ be the temperature of the seawater in the Mariana Trench d meters below the surface. Find a formula for $p(x)$, the temperature x km below the surface.

18. Let $f(t)$ be a man's height in meters when he turns t months old. Find a formula for his height $g(n)$ in centimeters when he turns n years old.

19. Let $A(t)$ be the altitude in meters of a balloonist t minutes after liftoff. Find a formula for

(a) $f(s)$, the altitude s seconds after liftoff.
(b) $g(h)$, the altitude h hours after liftoff.

20. Every day I take the same taxi over the same route from home to the train station. The trip is x miles, so the cost for the trip is $f(x)$. Match each story in (a)–(d) to a function in (i)–(iv) representing the amount paid to the driver.

(a) I received a raise yesterday, so today I gave my driver a five-dollar tip.
(b) I had a new driver today and he got lost. He drove five extra miles and charged me for it.
(c) I haven't paid my driver all week. Today is Friday and I'll pay what I owe for the week.
(d) The meter in the taxi went crazy and showed five times the number of miles I actually traveled.

(i) $5f(x)$ (ii) $f(x) + 5$
(iii) $f(5x)$ (iv) $f(x + 5)$

21. A company projects a total profit, $P(t)$ dollars, in year t. Explain the economic meaning of $r(t) = 0.5P(t)$ and $s(t) = P(0.5t)$.

22. Let $A = f(r)$ be the area of a circle of radius r.

(a) Write a formula for $f(r)$.
(b) Which expression represents the area of a circle whose radius is increased by 10%? Explain.

(i) $0.10f(r)$ (ii) $f(r+0.10)$ (iii) $f(0.10r)$
(iv) $f(1.1r)$ (v) $f(r)+0.10$

(c) By what percent does the area increase if the radius is increased by 10%?

In Problems 23–24, state which graph represents

(a) $f(x)$ **(b)** $f(-2x)$ **(c)** $f(-\frac{1}{2}x)$ **(d)** $f(2x)$

23. 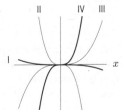   **24.**

25. Find a formula for the function in Figure 6.52 as a transformation of the function f in Figure 6.51.

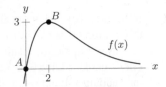

Figure 6.51

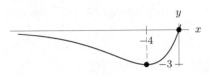

Figure 6.52

26. This problem investigates the effect of a horizontal stretch on the zeros of a function.

(a) Graph $f(x) = 4 - x^2$. Mark the zeros of f on the graph.
(b) Graph and find a formula for $g(x) = f(0.5x)$. What are the zeros of $g(x)$?
(c) Graph and find a formula for $h(x) = f(2x)$. What are the zeros of $h(x)$?
(d) Without graphing, what are the zeros of $f(10x)$?

27. In Figure 6.53, the point c is labeled on the x-axis. On the y-axis, locate and label output values:

(a) $g(c)$ (b) $2g(c)$ (c) $g(2c)$

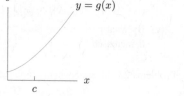

Figure 6.53

28. $g(x) = f(2x)$

29. $h(x) = f\left(\dfrac{1}{4}x\right)$

30. $k(x) = f(x+2)$ **31.** $m(x) = f(-x)$

32. Figure 6.54 shows the graphs of $f(x)$ and $g(x)$. It is claimed that $f(x)$ is a horizontal stretch of $g(x)$. If that could be true, find the stretch. If that could not be true, explain.

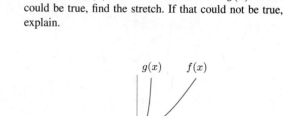

Figure 6.54

The function $f(x)$ has domain $-6 \le x \le 2$, and the average rate of change of $f(x)$ over the interval $-6 \le x \le 2$ is -3. For each transformation of $f(x)$ in Problems 28–31,

(a) State the domain of the function.

(b) Give the average rate of change of the function over its new domain found in part (a).

6.5   COMBINING TRANSFORMATIONS

In Sections 6.1–6.4, vertical and horizontal transformations were applied to graphs of functions. In this section we see what happens when several transformations are applied in succession.

In arithmetic, the result of a calculation depends on the order in which operations are performed. For example, adding 3 to 5 and then doubling the result gives a different result than doubling 5 and then adding 3 to the result, that is, $(5 + 3) \cdot 2 \ne 5 \cdot 2 + 3$.

The same is true when we apply a sequence of transformations to a function. For example, if we apply a horizontal shift followed by a horizontal stretch, we may get a different result than if we first applied the horizontal stretch followed by the horizontal shift.

Multiple Inside Changes

Inside changes lead to horizontal transformations. We see the effect of reversing the order of shifts and stretches (or compressions).

Example 1   Figure 6.55 shows the graph of a function g.

(a) Graph the function that is obtained by first shifting the graph of g horizontally right by 6 units and then compressing horizontally by a factor of $1/3$. Give a formula for this function.

(b) Graph the function that is obtained by first compressing the graph of g horizontally by a factor of $1/3$ and then shifting horizontally right by 6 units. Give a formula for this function.

(c) Compare the graphs in your answers to parts (a) and (b). How are they related?

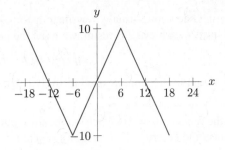

Figure 6.55: Graph of $y = g(x)$

Solution

(a) The first step is to shift the graph of g right by 6, giving the graph of an intermediate function, $w(x) = g(x - 6)$. The next step is to compress this graph by $1/3$, giving the graph of

$$y = w(3x) \qquad \text{compress intermediate graph by } 1/3$$
$$= g(3x - 6) \quad \text{since } w(x) = g(x - 6).$$

Notice that we do not really care about the intermediate function, w, beyond its role as the first step in the process. See Figure 6.56. A formula for the final result is $y = g(3x - 6)$.

(b) Here, the first step is to compress the graph of g horizontally by a factor of $1/3$, giving the graph of an intermediate function $v(x) = g(3x)$. The next step is to shift this graph to the right by 6, giving the graph of

$$y = v(x - 6) \qquad \text{shift intermediate graph right by } 6$$
$$= g\left(3(x - 6)\right). \quad \text{since } v(x) = g(3x)$$

Notice we only use the intermediate function, v, to keep track of the first step. See Figure 6.57. A formula for the final result is $y = g(3(x - 6))$.

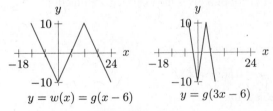

$y = w(x) = g(x - 6)$ $y = g(3x - 6)$

Figure 6.56: Graph of $y = g(3x - 6)$

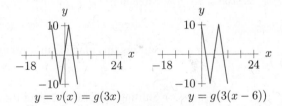

$y = v(x) = g(3x)$ $y = g(3(x - 6))$

Figure 6.57: Graph of $y = g(3(x - 6))$

(c) The final graphs in part (a) and (b) are the same shape and size, each extending 12 units in the x-direction and from -10 to 10 in the y-direction. However, they are in different positions. The graph in part (a) extends from -4 to 8, while the graph in part (b) extends from 0 to 12.

Example 1 shows that applying transformations in different orders can give different results. When we apply a horizontal shift and then a horizontal stretch or compression, the function is usually expressed in the the form $y = f(Bx - h)$, for example $y = g(3x - 6)$ in part (a). However, when we reverse the order and first apply a horizontal stretch or compression followed by a horizontal shift, the function is usually expressed in the form $y = f(B(x-h))$, for example $y = g(3(x-6))$

in part (b). In this section we usually rewrite transformations to apply the stretch/compression first, and then the shift. To achieve this result, we write the inside changes in the form

$$y = f(B(x - h)).$$

Then the horizontal stretch/compression factor is $1/|B|$ and the horizontal shift is h units.

Example 2   (a) Rewrite the function $y = f(2x - 6)$ in the form $y = f(B(x - h))$.

(b) Use the result to describe the graph of $y = f(2x - 6)$ as the result of first applying a horizontal stretch or compression to the graph of f and then applying a horizontal shift. What is the stretch/compression factor? What is the shift?

Solution   (a) We have $f(2x - 6) = f(2(x - 3))$.

(b) Thus, the graph of $y = f(2x - 6)$ can be obtained from the graph of $y = f(x)$ by first horizontally compressing it by a factor of $1/2$ and then shifting horizontally right by $h = 3$ units.

Multiple Outside Changes

We now see how two outside changes interact. Outside transformations lead to vertical transformations; first we see the effect of reversing the order of vertical shifts and vertical stretches (or compressions).

Example 3   (a) The graph of a function is obtained from the graph of $y = f(x)$ by first stretching vertically by a factor of 3 and then shifting upward by 2. Give a formula for the function in terms of f.

(b) The graph of a function is obtained from the graph of $y = f(x)$ by first shifting upward by 2 and then stretching vertically by a factor of 3. Give a formula for the function in terms of f.

(c) Are the results of parts (a) and (b) the same? If not, how are they related?

Solution   (a) Stretching the graph of f vertically by a factor of 3 gives the intermediate function

$$y = 3f(x);$$

shifting this function upward by 2 gives the result

$$y = 3f(x) + 2.$$

(b) Shifting upward by 2 gives the intermediate function

$$y = f(x) + 2;$$

stretching this function vertically by a factor of 3 gives the result

$$y = 3(f(x) + 2).$$

(c) The two functions are not the same. Since $y = 3(f(x) + 2) = 3f(x) + 6$, the two graphs are the same shape, but translated vertically by 4, the difference in the two shifts.

For outside changes, to apply the stretch/compression first, we write the function in the form

$$y = Af(x) + k.$$

Then the vertical stretch/compression factor is $|A|$ and the vertical shift is k.

Ordering Horizontal and Vertical Transformations

For transformations involving multiple inside and outside changes, it does not matter whether we do the inside changes first, or the outside changes. However, the order of the horizontal changes matters, as does the order of the vertical changes. We can follow the effect of a sequence of transformations on the graph by writing the function in the following form:

For nonzero constants A, B, h and k, the graph of the function

$$y = Af(B(x - h)) + k$$

is obtained by applying the transformations to the graph of $f(x)$ in the following order:
- Horizontal stretch/compression by a factor of $1/|B|$
- Horizontal shift by h units
- Vertical stretch/compression by a factor of $|A|$
- Vertical shift by k units

If $A < 0$, follow the vertical stretch/compression by a reflection about the x-axis.
If $B < 0$, follow the horizontal stretch/compression by a reflection about the y-axis.

Example 4 illustrates the use of these steps to graph multiple inside and outside changes.

Example 4   Figure 6.58 shows the graph of a function f.

(a) Put the function $r(x) = -\frac{1}{3}(f(2x - 8) + 3)$ in the form $y = Af(B(x - h)) + k$ and determine the values for constants A, B, h, and k.

(b) Express r as the result of applying a list of transformations to f, specifying the order in which the transformations are applied. Sketch a graph of r using the graph of f.

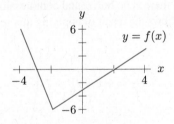

Figure 6.58: Graph of $y = f(x)$

Solution   (a) Expanding on the outside and factoring on the inside, we have

$$r(x) = -\frac{1}{3}f(2x - 8) - 1 = -\frac{1}{3}f\left(2(x - 4)\right) - 1,$$

so $A = -1/3, B = 2, h = 4$, and $k = -1$.

(b) See Figure 6.59. To find the graph of r, we carry out these steps:
- Horizontally compress the graph of f by $1/|B| = 1/2$.
- Horizontally shift the resulting graph to the right by $h = 4$.

- Vertically compress the resulting graph by $|A| = 1/3$ and reflect the graph about the x-axis.
- Vertically shift the resulting graph by $k = -1$.

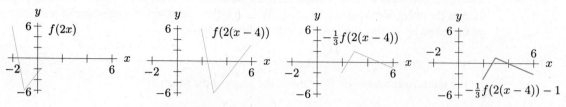

Figure 6.59: Graph of $y = -\frac{1}{3}(f(2x - 8) + 3)$

In Section 3.2 we found it useful to express a quadratic function in vertex form. In the next example, we revisit this idea in the context of transformations.

Example 5   (a) Let $y = 5(x + 2)^2 + 7$. Determine the values of $A, B, h,$ and k when y is put in the form $y = Af(B(x - h)) + k$ with $f(x) = x^2$. List the transformations applied to $f(x) = x^2$ to give $y = 5(x + 2)^2 + 7$.

(b) Using your answers in part (a), sketch a graph of $y = 5(x + 2)^2 + 7$, labeling the vertex.

Solution   (a) If $f(x) = x^2$, we see $y = 5(x + 2)^2 + 7 = 5f(x + 2) + 7$, so $A = 5$, $B = 1$, $h = -2$, and $k = 7$. Based on the values of these constants, we carry out these steps:

- Horizontal shift 2 to the left of the graph of $f(x) = x^2$.
- Vertical stretch of the resulting graph by a factor of 5.
- Vertical shift of the resulting graph up by 7.

Since $B = 1$, there is no horizontal compression, stretch, or reflection.

(b) Figure 6.60 shows the result of applying this sequence of transformations to the graph of f.

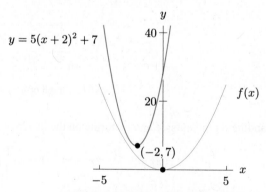

Figure 6.60: Graphs of $y = x^2$ and
$y = 5(x + 2)^2 + 7$

Exercises and Problems for Section 6.5

Skill Refresher

In Exercises S1–S4, solve for the constant h.

S1. $4x + 12 = 4(x - h)$ **S2.** $\frac{1}{5}t - 10 = \frac{1}{5}(t - h)$

S3. $-3z + 10 = -3(z - h)$ **S4.** $-\frac{1}{9}x - 4 = -\frac{1}{9}(x - h)$

S5. Let $f(x) = \sqrt[3]{x}$. Evaluate each expression at $x = 1$.

  (a) $f(8x) - 3$ **(b)** $8f(x - 3)$

  (c) $8f(x) - 3$ **(d)** $8(f(x) - 3)$

  (e) $f(8(x - 3))$ **(f)** $f(8x - 3)$

S6. Write a formula for each transformations of $Q(t) = e^t$.

  (a) $y = -7Q(t - 4)$ **(b)** $y = -7Q(t) - 4$

  (c) $y = -7(Q(t) - 4)$ **(d)** $y = Q(-7t) - 4$

  (e) $y = Q(-7(t - 4))$ **(f)** $y = \frac{1}{4}Q(-7t + 2) - 4$

In Exercises S7–S10, rewrite as $y = Af(B(x - h)) + k$ and give values for A, B, h, and k.

S7. $y = f(-2x) + 9$ **S8.** $y = -f(2x - 6) + 9$

S9. $y = 6f\left(-\frac{1}{3}x - 9\right)$

S10. $y = -5(f(-x - 7) + 2)$

Exercises

1. Describe $y = f(3x - 2)$ as the result of first applying a stretch or compression and then applying a shift to f.

2. Describe $y = 5(g(x) - 8)$ as the result of first applying a stretch or compression and then applying a shift to g.

3. $(6, -9)$. For each of the following functions, find a point on its graph:

  (a) $g(2x) - 5$ **(b)** $3g(x) + 1$

  (c) $-(g(\frac{1}{3}(x + 4)) - 8)$ **(d)** $\frac{1}{2}g(-5x - 15) - 8$

4. Table 6.24 gives values of x and $f(x)$. Supply the values of each function shown. In some cases, there may not be enough information to fill in a box.

Table 6.24

x	-2	-1	0	1	2
$f(x)$	-3	-4	2	0	5
$2f(x) + 3$					
$f(x - 1) + 1$					
$f(x + 2) - 1$					
$3f(2x + 2) - 1$					

5. Table 6.25 gives values of function v. Create a table giving five values of the function $w(t) = 40 - 2v(-0.5t)$.

Table 6.25

t	0	1	2	3	4
$v(t)$	20	17	16	19	23

6. Figure 6.61 shows the graph of $fx) = |x|$. Graph each transformation of $f(x)$:

  (a) $g(x) = f(x) + 1$ **(b)** $h(x) = f(x + 1)$

  (c) $j(x) = f(2x + 1) - 3$ **(d)** $k(x) = \frac{1}{2}f(2x - 4) + 1$

  (e) $m(x) = -\frac{1}{2}f(4x + 12) - 3$

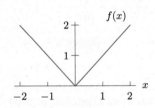

Figure 6.61

7. Figure 6.62 shows the graph of $fx) = 2^x$. Graph each transformation of $f(x)$:

  (a) $f(3x + 6)$ **(b)** $f(-\frac{1}{2}x - 1)$

  (c) $0.4f(-x + 1) - 2$ **(d)** $-f(\frac{1}{2}x + 4) + 1$

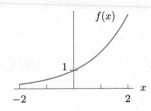

Figure 6.62

8. Using Figure 6.63, graph the following functions.

(a) $y = -f(x) + 2$ **(b)** $y = 2f(x)$

(c) $y = f(x - 3)$ **(d)** $y = -\dfrac{1}{2}f(x + 1) - 3$

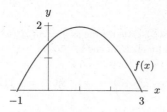

Figure 6.63

9. Using Figure 6.64, sketch $y = 2f(0.5x) + 20$.

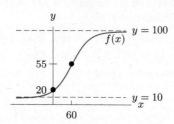

Figure 6.64

In Exercises 10–11, use Figure 6.65 to graph the function.

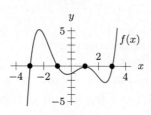

Figure 6.65

12. Using Figure 6.66, graph each of the following functions on separate sets of axes, together with the graph of the original function. Label intercepts and asymptotes.

(a) $y = 3f(x)$ **(b)** $y = f(x - 1)$

(c) $y = f(x) - 1$ **(d)** $y = -2f(x)$

(e) $y = \frac{1}{2}f(x + 2) - 1$ **(f)** $y = -f(-x)$

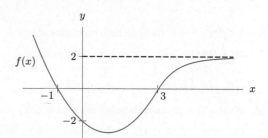

Figure 6.66

13. The graph of v has a horizontal asymptote at $y = -4$ and a vertical asymptote at $t = 5$. Give the asymptotes of $w(t) = 3 - 0.5v(-2t)$.

14. The function $p(t)$ has domain $1 \le t \le 12$ and range $-40 < p \le 160$. What is the new domain and range of

(a) $p(\frac{1}{5}t + 4)$?   **(b)** $-\frac{1}{10}p(2t) + 50$?

In Exercises 15–16, sketch and label graphs of the functions using Figure 6.67. Briefly describe the relationship between your graph and the graph of f.

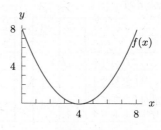

Figure 6.67

10. $y = -2f(-0.5x)$ **11.** $h(x) = f(2x - 1)$ **15.** $h(x) = f(2x + 6)$.   **16.** $q(x) = f(2(x + 6))$.

Problems

17. Figure 6.68 shows the graph of a function f.

  (a) Graph the function that is obtained by first shifting the graph of f vertically upward by 3 units and then stretching it vertically by a factor of 2.

  (b) Graph the function that is obtained by first stretching the graph of f vertically by a factor of 2 and then shifting up vertically by 3 units.

  (c) Compare your answers in parts (a) and (b).

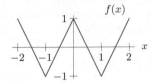

Figure 6.68

18. Is $y = f(2x - 6)$ the function obtained from f by a horizontal compression by a factor of $1/2$ followed by a horizontal shift of 6 units to the right? Explain why or why not.

19. Is the function $y = 5(g(x) - 2)$ obtained from g by a vertical stretch by a factor of 5 followed by a vertical shift of 2 units downward? If not, what vertical shift is needed?

20. The *Heaviside step function*, $H(x)$, is defined as follows:

$$H(x) = 1 \text{ for } x \geq 0$$
$$H(x) = 0 \text{ for } x < 0.$$

Graph the Heaviside function, then sketch graphs of the following transformations of H:

  (a) $y = H(x) - 2$ **(b)** $y = H(x + 2)$
  (c) $y = -3H(-x) + 4$

21. The graph of g is found by shifting the graph of f to the left by 4 units, then reflecting it vertically across the x-axis, then shifting it up by 2 units, then finally stretching it vertically by a factor of 3. Find a formula for g in terms of f.

22. The graph of g is the graph of f shifted right by 3 units, then reflected vertically across the x-axis, then shifted down by 2 units, then stretched vertically by a factor of 2. Find a formula for g in terms of f.

23. The graph of g is found by shifting the graph of f up by 2 units and left by 3 units. The graph of h is found by reflecting the graph of g horizontally, then reflecting it vertically and stretching it vertically by a factor of 2. Find a formula for h in terms of f.

In Problems 24–25, the points $(-12, 20)$, $(0, 6)$, $(36, -2)$ lie on the graph of f.

24. List three points on the graph of $g(x) = 10 - 2f(-3x)$.

25. The graph of f is found by shifting the graph of h to the left by 3 units, then stretching it vertically by a factor of 2, then shifting it up by 6 units. Find three points on the graph of h.

26. Use shifts, reflections, and vertical stretches to graph each parabola without a calculator. Then write each equation in standard form:

  (a) $y = (x + 3)^2 - 4$ **(b)** $y = -2(x + 1)^2 + 3$

27. Sketch $y = 160 - 4f(-x/10)$ if $f(x) = 20 \cdot 2^x$.

28. Let $h(t) = t^2$. Parts (a)–(c) investigate the effects of changing the order of horizontal transformations.

  (a) Give a formula in vertex form for the quadratic function obtained by first shifting the function $h(t)$ to the right 6 units and then compressing horizontally by a factor of $1/2$.

  (b) Give a formula in vertex form for the quadratic function obtained by first compressing the function $h(t)$ horizontally by a factor of $1/2$ and then shifting to the right 6 units.

  (c) If you first horizontally compress $h(t)$ by a factor of $1/2$, by how much and in what direction would you next need to shift horizontally in order to get the same result as in part (a)?

29. Which (if any) of the following transformations of f is not the same as the others?

  (a) Shift f up by 3, then stretch it vertically by a factor of 2, then reflect it vertically.

  (b) Reflect f vertically, then shift it down by 3, then stretch it vertically by a factor of 2.

  (c) Stretch f vertically by a factor of 2, then shift it up by 6, then reflect it vertically.

  (d) Reflect f vertically, then stretch it vertically by a factor of 2, then shift it down by 6.

30. Let $f(x) = e^x$ and $g(x) = 5e^{x-2}$. If $g(x) = kf(x)$, find k.

31. The log function has the property that the graph resulting from a horizontal stretch can also be obtained by a vertical shift.

  (a) Graph $f(x) = \log x$ and $g(x) = \log(10x)$ and determine the vertical shift.

  (b) Explain how you could have predicted the answer to part (a) from the properties of logarithms.

  (c) If $h(x) = \log(ax)$, what is the vertical shift k making $h(x) = \log(x) + k$?

32. Applying a horizontal stretch by a factor of k (where k is a constant such that $k > 1$) to $f(x) = \ln x$ is equivalent to applying what shift to f? Give both the amount and the direction of the shift.

33. Shifting $g(x) = e^x$ to the right k units (where k is a constant such that $k > 0$) is equivalent to applying what stretch or compression to g? Be sure you describe the amount and direction of the stretch or compression needed.

34. (a) The point $(-2, 5)$ lies on the graph of $y = r(x)$. What are the coordinates of the transformed point on the graph of $y = 3(r(x) + 2)$?
   (b) Express the function $y = 3(r(x)+2)$ as the result of first applying a vertical stretch or compression and then applying a vertical shift to the function r. What is the stretch/compression? What is the shift?

35. (a) Describe the graph of $y = 2f(x) + 8$ as the result of applying a stretch or compression to the graph of f, then applying a shift.
   (b) Now describe this graph as the result of applying a shift to the graph of f, then applying a stretch or compression.

36. (a) Describe the graph of $y = f\left(\frac{1}{3}x + 4\right)$ as the result of applying a stretch or compression to f, then applying a shift.
   (b) Describe this graph as the result of applying a shift to f, then applying a stretch or compression.

37. The function $d(t)$ graphed in Figure 6.69 gives the winter temperature in °F at a high school, t hours after midnight.

   (a) Describe in words the heating schedule for this building during the winter months.
   (b) Graph $c(t) = 142 - d(t)$.
   (c) Explain why c might describe the cooling schedule for summer months.

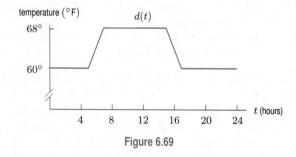

temperature (°F)

$d(t)$

Figure 6.69

38. Let $D(t)$ denote the depth, in meters, of the water at a fixed location in a bay t hours from noon. Find a formula for each function below by applying transformation(s) to $D(t)$.

   (a) $f(t)$, the depth of the tide in kilometers.

(b) $g(x)$, the depth of the tide in kilometers x minutes from noon.
(c) $j(x)$, the depth of the tide in kilometers x minutes from 2 pm.

39. Let f be defined by the graph in Figure 6.70. Find formulas (in terms of f) for the following transformations of f and sketch a graph of each. Show that these transformations lead to different outcomes.

   (a) First shift the graph of f upward by 3 units, then reflect it across the x-axis.
   (b) First reflect the graph of f across the x-axis. Then, shift it upward by 3 units.

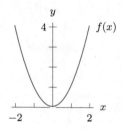

Figure 6.70

40. (a) Graph $h(x) = -2x^2 - 8x - 8$.
   (b) Compare the graphs of $h(x)$ and $f(x) = x^2$. How are these two graphs related? Be specific.

For Problems 41–42, find a formula for the family of functions obtained from $f(x)$ by: **(a)** Stretching vertically **(b)** Stretching vertically and shifting horizontally. Compare the graph of a typical member of the family and the graph of $f(x)$. Include intercepts and asymptotes in your discussion. Are the two families the same?

41. $f(x) = x$ **42.** $f(x) = 2^x$

In Problems 43–45, you are given that $g(x) = r \cdot f(sx) + j$, where r, s, j are constants.

43. For the linear function $f(x) = b + mx$, is g also linear? If so, write g in the form $g(x) = B + Mx$ and state the values of B and M.

44. For the exponential function $f(x) = ae^{kx}$, is g also exponential? If so, write g in the form $g(x) = Ae^{Kx}$ and state the values of A and K.

45. For the quadratic function $f(x) = a(x - h)^2 + k$, is g also quadratic? If so, write g in the form $g(x) = A(x - H)^2 + K$ and state the values of A, H, and K.

CHAPTER SUMMARY

- **Vertical and Horizontal Shifts**
  Vertical: $y = g(x) + k$.
  Upward if $k > 0$; downward if $k < 0$.
  Horizontal: $y = g(x + k)$.
  Left if $k > 0$; right if $k < 0$.

- **Reflections**
  Across x-axis: $y = -f(x)$.
  Across y-axis: $y = f(-x)$.

- **Symmetry**
  About y-axis: $f(-x) = f(x)$; even function.
  About the origin: $f(-x) = -f(x)$; odd function.

- **Stretches and Compressions**
  Vertical: $y = kf(x)$. Stretch if $|k| > 0$; compress if

  $0 < |k| < 1$; reflect across x-axis if $k < 0$.
  Horizontal: $y = f(kx)$. Compress if $|k| > 0$; stretch if
  $0 < |k| < 1$; reflect across y-axis if $k < 0$.

- **Combining Transformations**
  Standard form: $y = Af(B(x - h)) + k$.
  Order of changes to graph of f:
      Horizontal stretch/compression by a factor of $1/|B|$
      Horizontal shift by h units
      Vertical stretch/compression by a factor of $|A|$
      Vertical shift by k units
  If $A < 0$, reflect about the x-axis.
  If $B < 0$, reflect about the y-axis.

REVIEW EXERCISES AND PROBLEMS FOR CHAPTER SIX

Exercises

1. Suppose $x = 2$. Determine the value of the input of the function f in each of the following expressions:

   (a) $f(2x)$ (b) $f(\frac{1}{2}x)$ (c) $f(x+3)$ (d) $f(-x)$

2. Determine the value of x in each of the following expressions that leads to an input of 2 to the function f:

   (a) $f(2x)$ (b) $f(\frac{1}{2}x)$ (c) $f(x+3)$ (d) $f(-x)$

3. The point $(2, 5)$ is on the graph of $y = f(x)$. Give the coordinates of one point on the graph of each of the following functions.

   (a) $y = f(x - 4)$ (b) $y = f(x) - 4$
   (c) $y = f(4x)$ (d) $y = 4f(x)$

4. The point $(-3, 4)$ is on the graph of $y = g(x)$. Give the coordinates of one point on the graph of each of the following functions.

   (a) $y = g(\frac{1}{3}x)$ (b) $y = \frac{1}{3}g(x)$
   (c) $y = g(-3x)$ (d) $y = -g(3x)$

Are the functions in Exercises 5–10 even, odd, or neither?

5. $a(x) = \dfrac{1}{x}$

6. $m(x) = \dfrac{1}{x^2}$

7. $e(x) = x + 3$

8. $p(x) = x^2 + 2x$

9. $b(x) = |x|$

10. $q(x) = 2^{x+1}$

11. Let $f(x) = 1 - x$. Evaluate and simplify:

   (a) $f(2x)$ (b) $f(x + 1)$ (c) $f(1 - x)$
   (d) $f(x^2)$ (e) $f(1/x)$ (f) $f(\sqrt{x})$

12. Fill in all the blanks in Table 6.26 for which you have sufficient information.

Table 6.26

x	-3	-2	-1	0	1	2	3
$f(x)$	-4	-1	2	3	0	-3	-6
$f(-x)$							
$-f(x)$							
$f(x) - 2$							
$f(x - 2)$							
$f(x) + 2$							
$f(x + 2)$							
$2f(x)$							
$-f(x)/3$							

Problems

In Problems 13–14, use Figure 6.71 to sketch the function.

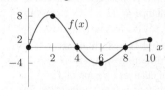

Figure 6.71

13. $y = f(x + 2) + 2$ **14.** $y = -2f(-x)$

In Problems 15–16, use Figure 6.71 to find a possible formula for the transformation of f shown.

15.

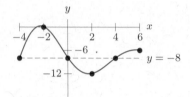

16.

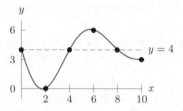

17. The function $f(x)$ contains the point $(-3, 1)$. The function $g(x)$ is obtained by applying a single transformation to the graph of $f(x)$ such that $g(x)$ contains the point $(3, 1)$. Describe the transformation that is applied to $f(x)$ in order to get the function $g(x)$ if

  (a) $g(x)$ is obtained by applying only one reflection to the graph of $f(x)$.
  (b) $g(x)$ is obtained by applying only one shift to the graph of $f(x)$.

18. Let $D(p)$ be the number of iced cappuccinos sold each week by a coffeehouse when the price is p cents.

  (a) What does the expression $D(225)$ represent?
  (b) Do you think that $D(p)$ is an increasing function or a decreasing function? Why?
  (c) What does the following equation tell you about p?
    $D(p) = 180$
  (d) The coffeehouse sells n iced cappuccinos when they charge the average price in their area, t cents. Thus, $D(t) = n$. What is the meaning of the following expressions: $D(1.5t)$, $1.5D(t)$, $D(t+50)$, $D(t)+50$?

19. Without a calculator, match each of the functions (a)–(f) with one of the graphs (I)–(VI).

  (a) $y = e^x$ **(b)** $y = e^{5x}$ **(c)** $y = 5e^x$
  (d) $y = e^{x+5}$ **(e)** $y = e^{-x}$ **(f)** $y = e^x + 5$

(I) 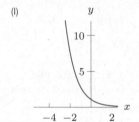   (II)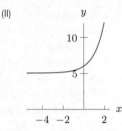

(III) 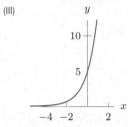   (IV)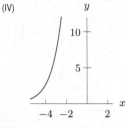

(V) 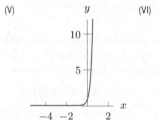   (VI)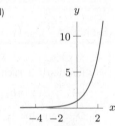

20. The graph in Figure 6.72 gives the number of hours of daylight in Charlotte, North Carolina on day d of the year, where $d = 0$ is January 1. Graph the number of hours of daylight in Buenos Aires, Argentina, which is as far south of the equator as Charlotte is north. [Hint: When it is summer in the Northern Hemisphere, it is winter in the Southern Hemisphere.]

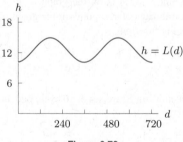

Figure 6.72

21. During a hurricane, a brick breaks loose from the top of a chimney, 38 feet above the ground. As the brick falls, its distance from the ground after t seconds is given by:

$$d(t) = -16t^2 + 38.$$

(a) Find formulas for $d(t) - 15$ and $d(t - 1.5)$.

(b) On the same axes, graph $d(t)$, $d(t) - 15$, $d(t - 1.5)$.

(c) Suppose $d(t)$ represents the height of a brick which began to fall at noon. What might $d(t) - 15$ represent? $d(t - 1.5)$?

(d) Using algebra, determine when the brick hits the ground:

  (i) If $d(t)$ represents the distance of the brick from the ground,

  (ii) If $d(t) - 15$ represents the distance of the brick from the ground.

(e) Use one of your answers in part (d) to determine when the brick hits the ground if $d(t - 1.5)$ represents its distance above the ground at time t.

The functions graphed in Problems 22–23 are transformations of some basic function. Give a possible formula for each one.

22.

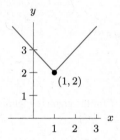

23.

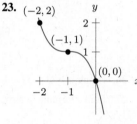

In Problems 24–25, use Figure 6.73 to find a formula for the transformations of $h(x)$.

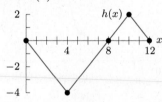

Figure 6.73

24.

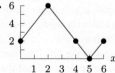

25.

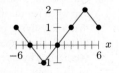

Problems 26–30 use Table 6.27 which gives the total cost, $C = f(n)$, for a carpenter to build n wooden chairs.

Table 6.27

n	0	10	20	30	40	50
$f(n)$	5000	6000	6800	7450	8000	8500

26. Evaluate the following expressions. Explain in everyday terms what they mean.

(a) $f(10)$ (b) $f(x)$ if $x = 30$

(c) z if $f(z) = 8000$ (d) $f(0)$

27. Find approximate values for p and q if $f(p) = 6400$ and $q = f(26)$.

28. Let $d_1 = f(30) - f(20)$, $d_2 = f(40) - f(30)$, and $d_3 = f(50) - f(40)$.

(a) Evaluate d_1, d_2 and d_3.

(b) What do these numbers tell you about the carpenter's cost of building chairs?

29. Graph $f(n)$. Label the quantities you found in Problems 26–28 on your graph.

30. The carpenter currently builds k chairs per week.

(a) What do the following expressions represent?

  (i) $f(k + 10)$ (ii) $f(k) + 10$
  (iii) $f(2k)$ (iv) $2f(k)$

(b) If the carpenter sells his chairs at 80% above cost, plus an additional 5% sales tax, write an expression for his gross income (including sales tax) each week.

31. In Figure 6.74, the value of d is labeled on the x-axis. Locate the following quantities on the y-axis:

(a) $g(d)$ (b) $g(-d)$ (c) $-g(-d)$

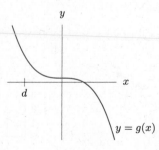

Figure 6.74

32. In Figure 6.75, the values c and d are labeled on the x-axis. On the y-axis, locate the following quantities:

(a) $h(c)$ **(b)** $h(d)$

(c) $h(c + d)$ **(d)** $h(c) + h(d)$

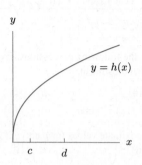

Figure 6.75

In Problems 33–35, use Figure 6.76 to find a formula for the graphs in terms of h.

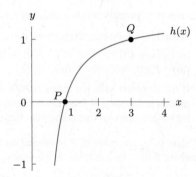

Figure 6.76

35.

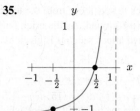

For Problems 36–37 use the graph of $y = f(x)$ in Figure 6.77.

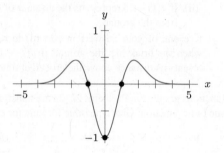

Figure 6.77

36. Graph $y = 2 - f(x - 2)$.

37. Find a formula in terms of f for the graph in Figure 6.78.

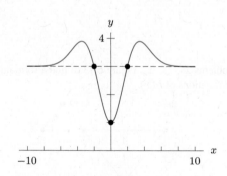

Figure 6.78

38. Gwendolyn, a pleasant parabola, was taking a peaceful nap when her dream turned into a nightmare: she dreamt that a low-flying pterodactyl was swooping toward her. Startled, she flipped over the horizontal axis, darted up (vertically) by three units, and to the left (horizontally) by two units. Finally she woke up and realized that her equation was $y = (x - 1)^2 + 3$. What was her equation before she had the bad dream?

33.

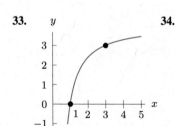

34.

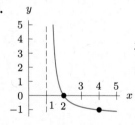

39. Suppose $w = j(x)$ is the average daily quantity of water (in gallons) required by an oak tree of height x feet.

    (a) What does the expression $j(25)$ represent? What about $j^{-1}(25)$?

    (b) What does the following equation tell you about v: $j(v) = 50$. Rewrite this statement in terms of j^{-1}.

    (c) Oak trees are on average z feet high and a tree of average height requires p gallons of water. Represent this fact in terms of j and then in terms of j^{-1}.

    (d) Using the definitions of z and p from part (c), what do the following expressions represent?

$$j(2z), \quad 2j(z), \quad j(z+10), \quad j(z)+10,$$
$$j^{-1}(2p), \quad j^{-1}(p+10), \quad j^{-1}(p)+10.$$

Table 6.28 gives values of $T = f(d)$, the average temperature (in °C) at a depth d meters in a borehole in Belleterre, Quebec. The functions in Problems 40–45 describe boreholes near Belleterre. Construct a table of values for each function and describe in words what it tells you about the borehole.[2]

Table 6.28

d, depth (m)	25	50	75	100
T, temp (°C)	5.5	5.2	5.1	5.1
d, depth (m)	125	150	175	200
T, temp (°C)	5.3	5.5	5.75	6

40. $g(d) = f(d) - 3$ **41.** $h(d) = f(d+5)$

42. $m(d) = f(d - 10)$ **43.** $n(d) = 1.5f(d)$

44. $p(d) = f(0.8d)$ **45.** $q(d) = 1.5f(d) + 2$

CHECK YOUR UNDERSTANDING

Are the statements in Problems 1–23 true or false? Give an explanation for your answer.

1. If $g(x) = f(x) + 3$ then the graph of $g(x)$ is a vertical shift of the graph of f.

2. If $g(t) = f(t - 2)$ then the graph of $g(t)$ can be obtained by shifting the graph of f two units to the left.

3. If $g(x) = f(x) + k$ and k is negative, the graph of $g(x)$ is the same as the graph of f, but shifted down.

4. Vertical and horizontal shifts are called translations.

5. The reflection of $y = x^2$ across the x-axis is $y = -x^2$.

6. If $f(x)$ is an odd function, then $f(x) = f(-x)$.

7. The graphs of odd functions are symmetric about the y-axis.

8. The graph of $y = -f(x)$ is the reflection of the graph of $y = f(x)$ across the x-axis.

9. The graph of $y = f(-x)$ is the reflection of the graph of $y = f(x)$ across the y-axis.

10. If the graph of a function f is symmetric about the y-axis then $f(x) = f(-x)$.

11. Figure 6.79 suggests that $g(x) = f(x+2) + 1$.

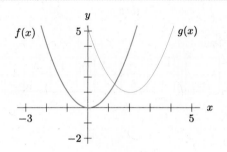

Figure 6.79

12. If $g(x) = x^2 + 4$ then $g(x - 2) = x^2$.

13. For any function f, we have $f(x + k) = f(x) + k$.

14. Figure 6.80 could be the graph of $f(x) = |x - 1| - 2$.

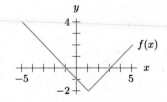

Figure 6.80

[2]Hugo Beltrami of St. Francis Xavier University and David Chapman of the University of Utah posted this data at http://esrc.stfx.ca/borehole/node3.html, accessed December 20, 2005.

15. Let $f(x) = 3^x$. If the graph of $f(x)$ is reflected across the x-axis and then shifted up four units, the new graph has the equation $y = -3^x + 4$.

16. If $q(p) = p^2 + 2p + 4$ then $-q(-p) = p^2 - 2p + 4$.

17. Multiplying a function by a constant k, with $k > 1$, vertically stretches its graph.

18. If $g(x) = kf(x)$, then on any interval the average rate of change of g is k times the average rate of change of f.

19. Figure 6.81 suggests that $g(x) = -2f(x + 1) + 3$.

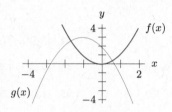

Figure 6.81

20. Using Table 6.29, we can conclude that if $g(x) = -\frac{1}{2}f(x + 1) - 3$, then $g(-2) = -10$.

Table 6.29

x	-3	-2	-1	0	1	2	3
$f(x)$	10	6	4	1	-2	-4	-10

21. Shifting the graph of a function up by one unit and then compressing it vertically by a factor of $\frac{1}{2}$ produces the same result as first compressing the graph by a factor of $\frac{1}{2}$ and then shifting it up by one unit.

22. Figure 6.82 suggests that $g(x) = 3f(\frac{1}{2}x)$.

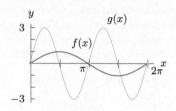

Figure 6.82

23. For the function given in Table 6.30, for $x = -2$, we have $3f(2x) + 1 = -2f(\frac{1}{2}x)$.

Table 6.30

x	-4	-3	-2	-1	0	1	2
$f(x)$	1	4	0	-2	0	0	-2

Chapter Ten

COMPOSITIONS, INVERSES, AND COMBINATIONS OF FUNCTIONS

Contents

10.1 COMPOSITION OF FUNCTIONS

Recall that composition of functions was introduced in Section 2.4.

> The function $f(g(t))$ is said to be a **composition** of f with g. The function $f(g(t))$ is defined by using the output of the function g as the input to f.

The composite function $f(g(t))$ is only defined for values in the domain of g whose $g(t)$ values are in the domain of f.

For example, recall the London Eye Ferris wheel example from Section 7.1. We wished to find the height on the Ferris wheel at a particular time. If $H = f(\theta)$ represents the height on the Ferris wheel (in feet) as a function of angular position (in degrees) and $\theta = g(t)$ represents the angular position as a function of time (in minutes), then the composition of f with g gives a function $H = f(g(t))$ that represents the height on the Ferris wheel as a function of time.

Formulas for Composite Functions

A therapeutic drug has the side effect of raising a patient's heart rate. The relation between Q, the amount of drug in the patient's body (in milligrams), and r, the patient's heart rate (in beats per minute), is given by the formula

$$r = f(Q) = 60 + 0.2Q.$$

Over time, the level of the drug in the patient's bloodstream falls. The drug level as a function of time t, in hours since the initial injection, is

$$Q = g(t) = 250(0.8)^t.$$

Since heart rate depends on the drug level and drug level depends on time, the heart rate also depends on time. To find a formula for heart rate as a function of time, we use the function $g(t)$ as the input to f. Thus,

$$r = f(\underbrace{\text{input}}_{g(t)}) = 60 + 0.2(\underbrace{\text{input}}_{g(t)}),$$

so

$$r = f(g(t)) = 60 + 0.2g(t).$$

Substituting the formula for $g(t)$ gives

$$r = h(t) = f(g(t)) = 60 + 0.2 \cdot \underbrace{250(0.8)^t}_{g(t)}$$

so

$$r = h(t) = 60 + 50(0.8)^t.$$

Notice that the units of the input in this composite function are hours (the same units as the input in the inside function g), and the units of the output of the composite function are beats per minute (the same units as the output of the outside function f).

So far we have considered examples of two functions composed together, but there is no limit on the number of functions that can be composed. Functions can even be composed with themselves.

Example 1   Let $p(x) = \sin x + 1$ and $q(x) = x^2 - 3$. Find a formula in terms of x for $w(x) = p(p(q(x)))$.

Solution   We work from inside the parentheses outward. First we find $p(q(x))$, and then input the result to p.

$$w(x) = p(p(q(x)))$$
$$= p(p(x^2 - 3))$$
$$= p(\underbrace{\sin(x^2 - 3) + 1}_{\text{Input for } p})$$
$$= \sin(\sin(x^2 - 3) + 1) + 1. \qquad \text{Because } p(\text{Input}) = \sin(\text{Input}) + 1$$

Composition of Functions Defined by Tables

Often we do not have a formula for a function, but we can arrange the values of the function we do know in a table. In the next example, we compose functions that are defined using tables.

Example 2   Complete Table 10.1. Assume that $f(x)$ is invertible.

Table 10.1

x	$f(x)$	$g(x)$	$g(f(x))$
0	2	3	2
1	3	1	3
2	1	2	?

Solution   We will first look at $g(f(2))$. From the table we see that $f(2) = 1$. Therefore, we have $g(f(2)) = g(1)$. Since $g(1) = 1$, we can fill in the entry for $g(f(2))$ the following way: $g(f(2)) = g(1) = 1$.

To find $g(2)$, we have to use information about $g(f(x))$. We first need to find a value of x such that $f(x) = 2$. That means that we are looking for $f^{-1}(2)$. From the table we see that $f^{-1}(2) = 0$, or equivalently, $f(0) = 2$. Therefore, $g(2) = g(f(0))$. From the table we see that $g(f(0)) = 2$. Thus, $g(2) = 2$.

Composition of Functions Defined by Graphs

So far we have composed functions defined by tables and formulas. We can also compose functions defined by graphs.

Example 3   Let u and v be two functions defined by the graphs in Figure 10.1. Evaluate:

(a) $v(u(-1))$ (b) $u(v(5))$ (c) $v(u(0)) + u(v(4))$

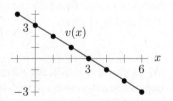

Figure 10.1: Evaluate the composition of functions u and v defined by their graphs

Solution   (a) To evaluate $v(u(-1))$, start with $u(-1)$. From Figure 10.1, we see that $u(-1) = 1$. Thus,

$$v(u(-1)) = v(1).$$

From the graph we see that $v(1) = 2$, so

$$v(u(-1)) = 2.$$

(b) Since $v(5) = -2$, we have $u(v(5)) = u(-2) = 0$.

(c) Since $u(0) = 0$, we have $v(u(0)) = v(0) = 3$.
Since $v(4) = -1$, we have $u(v(4)) = u(-1) = 1$.
Thus $v(u(0)) + u(v(4)) = 3 + 1 = 4$.

Decomposition of Functions

Sometimes we reason backward to find the functions that went into a composition. This process is called *decomposition*.

Example 4   Let $h(x) = f(g(x)) = e^{x^2+1}$. Find possible formulas for $f(x)$ and $g(x)$.

Solution   In the formula $h(x) = e^{x^2+1}$, the expression $x^2 + 1$ is in the exponent. We can take the inside function to be $g(x) = x^2 + 1$. This means that we can write

$$h(x) = e\underbrace{x^2 + 1}_{g(x)} = e^{g(x)}.$$

Then the outside function is $f(x) = e^x$. We check that composing f and g gives h:

$$f(g(x)) = f(x^2 + 1) = e^{x^2+1} = h(x).$$

There are many possible solutions to Example 4. For example, we might choose $f(x) = e^{x+1}$ and $g(x) = x^2$. Then

$$f(g(x)) = e^{g(x)+1} = e^{x^2+1} = h(x).$$

Alternatively, we might choose $f(x) = e^{x^2+1}$ and $g(x) = x$. Although this satisfies the condition that $h(x) = f(g(x))$, it is not very useful, because f is the same as h. This kind of decomposition is referred to as *trivial*. Another example of a trivial decomposition of $h(x)$ is $f(x) = x$ and $g(x) = e^{x^2+1}$.

We saw in Example 1 that we can compose more than two functions. Similarly, it may be possible to decompose a function into more than two simpler functions.

Example 5   Let $p(z) = \sin^2(\ln z)$. Decompose $p(z)$ into three simpler functions by giving formulas for $f(z)$, $g(z)$, and $h(z)$ where

$$p(z) = f(g(h(z))).$$

Solution   We work from inside the parentheses outward. In the formula $p(z) = \sin^2(\ln z)$, we have the expression $\ln z$ inside the $\sin^2$ function. In the formula $p(z) = f(g(h(z)))$, the innermost function is $h(z)$. Thus, we let

$$h(z) = \ln z.$$

In the formula $p(z) = \sin^2(\ln z)$, the operation $\sin^2$ applied to the innermost expression $\ln z$ means we first take the sin of $\ln z$ and then square the result. In other words, $p(z) = (\sin(\ln z))^2$. Thus, we let

$$g(\text{Input}) = \sin(\text{Input})$$
$$g(z) = \sin z.$$

So we have

$$g(h(z)) = g(\ln z) = \sin(\ln z).$$

Finally, since $p(z) = \sin^2(\ln z) = (\sin(\ln z))^2$, we square the expression $\sin(\ln z)$ and let

$$f(\text{Input}) = \text{Input}^2$$
$$f(z) = z^2.$$

To check, we compute

$$f(g(h(z))) = f(g(\ln z)) \qquad \text{Since } h(z) = \ln z$$
$$= f(\underbrace{\sin(\ln z)}_{\text{Input for } f}) \qquad \text{Since } g(\ln z) = \sin(\ln z)$$
$$= \sin^2(\ln z). \qquad \text{Since } f(\sin(\ln z)) = (\sin(\ln z))^2$$

Exercises and Problems for Section 10.1

Exercises

In Exercises 1–2, find and simplify for $f(x) = 2^x$ and $g(x) = \dfrac{x}{x+1}$.

1. $f(g(x))$

2. $g(f(x))$

3. Let $f(x) = \sin 4x$ and $g(x) = \sqrt{x}$. Find formulas for $f(g(x))$ and $g(f(x))$.

4. Let $m(x) = 3 + x^2$ and $n(x) = \tan x$. Find formulas for $m(n(x))$ and $n(m(x))$.

5. Find a formula in terms of x for the function $w(x) = p(p(x))$, where $p(x) = 2x + 1$.

6. Use Table 10.2 to construct a table of values for $r(x) = p(q(x))$.

Table 10.2

x	0	1	2	3	4	5
$p(x)$	1	0	5	2	3	4
$q(x)$	5	2	3	1	4	8

7. Let p and q be the functions in Exercise 6. Construct a table of values for $s(x) = q(p(x))$.

In Exercises 8–13, let $f(x) = 3x^2$, $g(x) = 9x - 2$, $m(x) = 4x$, and $r(x) = \sqrt{3x}$. Find and simplify the composite function.

8. $r(g(x))$

9. $f(r(x))$

10. $r(f(x))$

11. $g(f(x))$

12. $g(m(f(x)))$

13. $f(m(g(x)))$

In Exercises 14–18, identify the function $f(x)$.

14. $h(x) = e^{f(x)} = e^{\sin x}$

15. $j(x) = \sqrt{f(x)} = \sqrt{\ln(x^2 + 4)}$

16. $k(x) = \sin(f(x)) = \sin(x^3 + 3x + 1)$

17. $l(x) = (f(x))^2 = \cos^2 2x$

18. $m(x) = \ln f(x) = \ln(5 + 1/x)$

Problems

In Problems 19–22, give a practical interpretation in words of the function.

19. $f(h(t))$, where $A = f(r)$ is the area of a circle of radius r and $r = h(t)$ is the radius of the circle at time t.

20. $k(g(t))$, where $L = k(H)$ is the length of a steel bar at temperature H and $H = g(t)$ is temperature at time t.

21. $R(Y(q))$, where R gives a farmer's revenue as a function of corn yield per acre, and Y gives the corn yield as a function of the quantity, q, of fertilizer.

22. $t(f(H))$, where $t(v)$ is the time of a trip at velocity v, and $v = f(H)$ is velocity at temperature H.

23. Suppose $u(v(x)) = \dfrac{1}{x^2 - 1}$ and $v(u(x)) = \dfrac{1}{(x-1)^2}$. Find possible formulas for $u(x)$ and $v(x)$.

In Problems 24–27, suppose that $f(x) = g(h(x))$. Find possible formulas for $g(x)$ and $h(x)$ (There may be more than one possible answer. Assume $g(x) \neq x$ and $h(x) \neq x$.)

24. $f(x) = (x + 3)^2$

25. $f(x) = \sqrt{1 + \sqrt{x}}$

26. $f(x) = 9x^2 + 3x$

27. $f(x) = \dfrac{1}{x^2 + 8x + 16}$

28. Complete Table 10.3 given that $h(x) = f(g(x))$.

Table 10.3

x	$f(x)$	$g(x)$	$h(x)$
0	1	2	5
1	9	0	
2		1	

29. Complete the table given $h(x) = g(f(x))$.

x	$f(x)$	$g(x)$	$h(x)$
0	2	1	3
1	1	0	0
2	4	3	2
3	0	4	1
4	3	2	4

30. Complete Table 10.4 given that $w(t) = v(u(t))$.

Table 10.4

t	u	v	w
0	2	3	—
1	—	—	2
2	1	1	4
3	—	2	0
4	0	0	—

In Problems 31–33, let $x > 0$ and $k(x) = e^x$. Find a possible formula for $f(x)$.

31. $k(f(x)) = e^{2x}$

32. $f(k(x)) = e^{2x}$

33. $k(f(x)) = x$

In Problems 34–37, find a simplified formula for the difference quotient

$$\frac{f(x+h) - f(x)}{h}.$$

34. $f(x) = x^2 + x$

35. $f(x) = \sqrt{x}$

36. $f(x) = \dfrac{1}{x}$

37. $f(x) = 2^x$

38. Using Figure 10.2, estimate the following:

(a) $f(g(2))$ (b) $g(f(2))$ (c) $f(f(3))$ (d) $g(g(3))$

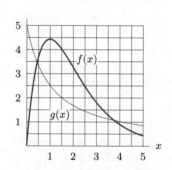

Figure 10.2

39. Use Figure 10.3 to calculate the following:

(a) $f(f(1))$ (b) $g(g(1))$

(c) $f(g(2))$ (d) $g(f(2))$

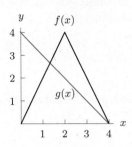

Figure 10.3

40. Use Figure 10.3 to find all solutions to the equations:

(a) $f(g(x)) = 0$ (b) $g(f(x)) = 0$

41. Let $f(x)$ and $g(x)$ be the functions in Figure 10.3.

(a) Graph the functions $f(g(x))$ and $g(f(x))$.
(b) On what interval(s) is $f(g(x))$ increasing?
(c) On what interval(s) is $g(f(x))$ increasing?

In Problems 42–45, use the information from Figures 10.4 and 10.5 to graph the functions.

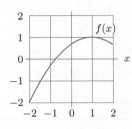 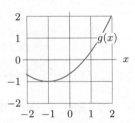

Figure 10.4   **Figure 10.5**

42. $f(g(x))$ **43.** $g(f(x))$ **44.** $f(f(x))$ **45.** $g(g(x))$

46. Find $f(f(1))$ for

$$f(x) = \begin{cases} 2 & \text{if } x \le 0 \\ 3x + 1 & \text{if } 0 < x < 2 \\ x^2 - 3 & \text{if } x \ge 2 \end{cases}$$

47. If $s(x) = 5 + \dfrac{1}{x+5} + x$, $k(x) = x + 5$, and $s(x) = v(k(x))$, what is $v(x)$?

48. Let $f(x) = 12 - 4x$, $g(x) = 1/x$, and $h(x) = \sqrt{x - 4}$. Find the domain of the functions:

(a) $g(f(x))$ (b) $h(f(x))$

Decompose the functions in Problems 49–54 into $u(v(x))$ for given u or v.

49. $y = \dfrac{1 + x^2}{2 + x^2}$ given that

(a) $v(x) = x^2$ (b) $v(x) = x^2 + 1$

50. $y = e^{-\sqrt{x}}$ given that

(a) $u(x) = e^x$ (b) $v(x) = \sqrt{x}$

51. $y = \sqrt{1 - x^3}$ given that

(a) $u(x) = \sqrt{1 + x^3}$ (b) $v(x) = x^3$

52. $y = 2^{x+1}$ given that

(a) $u(x) = 2x$ (b) $v(x) = -x$

53. $y = \sin^2 x$ given that

(a) $u(x) = x^2$ (b) $v(x) = x^2$

54. $y = e^{2\cos x}$ given that

(a) $u(x) = e^x$ (b) $v(x) = \cos x$

55. (a) Use Table 10.5 and Figure 10.6 to calculate:

(i) $f(g(4))$ (ii) $g(f(4))$
(iii) $f(f(0))$ (iv) $g(g(0))$

(b) Solve $g(g(x)) = 1$ for x.

Table 10.5

x	0	1	2	3	4	5
$f(x)$	2	5	3	4	1	0

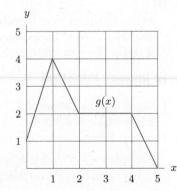

Figure 10.6

56. You have two money machines, both of which increase any money inserted into them. The first machine doubles your money. The second adds five dollars. The money that comes out is described by $d(x) = 2x$ in the first case and $a(x) = x + 5$ in the second, where x is the number of dollars inserted. The machines can be hooked up so that the money coming out of one machine goes into the other. Find formulas for each of the two possible composition machines. Is one machine more profitable than the other?

57. Let $p(t) = 10(0.01)^t$ and $q(t) = \log t^2$. Solve the equation $q(p(t)) = 0$ for t.

58. Let $f(t) = \sin t$ and $g(t) = 3t - \pi/4$. Solve the equation $f(g(t)) = 1$ for t in the interval $0 \le t \le 2\pi/3$.

59. Let $f(x) = \sqrt{x}$ and $g(x) = x^2$. Calculate the domain of $f(g(x))$ and the domain of $g(f(x))$.

60. The graphs for $y = f(x)$ and $y = g(x)$ are shown in Figure 10.7.

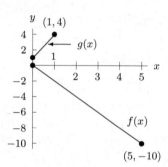

Figure 10.7

(a) Write an equation for $f(x)$.

(b) State the domain and range of $f(x)$.
(c) Write an equation for $g(x)$.
(d) State the domain and range of $g(x)$.
(e) Write an equation for $h(x) = f(g(x))$.
(f) State the domain and range of $h(x)$.
(g) Draw the graph of $h(x)$.

61. Letting $r(x) = 3x^3 - 4x^2$, find $q(x)$ given that
$$q(r(x)) = \frac{8x^3}{16x^2}.$$

In Problems 62–63, find a simplified formula for g given that $f(x) = \dfrac{x+1}{x+3}$.

62. $g(x) = f(h(x))$ where $h(x) = 3x^2 - 1$.

63. $f(x) = g(x) + \dfrac{2x+4}{x+3}$.

64. Which of the following statements must be true in order for the point $(2, 5)$ to be on the graph of $h(x) = g\left(f(x)\right)$?

(a) The domain of f includes 2.
(b) The domain of g includes 2.
(c) The range of f includes 5.
(d) The range of g includes 5.
(e) The function g is invertible.

65. Which of the following statements must be true in order for $h(x) = g\left(f(x)\right)$ to be defined for all x?

(a) The domain of f is all x.
(b) The domain of g is all x.
(c) The range of f is all y.
(d) The range of g is all y.
(e) The range of f is within the domain of g.

10.2 INVERTIBILITY AND PROPERTIES OF INVERSE FUNCTIONS

Inverse functions were introduced in Section 2.4. In Section 5.1, we defined the logarithm as the inverse function of the exponential function. In Section 8.4, we defined the arccosine as the inverse of cosine. We now study inverse functions in general.

Definition of Inverse Function

Recall that the statement $f^{-1}(50) = 20$ means that $f(20) = 50$. In fact, the values of f^{-1} are determined in just this way. In general,

Suppose $Q = f(t)$ is a function with the property that each value of Q determines exactly one value of t. Then f has an **inverse function**, f^{-1}, and

$$f^{-1}(Q) = t \quad \text{if and only if} \quad Q = f(t).$$

If a function has an inverse, it is said to be **invertible**.

The definitions of the logarithm and of the inverse cosine have the same form as the definition of f^{-1}. Since $y = \log x$ is the inverse function of $y = 10^x$, we have

$$x = \log y \quad \text{if and only if} \quad y = 10^x,$$

and since $y = \cos^{-1} t$ is the inverse function of $y = \cos t$,

$$t = \cos^{-1} y \quad \text{if and only if} \quad y = \cos t.$$

Example 1   Find a solution to the equation $\sin x = 0.8$ using an inverse function.

Solution   A solution is $x = \sin^{-1}(0.8)$. A calculator (set in radians) gives $x = \sin^{-1}(0.8) \approx 0.927$.

Finding a Formula for an Inverse Function

As we have seen in Section 2.4, it is sometimes possible to find a formula for an inverse function f^{-1} from a formula for f.

Example 2   Suppose you deposit $500 into a savings account that pays 4% interest compounded annually. The balance, in dollars, in the account after t years is given by $B = f(t) = 500(1.04)^t$.

(a) Find a formula for $t = f^{-1}(B)$.
(b) What does the inverse function represent in terms of the account?

Solution   (a) To find a formula for f^{-1}, we solve for t in terms of B:

$$B = 500(1.04)^t$$

$$\frac{B}{500} = (1.04)^t$$

$$\log\left(\frac{B}{500}\right) = t \log 1.04 \qquad \text{Taking logs of both sides}$$

$$t = \frac{\log(B/500)}{\log 1.04}.$$

Thus, a formula for the inverse function is

$$t = f^{-1}(B) = \frac{\log(B/500)}{\log 1.04}.$$

(b) The function $t = f^{-1}(B)$ gives the number of years for the balance to grow to $\$B$.

In the previous example the variables of the function $B = f(t)$ had contextual meaning, so the inverse function was written as $t = f^{-1}(B)$. In abstract mathematical examples, a function $y = f(x)$ will often have its inverse function written with x as the independent variable.

Example 3   Find the inverse of the function

$$f(x) = \frac{3x}{2x + 1}.$$

Solution   First, we solve the equation $y = f(x)$ for x:

$$y = \frac{3x}{2x+1}$$
$$2xy + y = 3x$$
$$2xy - 3x = -y$$
$$x(2y - 3) = -y$$
$$x = \frac{-y}{2y - 3} = \frac{y}{3 - 2y}.$$

As before, we write $x = f^{-1}(y) = \dfrac{y}{3 - 2y}.$

Since y is now the independent variable, by convention we rewrite the inverse function with x as the independent variable. We have

$$f^{-1}(x) = \frac{x}{3 - 2x}.$$

Noninvertible Functions: Horizontal Line Test

Not every function has an inverse function. A function $Q = f(t)$ has no inverse if it returns the same Q-value for two different t-values. When that happens, the value of t cannot be uniquely determined from the value of Q.

For example, if $q(x) = x^2$ then $q(-3) = 9$ and $q(+3) = 9$. This means that we cannot say what the value $q^{-1}(9)$ would be. (Is it $+3$ or -3?) Thus, q is not invertible. In Figure 10.8, notice that the horizontal line $y = 9$ intersects the graph of $q(x) = x^2$ at two different points: $(-3, 9)$ and $(3, 9)$. This corresponds to the fact that the function q returns $y = 9$ for two different x-values, $x = +3$ and $x = -3$.

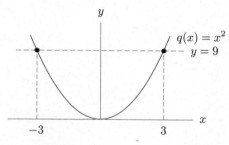

Figure 10.8: The graph of $q(x) = x^2$ fails the horizontal line test

We have the following general result:

> **The Horizontal Line Test** If there is a horizontal line that intersects a function's graph in more than one point, then the function does not have an inverse. If every horizontal line intersects a function's graph at most once, then the function has an inverse.

Evaluating an Inverse Function Graphically

Finding a formula for an inverse function can be difficult. However, this does not mean that the inverse function does not exist. Even without a formula, it may be possible to find values of the inverse function.

Example 4   Let $u(x) = x^3 + x + 1$. Explain why a graph suggests the function u is invertible. Assuming u has an inverse, estimate $u^{-1}(4)$.

Solution   To show that u is invertible, we could try to find a formula for u^{-1}. To do this, we would solve the equation $y = x^3 + x + 1$ for x. Unfortunately, this is difficult. However, the graph in Figure 10.9 suggests that u passes the horizontal line test and therefore that u is invertible. To estimate $u^{-1}(4)$, we find an x-value such that

$$x^3 + x + 1 = 4.$$

In Figure 10.9, the graph of $y = u(x)$ and the horizontal line $y = 4$ intersect at the point $x \approx 1.213$. Thus, tracing along the graph, we estimate $u^{-1}(4) \approx 1.213$.

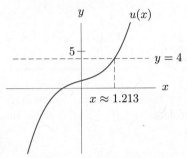

Figure 10.9: The graph of $u(x)$ passes the horizontal line test. Since $u(1.213) \approx 4$, we have $u^{-1}(4) \approx 1.213$

In Example 4, even without a formula for u^{-1}, we can approximate $u^{-1}(a)$ for any value of a.

Example 5   Let $P(x) = 2^x$.

(a) Show that P is invertible.
(b) Find a formula for $P^{-1}(x)$.
(c) Sketch the graphs of P and P^{-1} on the same axes.
(d) What are the domain and range of P and P^{-1}?

Solution   (a) Since P is an exponential function with base 2, it is always increasing, and therefore passes the horizontal line test. (See the graph of P in Figure 10.10.) Thus, P has an inverse function.
(b) To find a formula for $P^{-1}(x)$, we solve for x in the equation

$$2^x = y.$$

We take the log of both sides to get

$$\log 2^x = \log y$$
$$x \log 2 = \log y$$
$$x = P^{-1}(y) = \frac{\log y}{\log 2}.$$

Thus, we have a formula for P^{-1} with y as the input. To graph P and P^{-1} on the same axes, we write P^{-1} as a function of x:

$$P^{-1}(x) = \frac{\log x}{\log 2} = \frac{1}{\log 2} \cdot \log x = 3.322 \log x.$$

(c) Table 10.6 gives values of $P(x)$ for $x = -3, -2, \ldots, 3$. Interchanging the columns of Table 10.6 gives Table 10.7 for $P^{-1}(x)$. We use these tables to sketch Figure 10.10.

Table 10.6 *Values of*
$P(x) = 2^x$

x	$P(x) = 2^x$
−3	0.125
−2	0.25
−1	0.5
0	1
1	2
2	4
3	8

Table 10.7 *Values of*
$P^{-1}(x)$

x	$P^{-1}(x)$
0.125	−3
0.25	−2
0.5	−1
1	0
2	1
4	2
8	3

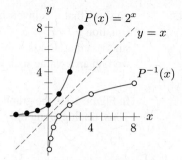

Figure 10.10: The graphs of
$P(x) = 2^x$ and its inverse are
symmetrical across the line $y = x$

(d) The domain of P, an exponential function, is all real numbers, and its range is all positive numbers. The domain of P^{-1}, a logarithmic function, is all positive numbers and its range is all real numbers.

The Graph, Domain, and Range of an Inverse Function

In Figure 10.10, we see that the graph of P^{-1} is the mirror-image of the graph of P across the line $y = x$. In general, this is true if the x- and y-axes have the same scale. To understand why this occurs, consider how a function is related to its inverse.

If f is an invertible function with, for example, $f(2) = 5$, then $f^{-1}(5) = 2$. Thus, the point $(2, 5)$ is on the graph of f and the point $(5, 2)$ is on the graph of f^{-1}. Generalizing, if (a, b) is any point on the graph of f, then (b, a) is a point on the graph of f^{-1}. Figure 10.11 shows how reflecting the point (a, b) across the line $y = x$ gives the point (b, a). Consequently, the graph of f^{-1} is the reflection of the graph of f across the line $y = x$.

Notice that outputs from a function are inputs to its inverse function. Similarly, outputs from the inverse function are inputs to the original function. This is expressed in the statement $f^{-1}(b) = a$ if and only if $f(a) = b$, and also in the fact that we can obtain a table for f^{-1} by interchanging the columns of a table for f. Consequently, the domain and range for f^{-1} are obtained by interchanging the domain and range of f. In other words,

---

Graph of f^{-1} is reflection of graph of f across the line $y = x$.

Domain of f^{-1} = Range of f and   Range of f^{-1} = Domain of f.

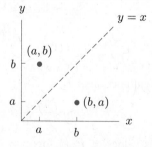

Figure 10.11: The reflection of the point (a, b) across the line $y = x$ is the point (b, a)

As we saw in Example 5, the function P has all real numbers as its domain and all positive numbers as its range; the function P^{-1} has all positive numbers as its domain and all real numbers as its range.

A Property of Inverse Functions

The fact that Tables 10.6 and 10.7 contain the same values, but with the columns switched, reflects the special relationship between the values of $P(x)$ and $P^{-1}(x)$. For the function in Example 5

$$P^{-1}(2) = 1 \quad \text{and} \quad P(1) = 2 \quad \text{so} \quad P^{-1}(P(1)) = 1,$$

and

$$P^{-1}(0.25) = -2 \quad \text{and} \quad P(-2) = 0.25 \quad \text{so} \quad P^{-1}(P(-2)) = -2.$$

This result holds for any input x, so in general,

$$P^{-1}(P(x)) = x.$$

In addition, $P(P^{-1}(2)) = 2$ and $P(P^{-1}(0.25)) = 0.25$, and for any x

$$P(P^{-1}(x)) = x.$$

Similar reasoning holds for any other invertible function, suggesting the general result:

If $y = f(x)$ is an invertible function and $y = f^{-1}(x)$ is its inverse, then
- $f^{-1}(f(x)) = x$ for all values of x for which $f(x)$ is defined,
- $f(f^{-1}(x)) = x$ for all values of x for which $f^{-1}(x)$ is defined.

This property tell us that composing a function and its inverse function returns the original value as the end result. We can use this property to decide whether two functions are inverses.

Example 6   (a) Check that $f(x) = \dfrac{x}{2x+1}$ and $f^{-1}(x) = \dfrac{x}{1-2x}$ are inverse functions of each other.

(b) Graph f and f^{-1} on axes with the same scale. What are the domains and ranges of f and f^{-1}?

Solution   (a) To check that these functions are inverses, we compose

$$f^{-1}(f(x)) = \frac{f(x)}{1-2f(x)} = \frac{\dfrac{x}{2x+1}}{1-2\left(\dfrac{x}{2x+1}\right)}$$

$$= \frac{\dfrac{x}{2x+1}}{\dfrac{2x+1}{2x+1} - \dfrac{2x}{2x+1}}$$

$$= \frac{\dfrac{x}{2x+1}}{\dfrac{1}{2x+1}}$$

$$= x.$$

Similarly, you can check that $f(f^{-1}(x)) = x$.

(b) The graphs of f and f^{-1} in Figure 10.12 are symmetric about the line $y = x$.

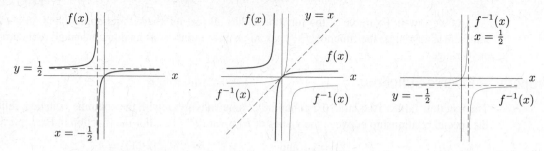

Figure 10.12: The graph of $f(x) = x/(2x + 1)$ and the inverse $f^{-1}(x) = x/(1 - 2x)$

The function $f(x) = x/(2x + 1)$ is undefined at $x = -1/2$, so its domain consists of all real numbers except $-1/2$. Figure 10.12 suggests that f has a horizontal asymptote at $y = 1/2$ which it does not cross and that its range is all real numbers except $1/2$.

Because the inverse function $f^{-1}(x) = x/(1 - 2x)$ is undefined at $x = 1/2$, its domain is all real numbers except $1/2$. Note that this is the same as the range of f. The graph of f^{-1} appears to have a horizontal asymptote which it does not cross at $y = -1/2$, suggesting that its range is all real numbers except $-1/2$. Note that this is the same as the domain of f.

The ranges of the functions f and f^{-1} can be confirmed algebraically.

Restricting the Domain

A function that fails the horizontal line test is not invertible. For this reason, the function $f(x) = x^2$ does not have an inverse function. However, by considering only part of the graph of f, we can eliminate the duplication of y-values. Suppose we consider the half of the parabola with $x \geq 0$. See Figure 10.13. This part of the graph does pass the horizontal line test because there is only one (positive) x-value for each y-value in the range of f.

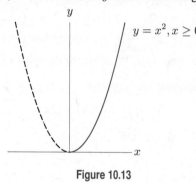

Figure 10.13

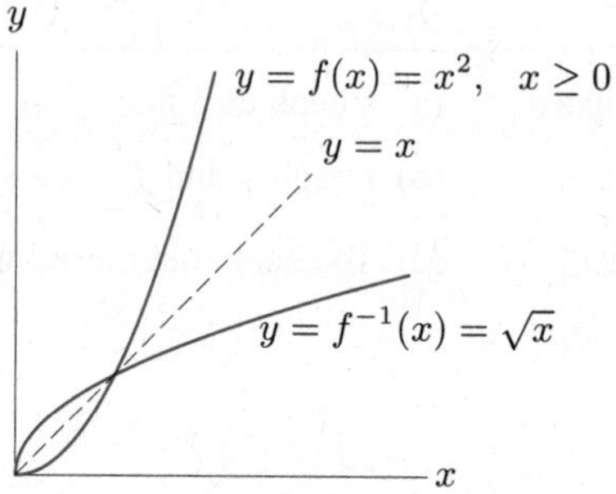

Figure 10.14

We can find an inverse for $f(x) = x^2$ on its restricted domain,[1] $x \geq 0$. Using the fact that $x \geq 0$ and solving $y = x^2$ for x gives

$$x = \sqrt{y}.$$

Thus a formula for the inverse function is

$$x = f^{-1}(y) = \sqrt{y}.$$

Rewriting the formula for f^{-1} with x as the input, we have

$$f^{-1}(x) = \sqrt{x}.$$

The graphs of f and f^{-1} are shown in Figure 10.14. Note that the domain of f is the the range of f^{-1}, and the domain of f^{-1} ($x \geq 0$) is the range of f.

---

[1] Technically, changing the domain results in a new function, but we will continue to call it $f(x)$.

In Section 8.4 we restricted the domains of the sine, cosine, and tangent functions in order to define their inverse functions:

$$y = \sin^{-1} x \quad \text{if and only if} \quad x = \sin y \quad \text{and} \quad -\frac{\pi}{2} \le y \le \frac{\pi}{2}$$

$$y = \cos^{-1} x \quad \text{if and only if} \quad x = \cos y \quad \text{and} \quad 0 \le y \le \pi$$

$$y = \tan^{-1} x \quad \text{if and only if} \quad x = \tan y \quad \text{and} \quad -\frac{\pi}{2} < y < \frac{\pi}{2}.$$

The graphs of each of the inverse trigonometric functions are shown in Figures 10.15-10.17. Note the symmetry about the line $y = x$ for each trigonometric function and its inverse.

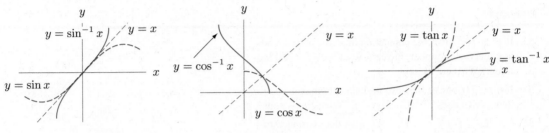

Figure 10.15   Figure 10.16   Figure 10.17

In each case, the restricted domain of the function is the range of the inverse function. In addition, the domain of the inverse is the range of the original function. For example,

$$y = \sin x \quad \text{has restricted domain} \; -\frac{\pi}{2} \le x \le \frac{\pi}{2} \quad \text{and} \quad \text{range} \quad -1 \le y \le 1$$

$$y = \sin^{-1} x \quad \text{has domain} \quad -1 \le x \le 1 \quad \text{and} \quad \text{range} \quad -\frac{\pi}{2} \le y \le \frac{\pi}{2}.$$

Exercises and Problems for Section 10.2

Exercises

In Exercises 1–6, use a graph to decide whether or not the function is invertible.

1. $y = x^6 + 2x^2 - 10$

2. $y = x^4 - 6x + 12$

3. $y = e^{x^2}$

4. $y = \cos(x^3)$

5. $y = |x|$

6. $y = x + \ln x$

In Exercises 7–14, check that the functions are inverses.

7. $f(x) = \frac{x}{4} - \frac{3}{2}$ and $g(t) = 4\left(t + \frac{3}{2}\right)$

8. $f(x) = 1 + 7x^3$ and $f^{-1}(x) = \sqrt[3]{\dfrac{x-1}{7}}$

9. $g(x) = 1 - \dfrac{1}{x-1}$ and $g^{-1}(x) = 1 + \dfrac{1}{1-x}$

10. $h(x) = \sqrt{2x}$ and $k(t) = \dfrac{t^2}{2}$, for $x, t \ge 0$

11. $f(x) = e^{x+1}$ and $f^{-1}(x) = \ln x - 1$

12. $f(x) = e^{2x}$ and $f^{-1}(x) = \dfrac{\ln x}{2}$

13. $f(x) = e^{x/2}$ and $f^{-1}(x) = 2\ln x$

14. $f(x) = \ln(x/2)$ and $f^{-1}(x) = 2e^x$

In Exercises 15–31, find a formula for the inverse function. Assume these functions are defined on domains on which they are invertible.

15. $f(x) = x + 5$

16. $g(x) = 1 - x$

17. $h(x) = \sqrt{x}$

18. $j(x) = \dfrac{1}{x}$

19. $f(x) = 3x - 7$

20. $k(x) = \dfrac{x}{x-1}$

21. $l(x) = \sqrt{1 - 2x^2}$

22. $m(x) = \dfrac{1}{x} - x$

29. $h(x) = \log\left(\dfrac{x+5}{x-4}\right)$

30. $f(x) = \cos\sqrt{x}$

23. $n(x) = (1 + x^2)^2$

24. $o(x) = 1/(1 + \dfrac{1}{x})$

31. $g(x) = 2^{\sin x}$

25. $j(x) = \sqrt{1 + \sqrt{x}}$

26. $h(x) = \dfrac{2x+1}{3x-2}$

32. Check that the functions $R = f(T) = 150 + 5T$ and $T = f^{-1}(R) = \frac{1}{5}R - 30$ satisfy the identities

27. $k(x) = \dfrac{3 - \sqrt{x}}{\sqrt{x} + 2}$

28. $g(x) = \dfrac{\ln x - 5}{2\ln x + 7}$

$$f^{-1}(f(T)) = T \quad \text{and} \quad f(f^{-1}(R)) = R.$$

Problems

33. If $P = f(t)$ gives the population of a city, in thousands, as a function of time, t, in years, what does $f^{-1}(P)$ represent? What are its units?

34. If $C = f(q)$ gives the cost, in dollars, to manufacture q items, what does $f^{-1}(C)$ represent? What are its units?

35. Let $R = f(T) = 150 + 5T$ give the resistance of a circuit element as a function of temperature.

(a) Find a formula for $T = f^{-1}(R)$.
(b) Make a table of values showing values of f. Make another table showing values of f^{-1}. Explain the relationship between the tables.

36. The police can determine the speed a car was traveling from the length of the skid marks it leaves. The function they use is $S = f(L) = 2\sqrt{(5L)}$ where S is speed (mph) and L is the length of the skid marks (feet).

(a) If skid marks of length 125 feet are measured, what was the speed of the car?
(b) Find a formula for the inverse function.
(c) If the car had been traveling at 80 mph, how long would the skid marks be?

37. Let $f(x) = 5^x$.

(a) Evaluate $f(3)$ and $f^{-1}(1/25)$ exactly.
(b) Approximate the value of $f^{-1}(10)$.

38. Let $P = f(t) = 37.8(1.044)^t$ be the population of a town (in thousands) in year t.

(a) Describe the town's population in words.
(b) Evaluate $f(50)$. What does this quantity tell you about the population?
(c) Find a formula for $f^{-1}(P)$ in terms of P.
(d) Evaluate $f^{-1}(50)$. What does this quantity tell you about the population?

39. Figure 10.18 defines the function f. Rank the following quantities in order from least to greatest:

$$0, f(0), f^{-1}(0), 3, f(3), f^{-1}(3).$$

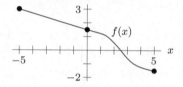

Figure 10.18

40. Let $C = f(q) = 200 + 0.1q$ give the cost in dollars to manufacture q kg of a chemical. Find and interpret $f^{-1}(C)$.

41. Let $P = f(t) = 10e^{0.02t}$ give the population in millions at time t in years. Find and interpret $f^{-1}(P)$.

42. The noise level, N, of a sound in decibels is given by

$$N = f(I) = 10\log\left(\dfrac{I}{I_0}\right),$$

where I is the intensity of the sound and I_0 is a constant. Find and interpret $f^{-1}(N)$.

43. A research facility on the Isle of Shoals has 800 gallons of fresh water for a two-month period.

(a) There are 7 members of the research team and each is allotted 2 gallons of water per day for cooking and drinking. Find a formula for $f(t)$, the amount of fresh water left on the island after t days has elapsed.
(b) Evaluate and interpret the following expressions:

(i) $f(0)$ (ii) $f^{-1}(0)$
(iii) t if $f(t) = \dfrac{1}{2}f(0)$ (iv) $800 - f(t)$

44. The rating, r, of an earthquake of intensity I is given by $r = f(I) = \log(I/I_0)$, where I_0 is a constant. Find and interpret $f^{-1}(r)$.

45. Let $f(x) = e^x$ and $g(x) = \ln x$.

(a) Find $f(g(x))$ and $g(f(x))$. What can you conclude about the relationship between these two functions?

(b) Graph $f(x)$ and $g(x)$ together on axes with the same scales. What is the line of symmetry of the graph?

46. Let $p(t) = 10^t$ and $q(t) = \log t$.

(a) Find $p(q(t))$ and $q(p(t))$. What can you conclude about the relationship between these two functions?

(b) Graph $p(t)$ and $q(t)$ together on axes with the same scales. What is the line of symmetry of the graph?

47. Table 10.8 gives the number N of cows in a herd.

(a) Find an exponential function that approximates the data.

(b) Find the inverse function of the function in part (a).

(c) When do you predict that the herd will contain 400 cows?

Table 10.8

t (years)	0	1	2
$N = P(t)$ (cows)	150	165	182

48. There is a linear relationship between the number of units, $N(x)$, of a product that a company sells and the amount of money, x, spent on advertising. If the company spends \$25,000 on advertising, it sells 400 units, and for each additional \$5,000 spent, it sells 20 units more.

(a) Calculate and interpret $N(20,000)$.

(b) Find a formula for $N(x)$ in terms of x.

(c) Give interpretations of the slope and the x- and y-intercepts of $N(x)$ if possible.

(d) Calculate and interpret $N^{-1}(500)$.

(e) An internal audit reveals that the profit made by the company on the sale of 10 units of its product, before advertising costs have been accounted for, is \$2,000. What are the implications regarding the company's advertising campaign? Discuss.

49. A hot brick is removed from a kiln at $200°$C above room temperature. Over time, the brick cools off. After 2 hours have elapsed, the brick is $20°$C above room temperature. Let t be the time in hours since the brick was removed from the kiln. Let $y = H(t)$ be the difference between the brick's and the room's temperature at time t. Assume that $H(t)$ is an exponential function.

(a) Find a formula for $H(t)$.

(b) How many degrees does the brick's temperature drop during the first quarter hour? During the next quarter hour?

(c) Find and interpret $H^{-1}(y)$.

(d) How much time elapses before the brick's temperature is $5°$C above room temperature?

(e) Interpret the physical meaning of the horizontal asymptote of $H(t)$.

50. The *quadratic mean* (or RMS) of x and the constant A is given by $f(x) = 0.5(x^2 + A^2)^{0.5}$. Assuming $x \geq 0$, find a formula for $f^{-1}(x)$.

51. The *harmonic mean* of x and the constant A is given by $f(x) = 0.5(x^{-1} + A^{-1})^{-1}$. Find a formula for $f^{-1}(x)$.

52. Values of f and g are in Table 10.9. Based on this table:

(a) Is $f(x)$ invertible? If not, explain why; if so, construct a table of values of $f^{-1}(x)$ for all values of x for which $f^{-1}(x)$ is defined.

(b) Answer the same question as in part (a) for $g(x)$.

(c) Make a table of values for $h(x) = f(g(x))$, with $x = -3, -2, -1, 0, 1, 2, 3$.

(d) Explain why you cannot define a function $j(x)$ by the formula $j(x) = g(f(x))$.

Table 10.9

x	-3	-2	-1	0	1	2	3
$f(x)$	9	7	6	-4	-5	-8	-9
$g(x)$	3	1	3	2	-3	-1	3

Problems 53–54 involve the *Lambert W function*,[2] defined by $W(x) = f^{-1}(x)$ where $f(x) = xe^x$ with $x \geq -1$. Since $f\left(f^{-1}(x)\right) = x$, this means $W(x)e^{W(x)} = x$.

53. Find three points on the graph of W by finding $f(-1)$, $f(0)$, and $f(1)$.

54. Given that $W(10) = 1.746$, find a solution to the equation $te^{2t} = 5$.

55. Suppose $P = f(t)$ is the population (in thousands) in year t, and that $f(7) = 13$ and $f(12) = 20$,

(a) Find a formula for $f(t)$ assuming f is exponential.

(b) Find a formula for $f^{-1}(P)$.

(c) Evaluate $f(25)$ and $f^{-1}(25)$. Explain what these expressions mean in terms of population.

---

[2] See http://en.wikipedia.org/wiki/Lambert%27s_W_function, accessed April 30, 2008.

56. A gymnast at Ringling Bros. and Barnum & Bailey Circus is fired straight up in the air from a cannon. While she is in the air, a trampoline is moved into the spot where the cannon was. Figure 10.19 is a graph of the gymnast's height, h, as a function of time, t.

(a) Approximately what is her maximum height?
(b) Approximately when does she land on the trampoline?
(c) Restrict the domain of $h(t)$ so that $h(t)$ has an inverse. That is, pick a piece of the graph on which $h(t)$ does have an inverse. Graph this new restricted function.
(d) Change the story to go with your graph in part (c).
(e) Graph the inverse of the function in part (c). Explain in your story why it makes sense that the inverse is a function.

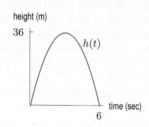

height (m)

36

$h(t)$

time (sec)

6

Figure 10.19

57. A 100-ml solution contains 99% alcohol and 1% water. Let $y = C(x)$ be the concentration of alcohol in the

solution after x ml of alcohol are removed, so

$$C(x) = \frac{\text{Amount of alcohol}}{\text{Amount of solution}}.$$

(a) What is $C(0)$?
(b) Find a formula in terms of x for $C(x)$.
(c) Find a formula in terms of y for $C^{-1}(y)$.
(d) Explain the physical significance of $C^{-1}(y)$.

58. (a) How much alcohol do you think should be removed from the 99% solution in Problem 57 in order to obtain a 98% solution? (Make a guess.)
(b) Express the exact answer to part (a) using the function C^{-1} you found in Problem 57.
(c) Determine the exact answer to part (a). Are you surprised by your result?

The predicted pulse in beats per minute (bpm) of a healthy person fifteen minutes after consuming q milligrams of caffeine is given by $r = f(q)$. The amount of caffeine in a serving of coffee is q_c, and $r_c = f(q_c)$. Assume that f is an increasing function for non-toxic levels of caffeine. What do the statements in Problems 59–64 tell you about caffeine and a person's pulse?

59. $f(2q_c)$

60. $f^{-1}(r_c + 20)$

61. $2f^{-1}(r_c) + 20$

62. $f(q_c) - f(0)$

63. $f^{-1}(r_c + 20) - q_c$

64. $f^{-1}(1.1f(q_c))$

10.3 COMBINATIONS OF FUNCTIONS

Like numbers, functions can be combined using addition, subtraction, multiplication, and division.

The Difference of Two Functions Defined by Formulas: A Measure of Prosperity

We can define new functions as the sum or difference of two functions. In Chapter 4, we discussed Thomas Malthus, who predicted widespread food shortages because he believed that human populations increase exponentially, whereas the food supply increases linearly. We considered a country with population $P(t)$ million in year t. The population is initially 2 million and grows at the rate of 4% per year, so

$$P(t) = 2(1.04)^t.$$

Let $N(t)$ be the number of people (in millions) that the country can feed in year t. The annual food supply is initially adequate for 4 million people and it increases by enough for an additional 0.5 million people every year. Thus

$$N(t) = 4 + 0.5t.$$

This country first experiences shortages in about 78 years. (See Figure 10.20.) When is it most prosperous?

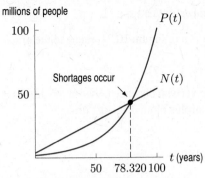

Figure 10.20: Predicted population, $P(t)$, and number of people who can be fed, $N(t)$, over a 100-year period

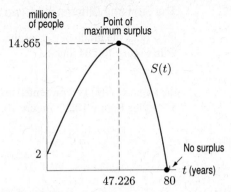

Figure 10.21: Surplus graphed using the formula $S(t) = 4 + 0.5t - 2(1.04)^t$

The answer depends on how we decide to measure prosperity. We could measure prosperity in one of the following ways:

- By the food surplus—that is, the amount of food the country has over and above its needs. This surplus food could be warehoused or exported in trade.

- By the per capita food supply—that is, how much food there is per person. (The term *per capita* means per person, or literally, "per head.") This indicates the portion of the country's wealth each person might enjoy.

First, we choose to measure prosperity in terms of food surplus, $S(t)$, in year t, where

$$S(t) = \underbrace{\text{Number of people that can be fed}}_{N(t)} - \underbrace{\text{Number of people living in the country}}_{P(t)}$$

so

$$S(t) = N(t) - P(t).$$

For example, to determine the surplus in year $t = 25$, we evaluate

$$S(25) = N(25) - P(25).$$

Since $N(25) = 4 + 0.5(25) = 16.5$ and $P(25) = 2(1.04)^{25} \approx 5.332$, we have

$$S(25) \approx 16.5 - 5.332 = 11.168.$$

Thus, in year 25 the food surplus could feed 11.168 million additional people.

We use the formulas for N and P to find a formula for S:

$$S(t) = \underbrace{N(t)}_{4+0.5t} - \underbrace{P(t)}_{2(1.04)^t},$$

so

$$S(t) = 4 + 0.5t - 2(1.04)^t.$$

A graph of S is shown in Figure 10.21. The maximum surplus occurs sometime during the 48th year. In that year, there is surplus food sufficient for an additional 14.865 million people.

The Sum and Difference of Two Functions Defined by Graphs

How does the graph of the surplus function S, shown in Figure 10.21, relate to the graphs of N and P in Figure 10.20? Since

$$S(t) = N(t) - P(t),$$

the value of $S(t)$ is represented graphically as the vertical distance between the graphs of $N(t)$ and $P(t)$. See Figure 10.22. Figure 10.23 shows the surplus plotted against time.

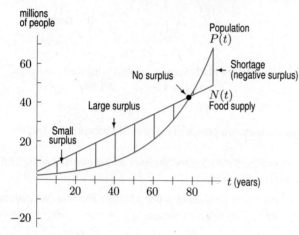

Figure 10.22: Surplus, $S(t) = N(t) - P(t)$, as vertical distance between $N(t)$ and $P(t)$ graphs

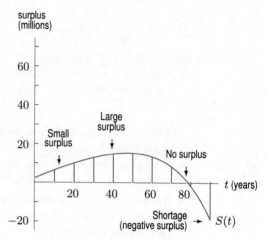

Figure 10.23: Surplus as a function of time

From year $t = 0$ to $t \approx 78.320$, the food supply is more than the population needs. Therefore the surplus, $S(t)$, is positive on this time interval. At time $t = 78.320$, the food supply is exactly sufficient for the population, so $S(t) = 0$, resulting in the horizontal intercept $t = 78.320$ on the graph of $S(t)$ in Figure 10.23. For times $t > 78.320$, the food supply is less than the population needs. Therefore the surplus is negative, representing a food shortage.

In the next example we consider a sum of two functions.

Example 1   Let $f(x) = x$ and $g(x) = \dfrac{1}{x}$. By adding vertical distances on the graphs of f and g, sketch

$$h(x) = f(x) + g(x) \quad \text{for } x > 0.$$

Solution   The graphs of f and g are shown in Figure 10.24. For each value of x, we add the vertical distances that represent $f(x)$ and $g(x)$ to get a point on the graph of $h(x)$. Compare the graph of $h(x)$ to the values shown in Table 10.10.

Table 10.10   *Adding function values*

x	$\frac{1}{4}$	$\frac{1}{2}$	1	2	4
$f(x) = x$	$\frac{1}{4}$	$\frac{1}{2}$	1	2	4
$g(x) = 1/x$	4	2	1	$\frac{1}{2}$	$\frac{1}{4}$
$h(x) = f(x) + g(x)$	$4\frac{1}{4}$	$2\frac{1}{2}$	2	$2\frac{1}{2}$	$4\frac{1}{4}$

Note that as x increases, $g(x)$ decreases toward zero, so the values of $h(x)$ get closer to the values of $f(x)$. On the other hand, as x approaches zero, $h(x)$ gets closer to $g(x)$.

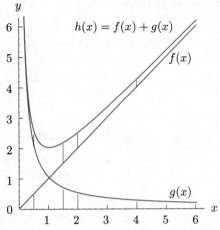

Figure 10.24: Graph of $h(x) = f(x) + g(x)$ constructed by adding vertical distances under f and g

Factoring a Function's Formula into a Product

It is often useful to be able to express a given function as a product of functions.

Example 2   Find exactly all the zeros of the function

$$p(x) = 2^x \cdot 6x^2 - 2^x \cdot x - 2^{x+1}.$$

Solution   We could approximate the zeros by finding the points where the graph of the function p crosses the x-axis. Unfortunately, these solutions are not exact. Alternatively, we can express p as a product. Using the fact that

$$2^{x+1} = 2^x \cdot 2^1 = 2 \cdot 2^x,$$

we rewrite the formula for p as

$$p(x) = 2^x \cdot 6x^2 - 2^x x - 2 \cdot 2^x$$
$$= 2^x(6x^2 - x - 2) \qquad \text{Factoring out } 2^x$$
$$= 2^x(2x + 1)(3x - 2). \qquad \text{Factoring the quadratic}$$

Thus p is the product of the exponential function 2^x and two linear functions. Since p is a product, it equals zero if one or more of its factors equals zero. But 2^x is never equal to 0, so $p(x)$ equals zero if and only if one of the linear factors is zero:

$$\begin{array}{cc} (2x + 1) = 0 & \text{or } (3x - 2) = 0 \\ x = -\dfrac{1}{2} & x = \dfrac{2}{3}. \end{array}$$

The Quotient of Functions Defined by Formulas and Graphs: Prosperity

Now let's think about our second proposed measure of prosperity, the per capita food supply, $R(t)$. With this definition of prosperity

$$R(t) = \frac{\text{Number of people that can be fed}}{\text{Number of people living in the country}} = \frac{N(t)}{P(t)}.$$

For example,

$$R(25) = \frac{N(25)}{P(25)} = \frac{16.5}{5.332} \approx 3.1.$$

This means that in year 25, everybody in the country could, on average, have more than three times as much food as he or she needs. The formula for $R(t)$ is

$$R(t) = \frac{N(t)}{P(t)} = \frac{4 + 0.5t}{2(1.04)^t}.$$

From the graph of R in Figure 10.25, we see that the maximum per capita food supply occurs during the 18th year. Notice this maximum prosperity prediction is different from the one made using the surplus function $S(t)$.

However, both prosperity models predict that shortages begin after time $t = 78.320$. This is not a coincidence. The food surplus model predicts shortages when $S(t) = N(t) - P(t) < 0$, or $N(t) < P(t)$. The per capita food supply model predicts shortages when $R(t) < 1$, meaning that the amount of food available per person is less than the amount necessary to feed 1 person. Since $R(t) = \dfrac{N(t)}{P(t)} < 1$ is true only when $N(t) < P(t)$, the same condition leads to shortages.

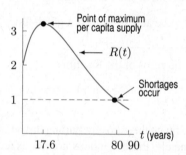

Figure 10.25: Per capita food supply,
$R(t) = \frac{N(t)}{P(t)}$

The Quotient of Functions Defined by Tables: Per Capita Crime Rate

Table 10.11 gives the number of violent crimes committed in two cities between 2005 and 2010. It appears that crime in both cities is on the rise and that there is less crime in City B than in City A.

Table 10.11   *Number of violent crimes committed each year in two cities*

Year	2005	2006	2007	2008	2009	2010
t, years since 2005	0	1	2	3	4	5
Crimes in City A	793	795	807	818	825	831
Crimes in City B	448	500	525	566	593	652

Table 10.12 gives the population for these two cities from 2005 to 2010. The population of City A is larger than that of City B and both cities are growing.

Table 10.12   *Population of the two cities*

Year	2005	2006	2007	2008	2009	2010
t, years since 2000	0	1	2	3	4	5
Population of City A	61,000	62,100	63,220	64,350	65,510	66,690
Population of City B	28,000	28,588	29,188	29,801	30,427	31,066

Can we attribute the growth in crime in both cities to the population growth? Can we attribute the larger number of crimes in City A to its larger population? To answer these questions, we consider the per capita crime rate in each city.

Let's define $N_A(t)$ to be the number of crimes in City A during year t (where $t = 0$ means 2005). Similarly, let's define $P_A(t)$ to be the population of City A in year t. Then the per capita crime rate in City A, $r_A(t)$, is given by

$$r_A(t) = \frac{\text{Number of crimes in year } t}{\text{Number of people in year } t} = \frac{N_A(t)}{P_A(t)}.$$

We have defined a new function, $r_A(t)$, as the quotient of $N_A(t)$ and $P_A(t)$. For example, the data in Tables 10.11 and 10.12 shows that the per capita crime rate for City A in year $t = 0$ is

$$r_A(0) = \frac{N_A(0)}{P_A(0)} = \frac{793}{61,000} = 0.0130 \text{ crimes per person.}$$

Similarly, the per capita crime rate for the year $t = 1$ is

$$r_A(1) = \frac{N_A(1)}{P_A(1)} = \frac{795}{62,100} = 0.0128 \text{ crimes per person.}$$

Thus, the per capita crime rate in City A actually decreased from 0.0130 crimes per person in 2005 to 0.0128 crimes per person in 2006.

Example 3

(a) Make a table of values for $r_A(t)$ and $r_B(t)$, the per capita crime rates of Cities A and B.
(b) Use the table to decide which city is more dangerous.

Solution

(a) Table 10.13 gives values of $r_A(t)$ for $t = 0, 1, \ldots, 5$. The per capita crime rate in City A declined between 2005 and 2010 despite the fact that the total number of crimes rose during this period. Table 10.13 also gives values of $r_B(t)$, the per capita crime rate of City B, defined by

$$r_B(t) = \frac{N_B(t)}{P_B(t)},$$

where $N_B(t)$ is the number of crimes in City B in year t and $P_B(t)$ is the population of City B in year t. For example, the per capita crime rate in City B in year $t = 0$ is

$$r_B(0) = \frac{N_B(0)}{P_B(0)} = \frac{448}{28,000} = 0.016 \text{ crimes per person.}$$

Table 10.13 *Values of $r_A(t)$ and $r_B(t)$, the per capita violent crime rates of Cities A and B*

Year	2005	2006	2007	2008	2009	2010
t, years since 2005	0	1	2	3	4	5
$r_A(t) = N_A(t)/P_A(t)$	0.0130	0.0128	0.01276	0.01271	0.01259	0.01246
$r_B(t) = N_B(t)/P_B(t)$	0.01600	0.01749	0.01799	0.01899	0.01949	0.02099

(b) From Table 10.13, we see that between 2005 and 2010, City A has a lower per capita crime rate than City B. The crime rate of City A is decreasing, whereas the crime rate of City B is increasing. Thus, even though Table 10.11 indicates that there are more crimes committed in City A, Table 10.13 tells us that City B is, in some sense, more dangerous. Table 10.13 also tells us that, even though the number of crimes is rising in both cities, City A is getting safer, while City B is getting more dangerous.

Exercises and Problems for Section 10.3

Exercises

In Exercises 1–6, find the following functions.

(a) $f(x) + g(x)$ (b) $f(x) - g(x)$
(c) $f(x)g(x)$ (d) $f(x)/g(x)$

1. $f(x) = x + 1$ $g(x) = 3x^2$
2. $f(x) = x^2 + 4$ $g(x) = x + 2$
3. $f(x) = x + 5$ $g(x) = x - 5$
4. $f(x) = x^2 + 4$ $g(x) = x^2 + 2$
5. $f(x) = x^3$ $g(x) = x^2$
6. $f(x) = \sqrt{x}$ $g(x) = x^2 + 2$

In Exercises 7–12, find simplified formulas using

$$u(x) = 2x - 1, \quad v(x) = 1 - x, \quad \text{and} \quad w(x) = \frac{1}{x}.$$

7. $f(x) = u(x) + v(x)$
8. $g(x) = v(x)w(x)$
9. $h(x) = 2u(x) - 3v(x)$
10. $j(x) = \dfrac{u(x)}{w(x)}$

11. $k(x) = (v(x))^2$

12. $l(x) = u(x) - v(x) - w(x)$

In Exercises 13–16, let $u(x) = e^x$ and $v(x) = 2x + 1$. Find a simplified formula for the function.

13. $f(x) = u(x)v(x)$ 14. $g(x) = u(x)^2 + v(x)^2$

15. $h(x) = (v(u(x)))^2$ 16. $k(x) = v(u(x)^2)$

Find formulas for the functions in Exercises 17–22. Let $f(x) = \sin x$ and $g(x) = x^2$.

17. $f(x) + g(x)$ 18. $g(x)f(x)$

19. $f(x)/g(x)$ 20. $f(g(x))$

21. $g(f(x))$ 22. $1 - (f(x))^2$

Problems

23. Use Table 10.14 to make tables of values for $x = -1, 0, 1, 2, 3, 4$ for the following functions.

(a) $h(x) = f(x) + g(x)$ (b) $j(x) = 2f(x)$

(c) $k(x) = (g(x))^2$ (d) $m(x) = g(x)/f(x)$

Table 10.14

x	−1	0	1	2	3	4
$f(x)$	−4	−1	2	5	8	11
$g(x)$	4	1	0	1	4	9

24. Let $f(x) = x + 1$ and $g(x) = x^2 - 1$. In parts (a)–(e), write a formula in terms of $f(x)$ and $g(x)$ for the function. Then evaluate the formula for $x = 3$. Write a formula in terms of x for each function. Check your formulas for $x = 3$.

(a) $h(x)$ is the sum of $f(x)$ and $g(x)$.
(b) $j(x)$ is the difference between $g(x)$ and twice $f(x)$.
(c) $k(x)$ is the product of $f(x)$ and $g(x)$.
(d) $m(x)$ is the ratio of $g(x)$ to $f(x)$.
(e) $n(x)$ is defined by $n(x) = (f(x))^2 - g(x)$.

25. Let $f(t)$ be the number of men and $g(t)$ be the number of women in Canada in year t. Let $h(t)$ be the average income, in Canadian dollars, of women in Canada in year t.

(a) Find the function $p(t)$, which gives the number of people in Canada in year t.
(b) Find the total amount of money $m(t)$ earned by Canadian women in year t.

Evaluate the expressions in Problems 26–27 using Figures 10.26 and 10.27, giving estimates if necessary.

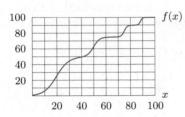

Figure 10.26

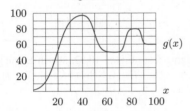

Figure 10.27

26. $f(g(65))$

27. $v(50)$ where $v(x) = g(x)f(x)$

28. Let $f(x) = \dfrac{1}{x+1}$. Find and simplify $f\left(\dfrac{1}{x}\right) + \dfrac{1}{f(x)}$.

29. Use Table 10.15 to make tables of values for the following functions.

(a) $f(x) = r(x) + t(x)$ (b) $g(x) = 4 - 2s(x)$
(c) $h(x) = r(x)t(x)$ (d) $j(x) = \dfrac{r(x) - t(x)}{s(x)}$

(e) $k(x) = r(x)^2$ (f) $l(x) = r(x) + s(x)t(x)$

Table 10.15

x	-2	-1	0	1	2	3
$r(x)$	4	5	6	7	8	9
$s(x)$	-2	2	-2	2	-2	2
$t(x)$	8	5	7	-3	2	13

30. Find formulas for H and h given that:

$$F(x) = \cos x \qquad f(x) = -\sin x$$
$$G(x) = \sqrt{x} \qquad g(x) = \frac{1}{2\sqrt{x}}$$
$$H(x) = F(G(x)); \quad h(x) = f(G(x)) \cdot g(x).$$

31. Judging from Figure 10.28, sketch a graph of $h(x) = f(x)g(x)$. [Hint: Note where $g(x) = 0$ and $g(x) = 1$.]

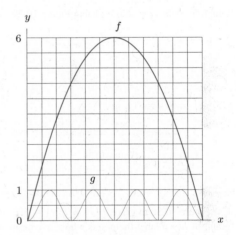

Figure 10.28

Create tables for the functions in Problems 32–33 based on Table 10.16.

Table 10.16

x	0	1	2	3	4	5
$v(x)$	4	3	3	5	4	4
$w(x)$	2	1	3	4	0	5

32. $p(x) = v(x)w(x)$ **33.** $q(x) = w^{-1}(v(x))$

34. In 1961 and 1962, large amounts of the radioactive isotope carbon-14 were produced by tests of nuclear bombs.[3] If t is years since 1963, the amount of carbon-14, as a percent in excess of the normal level, is given by

$$C(t) = 108(e^{-0.1t} - e^{-0.7t}).$$

(a) Graph the function.
(b) Approximately when was the level of carbon-14 the highest?
(c) What happens to the level of carbon-14 in the long run?

35. An average of 50,000 people visit Riverside Park each day in the summer. The park charges $15.00 for admission. Consultants predict that for each $1.00 increase in the entrance price, the park would lose an average of 2500 customers per day. Express the daily revenue from ticket sales as a function of the number of $1.00 price increases. What ticket price maximizes the revenue from ticket sales?

36. Graph $h(x) = f(x) + g(x)$ using Figure 10.29.

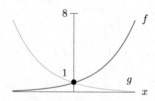

Figure 10.29

37. Use Figure 10.30 to graph $h(x) = g(x) - f(x)$. On the graph of $h(x)$, label the points whose x-coordinates are $x = a$, $x = b$, and $x = c$. Label the y-intercept.

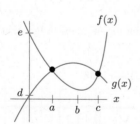

Figure 10.30

38. Table 10.17 gives the upper household income limits for the twentieth and the lower household income limits of the ninety-fifth percentiles t years after 2000.[4] For instance, $P_{20}(5) = 19,178$ tells us that in 2005 the maximum income for a household in the poorest 20% of all households was $19,178. Let $f(t) = P_{95}(t) - P_{20}(t)$ and $g(t) = P_{95}(t)/P_{20}(t)$.

(a) Make tables of values for f and g.
(b) Describe in words what f and g tell you about household income.

Table 10.17

t (yrs)	0	1	2
$P_{20}(t)(\$)$	17,920	17,970	17,916
$P_{95}(t)(\$)$	145,220	150,449	150,002

t (yrs)	3	4	5
$P_{20}(t)$ (\$)	17,984	18,486	19,178
$P_{95}(t)$ (\$)	154,120	157,152	166,000

39. Sketch two linear functions whose product is the function f graphed in Figure 10.31(a). Explain why this is not possible for the function q graphed in Figure 10.31(b).

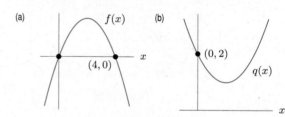

Figure 10.31

40. Judging from Figure 10.32, sketch a graph of $h(x) = g(x) - f(x)$. (Hint: Note where $g(x) = f(x)$.)

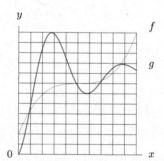

Figure 10.32

---

[3] Adapted from William Bolton, *Patterns in Physics* (New York: McGraw-Hill, 1974).
[4] US Census Bureau, www.census.gov/hhes/www/income/histinc/h01ar.html, accessed November 18, 2009.

41. Find simplified formulas for H and h given that:

$$F(x) = e^{-x^2} \qquad f(x) = -2xe^{-x^2}$$
$$G(x) = x^4 \qquad g(x) = 4x^3$$
$$H(x) = \frac{F(x)}{G(x)} \qquad h(x) = \frac{f(x)G(x) - F(x)g(x)}{(G(x))^2}.$$

42. At the Mauna Loa Observatory, measurements of CO_2 levels (ppm) in the atmosphere reveal a slow exponential increase due to deforestation and burning of fossil fuels, and a periodic seasonal variation.

(a) In 1960, the average CO_2 level was 316.75 parts per million and was rising by 0.4% per year. Write the average annual CO_2 level as an exponential function of time, t, in years since 1960.

(b) Each year, the CO_2 level oscillates once between 3.25 ppm above and 3.25 ppm below the average level. Write a sinusoidal function for the seasonal variation in CO_2 levels in terms of time, t.

(c) Graph the sum of your functions in parts (a) and (b).

43. Table 10.18 gives data on strawberry production from 2004 through 2008,[5] where t is in years since 2004. Let $f_{CA}(t)$, $f_{FL}(t)$, and $f_{US}(t)$ be the harvested area in year t for strawberries grown in California, Florida, and the US overall, respectively. Likewise, let $g_{CA}(t)$, $g_{FL}(t)$, and $g_{US}(t)$ give the yield in thousands of pounds per acre for these three regions.

(a) Let $h_{CA}(t) = f_{CA}(t) \cdot g_{CA}(t)$. Create a table of values for $h_{CA}(t)$ for $0 \le t \le 4$. Describe in words what $h_{CA}(t)$ tells you about strawberry production.

(b) Let $p(t)$ be the fraction of all US strawberries (by weight) grown in Florida and California in year t. Find a formula for $p(t)$ in terms of f_{CA}, f_{FL}, f_{US}. Use Table 10.18 to make a table of values for $p(t)$.

Table 10.18

	Harvested area (acres)			Yield (1000 lbs per acre)		
t	CA	FL	US total	CA	FL	US total
0	33,200	7,100	51,400	59.0	23.0	43.1
1	34,300	7,300	52,200	60.0	24.5	44.5
2	35,800	7,300	53,460	59.0	28.0	45.0
3	35,500	6,600	52,180	60.5	32.0	46.9
4	37,600	6,900	54,470	60.5	26.0	46.5

44. In Figure 10.33, the line l_2 is fixed and the point P moves along l_2. Define $f(\theta)$ as the y-coordinate of P.

(a) Find a formula for $f(\theta)$ if $0 < \theta < \pi/2$. [Hint: Use the equation for l_2.]

(b) Graph $y = f(\theta)$ on the interval $-\pi \le \theta \le \pi$.

(c) How does the y-coordinate of P change as θ changes? Is $y = f(\theta)$ periodic?

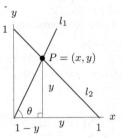

Figure 10.33

45. Let $f(x) = kx^2 + B$ and $g(x) = C^{2x}$ and

$$h(x) = kx^2C^{2x} + BC^{2x} + C^{2x}.$$

Suppose $f(3) = 7$ and $g(3) = 5$. Evaluate $h(3)$.

In Problems 46–52, you hire either Ace Construction or Space Contractors to build office space. Let $f(x)$ be the average total cost in dollars of building x square feet of office space, as estimated by Ace. Let $h(x)$ be the total number of square feet of office space you can build with x dollars, as estimated by Space.

46. Describe in words what the following statement tells you: $f(2000) = 200,000$.

47. Let $g(x) = f(x)/x$. Using the information from Problem 46, evaluate $g(2000)$, and describe in words what $g(2000)$ represents. [Hint: Think about the units.]

48. Ace tells you that, due to the economies of scale, "Building twice as much office space always costs less than twice as much." Express this statement symbolically, in terms of f and x. [Hint: If you are building x square feet, how do you represent the cost? How would you represent twice the cost? How do you represent the cost of building twice as many square feet?]

49. Suppose that $q > p$ and $p > 1$. Assuming that the contractor's statement in Problem 48 is correct, rank the following in increasing order, using inequality signs: $f(p)$, $g(p)$, $f(q)$, $g(q)$.

50. What does the statement $h(200,000) = 1500$ tell you?

51. Let $j(x)$ be the average cost in dollars per square foot of office space as estimated by Space Contractors. Give a formula for $j(x)$. (Your formula will have $h(x)$ in it.)

52. Research reveals that $h(f(x)) < x$ for every value of x you check. Explain the implications of this statement. [Hint: Which company seems more economical?]

---

[5] usda.mannlib.cornell.edu/usda/nass/NoncFruitNu//2000s/2009/NoncFruiNu-07-08-2009.pdf, accessed November 27, 2009.

CHAPTER SUMMARY

- **Composition of Functions**
  Notation: $h(t) = f(g(t))$.
  Domain and range; Decomposition.
- **Inverse Functions**
  Definition: $f^{-1}(Q) = t$ if and only if $Q = f(t)$.
  Invertibility; horizontal line test.

Domain and range of an inverse function.
Restricting domain of a function to construct an inverse.
Graph of an inverse function.
$f^{-1}(f(x)) = x$ and $f(f^{-1}(x)) = x$.
- **Combinations of Functions**
  Sums, differences, products, quotients of functions.

REVIEW EXERCISES AND PROBLEMS FOR CHAPTER TEN

Exercises

1. Let $h(x) = 2^x$ and $k(x) = x^2$. Find formulas for $h(k(x))$ and $k(h(x))$.

Find formulas for the functions in Exercises 2–7 and simplify.
Let $f(x) = x^2 + 1$, $g(x) = \dfrac{1}{x-3}$, and $h(x) = \sqrt{x}$.

2. $f(g(x))$ **3.** $g(f(x))$ **4.** $f(h(x))$

5. $h(f(x))$ **6.** $g(g(x))$ **7.** $g(f(h(x)))$

8. Using Tables 10.19 and 10.20, complete Table 10.21:

Table 10.19

x	$f(x)$
0	0
$\pi/6$	$1/2$
$\pi/4$	$\sqrt{2}/2$
$\pi/3$	$\sqrt{3}/2$
$\pi/2$	1

Table 10.20

y	$g(y)$
0	$\pi/2$
$1/4$	π
$\sqrt{2}/4$	0
$1/2$	$\pi/3$
$\sqrt{2}/2$	$\pi/4$
$3/4$	0
$\sqrt{3}/2$	$\pi/6$
1	0

Table 10.21

x	$g(f(x))$
0	
$\pi/6$	
$\pi/4$	
$\pi/3$	
$\pi/2$	

9. For each of the following functions, use a graph to decide whether or not the function is invertible.

(a) $y = e^{x^2}$ (b) $y = \cos(x^3)$ (c) $y = x + \ln x$

Find the inverses of the functions in Exercises 10–22.

10. $h(x) = 12x^3$

11. $h(x) = \dfrac{x}{2x+1}$

12. $k(x) = 3 \cdot e^{2x}$

13. $g(x) = e^{3x+1}$

14. $n(x) = \log(x - 3)$

15. $h(x) = \ln(1 - 2x)$

16. $h(x) = \dfrac{\sqrt{x}}{\sqrt{x}+1}$

17. $g(x) = \dfrac{x-2}{2x+3}$

18. $f(x) = \sqrt{\dfrac{4-7x}{4-x}}$

19. $f(x) = \dfrac{\sqrt{x}+3}{11-\sqrt{x}}$

20. $f(x) = \ln\left(1 + \dfrac{1}{x}\right)$

21. $s(x) = \dfrac{3}{2 + \log x}$

22. $q(x) = \ln(x + 3) - \ln(x - 5)$

In Exercises 23–28, state whether the function is invertible. If so, give a formula for the inverse function.

23. $f(x) = 6x^2 - 2x - 3$ **24.** $q(x) = 3x^3 - 2$

25. $m(x) = 3x^3 - 2x^2 + 5x$ **26.** $p(x) = 5x^5 + 4$

27. $r(x) = e^x - 7$ **28.** $b(x) = \sqrt[3]{x} - 2$

29. Check that $h^{-1}(h(x)) = x$ if $h(x) = \sqrt{\dfrac{1-x}{x}}$ for $0 < x \leq 1$ and $h^{-1}(x) = \dfrac{1}{x^2+1}$ for $x \geq 0$.

30. Suppose $f(x) = \dfrac{x}{2x+1}$. Find a formula for $f^{-1}(x)$.

In Exercises 31–36, find simplified formulas if $f(x) = e^x$, $g(x) = 2x - 1$, and $h(x) = \sqrt{x}$.

31. $g(f(x))$ **32.** $g(x)f(x)$ **33.** $g(g(x))$

34. $f(g(h(x)))$ **35.** $f(g(x))h(x)$ **36.** $(f(h(x)))^2$

37. Find formulas for the following functions, given that

$$f(x) = x^2 + x, \qquad g(x) = 2x - 3. \qquad h(x) = \frac{x}{1-x}.$$

(a) $f(2x)$ (b) $g(x^2)$ (c) $h(1-x)$
(d) $(f(x))^2$ (e) $g^{-1}(x)$ (f) $(h(x))^{-1}$
(g) $f(x) \cdot g(x)$ (h) $h(f(x))$

In Exercises 38–40, find simplified formulas if $u(x) = \dfrac{1}{1+x^2}$, $v(x) = e^x$, and $w(x) = \ln x$.

38. $v(x)/u(x)$

39. $u(v(x)) \cdot w(v(x))$

40. $\dfrac{w(2+h) - w(2)}{h}$

In Exercises 41–46, find a simplified formula for the function. Let $m(x) = 3x^2 - x$, $n(x) = 2x$, and $o(x) = \sqrt{x+2}$.

41. $f(x) = m(x) + n(x)$ **42.** $g(x) = (o(x))^2$

43. $h(x) = n(x)o(x)$ **44.** $i(x) = m(o(x))n(x)$

45. $j(x) = (m(x))/n(x)$

46. $k(x) = m(x) - n(x) - o(x)$

In Exercises 47–50 find simplified formulas if $f(x) = x^{3/2}$, $g(x) = \dfrac{(3x-1)^2}{4}$, and $h(x) = \tan 2x$.

47. $f(x)h(x)$ **48.** $\dfrac{h(x)}{f(g(x))}$

49. $h(g(x)) - f(9x)$ **50.** $h(x/2) \cos x$

Problems

51. Complete Table 10.22 if $r(t) = q(p(t))$.

Table 10.22

t	$p(t)$	$q(t)$	$r(t)$
0	4	??	??
1	??	2	1
2	??	??	0
3	2	0	4
4	1	5	??
5	0	1	3

52. Complete Table 10.23, Table 10.24, and Table 10.25 given that $h(x) = g(f(x))$. Assume that different values of x lead to different values of $f(x)$.

Table 10.23

x	$f(x)$
-2	4
-1	
0	
1	5
2	1

Table 10.24

x	$g(x)$
1	
2	1
3	2
4	0
5	-1

Table 10.25

x	$h(x)$
-2	
-1	1
0	2
1	
2	-2

Decompose the functions in Problems 53–60 into two new functions, u and v, where v is the inside function, $u(x) \neq x$, and $v(x) \neq x$.

53. $f(x) = \sqrt{3 - 5x}$ **54.** $g(x) = \sin(x^2)$

55. $h(x) = \sin^2 x$ **56.** $k(x) = e^{\sin x} + \sin x$

57. $F(x) = (2x + 5)^3$ **58.** $G(x) = \dfrac{2}{1 + \sqrt{x}}$

59. $H(x) = 3^{2x-1}$ **60.** $J(x) = 8 - 2|x|$

61. Using your knowledge of the absolute value function, explain in a few sentences the relationship between the graph of $y = |\sin x|$ and the graph of $y = \sin x$.

62. Graph the following functions for $-2\pi \le x \le 2\pi$.

(a) $f(x) = \sin x$ (b) $g(x) = |\sin x|$
(c) $h(x) = \sin |x|$ (d) $i(x) = |\sin |x||$

(e) Do any two of these functions have identical graphs? If so, explain why this makes sense.

63. Suppose $p(x) = (1/x) + 1$ and $q(x) = x - 2$.

(a) Let $r(x) = p(q(x))$. Find a formula for $r(x)$ and simplify it.
(b) Write formulas for $s(x)$ and $t(x)$ such that $p(x) = s(t(x))$, where $s(x) \neq x$ and $t(x) \neq x$.
(c) Let a be different from 0 and -1. Find a simplified expression for $p(p(a))$.

64. Let $f(x) = \frac{1}{x}$ and $g(x) = \sin x$. Calculate the domain of $f(g(x))$ and the domain of $g(f(x))$.

65. Suppose that $h(x) = f(g(x))$, and that f is invertible. Complete the following table.

x	$f(x)$	$g(x)$	$h(x)$
0	9	1	
1	0		1
2	1	0	

In Problems 66–67, a population is given by the formula $P = f(t) = 20 + 0.4t$ where P is the number of people (in thousands) and t is the number of years since 1985.

66. Evaluate the following quantities. Explain in words what each tells you about the population.

   (a) $f(25)$ **(b)** $f^{-1}(25)$

   (c) Show how to estimate $f^{-1}(25)$ from a graph of f.

67. **(a)** Find a formula for $t = f^{-1}(P)$.

   (b) Construct tables of values for both functions for values of t from $t = 0$ years to $t = 20$ years, using five-year intervals.

68. Let $P = f(t) = 14 \cdot 2^{t/12}$ give the size in 1000s of an animal population in year t.

   (a) Find $f^{-1}(P)$.

   (b) Evaluate $f^{-1}(24)$. Say what this tells you about the population.

69. If $t = g(v)$ represents the time in hours it takes to drive to the next town at velocity v mph, what does $g^{-1}(t)$ represent? What are its units?

70. Let $f(x) = e^x$. Solve each of the following equations exactly for x.

   (a) $(f(x))^{-1} = 2$ **(b)** $f^{-1}(x) = 2$

   (c) $f(x^{-1}) = 2$

71. Simplify the expression $\cos^2(\arcsin t)$, using the property that inverses "undo" each other.

Solve the equations in Problems 72–77 exactly. Use an inverse function when appropriate.

72. $7\sin(3x) = 2$ **73.** $2^{x+5} = 3$

74. $x^{1.05} = 1.09$ **75.** $\ln(x + 3) = 1.8$

76. $\dfrac{2x + 3}{x + 3} = 8$ **77.** $\sqrt{x + \sqrt{x}} = 3$

78. Let $Q = f(t) = 20(0.96)^{t/3}$ be the number of grams of a radioactive substance remaining after t years.

   (a) Describe the behavior of the radioactive substance as a function of time.

   (b) Evaluate $f(8)$. Explain the meaning of this quantity in practical terms.

   (c) Find a formula for $f^{-1}(Q)$ in terms of Q.

   (d) Evaluate $f^{-1}(8)$. Explain the meaning of this quantity in practical terms.

79. **(a)** What is the formula for the area of a circle in terms of its radius?

   (b) Graph this function for the domain all real numbers.

   (c) What domain actually applies in this situation? On separate axes, graph the function for this domain.

   (d) Find the inverse of the function in part (c).

   (e) Graph the inverse function on the domain you gave in part (c) on the same axes used in part (c).

   (f) If area is a function of the radius, is radius a function of area? Explain carefully.

80. A company believes there is a linear relationship between the consumer demand for its products and the price charged. When the price was \$3 per unit, the quantity demanded was 500 units per week. When the unit price was raised to \$4, the quantity demanded dropped to 300 units per week. Let $D(p)$ be the quantity per week demanded by consumers at a unit price of \$p$.

   (a) Estimate and interpret $D(5)$.

   (b) Find a formula for $D(p)$ in terms of p.

   (c) Calculate and interpret $D^{-1}(5)$.

   (d) Give an interpretation of the slope of $D(p)$ in terms of demand.

   (e) Currently, the company can produce 400 units every week. What should the price of the product be if the company wants to sell all 400 units?

   (f) If the company produced 500 units per week instead of 400 units per week, would its weekly revenues increase, and if so, by how much?

81. Use Figure 10.34.

   (a) Evaluate $f(g(a))$.

   (b) Evaluate $g(f(c))$.

   (c) Evaluate $f^{-1}(b) - g^{-1}(b)$.

   (d) For what positive value(s) of x is $f(x) \leq g(x)$?

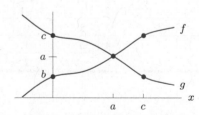

Figure 10.34

Chapter Eleven

POLYNOMIAL AND RATIONAL FUNCTIONS

Contents

11.1   POWER FUNCTIONS

Proportionality and Power Functions

The following two examples introduce proportionality and power functions.

Example 1   The area, A, of a circle is proportional to the square of its radius, r:

$$A = \pi r^2.$$

Example 2   The weight, w, of an object is inversely proportional to the square of the object's distance, d, from the earth's center:[1]

$$w = \frac{k}{d^2} = kd^{-2}.$$

For an object with weight 44 pounds on the surface of the earth, which is about 3959 miles from the earth's center, we get the data listed in Table 11.1 and graphed in Figure 11.1.

Table 11.1   *Weight of an object, w, inversely proportional to the square of the object's distance, d, from the earth's center*

d, miles	$w = f(d)$, lbs
4000	43.3
5000	27.8
6000	19.2
7000	14.1
8000	10.8

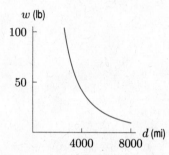

Figure 11.1: Weight, w, inversely proportional to the square of the object's distance, d, from the earth's center

---

A quantity y is **(directly) proportional to a power** of x if

$$y = kx^n, \qquad k \text{ and } n \text{ are constants.}$$

A quantity y is **inversely proportional** to x^n if

$$y = \frac{k}{x^n}, \qquad k \text{ and } n \text{ are constants.}$$

---

[1] There is a distinction between mass and weight. For example, astronauts in orbit may be weightless, but they still have mass.

The functions in Examples 1 and 2 are power functions. Generalizing, we define:

> A **power function** is a function of the form
>
> $$f(x) = kx^p,$$ where k and p are constants.

Example 3   Which of the following functions are power functions? For each power function, state the value of the constants k and p in the formula $y = kx^p$.

(a) $f(x) = 13\sqrt[3]{x}$ (b) $g(x) = 2(x+5)^3$ (c) $u(x) = \sqrt{\dfrac{25}{x^3}}$ (d) $v(x) = 6 \cdot 3^x$

Solution   The functions f and u are power functions; the functions g and v are not.

(a)   The function $f(x) = 13\sqrt[3]{x}$ is a power function because we can write its formula as

$$f(x) = 13x^{1/3}.$$

Here, $k = 13$ and $p = 1/3$.

(b)   Although the value of $g(x) = 2(x+5)^3$ is proportional to the cube of $x+5$, it is *not* proportional to a power of x. We cannot write $g(x)$ in the form $g(x) = kx^p$; thus, g is not a power function.

(c)   We can rewrite the formula for $u(x) = \sqrt{25/x^3}$ as

$$u(x) = \frac{\sqrt{25}}{\sqrt{x^3}} = \frac{5}{(x^3)^{1/2}} = \frac{5}{x^{3/2}} = 5x^{-3/2}.$$

Thus, u is a power function. Here, $k = 5$ and $p = -3/2$.

(d)   Although the value of $v(x) = 6 \cdot 3^x$ is proportional to a power of 3, the power is not a constant—it is the variable x. In fact, $v(x) = 6 \cdot 3^x$ is an exponential function, not a power function. Notice that $y = 6 \cdot x^3$ is a power function. However, $6 \cdot x^3$ and $6 \cdot 3^x$ are quite different.

The Effect of the Power p

We now study functions whose constant of proportionality is $k = 1$ so that we can focus on the effect of the power p.

Graphs of the Special Cases $y = x^0$ and $y = x^1$

The power functions corresponding to $p = 0$ and $p = 1$ are both linear. The graph of $y = x^0 = 1$ is a horizontal line through the point $(1, 1)$. The graph of $y = x^1 = x$ is a line through the origin with slope $+1$.

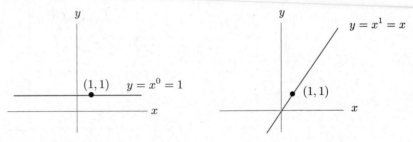

Figure 11.2: Graph of $y = x^0 = 1$ Figure 11.3: Graph of $y = x^1 = x$

Positive Integer Powers: $y = x^3,\ x^5,\ x^7 \ldots$ and $y = x^2,\ x^4, x^6 \ldots$

The graphs of all power functions with p a positive even integer have the same characteristic $\cup$-shape and are symmetric about the y-axis. For instance, the graphs of $y = x^2$ and $y = x^4$ in Figure 11.4 are similar in shape, although the graph of $y = x^4$ is flatter near the origin and steeper away from the origin than the graph of $y = x^2$.

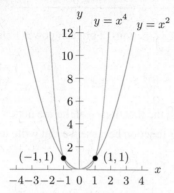

Figure 11.4: Graphs of positive even powers of x are $\cup$-shaped

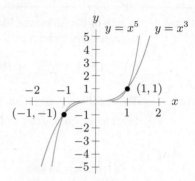

Figure 11.5: Graphs of positive odd powers of x are "chair-shaped"

The graphs of power functions with p a positive odd integer resemble the side view of a chair and are symmetric about the origin. Figure 11.5 shows the graphs of $y = x^3$ and $y = x^5$. The graph of $y = x^5$ is flatter near the origin and steeper far from the origin than the graph of $y = x^3$.

Negative Integer Powers: $y = x^{-1},\ x^{-3}, x^{-5}, \ldots$ and $y = x^{-2}, x^{-4}, x^{-6}, \ldots$

For negative powers, if we rewrite

$$y = x^{-1} = \frac{1}{x}$$

and

$$y = x^{-2} = \frac{1}{x^2},$$

then it is clear that as $x > 0$ increases, the denominators increase and the functions decrease. The graphs of power functions with odd negative powers, $y = x^{-3},\ x^{-5}, \ldots$, resemble the graph of $y = x^{-1} = 1/x$. The graphs of even integer powers, $y = x^{-4},\ x^{-6}, \ldots$, are similar in shape to the graph of $y = x^{-2} = 1/x^2$. See Figures 11.6 and 11.7.

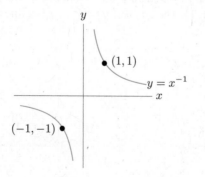

Figure 11.6: Graph of $y = x^{-1} = 1/x$

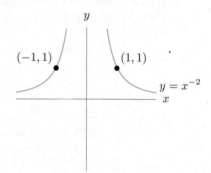

Figure 11.7: Graph of $y = x^{-2} = 1/x^2$

We see in Figures 11.6 and 11.7 that $y = 0$ is a horizontal asymptote and $x = 0$ is a vertical asymptote for the graphs of $y = 1/x$ and $y = 1/x^2$.

Numerically, the values of $1/x$ and $1/x^2$ can be made as close to zero as we like by choosing a sufficiently large x (positive or negative). See Table 11.2 for positive values of x. Graphically, this means that the curves $y = 1/x$ and $y = 1/x^2$ get closer and closer to the x-axis for large values of x. We write $y \to 0$ as $x \to \pm\infty$. Using limit notation, we see

$$\lim_{x \to \infty} \left(\frac{1}{x} \right) = 0, \quad \lim_{x \to -\infty} \left(\frac{1}{x} \right) = 0 \quad \text{and} \quad \lim_{x \to \infty} \left(\frac{1}{x^2} \right) = 0, \quad \lim_{x \to -\infty} \left(\frac{1}{x^2} \right) = 0.$$

Table 11.2 *Values of x^{-1} and x^{-2} approach zero as x grows large*

x	0	10	20	30	40	50
$y = 1/x$	Undefined	0.1	0.05	0.033	0.025	0.02
$y = 1/x^2$	Undefined	0.01	0.0025	0.0011	0.0006	0.0004

On the other hand, as x gets close to zero, the values of $1/x$ and $1/x^2$ get very large. See Table 11.3. Graphically, this means that the curves $y = 1/x$ and $y = 1/x^2$ get very close to the y-axis as x gets close to zero. From Figure 11.6, we see that[2]

$$\lim_{x \to 0^+} \left(\frac{1}{x} \right) = \infty \quad \text{and} \quad \lim_{x \to 0^-} \left(\frac{1}{x} \right) = -\infty.$$

From Figure 11.7, we see that

$$\lim_{x \to 0} \left(\frac{1}{x^2} \right) = \infty.$$

Table 11.3 *Values of x^{-1} and x^{-2} grow large as x approaches zero from the positive side*

x	0.1	0.05	0.01	0.001	0.0001	0
$y = 1/x$	10	20	100	1000	10,000	Undefined
$y = 1/x^2$	100	400	10,000	1,000,000	100,000,000	Undefined

Graphs of Positive Fractional Powers: $y = x^{1/2}, x^{1/3}, x^{1/4}, \ldots$

Figure 11.8 shows the graphs of $y = x^{1/2}$ and $y = x^{1/4}$. These graphs have the same shape, although $y = x^{1/4}$ is steeper near the origin and flatter away from the origin than $y = x^{1/2}$. The same can be said about the graphs of $y = x^{1/3}$ and $y = x^{1/5}$ in Figure 11.9. In general, if n is a positive integer, then the graph of $y = x^{1/n}$ resembles the graph of $y = x^{1/2}$ if n is even; if n is odd, the graph resembles the graph of $y = x^{1/3}$.

Notice that the graphs of $y = x^{1/2}$ and $y = x^{1/3}$ bend in a direction opposite to that of the graphs of $y = x^2$ and x^3. For example, the graph of $y = x^2$ is concave up, but the graph of $y = x^{1/2}$ is concave down. However, all these functions become infinitely large as x increases.

---

[2]Some authors say that these limits do not exist.

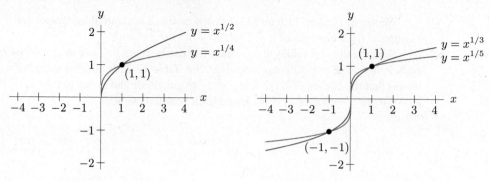

Figure 11.8: The graphs of $y = x^{1/2}$ and $y = x^{1/4}$ Figure 11.9: The graphs of $y = x^{1/3}$ and $y = x^{1/5}$

Example 4   From geometry, we know that the radius of a sphere is directly proportional to the cube root of its volume. In this example, we use that proportionality relationship. If a sphere of radius 18.2 cm has a volume of 25,252.4 cm^3, what is the radius of a sphere whose volume is 30,000 cm^3?

Solution   Since the radius of the sphere is proportional to the cube root of its volume, we know that

$$r = kV^{1/3}, \qquad \text{for } k \text{ constant.}$$

We also know that $r = 18.2$ cm when $V = 25,252.4$ cm^3; therefore

$$18.2 = k(25,252.4)^{1/3},$$

giving

$$k = \frac{18.2}{(25,252.4)^{1/3}} \approx 0.620.$$

Thus, when $V = 30,000$, we get $r = 0.620(30,000)^{1/3} \approx 19.3$, so the radius of the sphere is approximately 19.3 cm.

To compare the proportionality constant in Example 4 with that given by geometry, notice that since

$$V = \frac{4}{3}\pi r^3,$$

we have

$$r = \left(\frac{3}{4\pi}V\right)^{1/3} = \left(\frac{3}{4\pi}\right)^{1/3} V^{1/3}.$$

Thus, the constant of proportionality is $(3/(4\pi))^{1/3} = 0.620$, as before.

Finding the Formula for a Power Function

As is the case for linear and exponential functions, the formula of a power function can be found using two points on its graph.

Example 5   Water is leaking out of a container with a hole in the bottom. Torricelli's Law states that at any instant, the velocity v with which water escapes from the container is a power function of d, the depth of the water at that moment. When $d = 9$ feet, then $v = 24$ ft/sec; when $d = 1/4$ foot, then $v = 4$ ft/sec. Express v as a function of d.

Solution   Torricelli's Law tells us that $v = kd^p$, where k and p are constants. Since $v = 24$ when $d = 9$ we have $24 = k9^p$ and since $v = 4$ when $d = 1/4$ we have $4 = k(1/4)^p$. Taking the ratio gives

$$\frac{24}{4} = \frac{k9^p}{k(1/4)^p}$$
$$6 = 36^p.$$

Since $36^{1/2} = 6$, we must have $p = 1/2$, so $v = kd^{1/2}$. Substituting $v = 24$ and $d = 9$ gives

$$24 = k9^{1/2},$$

so $k = 8$. Therefore we have $v = 8d^{1/2}$. *Note:* Torricelli's Law is often written in the form $v = \sqrt{2gd}$, where $g = 32$ ft/sec^2 is the acceleration due to gravity.

Exercises and Problems for Section 11.1

Skill Refresher

Simplify the expressions in Exercises S1–S4.

S1. $\sqrt{36t^2}$

S2. $\left(3x\sqrt{x^3}\right)^2$

S3. $(0.1)^2 \left(4xy^2\right)^2$

S4. $7\left(5w^{1/2}\right)\left(2w^{1/3}\right)$

In Exercises S5–S6, solve for x.

S5. $\dfrac{10x^5}{x^2} = 2$

S6. $5x^{-2} = 500$

Are the statements in Exercises S7–S10 true or false?

S7. $t^3 t^4 = t^{12}$

S8. $(p^3)^8 = p^{11}$

S9. $\dfrac{m^8}{2m^2} = \dfrac{1}{2}m^4$

S10. $5z^{-4} = \dfrac{1}{5z^4}$

Exercises

Are the functions in Exercises 1–6 power functions? If so, write the function in the form $f(x) = kx^p$.

1. $g(x) = \dfrac{(-x^3)^3}{6}$

2. $R(t) = \dfrac{4}{\sqrt{16t}}$

3. $f(x) = 4(x + 7)^2$

4. $T(s) = (6s^{-2})(es^{-3})$

5. $h(x) = 22(7^x)^2$

6. $K(w) = \dfrac{w^4 \cdot}{4\sqrt{w^3}}$

7. Write $y = 3\left(\dfrac{2}{5\sqrt{7x}}\right)^4$ in the form $y = ax^p$ and state the values of a and p.

8. Write $y = \sqrt{\pi(2x)^3}$ in the form $y = ax^p$ and state the values of a and p.

Do the power functions in Exercises 9–12 appear to have odd, even, or fractional powers?

9.  x
10. 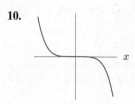 x

11. 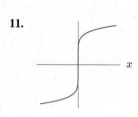 x
12. 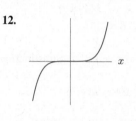 x

In Exercises 13–14, find a power function through the two points.

13. $(1, 3)$ $(4, 13)$ **14.** $(7, 8)$ $(1, 0.7)$

In Exercises 15–16, find possible formulas for the power functions with the properties given.

15. $f(1) = \frac{3}{2}$ and $f(2) = \frac{3}{8}$

16. $g\left(-\frac{1}{5}\right) = 25$ and $g(2) = -\frac{1}{40}$

17. Suppose c is directly proportional to the square of d. If $c = 45$ when $d = 3$, find the constant of proportionality and write the formula for c as a function of d. Use your formula to find c when $d = 5$.

18. Suppose c is inversely proportional to the square of d. If $c = 45$ when $d = 3$, find the constant of proportionality and write the formula for c as a function of d. Use your formula to find c when $d = 5$.

19. If y is directly proportional to x, and $y = 6$ when $x = 4$, find the constant of proportionality, write a formula for y in terms of x, and find x when $y = 8$.

20. If y is inversely proportional to x, and $y = 6$ when $x = 4$, find the constant of proportionality, write a formula for y in terms of x, and find x when $y = 8$.

In Exercises 21–24, find possible formulas for the power functions.

21.

x	2	3	4	5
$f(x)$	12	27	48	75

22.

x	-6	-2	3	4
$g(x)$	36	$4/3$	$-9/2$	$-32/3$

23.

x	0	1	2	3
$j(x)$	0	2	16	54

24.

x	-2	$-1/2$	$1/4$	4
$h(x)$	$-1/2$	-8	-32	$-1/8$

25. Find (a) $\lim_{x \to \infty} x^{-4}$ (b) $\lim_{x \to -\infty} 2x^{-1}$

26. Find (a) $\lim_{t \to \infty} (t^{-3} + 2)$ (b) $\lim_{y \to -\infty} (5 - 7y^{-2})$

Problems

27. Compare the graphs of $y = x^2$, $y = x^4$, and $y = x^6$. Describe the similarities and differences.

28. Describe the behavior of $y = x^{-10}$ and $y = -x^{10}$ as
(a) $x \to 0$ (b) $x \to \infty$ (c) $x \to -\infty$

29. Describe the behavior of $y = x^{-3}$ and $y = x^{1/3}$ as
(a) $x \to 0$ from the right   (b) $x \to \infty$

30. (a) Figure 11.10 shows $g(x)$, a mystery power function. If you learn that the point $(-1, 3)$ lies on its graph, do you have enough information to write a formula for $g(x)$?
(b) If you are told that the point $(1, -3)$ also lies on the graph, what new deductions can you make?

(c) If the point $(2, -96)$ lies on the graph g, in addition to the points already given, state three other points that also lie on it.

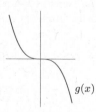
$g(x)$

Figure 11.10

31. Figure 11.11 shows the power function $y = c(t)$. Is $c(t) = 1/t$ the only possible formula for c? Could there be others?

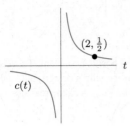

Figure 11.11

32. **(a)** Match the functions $x, x^2, x^3, x^{1/2}, x^{1/3}, x^{3/2}$ with the graphs in Figure 11.12. Justify your choice.
   (b) What is the relationship between the concavity of $y = x^2$ and $y = x^{1/2}$? Between the concavity of $y = x^3$ and $y = x^{1/3}$ for $x > 0$? Explain why this happens.

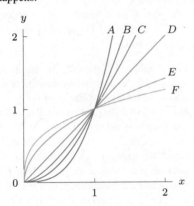

Figure 11.12

Problems 33–34 refer to the power functions f, g, w, v graphed in Figure 11.13. All four graphs contain the point $(1, 1)$.

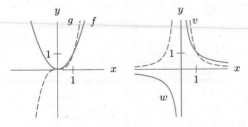

Figure 11.13

33. Rank the four functions in order of p, the power, from least to greatest.

34. For which (if any) of the four functions is the power p odd?

35. For the power function $F(x) = kx^n$, let $f(x) = nkx^{n-1}$. Find f given that $F(x) = \dfrac{1}{\sqrt[3]{7x}}$.

36. For the power function $f(x) = kx^n$, let $F(x) = \dfrac{kx^{n+1}}{n+1}$. Find F given that $f(x) = \dfrac{\sqrt[5]{x^2}}{4}$.

37. The cost of denim fabric is directly proportional to the amount that you buy. Let $C(x)$ be the cost, in dollars, of x yards of denim fabric.

   (a) Write a formula for the cost, $C(x)$, in terms of x. Your answer will contain a constant, k.
   (b) A particular type of denim costs $28.50 for 3 yards. Find k and rewrite the formula for $C(x)$ using it.
   (c) Graph $C(x)$.
   (d) How much does it cost to buy 5.5 yards of denim?

38. Three ounces of broiled ground beef contains 245 calories.[3] Is the number of calories directly or inversely proportional to the number of ounces? Explain your reasoning and write a formula for the proportion. How many calories are there in 4 ounces of broiled hamburger?

39. The circulation time of a mammal—that is, the average time it takes for all the blood in the body to circulate once and return to the heart—is governed by the equation

$$t = 17.4m^{1/4},$$

where m is the body mass of the mammal in kilograms, and t is the circulation time in seconds.[4]

   (a) Complete Table 11.4, which shows typical body masses in kilograms for various mammals.[5]
   (b) If the circulation time of one mammal is twice that of another, what is the relationship between their body masses?

---

[3] *The World Almanac Book of Facts*, 1999, p. 718.
[4] K. Schmidt-Nielsen, *Scaling, Why is Animal Size so Important?* (Cambridge: CUP, 1984).
[5] R. McNeill Alexander, *Dynamics of Dinosaurs and Other Extinct Giants* (New York: Columbia University Press, 1989).

Table 11.4

Animal	Body mass (kg)	Circulation time (sec)
Blue whale	91000	
African elephant	5450	
White rhinoceros	3000	
Hippopotamus	2520	
Black rhinoceros	1170	
Horse	700	
Lion	180	
Human	70	

40. In 2004, Agutter and Wheatley[6] reported

> The relationship between body mass, M, and standard metabolic rate, B, among living organisms remains controversial, though it is widely accepted that in many cases B is approximately proportional to the three-quarters power of M.

(a) Write a function that represents this relationship.

(b) The average mass of an African forest elephant is 4.6 metric tons[7] and that of a typical mouse is 20 grams. Use part (a) to determine how many times greater the metabolic rate of an elephant is than that of a mouse. (1 metric ton = 1,000,000 grams.)

41. The musical pitch, P, of a guitar string can be varied by changing its density, ρ. The pitch is inversely proportional to the square root of the density, so a string that is denser produces a lower pitch. Write an expression for the pitch in terms of the density.

42. A 30-second commercial during Super Bowl XLIV in 2010 cost advertisers up to $3 million. For the first Super Bowl in 1967, an advertiser could have purchased approximately 34.439 minutes of advertising time for the same amount of money.[8]

(a) Assuming that cost is proportional to time, find the cost of advertising, in dollars/second, during the 1967 and 2010 Super Bowls.

(b) How many times more expensive was Super Bowl advertising in 2010 than in 1967?

43. Driving at 55 mph, it takes approximately 3.5 hours to drive from Long Island to Albany, NY. Is the time the drive takes directly or inversely proportional to the speed? Explain your reasoning and write a formula for the proportion. To get to Albany in 3 hours, how fast would you have to drive?

44. Ship designers usually construct scale models before building a real ship. The formula that relates the speed u to the hull length l of a ship is

$$u = k\sqrt{l},$$

where k is a positive constant. This constant k varies depending on the ship's design, but scale models of a real ship have the same k as the real ship after which they are modeled.[9]

(a) How fast should a scale model with hull length 4 meters travel to simulate a real ship with hull length 225 meters traveling 9 meters/sec?

(b) A new ship is to be built whose speed is to be 10% greater than the speed of an existing ship with the same design. What is the relationship between the hull lengths of the new ship and the existing ship?

45. A volcano erupts in a powerful explosion. The sound from the explosion is heard in all directions for many hundreds of kilometers. The speed of sound is about 340 meters per second.

(a) Fill in Table 11.5 showing the distance, d, that the sound of the explosion has traveled at time t. Write a formula for d as a function of t.

(b) How long after the explosion will a person living 200 km away hear the explosion?

(c) Fill in Table 11.5 showing the land area, A, over which the explosion can be heard as a function of time. Write a formula for A as a function of t.

(d) The average population density around the volcano is 31 people per square kilometer. Write a formula for P as function of t, where P is the number of people who have heard the explosion at time t.

(e) Graph the function $P = f(t)$. How long will it take until 1 million people have heard the explosion?

Table 11.5

Time, t	5 sec	10 sec	1 min	5 min
Distance, d (km)				
Area, A (km^2)				

[6]P. S. Agutter and D. N. Wheatley, (2004) Metabolic scaling: consensus or controversy? *Theor. Biol. Med. Mod.* 1:13, PMID: 15546492

[7]www.pbs.org/wnet/nature/elephants/life.html, accessed June 14, 2010.

[8]www.dailfinance.com/2009/09/20/cbs-super-bowl-ad-sales-slip-behind-last-years-pace, accessed November 27, 2009.

[9]R. McNeill Alexander, *Dynamics of Dinosaurs and Other Extinct Giants* (New York: Columbia University Press, 1989).

46. Two oil tankers crash in the Pacific Ocean. The spreading oil slick has a circular shape, and the radius of the circle is increasing at 200 meters per hour.

    (a) Express the radius of the spill, r, as a power function of time, t, in hours since the crash.

    (b) Express the area of the spill, A, as a power function of time, t.

    (c) Clean-up efforts begin 7 hours after the spill. How large an area is covered by oil at that time?

47. In a microwave oven, cooking time is inversely proportional to the amount of power used. It takes 6.5 minutes to heat a frozen dinner at 750 watts.

    (a) Write a formula for the cooking time, t, as a function of power level, w.

    (b) Fill in Table 11.6 with the cooking times needed to heat the frozen dinner at various power levels.

    (c) Graph the function $t = f(w)$.

    (d) If it takes 2 minutes to heat a rhubarb crumble at 250 watts, how long will it take at 500 watts?

Table 11.6

Power, w (watts)	250	300	500	650
Time, t (mins)				

48. An average hailstone is a sphere of radius 0.3 centimeter. Severe thunderstorms can produce hailstones of radius 0.95 centimeter. The largest hailstone found in the US had radius 7.05 centimeters. Table 11.7 gives the masses of these hailstones in grams.[10]

    (a) Using the data given, check that mass, m, is proportional to the cube of the radius, r.

    (b) Find the constant of proportionality and write m as a function of r.

    (c) The largest recorded hailstone was found in India in 1939 and weighed 3.4 kilograms. What was its radius?

    (d) Calculate the density of ice in grams per cubic centimeter. [Hint: Density is mass per unit volume.]

Table 11.7

Radius, r (cm)	0.3	0.95	7.05
Mass, m (gm)	0.058	1.835	750

49. The following questions involve the behavior of the power function $y = x^{-p}$, for p a positive integer. If a distinction between even and odd values of p is significant, the significance should be indicated.

    (a) What is the domain of $y = x^{-p}$? What is the range?

    (b) What symmetries does the graph of $y = x^{-p}$ have?

    (c) What is the behavior of $y = x^{-p}$ as $x \to 0$?

    (d) What is the behavior of $y = x^{-p}$ for large positive values of x? For large negative values of x?

50. Let $f(x) = 16x^4$ and $g(x) = 4x^2$.

    (a) If $f(x) = g(h(x))$, find a possible formula for $h(x)$, assuming $h(x) \le 0$ for all x.

    (b) If $f(x) = j(2g(x))$, find a possible formula for $j(x)$, assuming $j(x)$ is a power function.

51. Consider the power function $y = t(x) = k \cdot x^{p/3}$ where p is any integer, $p \ne 0$.

    (a) For what values of p does $t(x)$ have domain restrictions? What are those restrictions?

    (b) What is the range of $t(x)$ if p is even? If p is odd?

    (c) What symmetry does the graph of $t(x)$ exhibit if p is even? If p is odd?

11.2 POLYNOMIAL FUNCTIONS

A *polynomial function* is a sum of power functions whose exponents are nonnegative integers. We use what we learned about power functions to study polynomials.

Example 1   You make five separate deposits of $1000 each into a savings account, one deposit per year, beginning today. What annual interest rate gives a balance in the account of $6000 five years from today? (Assume the interest rate is constant over these five years.)

Solution   Let r be the annual interest rate. Our goal is to determine what value of r gives you $6000 in five years. In year $t = 0$, you make a $1000 deposit. One year later, you have $1000 plus the interest earned on that amount. At that time, you add another $1000.

        To picture how this works, imagine the account pays 5% annual interest, compounded annually. Then, after one year, your balance would be

---

[10]C. Donald Ahrens, *Essentials of Meteorology* (Wadsworth: Belmont, CA, 1998).

$$\text{Balance} = (100\% \text{ of Initial deposit}) + (5\% \text{ of Initial deposit}) + \text{Second deposit}$$

$$= 105\% \text{ of } \underbrace{\text{Initial deposit}}_{\$1000} + \underbrace{\text{Second deposit}}_{\$1000}$$

$$= 1.05(1000) + 1000.$$

Let x represent the annual growth factor, $1 + r$. For example, if the account paid 5% interest, then $x = 1 + 0.05 = 1.05$. We write the balance after one year in terms of x:

$$\text{Balance after one year} = 1000x + 1000.$$

After two years, you would have earned interest on the first-year balance. This gives

$$\text{Balance after earning interest} = \underbrace{(1000x + 1000)}_{\text{First-year balance}}x = 1000x^2 + 1000x.$$

The third $1000 deposit brings your balance to

$$\text{Balance after two years} = 1000x^2 + 1000x + \underbrace{1000.}_{\text{Third deposit}}$$

A year's worth of interest on this amount, plus the fourth $1000 deposit, brings your balance to

$$\text{Balance after three years} = \underbrace{(1000x^2 + 1000x + 1000)}_{\text{Second-year balance}}x + \underbrace{1000}_{\text{Fourth deposit}}$$

$$= 1000x^3 + 1000x^2 + 1000x + 1000.$$

The pattern is this: Each of the $1000 deposits grows to $1000x^n$ by the end of its nth year in the bank. Thus,

$$\text{Balance after five years} = 1000x^5 + 1000x^4 + 1000x^3 + 1000x^2 + 1000x.$$

If the interest rate is chosen correctly, then the balance will be $6000 in five years. This gives us

$$1000x^5 + 1000x^4 + 1000x^3 + 1000x^2 + 1000x = 6000.$$

Dividing by 1000 and moving the 6 to the left side, we have the equation

$$x^5 + x^4 + x^3 + x^2 + x - 6 = 0.$$

Solving this equation for x determines how much interest we must earn. Using a computer or calculator, we find where the graph of $Q(x) = x^5 + x^4 + x^3 + x^2 + x - 6$ crosses the x-axis. Figure 11.14 shows that this occurs at $x \approx 1.0614$. Since $x = 1 + r$, this means $r = 0.0614$. So the account must earn 6.14% annual interest[11] for the balance to be $6000 at the end of five years.

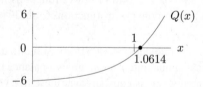

Figure 11.14: Finding where $Q(x)$ crosses the x-axis, for $x \geq 0$

You may wonder if Q crosses the x-axis more than once. For $x \geq 0$, graphing Q on a larger scale suggests that Q increases for all values of x and crosses the x-axis only once. For $x > 1$,

---

[11]This is 6.14% interest per year, compounded annually.

we expect Q to be an increasing function, because larger values of x indicate higher interest rates and therefore larger values of $Q(x)$. Having crossed the axis once, the graph of Q does not "turn around" to cross it again.

The function $Q(x) = x^5 + x^4 + x^3 + x^2 + x - 6$ is the sum of power functions; Q is called a *polynomial*. (Note that the expression -6 can be written as $-6x^0$, so it, too, is a power function.)

A General Formula for the Family of Polynomial Functions

The general formula for a polynomial function can be written as

$$p(x) = a_n x^n + a_{n-1} x^{n-1} + \ldots + a_1 x + a_0,$$

where n is called the *degree* of the polynomial and a_n is the *leading coefficient*. For example, the function

$$g(x) = 3x^2 + 4x^5 + x - x^3 + 1,$$

is a polynomial of degree 5 because the term with the highest power is $4x^5$. It is customary to write a polynomial with the powers in decreasing order from left to right:

$$g(x) = 4x^5 - x^3 + 3x^2 + x + 1.$$

The function g has one other term, $0 \cdot x^4$, which we don't bother to write down. The values of g's coefficients are $a_5 = 4, a_4 = 0, a_3 = -1, a_2 = 3, a_1 = 1$, and $a_0 = 1$. In summary:

The general formula for the family of polynomial functions can be written as

$$p(x) = a_n x^n + a_{n-1} x^{n-1} + \ldots + a_1 x + a_0,$$

where n is a positive integer called the **degree** of p and where $a_n \neq 0$.

- Each power function $a_i x^i$ in this sum is called a **term**.
- The constants $a_n, a_{n-1}, \ldots, a_0$ are called **coefficients**.
- The term a_0 is called the **constant term**. The term with the highest power, $a_n x^n$, is called the **leading term**.
- To write a polynomial in **standard form**, we arrange its terms from highest power to lowest power, going from left to right.

Like the power functions from which they are built, polynomials are defined for all values of x. Except for polynomials of degree zero (whose graphs are horizontal lines), the graphs of polynomials do not have horizontal or vertical asymptotes; they are smooth and unbroken. The shape of the graph depends on its degree; typical graphs are shown in Figure 11.15.

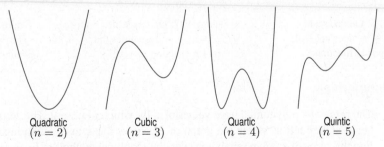

Quadratic
$(n = 2)$

Cubic
$(n = 3)$

Quartic
$(n = 4)$

Quintic
$(n = 5)$

Figure 11.15: Graphs of typical polynomials of degree n

The Long-Run Behavior of Polynomial Functions

We have seen that, as x grows large, $y = x^2$ increases fast, $y = x^3$ increases faster, and $y = x^4$ increases faster still. In general, power functions with larger positive powers eventually grow much faster than those with smaller powers. This tells us about the behavior of polynomials for large x. For instance, consider the polynomial $g(x) = 4x^5 - x^3 + 3x^2 + x + 1$. Provided x is large enough, the value of the term $4x^5$ is much larger than the value of the other terms combined. For example, if $x = 100$,

$$4x^5 = 4(100)^5 = 40{,}000{,}000{,}000,$$

and the other terms in $g(x)$ are

$$-x^3 + 3x^2 + x + 1 = -(100)^3 + 3(100)^2 + 100 + 1$$
$$= -1{,}000{,}000 + 30{,}000 + 100 + 1 = -969{,}899.$$

Therefore $p(100) = 39{,}999{,}030{,}101$, which is approximately equal to the value of the $4x^5$ term. In general, if x is large enough, the most important contribution to the value of a polynomial p is made by the leading term; we can ignore the lower power terms.

> When viewed on a large enough scale, the graph of the polynomial $p(x) = a_n x^n + a_{n-1} x^{n-1} + \cdots + a_1 x + a_0$ looks like the graph of the power function $y = a_n x^n$. This behavior is called the **long-run behavior** of the polynomial. Using limit notation, we write
>
> $$\lim_{x \to \infty} p(x) = \lim_{x \to \infty} a_n x^n \quad \text{and} \quad \lim_{x \to -\infty} p(x) = \lim_{x \to -\infty} a_n x^n.$$

Example 2   Find a window in which the graph of $f(x) = x^3 + x^2$ resembles the power function $y = x^3$.

Solution   Figure 11.16 gives the graphs of $f(x) = x^3 + x^2$ and $y = x^3$. On this scale, f does not look like a power function. On the larger scale in Figure 11.17, the graph of f resembles the graph of $y = x^3$. On this larger scale, the "bumps" in the graph of f are too small to be seen. On an even larger scale, as in Figure 11.18, the graph of f is indistinguishable from the graph of $y = x^3$.

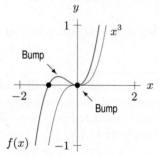

Figure 11.16: On this scale, $f(x) = x^3 + x^2$ does not look like a power function

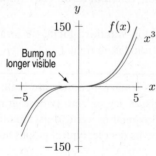

Figure 11.17: On this scale, $f(x) = x^3 + x^2$ resembles the power function $y = x^3$

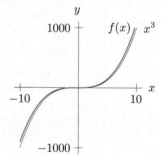

Figure 11.18: On this scale, $f(x) = x^3 + x^2$ is nearly indistinguishable from $y = x^3$

Zeros of Polynomials

The *zeros* of a polynomial p are values of x for which $p(x) = 0$. The zeros are also the x-intercepts, because they tell us where the graph of p crosses the x-axis. Factoring can sometimes be used to find the zeros of a polynomial; however, the graphical method of Example 1 can always be used. In addition, the long-run behavior of the polynomial can give us clues as to how many zeros (if any) there may be.

Example 3   Given the polynomial

$$q(x) = 3x^6 - 2x^5 + 4x^2 - 1,$$

where $q(0) = -1$, is there a reason to expect a solution to the equation $q(x) = 0$? If not, explain why not. If so, how do you know?

Solution   The equation $q(x) = 0$ must have at least two solutions. We know this because on a large scale, q looks like the power function $y = 3x^6$. (See Figure 11.19.) The function $y = 3x^6$ takes on large positive values as x grows large (either positive or negative). Since the graph of q is smooth and unbroken, it must cross the x-axis at least twice to get from $q(0) = -1$ to the positive values it attains as $x \to \infty$ and $x \to -\infty$.

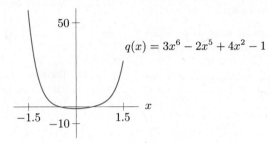

Figure 11.19: Graph must cross x-axis at least twice since $q(0) = -1$ and $q(x)$ looks like $3x^6$ for large x

A sixth-degree polynomial such as q in Example 3 can have as many as six real zeros. We consider the zeros of a polynomial in more detail in Section 11.3.

Exercises and Problems for Section 11.2

Exercises

Are the functions in Exercises 1–6 polynomials? If so, of what degree?

1. $y = 5^x - 2$ **2.** $y = 5 + x$

3. $y = 4x^2 + 2$ **4.** $y = 7t^6 - 8t + 7.2$

5. $y = 4x^4 - 3x^3 + 2e^x$ **6.** $y = 4x^2 - 7\sqrt{x^9} + 10$

For the polynomials in Exercises 7–9, state the degree, the number of terms, and describe the long-run behavior.

7. $y = 2x^3 - 3x + 7$

8. $y = 1 - 2x^4 + x^3$

9. $y = (x + 4)(2x - 3)(5 - x)$

10. Find

(a) $\lim_{x \to \infty} (3x^2 - 5x + 7)$ **(b)** $\lim_{x \to -\infty} (7x^2 - 9x^3)$

Problems

11. Estimate the zeros of $f(x) = x^4 - 3x^2 - x + 2$.

12. Estimate the minimum value of $g(x) = x^4 - 3x^3 - 8$.

13. Compare the graphs of $f(x) = x^3 + 5x^2 - x - 5$ and $g(x) = -2x^3 - 10x^2 + 2x + 10$ on a window that shows all intercepts. How are the graphs similar? Different? Discuss.

14. Let $u(x) = -\frac{1}{5}(x - 3)(x + 1)(x + 5)$ and $v(x) = -\frac{1}{5}x^2(x - 5)$.

(a) Graph u and v for $-10 \le x \le 10$, $-10 \le y \le 10$. How are the graphs similar? How are they different?

(b) Compare the graphs of u and v on the window $-20 \le x \le 20$, $-1600 \le y \le 1600$, the window $-50 \le x \le 50$, $-25,000 \le y \le 25,000$, and the window $-500 \le x \le 500$, $-25,000,000 \le y \le 25,000,000$. Discuss.

15. Find the equation of the line through the y-intercept of $y = x^4 - 3x^5 - 1 + x^2$ and the x-intercept of $y = 2x - 4$.

16. Let $f(x) = \left(\dfrac{1}{50{,}000}\right)x^3 + \left(\dfrac{1}{2}\right)x$.

 (a) For small values of x, which term of f is more important? Explain your answer.
 (b) Graph $y = f(x)$ for $-10 \le x \le 10$, $-10 \le y \le 10$. Is this graph linear? How does the appearance of this graph agree with your answer to part (a)?
 (c) How large a value of x is required for the cubic term of f to be equal to the linear term?

17. Find four different viewing windows on which $f(x) = (x + 2)(x - 1)(x - 3)^2$ resembles graphs (a)–(d).

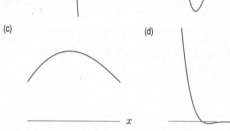

18.

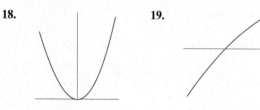

In Problems 18–21, find a viewing window on which the graph of $f(x) = x^3 + x^2$ resembles the plot.

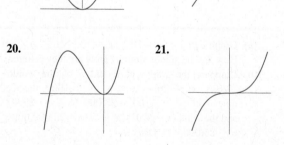

18.   **19.**

20.   **21.**

22. The polynomial function $f(x) = x^3 + x + 1$ is invertible—that is, this function has an inverse.

 (a) Graph $y = f(x)$. Explain how you can tell from the graph that f is invertible.
 (b) Find $f(0.5)$ and an approximate value for $f^{-1}(0.5)$.

23. If $f(x) = x^2$ and $g(x) = (x + 2)(x - 1)(x - 3)$, find all x for which $f(x) < g(x)$.

24. In calculus, we often consider pairs of polynomials. If $F(x) = 3x^4 - 4x^3 + 5x - 4$, find a_4, a_3, a_2, a_1, a_0. Then use these values to construct the cubic polynomial

$$f(x) = 4a_4x^3 + 3a_3x^2 + 2a_2x + a_1.$$

25. The town of Liddleville was founded in 1890. Its population y (in hundreds) was modeled, for t in years since 1890, by

$$y = 1 - 0.58t + 4.89t^2 - 1.872t^3 + 0.247t^4 - 0.0111t^5.$$

 (a) Graph the function for $0 \le t \le 8$, $-2 \le y \le 12$.
 (b) What was the population of Liddleville when it was founded?
 (c) When did the population of Liddleville reach zero? Give the year and the month.
 (d) What was the largest population of Liddleville after 1890? When did Liddleville reach that population? Give the month and year.
 (e) What population was predicted for 1898? Comment.

26. (a) The total cost, in millions of dollars, of producing x thousand units of an item is $C(x) = 4(x - 1)^2 + 4$. Graph $C(x)$.
 (b) The revenue (in millions of dollars) from selling x thousand units of the item is $R(x) = 10x$. What does this tell you about the price of each unit?
 (c) Profit is revenue minus cost. For what values of x does the firm make a profit? Break even? Lose money?

27. Let V represent the volume in liters of air in the lungs during a 5-second respiratory cycle. If t is time in seconds, V is given by

$$V = 0.1729t + 0.1522t^2 - 0.0374t^3.$$

 (a) Graph this function for $0 \le t \le 5$.
 (b) What is the maximum value of V on this interval? What is its practical significance?
 (c) Explain the practical significance of the t- and V-intercepts on the interval $0 \le t \le 5$.

28. The volume, V, in milliliters, of 1 kg of water as a function of temperature T is given, for $0 \le T \le 30°C$, by:

$$V = 999.87 - 0.06426T + 0.0085143T^2 - 0.0000679T^3.$$

(a) Graph V.
(b) Describe the shape of your graph. Does V increase or decrease as T increases? Does the graph curve upward or downward? What does the graph tell us about how the volume varies with temperature?
(c) At what temperature does water have the maximum density? How does that appear on your graph? (Density = Mass/Volume. In this problem, the mass of the water is 1 kg.)

29. Let f and g be polynomial functions. Are the following compositions also polynomial functions? Explain your answer.

$$f(g(x)) \quad \text{and} \quad g(f(x))$$

30. (a) Suppose $f(x) = ax^2 + bx + c$. What must be true about the coefficients if f is an even function?
(b) Suppose $g(x) = ax^3 + bx^2 + cx + d$. What must be true about the coefficients if g is an odd function?

31. Let g be a polynomial function of degree n, where n is a positive odd integer. For each of the following statements, write *true* if the statement is always true, *false* otherwise. If the statement is false, give an example that illustrates why it is false.

(a) g is an odd function.
(b) g has an inverse.
(c) $\lim\limits_{x \to \infty} g(x) = \infty$.
(d) If $\lim\limits_{x \to -\infty} g(x) = -\infty$, then $\lim\limits_{x \to \infty} g(x) = \infty$.

32. Let $f(x) = x - \dfrac{x^3}{6} + \dfrac{x^5}{120}$.

(a) Graph $y = f(x)$ and $y = \sin x$ for $-2\pi \le x \le 2\pi$, $-3 \le y \le 3$.
(b) The graph of f resembles the graph of $\sin x$ on a small interval. Based on your graphs from part (a), give the approximate interval.
(c) Your calculator uses a function similar to f in order to evaluate the sine function. How reasonable an approximation does f give for $\sin(\pi/8)$?

(d) Explain how you could use the function f to approximate the value of $\sin\theta$, where $\theta = 18$ radians. [Hint: Use the fact that the sine function is periodic.]

33. For certain x-values, the function $f(x) = 1/(1+x)$ can be well-approximated by the polynomial

$$p(x) = 1 - x + x^2 - x^3 + x^4 - x^5.$$

(a) Show that $p(0.5) \approx f(0.5) = 2/3$. To how many decimal places do $p(0.5)$ and $f(0.5)$ agree?
(b) Calculate $p(1)$. How well does $p(1)$ approximate $f(1)$?
(c) Graph $p(x)$ and $f(x)$ together on the same set of axes for $-1 \le x \le 1$. Based on your graph, for what range of values of x does $p(x)$ appear to give a good estimate for $f(x)$?

34. Table 11.8 gives v, the speed of sound (in m/sec) in water as a function of the temperature T (in °C).[12]

(a) An approximate linear formula for v is given by $v = 1402.385 + 5.038813T$. Over what temperature range does this formula agree with the values in Table 11.8 to within 1°C?
(b) The formula in part (a) can be improved by adding the quadratic term $-5.799136 \cdot 10^{-2}T^2$. Repeat part (a) using this adjusted formula.
(c) The formula in part (b) can be further improved by adding the cubic term $3.287156 \cdot 10^{-4}T^3$. Repeat part (a) using this adjusted formula.
(d) The speed of sound in water at 50°C is 1542.6 m/s. If we want to improve our formula still further by adding a quartic (fourth-degree) term, should this term be positive or negative?

Table 11.8

T	0	5	10	15	20	25	30
v	1402.4	1426.2	1447.3	1466.0	1482.4	1496.7	1509.2

11.3 THE SHORT-RUN BEHAVIOR OF POLYNOMIALS

The long-run behavior of a polynomial is determined by its leading term. However, polynomials with the same leading term may have very different short-run behaviors.

Example 1 Compare the graphs of the polynomials f, g, and h given by

$$f(x) = x^4 - 4x^3 + 16x - 16, \quad g(x) = x^4 - 4x^3 - 4x^2 + 16x, \quad h(x) = x^4 + x^3 - 8x^2 - 12x.$$

[12]Data from the Marczak formula at the UK National Physical Laboratory: www.npl.co.uk, accessed 2001.

Solution   Each of these functions is a fourth-degree polynomial, and each has x^4 as its leading term. Thus, all their graphs resemble the graph of x^4 on a large scale. See Figure 11.20.

However, on a smaller scale, the functions look different. See Figure 11.21. Two of the graphs go through the origin while the third does not. The graphs also differ from one another in the number of bumps each one has and in the number of times each one crosses the x-axis. Thus, polynomials with the same leading term look similar on a large scale, but may look dissimilar on a small scale.

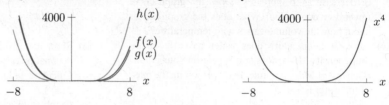

Figure 11.20: On a large scale, the polynomials f, g, and h resemble the power function $y = x^4$

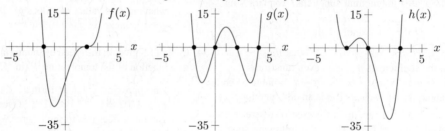

Figure 11.21: On a smaller scale, the polynomials f, g, and h look quite different from one another

Factored Form, Zeros, and the Short-Run Behavior of a Polynomial

To predict the long-run behavior of a polynomial, we use the highest-power term. To determine the zeros and the short-run behavior of a polynomial, we write it in factored form with as many linear factors as possible.

Example 2   Investigate the short-run behavior of the third-degree polynomial $u(x) = x^3 - x^2 - 6x$.

(a) Rewrite $u(x)$ as a product of linear factors.
(b) Find the zeros of $u(x)$.
(c) Describe the graph of $u(x)$. Where does it cross the x-axis? the y-axis? Where is $u(x)$ positive? Negative?

Solution   (a) By factoring out an x and then factoring the quadratic, $x^2 - x - 6$, we rewrite $u(x)$ as

$$u(x) = x^3 - x^2 - 6x = x(x^2 - x - 6) = x(x - 3)(x + 2).$$

Thus, we have expressed $u(x)$ as the product of three linear factors, x, $x - 3$, and $x + 2$.

(b) The polynomial equals zero if and only if at least one of its factors is zero. We solve the equation:

$$x(x - 3)(x + 2) = 0,$$

giving

$$x = 0, \quad \text{or} \quad x - 3 = 0, \quad \text{or} \quad x + 2 = 0,$$

so

$$x = 0, \quad \text{or} \quad x = 3, \quad \text{or} \quad x = -2.$$

These are the zeros, or x-intercepts, of u. To check, evaluate $u(x)$ for these x-values; you should get 0. There are no other zeros.

(c) To describe the graph of u, we give the x- and y-intercepts, and the long-run behavior.

The factored form, $u(x) = x(x - 3)(x + 2)$, shows that the graph crosses the x-axis at $x = 0, 3, -2$. The graph of u crosses the y-axis at $u(0) = 0^3 - 0^2 - 6 \cdot 0 = 0$; that is, at $y = 0$. For large values of x, the graph of $y = u(x)$ resembles the graph of its leading term, $y = x^3$. Figure 11.22 shows where u is positive and where u is negative.

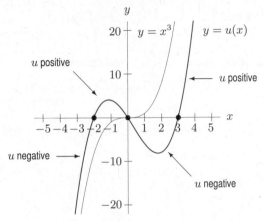

Figure 11.22: The graph of $u(x) = x^3 - x^2 - 6x$ has zeros at $x = -2, 0,$ and 3. Its long-run behavior resembles $y = x^3$

In Example 2, each linear factor produced a zero of the polynomial. Now suppose that we do not know the polynomial p, but we do know that it has zeros at $x = 0, -12, 31$. Then we know that the factored form of the polynomial must include the factors $(x - 0)$ or x, and $(x - (-12))$ or $(x + 12)$, and $(x - 31)$. It may include other factors too. In summary:

> Suppose p is a polynomial. If the formula for p has a **linear factor**, that is, a factor of the form $(x - k)$, then p has a zero at $x = k$.
>
> Conversely, if p has a **zero** at $x = k$, then p has a linear factor of the form $(x - k)$.

The Number of Factors, Zeros, and Bumps

The number of linear factors is always less than or equal to the degree of a polynomial. For example, a fourth-degree polynomial can have no more than four linear factors. This makes sense because if we had another factor in the product and multiplied out, the highest power of x would be greater than four. Since each zero corresponds to a linear factor, the number of zeros is less than or equal to the degree of the polynomial.

Between any two consecutive zeros of a polynomial, there is at least one bump. For example, in Figure 11.22, the function is zero at $x = 0$ and negative at $x = 1$, and must change direction to come back up and cross the x-axis at $x = 3$. Using calculus, it can be shown that any third-degree polynomial has no more than two bumps. In general:

> The graph of an nth-degree polynomial has at most n zeros and turns at most $(n - 1)$ times.

Multiple Zeros

The functions $s(x) = (x - 4)^2$ and $t(x) = (x + 1)^3$ are both polynomials in factored form. Each is a horizontal shift of a power function. We refer to the zeros of s and t as *multiple zeros*, because in each case the factor contributing the value of $y = 0$ occurs more than once. For instance, we say that $x = 4$ is a *double zero* of s, since

$$s(x) = (x - 4)^2 = \underbrace{(x - 4)(x - 4)}_{\text{Occurs twice}}.$$

Likewise, we say that $x = -1$ is a *triple zero* of t, since

$$t(x) = (x + 1)^3 = \underbrace{(x + 1)(x + 1)(x + 1)}_{\text{Occurs three times}}.$$

The graphs of s and t in Figures 11.23 and 11.24 show typical behavior near multiple zeros.

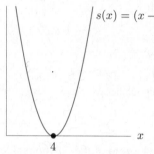

Figure 11.23: Double zero at $x = 4$

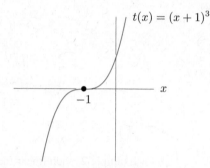

Figure 11.24: Triple zero at $x = -1$

In general:

If p is a polynomial with a repeated linear factor, then p has a **multiple zero**.
- If the factor $(x - k)$ occurs an even number of times, the graph of $y = p(x)$ does not cross the x-axis at $x = k$, but "bounces" off the x-axis at $x = k$. (See Figure 11.23.)
- If the factor $(x - k)$ occurs an odd number of times, the graph of $y = p(x)$ crosses the x-axis at $x = k$, but it looks flattened there. (See Figure 11.24.)

Example 3   Describe in words the zeros of the 4th-degree polynomials $f(x)$, $g(x)$, and $h(x)$, in Figure 11.25.

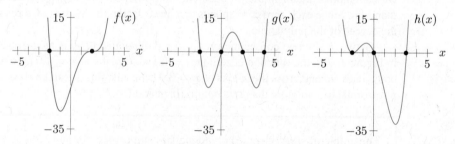

Figure 11.25: Three 4th-degree polynomials

Solution   The graph suggests that f has a single zero at $x = -2$. The flattened appearance near $x = 2$ suggests that f has a multiple zero there. Since the graph crosses the x-axis at $x = 2$ (instead of bouncing off it), this zero must occur an odd number of times. Since f is 4th degree, f has at most 4 factors, so there must be a triple zero at $x = 2$.

The graph of g has four single zeros. The graph of h has two single zeros (at $x = 0$ and $x = 3$) and a double zero at $x = -2$. The multiplicity of the zero at $x = -2$ is not higher than two because h is of degree $n = 4$.

Finding the Formula for a Polynomial from its Graph

The graph of a polynomial often enables us to find a possible formula for the polynomial.

Example 4   Find a possible formula for the polynomial function f graphed in Figure 11.26.

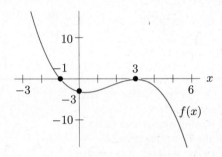

Figure 11.26: Features of the graph lead to a possible formula for this polynomial

Solution   Based on its long-run behavior, f is of odd degree greater than or equal to 3. The polynomial has zeros at $x = -1$ and $x = 3$. We see that $x = 3$ is a multiple zero of even power, because the graph bounces off the x-axis here instead of crossing it. Therefore, we try the formula

$$f(x) = k(x + 1)(x - 3)^2$$

where k represents a stretch factor. The shape of the graph shows that k must be negative.

To find k, we use the fact that $f(0) = -3$, so

$$f(0) = k(0 + 1)(0 - 3)^2 = -3,$$

which gives

$$9k = -3 \qquad \text{so} \qquad k = -\frac{1}{3}.$$

Thus, $f(x) = -\frac{1}{3}(x + 1)(x - 3)^2$ is a possible formula for this polynomial.

The formula for f we found in Example 4 is the polynomial of least degree we could have chosen. However, there are other polynomials, such as $y = -\frac{1}{27}(x + 1)(x - 3)^4$, with the same overall behavior as the function shown in Figure 11.26.

Exercises and Problems for Section 11.3

Exercises

In Exercises 1–4, find the zeros of the functions.

1. $y = x^3 + 7x^2 + 12x$

2. $y = (x^2 + 2x - 7)(x^3 + 4x^2 - 21x)$

3. $y = 7(x + 3)(x - 2)(x + 7)$

4. $y = a(x + 2)(x - b)$, where a, b are nonzero constants

5. Use the graph of $h(x)$ in Figure 11.21 on page 448 to determine the factored form of

$$h(x) = x^4 + x^3 - 8x^2 - 12x.$$

6. Use the graph of $g(x)$ in Figure 11.21 on page 448 to determine the factored form of

$$g(x) = x^4 - 4x^3 - 4x^2 + 16x.$$

7. Use the graph of $f(x)$ in Figure 11.21 on page 448 to determine the factored form of

$$f(x) = x^4 - 4x^3 + 16x - 16.$$

8. Factor $f(x) = 8x^3 - 4x^2 - 60x$ completely, and determine the zeros of f.

9. Find a possible formula for a polynomial with zeros at (and only at) $x = -2, 2, 5$, a y-intercept at $y = 5$, and long-run behavior of $y \to -\infty$ as $x \to \pm\infty$.

Without a calculator, graph the polynomials in Exercises 10–11. Label all the x-intercepts and y-intercepts.

10. $f(x) = -5(x^2 - 4)(25 - x^2)$

11. $g(x) = 5(x - 4)(x^2 - 25)$

Problems

12. (a) Let $f(x) = (2x - 1)(3x - 1)(x - 7)(x - 9)$. What are the zeros of this polynomial?
(b) Is it possible to find a viewing window that shows all of the zeros and all of the the turning points of f?
(c) Find two separate viewing windows that together show all the zeros and all the turning points of f.

13. (a) Experiment with various viewing windows to determine the zeros of $f(x) = 2x^4 + 9x^3 - 7x^2 - 9x + 5$. Then write f in factored form.
(b) Find a single viewing window that clearly shows all of the turning points of f.

14. Let $p(x) = x^4 + 10x^3 - 68x^2 + 102x - 45$. By experimenting with various viewing windows, determine the zeros of p and use this information to write $p(x)$ in factored form.

15. Without using a calculator, decide which of the equations A–E best describes the polynomial in Figure 11.27.

A $y = (x + 2)(x + 1)(x - 2)(x - 3)$
B $y = x(x + 2)(x + 1)(x - 2)(x - 3)$
C $y = -\frac{1}{2}(x + 2)(x + 1)(x - 2)(x - 3)$
D $y = \frac{1}{2}(x + 2)(x + 1)(x - 2)(x - 3)$
E $y = -(x + 2)(x + 1)(x - 2)(x - 3)$

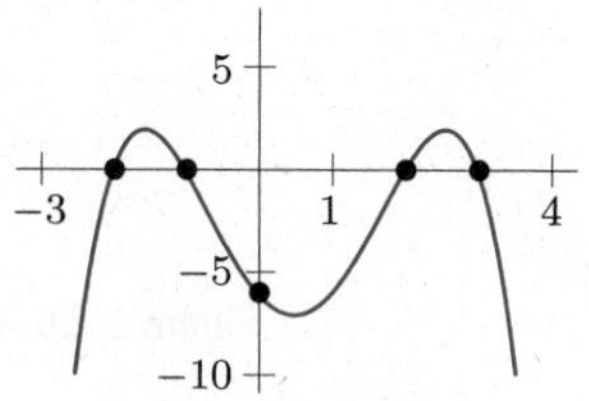

Figure 11.27

In Problems 16–21, find a possible formula for each polynomial with the given properties.

16. f has degree ≤ 2, $f(0) = 0$ and $f(1) = 1$.

17. f has degree ≤ 2, $f(0) = f(1) = f(2) = 1$.

18. f has degree ≤ 2, $f(0) = f(2) = 0$ and $f(3) = 3$.

19. f is third degree with $f(-3) = 0$, $f(1) = 0$, $f(4) = 0$, and $f(2) = 5$.

20. g is fourth degree, g has a double zero at $x = 3$, $g(5) = 0$, $g(-1) = 0$, and $g(0) = 3$.

21. Least possible degree through the points $(-3, 0)$, $(1, 0)$, and $(0, -3)$.

22. Which of these functions have inverses that are functions? Discuss.
(a) $f(x) = (x - 2)^3 + 4$.
(b) $g(x) = x^3 - 4x^2 + 2$.

Solution   If x is a large positive number, then

$$r(x) = \frac{\text{Big number} + 3}{\text{Same big number} + 2} \approx \frac{\text{Big number}}{\text{Same big number}} = 1.$$

For example, if $x = 100$, we have

$$r(x) = \frac{103}{102} = 1.0098\ldots \approx 1.$$

If $x = 10,000$, we have

$$r(x) = \frac{10,003}{10,002} = 1.00009998\ldots \approx 1,$$

For large positive x-values, $r(x) \approx 1$. Thus, for large enough values of x, the graph of $y = r(x)$ looks like the line $y = 1$, its horizontal asymptote. We write $\lim_{x \to \infty} r(x) = 1$. See Figure 11.30. However, for $x > 0$, the graph of r is above the line since the numerator is larger than the denominator.

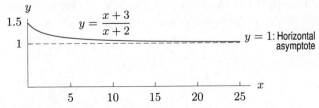

Figure 11.30: For large positive values of x, the graph of $r(x) = (x+3)/(x+2)$ looks like the horizontal line $y = 1$

Example 2   For positive x, describe the positive long-run behavior of the rational function

$$g(x) = \frac{3x + 1}{x^2 + x - 2}.$$

Solution   The leading term in the numerator is $3x$ and the leading term in the denominator is x^2. Thus for large enough values of x,

$$g(x) \approx \frac{3x}{x^2} = \frac{3}{x},$$

so

$$\lim_{x \to \infty} g(x) = \lim_{x \to \infty} \left(\frac{3}{x}\right) = 0.$$

Figure 11.31 shows the graphs of $y = g(x)$ and $y = 3/x$. For large values of x, the two graphs are nearly indistinguishable. Both graphs have a horizontal asymptote at $y = 0$.

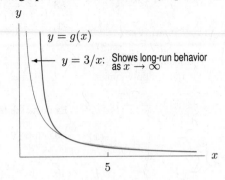

Figure 11.31: For large enough values of x, the function g looks like the function $y = 3x^{-1}$

What Causes Asymptotes?

The graphs of rational functions often behave differently from the graphs of polynomials. Polynomial graphs (except constant functions) cannot level off to a horizontal line as the graphs of rational functions can. In Example 1, the numerator and denominator are approximately equal for large x, producing the horizontal asymptote $y = 1$. In Example 2, the denominator grows faster than the numerator, driving the quotient toward zero.

The rapid rise (or fall) of the graph of a rational function near its vertical asymptote is due to the denominator becoming small (close to zero). It is tempting to assume that any function that has a denominator has a vertical asymptote. However, this is not true. To have a vertical asymptote, the denominator must equal zero. For example, suppose that

$$r(x) = \frac{1}{x^2 + 3}.$$

The denominator is always greater than 3; it is never 0. We see from Figure 11.32 that r does not have a vertical asymptote.

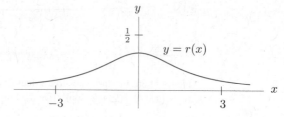

Figure 11.32: The rational function $r(x) = 1/(x^2 + 3)$ has no vertical asymptote

Exercises and Problems for Section 11.4

Skill Refresher

For Exercises S1–S4, perform the operations. Express answers in reduced form.

S1. $\dfrac{6}{y} + \dfrac{7}{y^3}$

S2. $\dfrac{13}{x-1} + \dfrac{14}{2x-2}$

S3. $\dfrac{\dfrac{1}{x} - \dfrac{2}{x^2}}{\dfrac{2x-4}{x^5}}$

S4. $\dfrac{9}{x^2 + 5x + 6} + \dfrac{12}{x+3}$

S5. $\dfrac{5}{(x-2)^2(x+1)} - \dfrac{18}{(x-2)}$

In Exercises S6–S9, simplify, if possible.

S6. $\dfrac{1/(x+y)}{x+y}$

S7. $\dfrac{(w+2)/2}{w+2}$

S8. $\dfrac{a^2 - b^2}{a^2 + b^2}$

S9. $\dfrac{x^{-1} + x^{-2}}{1 - x^{-2}}.$

Exercises

Are the functions in Exercises 1–7 rational functions? If so, write them in the form $p(x)/q(x)$, the ratio of polynomials.

1. $f(x) = \dfrac{x+2}{x^2-1}$

2. $f(x) = \dfrac{4^x + 3}{3^x - 1}$

3. $f(x) = \dfrac{x^2}{2} + \dfrac{1}{x}$

4. $f(x) = \dfrac{x^4 + 3^x - x^2}{x^3 - 2}$

5. $f(x) = \dfrac{\sqrt{x} + 1}{x + 1}$

6. $f(x) = \dfrac{x^3}{2x^2} + \dfrac{1}{6}$

7. $f(x) = \dfrac{9x - 1}{4\sqrt{x} + 7} + \dfrac{5x^3}{x^2 - 1}$

Evaluate the limits in Exercises 8–11.

8. $\lim\limits_{x \to \infty} (2x^{-3} + 4)$

9. $\lim\limits_{x \to \infty} (3x^{-2} + 5x + 7)$

10. $\lim\limits_{x \to \infty} \dfrac{4x + 3x^2}{4x^2 + 3x}$

11. $\lim\limits_{x \to -\infty} \dfrac{3x^2 + x}{2x^2 + 5x^3}$

Find the horizontal asymptote, if it exists, of the functions in Exercises 12–14.

12. $h(x) = 3 - \dfrac{1}{x} + \dfrac{x}{x+1}$

13. $f(x) = \dfrac{1}{1 + \dfrac{1}{x}}$

14. $g(x) = \dfrac{(1-x)(2+3x)}{2x^2 + 1}$

15. Compare and discuss the long-run behaviors of the following functions:

$$f(x) = \frac{x^2 + 1}{x^2 + 5}, \quad g(x) = \frac{x^3 + 1}{x^2 + 5}, \quad h(x) = \frac{x + 1}{x^2 + 5}.$$

Problems

16. Find a formula for $f^{-1}(x)$ given that

$$f(x) = \frac{4 - 3x}{5x - 4}.$$

17. Give examples of rational functions with even symmetry, odd symmetry, and neither. How does the symmetry of $f(x) = p(x)/q(x)$ depend on the symmetry of $p(x)$ and $q(x)$?

18. Let $r(x) = p(x)/q(x)$, where p and q are polynomials of degrees m and n, respectively. What conditions on m and n ensure that the following statements are true?

(a) $\displaystyle\lim_{x \to \infty} r(x) = 0$

(b) $\displaystyle\lim_{x \to \infty} r(x) = k$, with $k \neq 0$.

19. Let t be the time in weeks. At time $t = 0$, organic waste is dumped into a pond. The oxygen level in the pond at time t is given by

$$f(t) = \frac{t^2 - t + 1}{t^2 + 1}.$$

Assume $f(0) = 1$ is the normal level of oxygen.

(a) Graph this function.
(b) Describe the shape of the graph. What is the significance of the minimum for the pond?
(c) What eventually happens to the oxygen level?
(d) Approximately how many weeks must pass before the oxygen level returns to 75% of its normal level?

20. A small printing house agrees to publish a book of poems illustrated by the author. The printing house plans to recover its investment of $80,000 and make a profit of $40,000. The price of the book will depend on the number of copies they expect to sell.

(a) Fill in the table with the price per copy for each projected sales figure.

Number of copies sold	1000	2000	4000	6000
Price per copy				

(b) Give a formula for the price per copy, p, as a function of projected sales, s.
(c) Graph the function $p = f(s)$.

21. Bronze is an alloy, or mixture, of copper and tin. The alloy initially contains 3 kg copper and 9 kg tin. You add x kg of copper to this 12 kg of alloy. The concentration of copper in the alloy is a function of x:

$$f(x) = \text{Concentration of copper} = \frac{\text{Total amount of copper}}{\text{Total amount of alloy}}.$$

(a) Find a formula for f in terms of x, the amount of copper added.
(b) Evaluate the following expressions and explain their significance for the alloy:

  (i) $f(\frac{1}{2})$ (ii) $f(0)$ (iii) $f(-1)$
  (iv) $f^{-1}(\frac{1}{2})$ (v) $f^{-1}(0)$

(c) Graph $f(x)$ for $-5 \leq x \leq 5$, $-0.25 \leq y \leq 0.5$. Interpret the intercepts in the context of the alloy.
(d) Graph $f(x)$ for $-3 \leq x \leq 100$, $0 \leq y \leq 1$. Describe the appearance of your graph for large x-values. Does the appearance agree with what you expect to happen when large amounts of copper are added to the alloy?

22. A chemist is studying the properties of a bronze alloy (mixture) of copper and tin. She begins with 2 kg of an alloy that is one-half tin. Keeping the amount of copper constant, she adds small amounts of tin to the alloy. Letting x be the total amount of tin added, define

$$C(x) = \text{Concentration of tin} = \frac{\text{Total amount of tin}}{\text{Total amount of alloy}}.$$

(a) Find a formula for $C(x)$.
(b) Evaluate $C(0.5)$ and $C(-0.5)$. Explain the physical significance of these quantities.
(c) Graph $y = C(x)$, labeling all interesting features. Describe the physical significance of the features you have labeled.

23. The population of Mathville has been increasing since 2010 when it was 12,000. If the population t years after 2010 is

$$P(t) = 20 \left(\frac{4t + 3}{2t + 5} \right) \text{ thousand,}$$

when will the population of Mathville reach 20,000? When will it reach 50,000?

24. A car is driven for 60 miles. The first 10 miles are through a large city at a speed of 40 mph; once out of the city a speed of V mph is maintained.

(a) Calculate the average speed for the 60-mile trip.
(b) If you want to average 60 mph for the trip, how fast need you go during the last 50 miles?

25. An alcohol solution consists of 5 gallons of pure water and x gallons of alcohol, $x > 0$. Let $f(x)$ be the ratio of the volume of alcohol to the total volume of liquid. [Note that $f(x)$ is the concentration of the alcohol in the solution.]

(a) Find a possible formula for $f(x)$.
(b) Evaluate and interpret $f(7)$ in the context of the mixture.
(c) What is the zero of f? Interpret your result in the context of the mixture.
(d) Find an equation for the horizontal asymptote of f. Explain its significance in the context of the mixture.

26. The total cost $C(n)$ for a producer to manufacture n units of a good is given by

$$C(n) = 5000 + 50n.$$

The average cost of producing n units is $a(n) = C(n)/n$.

(a) Evaluate and interpret the economic significance of:

   (i) $C(1)$ (ii) $C(100)$
  (iii) $C(1000)$ (iv) $C(10000)$

(b) Evaluate and interpret the economic significance of:

   (i) $a(1)$ (ii) $a(100)$
  (iii) $a(1000)$ (iv) $a(10000)$

(c) Based on part (b), what trend do you notice in the values of $a(n)$ as n gets large? Explain this trend in economic terms.

27. Figure 11.33 shows the cost function, $C(n)$, from Problem 26, and a line, l, that passes through the origin.

(a) What is the slope of line l?
(b) How does line l relate to $a(n_0)$, the average cost of producing n_0 units (as defined in Problem 26)?

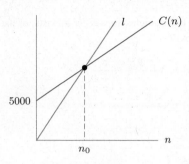

Figure 11.33

28. Typically, the average cost of production (as defined in Problem 26) decreases as the level of production increases. Is this always the case for the goods whose total cost function is graphed in Figure 11.34? Use the result of Problem 27 and explain your reasoning.

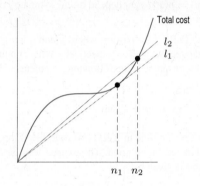

Figure 11.34

29. It costs a company $30,000 to begin production of a good, plus $3 for every unit of the good produced. Let x be the number of units produced by the company.

(a) Find a formula for $C(x)$, the total cost for the production of x units of the good.
(b) Find a formula for the company's average cost per unit, $a(x)$.
(c) Graph $y = a(x)$ for $0 < x \leq 50{,}000$, $0 \leq y \leq 10$. Label the horizontal asymptote.
(d) Explain in economic terms why the graph of a has the long-run behavior that it does.
(e) Explain in economic terms why the graph of a has the vertical asymptote that it does.
(f) Find a formula for $a^{-1}(y)$. Give an economic interpretation of $a^{-1}(y)$.
(g) The company makes a profit if the average cost of its good is less than $5 per unit. Find the minimum number of units the company can produce and make a profit.

30. Find a rational function of the form

$$R(x) = \frac{1}{1 + cx}$$

whose values equal those of $f(x) = e^x$ at $x = 0$ and $x = 1$. Plot and compare your approximation on the interval $(0, 1)$ and comment on the result.

11.5 THE SHORT-RUN BEHAVIOR OF RATIONAL FUNCTIONS

The short-run behavior of a polynomial can often be determined from its factored form. The same is true of rational functions. If r is a rational function given by

$$r(x) = \frac{p(x)}{q(x)}, \qquad p, q \text{ polynomials},$$

then the short-run behaviors of p and q tell us about the short-run behavior of r.

The Zeros and Vertical Asymptotes of a Rational Function

A fraction is equal to zero if and only if its numerator equals zero (and its denominator does not equal zero). Thus, the rational function $r(x) = p(x)/q(x)$ has a zero wherever p has a zero, provided q does not have a zero there.

Just as we can find the zeros of a rational function by looking at its numerator, we can find the vertical asymptotes by looking at its denominator. A rational function is large wherever its denominator is small. This means that r has a vertical asymptote wherever its denominator has a zero, provided its numerator does not also have a zero there.

Example 1 Find the zeros and vertical asymptotes of the rational function $r(x) = \dfrac{x + 3}{x + 2}$.

Solution We see that $r(x) = 0$ if

$$\frac{x + 3}{x + 2} = 0.$$

This ratio equals zero only if the numerator is zero (and the denominator is not zero), so

$$x + 3 = 0$$
$$x = -3.$$

The only zero of r is $x = -3$. To check, note that $r(-3) = 0/(-1) = 0$. The denominator has a zero at $x = -2$, so the graph of $r(x)$ has a vertical asymptote there. Note that as x approaches -2 from the left $r(x)$ tends toward $-\infty$ and as x approaches -2 from the right $r(x)$ tends toward ∞.

Example 2 Graph $r(x) = \dfrac{25}{(x + 2)(x - 3)^2}$, showing all the important features.

Solution Since the numerator of this function is never zero, r has no zeros, meaning that the graph of r never crosses the x-axis. The graph of r has vertical asymptotes at $x = -2$ and $x = 3$ because this is where the denominator is zero. What does the graph of r look like near its asymptote at $x = -2$?

At $x = -2$, the numerator is 25 and the value of the factor $(x - 3)^2$ is $(-2 - 3)^2 = 25$. Thus, near $x = -2$,

$$r(x) = \frac{25}{(x+2)(x-3)^2} \approx \frac{25}{(x+2)(25)} = \frac{1}{x+2}.$$

So, near $x = -2$, the graph of r looks like the graph of $y = 1/(x+2)$. Note that the graph of $y = 1/(x+2)$ is the graph of $y = 1/x$ shifted to the left by 2 units. We see that

$$\lim_{x \to -2^-} r(x) = -\infty \quad \text{and} \quad \lim_{x \to -2^+} r(x) = \infty.$$

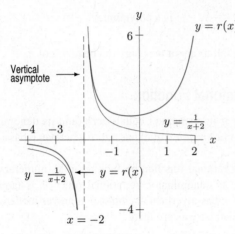

Figure 11.35: The rational function r resembles the shifted power function $1/(x+2)$ near the asymptote at $x = -2$

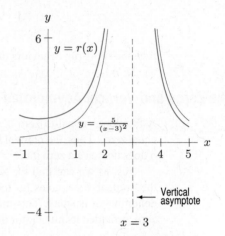

Figure 11.36: The rational function r resembles the shifted power function $5/(x-3)^2$ near the asymptote at $x = 3$

What does the graph of r look like near its vertical asymptote at $x = 3$? Near $x = 3$, the numerator is 25 and value of the factor $(x + 2)$ is approximately $(3 + 2) = 5$. Thus, near $x = 3$,

$$r(x) \approx \frac{25}{(5)(x-3)^2} = \frac{5}{(x-3)^2}.$$

Near $x = 3$, the graph of r looks like the the graph of $y = 5/(x-3)^2$. We see that

$$\lim_{x \to 3} r(x) = \infty.$$

The graph of $y = 5/(x-3)^2$ is the graph of $y = 5/x^2$ shifted to the right 3 units. Since

$$r(0) = \frac{25}{(0+2)(0-3)^2} = \frac{25}{18} \approx 1.4,$$

the graph of r crosses the y-axis at $25/18$. The long-run behavior of r is given by the ratio of the leading term in the numerator to the leading term in the denominator. The numerator is 25, and if we multiply out the denominator, we see that its leading term is x^3. Thus, the long-run behavior of r is given by $y = 25/x^3$, which has a horizontal asymptote at $y = 0$. See Figure 11.37. We see that

$$\lim_{x \to \pm\infty} r(x) = 0.$$

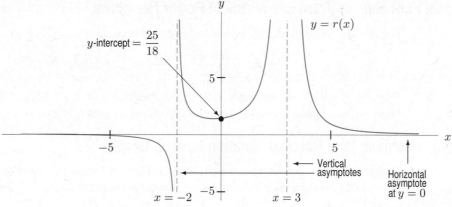

Figure 11.37: A graph of the rational function $r(x) = \dfrac{25}{(x+2)(x-3)^2}$, showing intercepts and asymptotes

The Graph of a Rational Function

We can now summarize what we have learned about the graphs of rational functions.

If r is a rational function given by $r(x) = \dfrac{p(x)}{q(x)}$, where p and q are polynomials with different zeros, then:

- The **long-run behavior** and **horizontal asymptote** (if any) of r are given by the ratio of the leading terms of p and q.
- The **zeros** of r are the same as the zeros of the numerator, p.
- The graph of r has a **vertical asymptote** at each of the zeros of the denominator, q.

If p and q have zeros at the same x-values, the rational function may behave differently. See the discussion about holes in graphs on page 465.

Can a Graph Cross an Asymptote?

The graph of a rational function never crosses a vertical asymptote. However, the graphs of some rational functions cross their horizontal asymptotes. The difference is that a vertical asymptote occurs where the function is undefined, so there can be no y-value there, whereas a horizontal asymptote represents the limiting value of the function as $x \to \pm\infty$. There is no reason that the function cannot take on this limiting y-value for some finite x-value. For example, the graph of $r(x) = \dfrac{x^2 + 2x - 3}{x^2}$ crosses the line $y = 1$, its horizontal asymptote; the graph does not cross the vertical asymptote, the y-axis. See Figure 11.38.

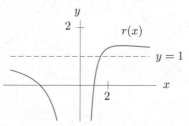

Figure 11.38: A rational function can cross its horizontal asymptote

Rational Functions as Transformations of Power Functions

The average cost function on page 455 can be written as

$$a(q) = \frac{2{,}500{,}000 + 2000q}{q} = 2{,}500{,}000q^{-1} + 2000.$$

Thus, the graph of a is the graph of the power function $y = 2{,}500{,}000q^{-1}$ shifted up 2000 units. Many rational functions can be viewed as translations of power functions.

Finding a Formula for a Rational Function from its Graph

The graph of a rational function can give a good idea of its formula. Zeros of the function correspond to factors in the numerator and vertical asymptotes correspond to factors in the denominator.

Example 3   Find a possible formula for the rational function, $g(x)$, graphed in Figure 11.39.

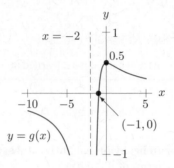

Figure 11.39: The graph of $y = g(x)$, a rational function

Solution   From the graph, we see that g has a zero at $x = -1$ and a vertical asymptote at $x = -2$. This means that the numerator of g has a zero at $x = -1$ and the denominator of g has a zero at $x = -2$. The zero of g does not seem to be a multiple zero because the graph crosses the x-axis instead of bouncing and does not have a flattened appearance. Thus, we conclude that the numerator of g has one factor of $(x + 1)$.

The values of $g(x)$ have the same sign on both sides of the vertical asymptote. Thus, the behavior of g near its vertical asymptote is more like the behavior of $y = 1/(x + 2)^2$ than like $y = 1/(x + 2)$. We conclude that the denominator of g has a factor of $(x + 2)^2$. This suggests

$$g(x) = k \cdot \frac{x + 1}{(x + 2)^2},$$

where k is a stretch factor. To find the value of k, use the fact that $g(0) = 0.5$. So

$$0.5 = k \cdot \frac{0 + 1}{(0 + 2)^2}$$

$$0.5 = k \cdot \frac{1}{4}$$

$$k = 2.$$

Thus, a possible formula for g is $g(x) = \dfrac{2(x + 1)}{(x + 2)^2}$.

When Numerator and Denominator Have the Same Zeros: Holes

The rational function $h(x) = \dfrac{x^2 + x - 2}{x - 1}$ is undefined at $x = 1$ because the denominator equals zero at $x = 1$. However, the graph of h does not have a vertical asymptote at $x = 1$ because the numerator of h also equals zero at $x = 1$. At $x = 1$,

$$h(1) = \frac{x^2 + x - 2}{x - 1} = \frac{1^2 + 1 - 2}{1 - 1} = \frac{0}{0},$$

and this ratio is undefined. What does the graph of h look like? Factoring the numerator of h gives

$$h(x) = \frac{(x - 1)(x + 2)}{x - 1} = \frac{x - 1}{x - 1}(x + 2).$$

For any $x \neq 1$, we can cancel $(x - 1)$ top and bottom and rewrite the formula for h as

$$h(x) = x + 2, \qquad \text{provided } x \neq 1.$$

Thus, the graph of h is the line $y = x + 2$ except at $x = 1$, where h is undefined. The line $y = x + 2$ contains the point $(1, 3)$, but the graph of h does not. Therefore, we say that the graph of h has a *hole* in it at the point $(1, 3)$. See Figure 11.40.

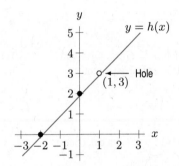

Figure 11.40: The graph of $y = h(x)$ is the line $y = x + 2$, except at the point $(1, 3)$, where it has a hole

Exercises and Problems for Section 11.5

Exercises

For the rational functions in Exercises 1–4, find all zeros and vertical asymptotes and describe the long-run behavior, then graph the function.

1. $y = \dfrac{x - 4}{x^2 - 9}$

2. $y = \dfrac{x^2 - 4}{x - 9}$

3. $y = \dfrac{x + 3}{x + 5}$

4. $y = \dfrac{x + 3}{(x + 5)^2}$

In Exercises 5–8, what are the x-intercepts, y-intercepts, and horizontal and vertical asymptotes (if any)?

5. $h(x) = \dfrac{x^2 - 4}{x^3 + 4x^2}$

6. $k(x) = \dfrac{x(4 - x)}{x^2 - 6x + 5}$

7. $f(x) = \dfrac{x - 2}{x - 4}$

8. $g(x) = \dfrac{x^2 - 9}{x^2 + 9}$

9. Let $G(x) = \dfrac{2x}{x+4}$.

   (a) Complete Table 11.10 for x-values close to -4. What happens to the values of $G(x)$ as x approaches -4 from the left? From the right?

Table 11.10

x	-5	-4.1	-4.01	-4	-3.99	-3.9	-3
$G(x)$							

   (b) Complete Tables 11.11 and 11.12. What happens to the values of $G(x)$ as x takes very large positive values? As x takes very large negative values?

Table 11.11

x	5	10	100	1000
$G(x)$				

Table 11.12

x	-5	-10	-100	-1000
$G(x)$				

   (c) Without a calculator, graph $y = G(x)$. Give equations for the horizontal and vertical asymptotes.

10. Let $g(x) = \dfrac{1}{(x+2)^2}$.

   (a) Complete Table 11.13 for x-values close to -2. What happens to the values of $g(x)$ as x approaches -2 from the left? From the right?

Table 11.13

x	-3	-2.1	-2.01	-2	-1.99	-1.9	-1
$g(x)$							

   (b) Complete Tables 11.14 and 11.15. What happens to the values of $g(x)$ as x takes very large positive values? As x takes very large negative values?

Table 11.14

x	5	10	100	1000
$g(x)$				

Table 11.15

x	-5	-10	-100	-1000
$g(x)$				

   (c) Without a calculator, graph $y = g(x)$. Give equations for the horizontal and vertical asymptotes.

Problems

Graph the functions in Problems 11–12 without a calculator.

11. $y = 2 + \dfrac{1}{x}$ **12.** $y = \dfrac{2x^2 - 10x + 12}{x^2 - 16}$

In Problems 13–14, estimate the one-sided limits:

(a) $\displaystyle \lim_{x \to a^+} f(x)$ **(b)** $\displaystyle \lim_{x \to a^-} f(x)$

13. $f(x) = \dfrac{x}{5 - x}$ with $a = 5$

14. $f(x) = \dfrac{5 - x}{(x - 2)^2}$ with $a = 2$

15. Without a calculator, match the functions (a)–(f) with their graphs in (i)–(vi) by finding the zeros, asymptotes, and end behavior for each function.

   (a) $y = \dfrac{-1}{(x - 5)^2} - 1$ **(b)** $y = \dfrac{x - 2}{(x + 1)(x - 3)}$

   (c) $y = \dfrac{2x + 4}{x - 1}$ **(d)** $y = \dfrac{1}{x + 1} + \dfrac{1}{x - 3}$

   (e) $y = \dfrac{1 - x^2}{x - 2}$ **(f)** $y = \dfrac{1 - 4x}{2x + 2}$

(i)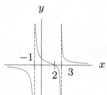

(ii)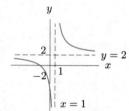

(iii)

(iv)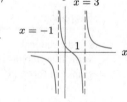

(v)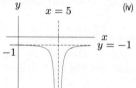

(vi)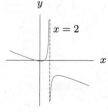

16. Let $f(x) = x^2 - 4$, $g(x) = x^2 + 4$, and $h(x) = x + 5$. Without a calculator, match the functions in (a)–(f) to the descriptions in (i)–(viii). Some of the functions may match none of the descriptions.

(a) $y = \dfrac{f(x)}{g(x)}$ (b) $y = \dfrac{g(x)}{f(x)}$ (c) $y = \dfrac{h(x)}{f(x)}$

(d) $y = f\left(\dfrac{1}{x}\right)$ (e) $y = \dfrac{g(x)}{h(x)}$ (f) $y = \dfrac{h(x^2)}{h(x)}$

(g) $y = \dfrac{1}{g(x)}$ (h) $y = f(x){\cdot}g(x)$

(i) Horizontal asymptote at $y = 0$ and one zero at $x = -5$.

(ii) No horizontal asymptote, no zeros, and a vertical asymptote at $x = -5$.

(iii) Zeros at $x = -5$, $x = -2$, and $x = 2$.

(iv) No zeros, a horizontal asymptote at $y = 0$, and a vertical asymptote at $x = -5$.

(v) Two zeros, no vertical asymptotes, and a horizontal asymptote at $y = 1$.

(vi) No zeros, no vertical asymptotes, and a horizontal asymptote at $y = 1$.

(vii) Horizontal asymptote at $y = -4$.

(viii) No horizontal asymptotes, two zeros, and a vertical asymptote at $x = -5$.

In Problems 17–18,

(a) Estimate $\lim\limits_{x \to \infty} f(x)$ and $\lim\limits_{x \to -\infty} f(x)$.

(b) What does the vertical asymptote tell you about limits?

17.

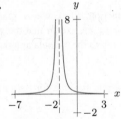

18.

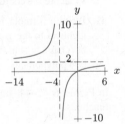

19. Suppose that n is a constant and that $f(x)$ is a function defined when $x = n$. Complete the following sentences.

(a) If $f(n)$ is large, then $\dfrac{1}{f(n)}$ is ...

(b) If $f(n)$ is small, then $\dfrac{1}{f(n)}$ is ...

(c) If $f(n) = 0$, then $\dfrac{1}{f(n)}$ is ...

(d) If $f(n)$ is positive, then $\dfrac{1}{f(n)}$ is ...

(e) If $f(n)$ is negative, then $\dfrac{1}{f(n)}$ is ...

20. (a) Use the results of Problem 19 to graph $y = 1/f(x)$ given the graph of $y = f(x)$ in Figure 11.41.

(b) Find a possible formula for the function in Figure 11.41. Use this formula to check your graph for part (a).

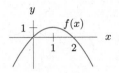

Figure 11.41

21. Use the graph of f in Figure 11.42 to graph

(a) $y = -f(-x) + 2$ (b) $y = \dfrac{1}{f(x)}$

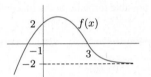

Figure 11.42

Problems 22–24 show a transformation of $y = 1/x$.

(a) Find a possible formula for the graph.

(b) Write the formula from part (a) as the ratio of two linear polynomials.

(c) Find the coordinates of the intercepts of the graph.

22.

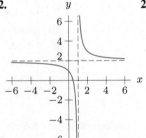

23.

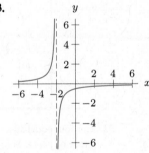

24.

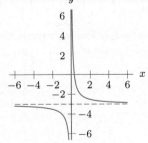

Each of the functions in Problems 25–27 is a transformation of $y = 1/x^p$. For each function, determine p, describe the transformation in words, and graph the function, labeling any intercepts and asymptotes.

25. $f(x) = \dfrac{1}{x-3} + 4$

26. $g(x) = -\dfrac{1}{(x-2)^2} - 3$

27. $h(x) = \dfrac{1}{x-1} + \dfrac{2}{1-x} + 2$

Problems 28–31 give values of transformations of either $y = 1/x$ or $y = 1/x^2$. In each case

(a) Determine if the values are from a transformation of $y = 1/x$ or $y = 1/x^2$. Explain your reasoning.

(b) Find a possible formula for the function.

28.

x	y
-1000	1.000001
-100	1.00001
-10	1.01
10	1.01
100	1.0001
1000	1.000001

29.

x	y
1.5	-1.5
1.9	-9.5
1.95	-19.5
2	Undefined
2.05	20.5
2.1	10.5
2.5	2.5

30.

x	y
2.7	12.1
2.9	101
2.95	401
3	Undefined
3.05	401
3.1	101
3.3	12.1

31.

x	y
-1000	0.499
-100	0.490
-10	0.400
10	0.600
100	0.510
1000	0.501

32. Cut four equal squares from the corners of a $8.5'' \times 11''$ piece of paper. Fold up the sides to create an open box. Find the dimensions of the box with the maximum volume per surface area.

Find possible formulas for the functions in Problems 33–38.

33.

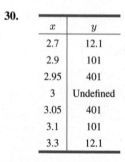

34.

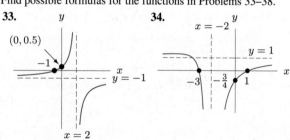

35.

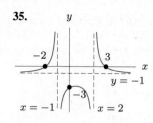

36.

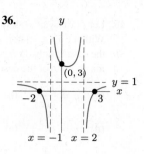

37.

38.

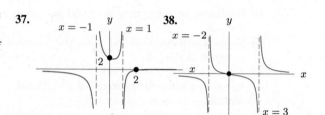

39. The graph of $f(x) = \dfrac{18 - 11x + x^2}{x - 2}$ is a line with a hole in it. What is the equation of the line? What are the coordinates of the hole?

40. The graph of $g(x) = \dfrac{x^3 + 5x^2 + x + 5}{x + 5}$ is a parabola with a hole in it. What is the equation of the parabola? What are the coordinates of the hole?

41. Write a formula for a function, $h(x)$, whose graph is identical to the graph of $y = x^3$, except that the graph of h has a hole at $(2, 8)$. Express the formula as a ratio of two polynomials

In Problems 42–44, find a possible formula for the rational functions.

42. This function has zeros at $x = 2$ and $x = 3$. It has a vertical asymptote at $x = 5$. It has a horizontal asymptote of $y = -3$.

43. The graph of $y = g(x)$ has two vertical asymptotes: one at $x = -2$ and one at $x = 3$. It has a horizontal asymptote of $y = 0$. The graph of g crosses the x-axis once, at $x = 5$.

44. The graph of $y = h(x)$ has two vertical asymptotes: one at $x = -2$ and one at $x = 3$. It has a horizontal asymptote of $y = 1$. The graph of h touches the x-axis once, at $x = 5$.

11.6   COMPARING POWER, EXPONENTIAL, AND LOG FUNCTIONS

In preceding chapters, we encountered exponential and logarithmic functions. In this section, we compare the long- and short-run behaviors of these functions and power functions.

Comparing Power Functions

For power functions $y = kx^p$ for large x, the higher the power of x, the faster the function climbs. See Figure 11.43. Not only are the higher powers larger, but they are *much* larger. This is because if $x = 100$, for example, 100^5 is one hundred times as big as 100^4, which is one hundred times as big as 100^3. As x gets larger (written as $x \to \infty$), any positive power of x grows much faster than all lower powers of x. We say that, as $x \to \infty$, higher powers of x *dominate* lower powers.

As x approaches zero (written $x \to 0$), the situation is reversed. Figure 11.44 is a close-up view near the origin. For x between 0 and 1, x^3 is bigger than x^4, which is bigger than x^5. (Try $x = 0.1$ to confirm this.) For values of x near zero, smaller powers dominate.

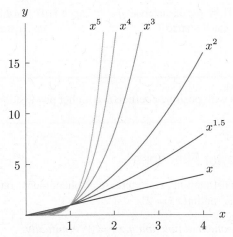

Figure 11.43: For large x: Large powers of x dominate

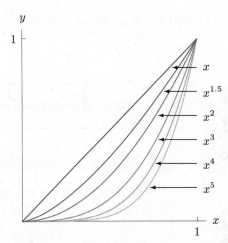

Figure 11.44: For $0 \le x \le 1$: Small powers of x dominate

In Chapter 6 we saw the effect of k on the graph of $f(x) = kx^p$. The coefficient k stretches or compresses the graph vertically; if k is negative, the graph is reflected across the x-axis. How does the value of k affect the long-term growth rate of $f(x) = kx^p$? Is the growth of a power function affected more by the size of the coefficient or by the size of the power?

Example 1   Let $f(x) = 100x^3$ and $g(x) = x^4$ for $x > 0$. Compare the long-term behavior of these two functions using graphs.

Solution   For $x < 10$, Figure 11.45 suggests that f is growing faster than g and that f dominates g. Eventually, however, the fact that g has a higher power than f asserts itself. In Figure 11.46, we see that $g(x)$ has caught up to $f(x)$ at $x = 100$. In Figure 11.47, we see that for $x > 100$, values of g are larger than values of f.

Could the graphs of f and g intersect again for some value of $x > 100$? To show that this cannot be the case, solve the equation $g(x) = f(x)$:

$$x^4 = 100x^3$$
$$x^4 - 100x^3 = 0$$
$$x^3(x - 100) = 0.$$

Since the only solutions to this equation are $x = 0$ and $x = 100$, the graphs of f and g do not cross for $x > 100$.

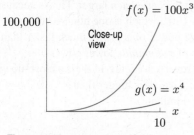

Figure 11.45: On this interval, f climbs faster than g

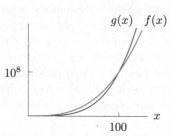

Figure 11.46: On this interval, g catches up to f

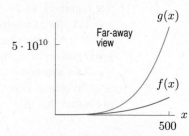

Figure 11.47: On this interval, g ends up far ahead of f

When comparing power functions with positive coefficients, higher powers dominate.

Comparing Exponential Functions and Power Functions

Both power functions and exponential functions can increase at phenomenal rates. For example, Table 11.16 shows values of $f(x) = x^4$ and $g(x) = 2^x$.

Table 11.16   *The exponential function $g(x) = 2^x$ eventually grows faster than the power function $f(x) = x^4$*

x	0	5	10	15	20
$f(x) = x^4$	0	625	10,000	50,625	160,000
$g(x) = 2^x$	1	32	1024	32,768	1,048,576

Despite the impressive growth in the value of the power function $f(x) = x^4$, in the long run $g(x) = 2^x$ grows faster. By the time $x = 20$, the value of $g(20) = 2^{20}$ is over six times as large as $f(20) = 20^4$. Figure 11.48 shows the exponential function $g(x) = 2^x$ catching up to $f(x) = x^4$.

But what about a more slowly growing exponential function? After all, $y = 2^x$ increases at a 100% growth rate. Figure 11.49 compares $y = x^4$ to the exponential function $y = 1.005^x$. Despite the fact that this exponential function creeps along at a 0.5% growth rate, at around $x = 7000$, it overtakes the power function. In summary,

---

Any positive increasing exponential function eventually grows faster than *any* power function.

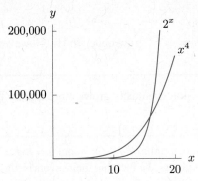

Figure 11.48: The exponential function $y = 2^x$ dominates the power function $y = x^4$

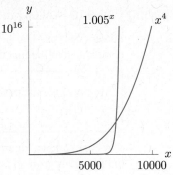

Figure 11.49: The exponential function $y = 1.005^x$ dominates the power function $y = x^4$

Decreasing Exponential Functions and Decreasing Power Functions

Just as an increasing exponential function eventually outpaces any increasing power function, an exponential decay function wins the race toward the x-axis. In general:

> *Any* positive decreasing exponential function eventually approaches the horizontal axis faster than any positive decreasing power function.

For example, let's compare the long-term behavior of the decreasing exponential function $y = 0.5^x$ with the decreasing power function $y = x^{-2}$. By rewriting

$$y = 0.5^x = \left(\frac{1}{2}\right)^x = \frac{1}{2^x} \qquad \text{and} \qquad y = x^{-2} = \frac{1}{x^2}$$

we can see the comparison more easily. In the long run, the smallest of these two fractions is the one with the largest denominator. The fact that 2^x is eventually larger than x^2 means that $1/2^x$ is eventually smaller than $1/x^2$.

Figure 11.50 shows $y = 0.5^x$ and $y = x^{-2}$. Both graphs have the x-axis as a horizontal asymptote. As x increases, the exponential function $y = 0.5^x$ approaches the x-axis faster than the power function $y = x^{-2}$. Figure 11.51 shows what happens for large values of x. The exponential function approaches the x-axis so rapidly that it becomes invisible compared to $y = x^{-2}$.

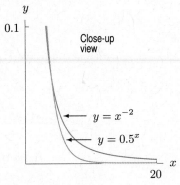

Figure 11.50: Graphs of $y = x^{-2}$ and $y = 0.5^x$

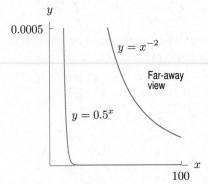

Figure 11.51: Graphs of $y = x^{-2}$ and $y = 0.5^x$

Comparing Log and Power Functions

Power functions like $y = x^{1/2}$ and $y = x^{1/3}$ grow quite slowly. However, they grow rapidly in comparison to log functions. In fact:

> *Any* positive increasing power function eventually grows more rapidly than $y = \log x$ and $y = \ln x$.

For example, Figure 11.52 shows the graphs of $y = x^{1/2}$ and $y = \log x$. The fact that exponential functions grow so fast should alert you to the fact that their inverses, the logarithms, grow very slowly. See Figure 11.53.

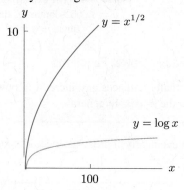

Figure 11.52: Graphs of $y = x^{1/2}$ and $y = \log x$

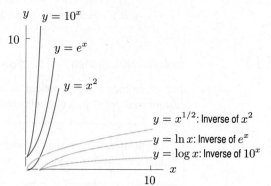

Figure 11.53: Graphs of $y = 10^x$, $y = e^x$, $y = x^2$, $y = x^{1/2}$, $y = \ln x$, and $y = \log x$

Exercises and Problems for Section 11.6

Exercises

Can the formulas in Exercises 1–6 be written in the form of an exponential function or a power function? If not, explain why the function does not fit either form.

1. $p(x) = (5^x)^2$

2. $q(x) = 5^{(x^2)}$

3. $m(x) = 3(3x + 1)^2$

4. $n(x) = 3 \cdot 2^{3x+1}$

5. $r(x) = 2 \cdot 3^{-2x}$

6. $s(x) = \dfrac{4}{5x^{-3}}$

7. Without a calculator, match the following functions with the graphs in Figure 11.54.

   (i) $y = x^5$ (ii) $y = x^2$ (iii) $y = x$ (iv) $y = x^3$

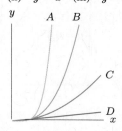

Figure 11.54

8. Without a calculator, match the following functions with the graphs in Figure 11.55.

   (i) $y = x^5$ (ii) $y = x^2$ (iii) $y = x$ (iv) $y = x^3$

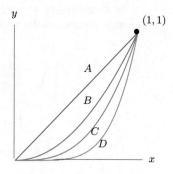

Figure 11.55

9. Let $f(x) = 3^x$ and $g(x) = x^3$.

(a) Complete the following table of values:

x	-3	-2	-1	0	1	2	3
$f(x)$							
$g(x)$							

(b) Describe the long-run behaviors of f and g as $x \to -\infty$ and as $x \to +\infty$.

Problems

14. The functions $y = x^{-3}$ and $y = 3^{-x}$ both approach zero as $x \to \infty$. Which function approaches zero faster? Support your conclusion numerically.

15. The functions $y = x^{-3}$ and $y = e^{-x}$ both approach zero as $x \to \infty$. Which function approaches zero faster? Support your conclusion numerically.

16. Let $f(x) = x^x$. Is f a power function, an exponential function, both, or neither? Discuss.

In Problems 17–19, find a possible formula for f if f is

(a) Linear   (b) Exponential   (c) Power function.

17. $f(1) = 18$ and $f(3) = 1458$

18. $f(1) = 16$ and $f(2) = 128$

19. $f(-1) = \frac{3}{4}$ and $f(2) = 48$

20. Data from four functions are in Tables 11.17–11.20. One function is linear, one is logarithmic, and the other two are power functions (one cubic and one quadratic). Find a formula for each function, and explain how you made your choices.

Table 11.17

x	$j(x)$
1.8	1.75
2.2	3.19
2.6	5.27
3.0	8.10
3.4	11.79

Table 11.18

x	$k(x)$
2.8	0.36
3.0	0.60
3.2	0.84
3.4	1.08
3.6	1.32

Table 11.19

x	$m(x)$
0.2	-0.699
0.6	-0.222
1.0	0.00
1.4	0.146
1.8	0.255

Table 11.20

x	$z(x)$
-4.0	6.4
-2	1.6
0	0
2	1.6
4	6.4

21. Match the graphs in Figure 11.56 with the functions $y = kx^{9/16}, y = kx^{3/8}, y = kx^{5/7}, y = kx^{3/11}$.

In Exercises 10–13, which function dominates as $x \to \infty$?

10. $y = ax^3, \quad y = bx^2, \quad a, b > 0$

11. $y = 7(0.99)^x, \quad y = 6x^{35}$

12. $y = 4e^x, \quad y = 2x^{50}$

13. $y = 50x^{1.1}, \quad y = 1000x^{1.08}$

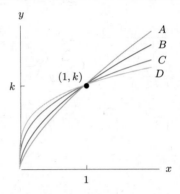

Figure 11.56

22. (a) Match the functions $f(x) = x^2, g(x) = 2x^2$, and $h(x) = x^3$ to their graphs in Figure 11.57.

(b) Do graphs A and B intersect for $x > 0$? If so, for what value(s) of x? If not, explain how you know.

(c) Do graphs C and A intersect for $x > 0$? If so, for what value(s) of x? If not, explain how you know.

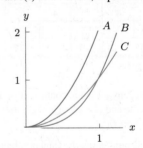

Figure 11.57

23. In Figure 11.58, find the values of m, t, and k.

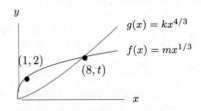

Figure 11.58

24. (a) Given $t(x) = x^{-2}$ and $r(x) = 40x^{-3}$, find v such that $t(v) = r(v)$.
(b) For $0 < x < v$, which is greater, $t(x)$ or $r(x)$?
(c) For $x > v$, which is greater, $t(x)$ or $r(x)$?

What is the long-run behavior of the functions in Problems 25–36?

25. $y = \dfrac{x^2 + 5}{x^8}$

26. $y = \dfrac{5 - t^2}{(7 + t + \sqrt{t})t^5}$

27. $y = \dfrac{2^t + 7}{5^t + 9}$

28. $y = \dfrac{3^{-t}}{4^t + 7}$

29. $y = \dfrac{x(x + 5)(x - 7)}{4 + x^2}$

30. $y = \dfrac{2^x + 3}{x^2 + 5}$

31. $y = \dfrac{\ln x}{\sqrt{x} + 5}$

32. $y = \dfrac{e^t + t^2}{\ln |t|}$

33. $y = \dfrac{e^x - e^{-x}}{2}$

34. $y = \dfrac{e^x - e^{-x}}{e^x + e^{-x}}$

35. $y = \dfrac{e^x + 5}{x^{100} + 50}$

36. $y = \dfrac{e^{2t}}{e^{3t} + 5}$

37. Table 11.21 gives approximate values for three functions, $f, g,$ and h. One is exponential, one is trigonometric, and one is a power function. Determine which is which and find possible formulas for each.

Table 11.21

x	-2	-1	0	1	2
$f(x)$	4	2	4	6	4
$g(x)$	20.0	2.5	0.0	-2.5	-20.0
$h(x)$	1.33	0.67	0.33	0.17	0.08

38. A woman opens a bank account with an initial deposit of $1000. At the end of each year thereafter, she deposits an additional $1000.

(a) The account earns 6% annual interest, compounded annually. Complete Table 11.22.

(b) Does the balance of this account grow linearly, exponentially, or neither? Justify your answer.

Table 11.22

Years elapsed	Start-of-year balance	End-of-year deposit	End-of-year interest
0	$1000.00	$1000	$60.00
1	$2060.00	$1000	$123.60
2	$3183.60	$1000	
3		$1000	
4		$1000	
5		$1000	

39. The annual percentage rate (APR) paid by the account in Problem 38 is r, where r does not necessarily equal 6%. Define $p_n(r)$ as the balance of the account after n years have elapsed. (For example, $p_2(0.06) = \$3183.60$, because, according to Table 11.22, the balance after 2 years is $3183.60 if the APR is 6%.)

(a) Find formulas for $p_5(r)$ and $p_{10}(r)$.
(b) What is APR if the woman in Problem 38 has $10,000 in 5 years?

40. Values of f and g are in Table 11.23 and 11.24. One function is of the form $y = a \cdot d^{p/q}$ with $p > q$; the other is of the form $y = b \cdot d^{p/q}$ with $p < q$. Which is which? How can you tell?

Table 11.23

d	2	2.2	2.4	2.6	2.8
$f(d)$	151.6	160.5	169.1	177.4	185.5

Table 11.24

d	10	10.2	10.4	10.6	10.8
$g(d)$	7.924	8.115	8.306	8.498	8.691

11.7 FITTING EXPONENTIALS AND POLYNOMIALS TO DATA

In Section 1.6 we used linear regression to find the equation for a line of best fit for a set of data. In this section, we fit an exponential or a power function to a set of data.

The Spread of AIDS

The data in Table 11.25 give the total number of deaths in the US from AIDS from 1981 to 1996. Figure 11.59 suggests that a linear function may not give the best possible fit for these data.

Table 11.25   *US deaths from AIDS, 1981–96*

t	N	t	N
1	159	9	90039
2	622	10	121577
3	2130	11	158193
4	5635	12	199287
5	12607	13	243923
6	24717	14	292586
7	41129	15	340957
8	62248	16	375904

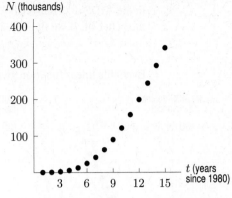

Figure 11.59: US deaths from AIDS, 1981–96

Fitting an Exponential

We first fit an exponential function to the data[13] in Table 11.25

$$N = ae^{kt},$$

where N is the total number of deaths t years after 1980.

Using exponential regression on a calculator or computer, we obtain[14]

$$N \approx 630e^{0.47t}.$$

Figure 11.60 shows how the graph of this formula fits the data points.

Fitting a Power Function

Now we fit the AIDS data with a power function of the form

$$N = at^p,$$

where a and p are constants. Some scientists have suggested that a power function may be a better model for the growth of AIDS than an exponential function.[15] Using power function regression on a calculator or a computer, we obtain

$$N \approx 107t^{3.005}.$$

Figure 11.60 shows the graph of this power function with the data.

Which Function Best Fits the Data?

Both the exponential function

$$N = 630e^{0.47t}$$

and the power function

$$N = 107t^{3.005}$$

---

[13] *HIV/AIDS Surveillance Report*, Year-end Edition, Vol. 9, No. 2, Table 13, US Department of Health and Human Services, Centers for Disease Control and Prevention, Atlanta. 2000–2004 data from *HIV/AIDS Surveillance Report*, Vol. 16, at www.cdc.gov/hiv/stats/hastlink.htm, accessed January 15, 2006. Data does not include 450 people whose dates of death are unknown.

[14] Calculator and computer answers for exponential regression may vary slightly due to different algorithms used.

[15] Stirling A. Colgate, E. Ann Stanley, James M. Hyman, Scott P. Layne, and Alifford Qualls, "Risk behavior-based model of the cubic growth of acquired immunodeficiency syndrome in the United States," *Proc. Natl. Acad. Sci. USA*, Vol. 86, June 1989, Population Biology.

fit the AIDS data reasonably well. By visual inspection alone, the power function arguably provides the better fit. If we fit a linear function to the original data we get

$$N = -97311 + 25946t.$$

Even this linear function gives a possible fit for $t \geq 4$, that is, for 1984 to 1996. (See Figure 11.60.)

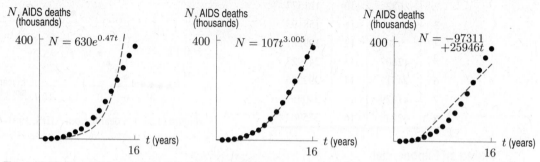

Figure 11.60: The AIDS data since 1981 together with an exponential model, a power-function model, and a linear model

Despite the fact that all three functions fit the data reasonably well up to 1996, it's important to realize that they give wildly different predictions for the future. If we use each model to estimate the total number of AIDS deaths by the year 2010 (when $t = 30$), the exponential model gives

$$N = 630e^{(0.47)30} \approx 837,322,467, \quad \text{about triple the current US population;}$$

the power model gives

$$N = 107(30)^{3.005} \approx 2,938,550, \quad \text{or about 1\% of the current population;}$$

and the linear model gives

$$N = -97311 + 25946 \cdot 30 = 681,069, \quad \text{or about 0.22\% of the current population.}$$

Which function is the best predictor of the future? To explore this question, let us add some more recent data to our previous data on AIDS deaths. See Table 11.26.

Table 11.26   US deaths from AIDS, 1997–2007

t	N
17	406,444
18	424,841
19	442,013
20	457,258
21	462,653
22	501,669
23	524,060
24	529,113
25	553,173
26	568,737
27	583,298

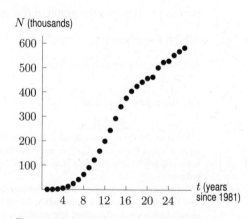

Figure 11.61: US deaths from AIDS, 1981–2007

When data from the entire period from 1981 to 2007 are plotted together (see Figure 11.61), we see that the rate of increase of AIDS deaths reaches a peak sometime around 1995 and then begins to taper off. Since none of the three types of functions we have used to model AIDS deaths exhibit this type of behavior, some other type of function is needed to describe the number of AIDS deaths accurately over the entire 26-year period.

This example illustrates that while a certain type of function may fit a set of data over a short period of time, care must be taken when using a mathematical model to make predictions about the future. An understanding of the processes leading to the data is crucial in answering any long-term question.

Exercises and Problems for Section 11.7

Exercises

1. Find a formula for the power function $f(x)$ such that $f(1) = 1$ and $f(2) = c$.

2. Find a formula for an exponential function $h(x)$.

x	2	3	4	5
$h(x)$	4.5948	7.4744	10.5561	13.7973

3. Find a formula for the power function $g(x)$.

x	2	3	4	5
$g(x)$	4.5948	7.4744	10.5561	13.7973

4. Table 11.27 shows the Maine lobster catch[16] (in millions of pounds) from 1970 to 2000.

   (a) With t in years since 1965, use a calculator or computer to fit the data with

   (i) A power function of the form $y = at^b$.

   (ii) A quadratic function of the form
   $$y = at^2 + bt + c.$$

   (b) Discuss which function is a better fit.

Table 11.27

Year	1970	1975	1980	1985	1990	1995	2000
t	5	10	15	20	25	30	35
Lobster	17	19	22	20	27	36	56

5. Students in the School of Forestry & Environmental Studies at Yale University collected data measuring sassafras trees. Table 11.28 lists the diameter at breast height (dbh, in cm) and the total dry weight (w, in gm) of different trees.[17]

   (a) Find a power function that fits the data.
   (b) Predict the total weight of a tree with a dbh of 20 cm.

   (c) If a tree has a total dry weight of 100,000 gm, what is its expected dbh?

Table 11.28

dbh	5	23.4	11.8	16.7	4.2	5.6
w	5,353	169,290	30,696	76,730	3,436	5,636
dbh	3.8	4.3	6.5	21.9	17.7	25.5
w	14,983	2,098	7,364	177,596	100,848	171,598

6. Anthropologists suggest that the relationship between the body weight and brain weight of primates can be modeled with a power function. Table 11.29 lists various body weights and the corresponding brain weights of different primates.[18]

   (a) Using Table 11.29, find a power function that gives the brain weight, Q (in mg), as a function of the body weight, b (in gm).
   (b) The erythrocebus (Patas monkey) has a body weight of 7800 gm. Estimate its brain weight.

Table 11.29

b	6667	960	6800	9500	1088
Q	56,567	18,200	110,525	120,100	20,700
b	2733	3000	6300	1500	665
Q	78,250	58,200	96,400	31,700	25,050

In Exercises 7–12, find an equation for y in terms of x.

7.

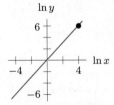

8.

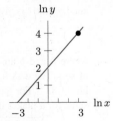

[16] Adapted from *The New York Times*, p. 16, May 31, 2001.

[17] www.yale.edu/fes519b/totoket/allom/allom.htm, accessed December 15, 2002.

[18] mac-huwis.lut.ac.uk/~wis/lectures/primate-adaptation/10PrimateBrains.pdf, accessed December 15, 2002.

9.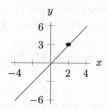

10.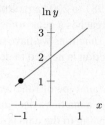

11.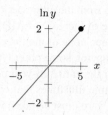

12.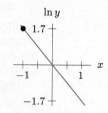

Problems

13. (a) Find a linear function that fits the data in Table 11.30. How good is the fit?

(b) The data in the table was generated using the power function $y = 5x^3$. Explain why (in this case) a linear function gives such a good fit to a power function. Does the fit remain good for other values of x?

Table 11.30

x	2.00	2.01	2.02	2.03	2.04	2.05
y	40.000	40.603	41.212	41.827	42.448	43.076

14. An analog radio dial can be measured in millimeters from left to right. Although the scale of the dial can be different from radio to radio, Table 11.31 gives typical measurements.

(a) Which radio band data appear linear? Graph and connect the data points for each band.

(b) Which radio band data appear exponential?

(c) Find a possible formula for the FM station number in terms of x.

(d) Find a possible formula for the AM station number in terms of x.

Table 11.31

x, millimeters	5	15	25	35	45	55
FM (mhz)	88	92	96	100	104	108
AM (khz/10)	53	65	80	100	130	160

15. A tube of soil is held horizontally and wetted at one end. The distance, x, which the water has reached from the end by time t is given by

$$x = at^b,$$

where a and b are constants that vary with the sample of soil. The data for such an experiment is given in Table 11.32.[19] For this soil it is known that $b \approx 0.4$. What value for a makes this a reasonable model?

Table 11.32   *Movement of wetting front*

Time (minutes)	0	1	2	4	8
Distance (cm)	0	3.7	4.5	6.0	8.0
Time (minutes)	16	32	64	128	256
Distance (cm)	10.6	13.8	18.6	24.3	32.0

16. In this problem you will fit a quartic polynomial to the AIDS data.

(a) With N as the total number of AIDS deaths in the US t years after 1980, use a calculator or computer to fit the data in Table 11.25 on page 475 with a polynomial of the form

$$N = at^4 + bt^3 + ct^2 + dt + e.$$

(b) Graph the data and your quartic for $0 \leq t \leq 16$. Comment on the fit.

(c) Graph the data and your quartic for $0 \leq t \leq 30$. Comment on the predictions made by this model.

17. The managers of a furniture store have compiled data showing the weekly demand for recliners at various prices.

(a) In Table 11.33, fill in the revenue generated by selling the number of recliners at the corresponding price.

(b) Find the quadratic function that best fits the data.

(c) According to the function you found, what price should the store charge for their recliners to maximize revenue? What is the maximum revenue?

Table 11.33

Recliner price ($)	399	499	599	699	799
Demand (recliners)	62	55	47	40	34
Revenue ($)					

[19] Adapted from I. A. Guerrini, "An example of motion in a course of physics for agriculture," *The Physics Teacher*, February 1984, 102–103.

18. The population of Armenia,[20] the smallest of the former Soviet republics, is shown from 2006 to 2010 in Table 11.34.

(a) Does the function giving the population as a function of time appear to be increasing or decreasing? Concave up or concave down?

(b) Find a power function that approximates this data with time, t, in years since 2005.

(c) Using your function, estimate the population in 2012. Have you used interpolation or extrapolation?

Table 11.34

Year	2006	2007	2008	2009	2010
Pop. (millions)	2.976	2.972	2.969	2.967	2.967

19. Cellular telephone use has increased over the past two decades. Table 11.35 gives the number of cellular telephone subscriptions, in thousands, from 1985 to 2007.[21]

(a) Fit an exponential function to this data with time in years since 1985.

(b) Based on your model, by what percent was the number of cell subscribers increasing each year?

(c) In the long run, what do you expect of the rate of growth? What does this mean in terms of the shape of the graph?

Table 11.35

Year	1985	1990	1995	2000	2005	2007
Subscriptions	340	5283	33786	109478	207896	255396

20. The use of one-way pagers declined as cell phones became more popular.[22] The number of users is given in Table 11.36 and plotted in Figure 11.62, along with a quadratic regression function.

(a) How well does the graph of the quadratic function fit the data?

(b) Find a cubic regression function. Does it fit better?

Table 11.36

Year	1990	1991	1992	1993	1994	1995
Users, millions	10	12	15	19	25	32
Year	1996	1997	1998	1999	2000	
Users, millions	38	43	44	43	37	

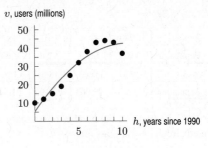

Figure 11.62

21. Table 11.37 gives the estimated population, in thousands, of the American colonies from 1650 to 1770.[23]

(a) Make a scatterplot of the data using $t = 0$ to represent the year 1650.

(b) Fit an exponential function to the data.

(c) Explain the meaning of the parameters in your model.

(d) Use your function to predict the population in 1750. Is it high or low?

(e) According to the US Census Bureau[24], the US population in 1800 was 5,308,483. Use your function to make a prediction for 1800. Is it high or low?

Table 11.37

Year	1650	1670	1690	1700
Population	50.4	111.9	210.4	250.9
Year	1720	1740	1750	1770
Population	466.2	905.6	1170.8	2148.1

22. The US Census Bureau began recording census data in 1790. Table 11.38 gives the population of the US in millions from 1790 to 1860.[25]

(a) With t = 0 representing the number of years since 1790, fit an exponential function to the data.

(b) The 1800 census value is 5.3 million. Find the population predicted by your function for 1800. Problem 21 gave a prediction of 5.5 million using the data for 1650 to 1750. Using the two data sets, explain the difference in predicted values.

(c) Use your function to project the population of the US in 2010. Is this prediction reasonable?

[20]http://www.census.gov/ipc/www/idb/country.php, accessed May 29, 2010.
[21]*World Almanac and Book of Facts*, 2009, p. 406.
[22]*The New York Times*, p. 16, April 11, 2002.
[23]*The World Almanac and Book of Facts, 2002*, New York, NY, p. 376.
[24]http://www.census.gov/, accessed January 15, 2003.
[25]http://www.census.gov/, accessed January 15, 2003.

Table 11.38

Year	1790	1800	1810	1820
Population	3.929	5.308	7.240	9.638
Year	1830	1840	1850	1860
Population	12.861	17.063	23.192	31.443

23. Table 11.39 gives N, the number of transistors per integrated circuit chip, t years after 1970.[26]

  (a) Plot N vs t and fit an exponential curve to the data.
  (b) According to the formula of your curve of best fit, approximately how often does the number of transistors double?

Table 11.39

Chip name	t	N
4004	1	2,300
8008	2	2,500
8080	4	4,500
8086	8	29,000
Intel286	12	134,000
Intel386	15	275,000
Intel486	19	1,200,000
Pentium	23	3,100,000
Pentium II	27	7,500,000
Pentium III	29	9,500,000
Pentium 4	30	42,000,000
Itanium	31	25,000,000
Itanium 2	33	220,000,000
Itanium 2 (9MB cache)	34	592,000,000
Dual Core Itanium	36	1,720,000,000
Xeon 7460	38	1,900,000,000
Xeon 7500	39	2,300,000,000

24. The US export of edible fishery produce, in thousands of metric tons, is shown in Table 11.40.[27] With t in years since 1935, fit the data with a function of the form

  (a) $y = at^b$ **(b)** $y = ab^t$ **(c)** $y = at^2 + bt + c$

  (d) Discuss the reliability for estimating 2010 exports with each function.

Table 11.40

Year	1940	1945	1950	1955	1960	1965	1970
Fish export	66	62	55	50	31	50	73
Year	1975	1980	1985	1990	1995	2000	2005
Fish export	109	275	305	883	929	982	1329

25. The data in Table 11.40 show a big jump in fish exports between 1985 and 1990. This suggests fitting a piecewise defined function. With t in years since 1935, fit a quadratic function to the data from

  (a) 1940 to 1985   **(b)** 1990 to 2005

  (c) Write a piecewise defined function using parts (a) and (b). Graph the function and the data.

26. (a) Using the data in Table 11.25 on page 475, plot $\ln N$ against t. If the original data were exponential, the points would lie on a line.
  (b) Fit a line to the graph from part (a).
  (c) From the equation of the line, obtain the formula for N as an exponential function of t.

27. (a) Let $N = at^p$, with a, p constant. Explain why if you plot $\ln N$ against $\ln t$, you get a line.
  (b) To decide if a function of the form $N = at^p$ fits some data, you plot $\ln N$ against $\ln t$. Explain why this plot is useful.

28. (a) Using the data in Table 11.25 on page 475, plot $\ln N$ against $\ln t$. If a power function fitted the original data, the points would lie on a line.
  (b) Fit a line to the graph from part (a).
  (c) From the equation of the line, obtain the formula for N as a power function of t.

29. According to the US Census Bureau, the 2008 mean income by age is as given in Table 11.41. [28]

  (a) Choose the best type of function to fit the data: linear, exponential, power, or quadratic.
  (b) Using a mid-range age value for each interval, find an equation to fit the data.
  (c) Interpolation estimates incomes for ages within the range of the data. Predict the income of a 37-year-old.
  (d) Extrapolation estimates incomes outside the range of data. Use your function to predict the income of a 10-year-old. Is it reasonable?

Table 11.41

Age	Mean income, dollars
15 to 24	14,268
25 to 34	36,146
35 to 44	47,520
45 to 54	49,570
55 to 64	46,408
65 to 74	33,286
75+ years	24,396

---

[26]The Intel Corporation, www.intel.com/museum/archives/history_docs/mooreslaw.htm, intel.com, www.geek.com.
[27]www.st.nmfs.gov/st1/trade/trade2001.pdf, accessed December 15, 2002 and www.st.nmfs.gov/st1/trade/documents/TRADE2005.pdf, accessed July 25, 2006.
[28]www.census.gov/hhes/www/income/histinc/p10ar.html, accessed November 27, 2009.

30. German physicist Arnd Leike of the University of Munich won the 2002 Ig Nobel prize in Physics for experiments with beer foam conducted with his students.[29] The data in Table 11.42 give the height (in cm) of beer foam after t seconds for three different types of beer, Erdinger Weissbier, Augustinerbräu München, and Budweiser Budvar. The heights are denoted h_e, h_a, and h_b, respectively.

  (a) Plot these points and fit exponential functions to them. Give the equations in the form $h = h_0 e^{-t/\tau}$.

  (b) What does the value of h_0 tell you for each type of beer? What does the value of τ tell you for each type of beer?

Table 11.42

t	h_e	h_a	h_b	t	h_e	h_a	h_b
0	17.0	14.0	14.0	120	10.7	6.0	7.0
15	16.1	11.8	12.1	150	9.7	5.3	6.2
30	14.9	10.5	10.9	180	8.9	4.4	5.5
45	14.0	9.3	10.0	210	8.3	3.5	4.5
60	13.2	8.5	9.3	240	7.5	2.9	3.5
75	12.5	7.7	8.6	300	6.3	1.3	2.0
90	11.9	7.1	8.0	360	5.2	0.7	0.9
105	11.2	6.5	7.5				

31. Table 11.43 gives the development time t (in days) for eggs of the pea weevil (*Bruchus pisorum*) at temperature H (°C).[30]

  (a) Plot these data and fit a power function.

  (b) Ecologists define the development rate $r = 1/t$ where t is the development time. Plot r against H, and fit a linear function.

  (c) At a certain temperature, the value of r drops to 0 and pea weevil eggs will not develop. What is this temperature according to the model from part (a)? Part (b)? Which model's prediction do you think is more reasonable?

Table 11.43

H, °C	10.7	14.4	16.2	18.1	21.4	23.7	24.7	26.9
t, days	38.0	19.5	15.6	9.6	9.5	7.3	4.5	4.5

32. In this problem, we will determine whether or not the compact disc data from Table 5.8 on page 210 can be well modeled using a power function of the form $l = kc^p$, where l and c give the number of LPs and CDs (in millions) respectively, and where k and p are constant.

  (a) Based on the plot of the data in Figure 5.24 on page 210, what do you expect to be true about the sign of the power p?

  (b) Fit a power function to the data. One data point may have to be omitted. Which point and why?

  (c) Let $y = \ln l$ and $x = \ln c$. Find a linear formula for y in terms of x by making substitutions in the equation $l = kc^p$.

  (d) Transform the data in Table 5.8 to create a table comparing $x = \ln c$ and $y = \ln l$. What data point must be omitted?

  (e) Plot your transformed data from part (d). Based on your plot, do you think a power function gives a good fit to the data? Explain.

33. In 1619, Kepler published his third law, which relates D, the distance of a planet from the Sun, to P, the period of the planet—the time it takes for the planet to orbit the Sun. Kepler conjectured that $P = kD^{3/2}$, where k is a constant that he determined empirically from experimental data. Table 11.44 represents modern observational data. Does this model fit the data? What is your estimate for k? What is the final form of Kepler's law?

Table 11.44 *The period and distance of a planet from the Sun*

Planet	Distance (kms $\times 10^6$)	Period (days)
Mercury	57.9	88
Venus	108.2	225
Earth	149.6	365
Mars	227.9	687
Jupiter	778.3	4329
Saturn	1427.0	10753
Uranus	2870.0	30660
Neptune	4497.0	60150
Pluto	5900.0	90670

---

[29]http://ignobel.com/ig/ig-pastwinners.html. The Ig Nobel prize is a spoof of the Nobel prize and honors researchers whose achievements "cannot or should not be reproduced." The data here is taken from *Demonstration of the Exponential Decay Law Using Beer Froth*, Arnd Leike, *European Journal of Physics*, vol. 23, January 2002, pp. 21-26.

[30]From website created by A. Sharov, http://www.ento.vt.edu/˜sharov/PopEcol/lec8/quest8.html, accessed November, 2001. The site attributes the data to Smith, A. M., 1992, *Environ. Entomol.* 21:314-321.

CHAPTER SUMMARY

- **Proportionality**
  Direct and indirect.
- **Power Functions**
  $y = kx^p$.
- **Polynomials**
  General formula:

  $$p(x) = a_n x^n + a_{n-1} x^{n-1} + \cdots + a_1 x + a_0$$

  All terms have non-negative, integer exponents. Leading term $a_n x^n$; coefficients $a_0, \ldots, a_n$; degree n.
  Long-run behavior: Like $y = a_n x^n$.
  Short-run behavior: Zeros corresponding to each factor; multiple zeros.

- **Rational Functions**
  Ratio of polynomials: $r(x) = \dfrac{p(x)}{q(x)}$.
  Long-run behavior: Horizontal asymptote of $r(x)$:
    Given by ratio of highest-degree terms.
  Short-run behavior: Vertical asymptote of $r(x)$:
    At zeros of $q(x)$ (if $p(x) \neq 0$).
  Short-run behavior: Zeros of $r(x)$:
    At zeros of $p(x)$ (if $q(x) \neq 0$).
  Using limits to understand short- and long-run behavior.
- **Comparing Functions**
  Exponential functions eventually dominate power functions. Power functions eventually dominate logs.
- **Fitting Exponentials and Polynomials to Data**

REVIEW EXERCISES AND PROBLEMS FOR CHAPTER ELEVEN

Exercises

In Exercises 1–4, does the function represent proportionality to a power of the independent variable? That is, can the function be written in the form $y = kx^p$ for the variables given in the problem? If so, identify the constant, k, and the power, p.

1. $y = \dfrac{\frac{1}{3}}{2x^7}$

2. $y = \dfrac{6}{-2/x^5}$

3. $z = 5(3)^x$

4. $C = 2q^3 - 5$

In Exercises 5–8, is y a power function of x? If so, write it in the form $y = kx^p$.

5. $y = 6x^3 + 2$

6. $3y = 9x^2$

7. $y - 9 = (x+3)(x-3)$

8. $y = 4(x-2)(x+2)+16$

Does the power function in Exercises 9–14 appear to have an odd power, an even power, or a power between 0 and 1?

9.

10.

11.

12.

13.

14.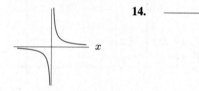

15. State the values of k and p if $r(x) = 2\sqrt[3]{7x}\sqrt[5]{x^2}$ is written in the form kx^p.

16. Find a possible formula for the power function $f(t)$ given that $f(3) = 5$ and $f(5) = 3$.

17. Show that the function $y = (x^2 - 4)(x^2 - 2x - 3)$ is a polynomial. What is its degree?

Describe in words the long-run behavior as $x \to \infty$ of the functions in Exercises 18–21. What power function does each resemble?

18. $y = 16x^3 - 4023x^2 - 2$

19. $y = 4x^4 - 2x^2 + 3$

20. $y = 5x^2/x^{3/2} + 2$

21. $y = 3x^3 + 2x^2/x^{-7} - 7x^5 + 2$

In Exercises 22–23, find the zeros of the functions.

22. $y = 3x^5 + 7x + 1$ **23.** $y = 2x^2 - 3x - 3$

Are the functions in Exercises 24–25 rational functions? If so, write them in the form $p(x)/q(x)$, the ratio of polynomials.

24. $f(x) = \dfrac{x^2}{x-3} - \dfrac{5}{x-3}$ **25.** $f(x) = \dfrac{x^2 + 4}{e^x}$

In Exercises 26–27, which function dominates as $x \to \infty$?

26. $y = 12x^3,\quad y = 7/x^{-4}$

27. $y = 4/e^{-x},\quad y = 17x^{43}$

28. Find

(a) $\displaystyle\lim_{x \to \infty} \frac{x(x^2 - 4)}{5 + 5x^3}$ (b) $\displaystyle\lim_{x \to -\infty} \frac{3x(x-1)(x-2)}{5 - 6x^4}$

29. Find

(a) $\displaystyle\lim_{x \to \infty} \frac{2x + 1}{x - 5}$ (b) $\displaystyle\lim_{x \to -\infty} \frac{2 + 5x}{6x + 3}$

30. For each of the following functions, state whether it is even, odd, or neither.

(a) $f(x) = x^2 + 3$ (b) $g(x) = x^3 + 3$

(c) $h(x) = 5/x$ (d) $j(x) = |x - 4|$

(e) $k(x) = \log x$ (f) $l(x) = \log(x^2)$

(g) $m(x) = 2^x + 2$ (h) $n(x) = \cos x + 2$

Problems

31. It is claimed that Figure 11.63 is the graph of a power function kx^p. If it is, estimate k and p. If it is not, explain why.

Figure 11.63

32. (a) One of the graphs in Figure 11.64 is $y = x^n$ and the other is $y = x^{1/n}$, where n is a positive integer. Which is which? How do you know?

(b) What are the coordinates of point A?

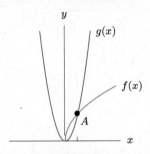

Figure 11.64

33. Without a calculator, match each graph (i)–(iv) with a function in Table 11.45.

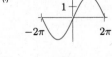

Table 11.45

(A) $y = 0.5\sin(2x)$	(J) $y = 2\sin(0.5x)$
(B) $y = -\ln x$	(K) $y = \ln(x - 1)$
(C) $y = 10(0.6)^x$	(L) $y = 2e^{-0.2x}$
(D) $y = 2\sin(2x)$	(M) $y = 1/(x - 6)$
(E) $y = \ln(-x)$	(N) $y = (x - 2)/(x^2 - 9)$
(F) $y = -15(3.1)^x$	(O) $y = 1/(x^2 - 4)$
(G) $y = 0.5\sin(0.5x)$	(P) $y = x/(x - 3)$
(H) $y = \ln(x + 1)$	(Q) $y = (x - 1)/(x + 3)$
(I) $y = 7(2.5)^x$	(R) $y = 1/(x^2 + 4)$

34. Without a calculator, match each graph (i)–(viii) with a function in Table 11.46.

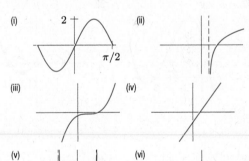

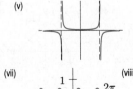

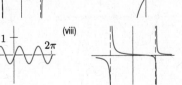

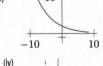

Table 11.46

(A) $y = 0.5\sin(2x)$	(M) $y = (x+3)/(x^2-4)$
(B) $y = 2\sin(2x)$	(N) $y = (x^2-4)/(x^2-1)$
(C) $y = 0.5\sin(0.5x)$	(O) $y = (x+1)^3 - 1$
(D) $y = 2\sin(0.5x)$	(P) $y = -2x - 4$
(E) $y = (x-2)/(x^2-9)$	(Q) $y = 3e^{-x}$
(F) $y = (x-3)/(x^2-1)$	(R) $y = -3e^x$
(G) $y = (x-1)^3 - 1$	(S) $y = -3e^{-x}$
(H) $y = 2x - 4$	(T) $y = 3e^{-x^2}$
(I) $y = -\ln x$	(U) $y = 1/(4-x^2)$
(J) $y = \ln(-x)$	(V) $y = 1/(x^2+4)$
(K) $y = \ln(x+1)$	(W) $y = (x+1)^3 + 1$
(L) $y = \ln(x-1)$	(X) $y = 2(x+2)$

41.
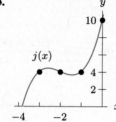

42.
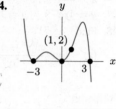

43.
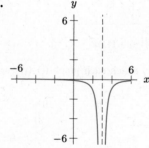

44.
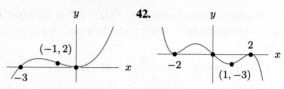

Find possible polynomial formulas in Problems 35–44.

35.
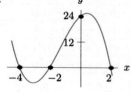

36.
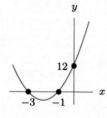

37.
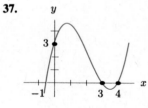

38.
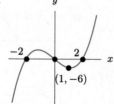

39.
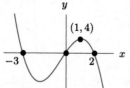

40.
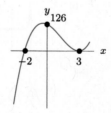

Problems 45–47 show a transformation of $y = 1/x^2$.

(a) Find a formula for the graph.

(b) Write the formula from part (a) as the ratio of two polynomials.

(c) Find the coordinates of any intercepts of the graph.

45.

46.

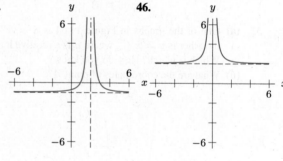

47.

48. Suppose that $g(2) = 24$ and $g(4) = 96$. Find a formula for g, assuming g is:

   (a) A power function.
   (b) A linear function.
   (c) An exponential function.

49. Let $f(x) = x^2 + 5x + 6$ and $g(x) = x^2 + 1$.

   (a) What are the zeros of f and g?
   (b) Let $r(x) = f(x)/g(x)$. Graph r. Does r have zeros? Vertical asymptotes? What is its long-run behavior as $x \to \pm\infty$?
   (c) Let $s(x) = g(x)/f(x)$. If you graph s in the window $-10 \le x \le 10$, $-10 \le y \le 10$, it appears to have a zero near the origin. Does it? Does s have a vertical asymptote? What is its long-run behavior?

50. Let $f(x) = (x-3)^2$, $g(x) = x^2 - 4$, $h(x) = x+1$, and $j(x) = x^2 + 1$. Without a calculator, match the functions described in (a)–(f) to the functions in (i)–(vi). Some of the descriptions may have no matching function or more than one matching function.

   (i) $p(x) = \dfrac{f(x)}{g(x)}$ (ii) $q(x) = \dfrac{h(x)}{g(x)}$

   (iii) $r(x) = f(x)h(x)$ (iv) $s(x) = \dfrac{g(x)}{j(x)}$

   (v) $t(x) = \dfrac{1}{h(x)}$ (vi) $v(x) = \dfrac{j(x)}{f(x)}$

   (a) Two zeros, no vertical asymptotes, and a horizontal asymptote.
   (b) Two zeros, no vertical asymptote, and no horizontal asymptote.
   (c) One zero, one vertical asymptote, and a horizontal asymptote.
   (d) One zero, two vertical asymptotes, and a horizontal asymptote.
   (e) No zeros, one vertical asymptote, and a horizontal asymptote at $y = 1$.
   (f) No zeros, one vertical asymptote, and a horizontal asymptote at $y = 0$.

51. Suppose f is a polynomial function of degree n, where n is a positive even integer. For each of the following statements, write *true* if the statement is always true, *false* otherwise. If the statement is false, give an example that illustrates why it is false.

   (a) f is an even function.
   (b) f has an inverse.
   (c) f cannot be an odd function.
   (d) If $f(x) \to +\infty$ as $x \to +\infty$, then $f(x) \to -\infty$ as $x \to -\infty$.

52. **(a)** Sketch a graph of $f(x) = x^4 - 17x^2 + 36x - 20$ for $-10 \le x \le 10$, $-10 \le y \le 10$.
   (b) Your graph should appear to have a vertical asymptote at $x = -5$. Does f actually have a vertical asymptote here? Explain.
   (c) How many zeros does f have? Can you find a window in which all of the zeros of f are clearly visible?
   (d) Write the formula of f in factored form.
   (e) How many turning points does the graph of f have? Can you find a window in which all the turning points of f are clearly visible? Explain.

In Problems 53–56, find a possible formula for the rational functions.

53. This function has zeros at $x = -3$ and $x = 2$, and vertical asymptotes at $x = -5$ and $x = 7$. It has a horizontal asymptote of $y = 1$.

54. The graph of $y = f(x)$ has one vertical asymptote, at $x = -1$, and a horizontal asymptote at $y = 1$. The graph of f crosses the y-axis at $y = 3$ and crosses the x-axis once, at $x = -3$.

55.

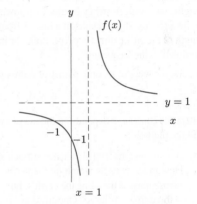

56.

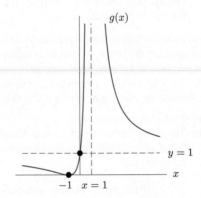

Find possible formulas for the polynomials and rational functions in Problems 57–60.

57. The zeros of f are $x = -3$, $x = 2$, and $x = 5$, and the y-intercept is $y = -6$.

58. This function has zeros at $x = -3$, $x = 2$, $x = 5$, and a double zero at $x = 6$. It has a y-intercept of 7.

59. The polynomial $h(x) = 7$ at $x = -5, -1, 4$, and the y-intercept is 3. [Hint: Visualize h as a vertically shifted version of another polynomial.]

60. The graph of w intercepts the graph of $v(x) = 2x + 5$ at $x = -4, 1, 3$ and has a y-intercept of 2. [Hint: Let $w(x) = p(x) + v(x)$ where p is another polynomial.]

61. On a map, $1/2$ inch represents 5 miles. Is the map distance between two locations directly or inversely proportional to the actual distance that separates the two locations? Explain your reasoning and write a formula for the proportion. How far apart are two towns if the distance between these two towns on the map is 3.25 inches?

62. When a guitar string is plucked, the frequency of the note produced can be adjusted by varying the length of the string. The frequency is inversely proportional to the length, so a longer string results in a lower frequency, while a shorter string results in a higher frequency. Is the length of the string directly proportional or inversely proportional to the frequency?

63. A person's weight, w, on a planet of radius d is given by

$$w = kd^{-2}, \quad k > 0,$$

where the constant k depends on the masses of the person and the planet.

(a) A man weighs 180 lb on the surface of the earth. How much does he weigh on the surface of a planet whose mass is the same the earth's, but whose radius is three times as large? One-third as large?

(b) What fraction of the earth's radius must an equally massive planet have if, on this planet, the weight of the man in part (a) is one ton?

64. One of Kepler's three laws of planetary motion states that the square of the period, P, of a body orbiting the sun is proportional to the cube of its average distance, d, from the sun. The earth has a period of 365 days and its distance from the sun is approximately 93,000,000 miles.

(a) Find P as a function of d.

(b) The planet Jupiter has an average distance from the sun of 483,000,000 miles. How long in earth days is a Jupiter year?

65. The town of Smallsville was founded in 1900. Its population y (in hundreds) is given by the equation

$$y = -0.1x^4 + 1.7x^3 - 9x^2 + 14.4x + 5,$$

where x is the number of years since 1900. Use a the graph in the window $0 \leq x \leq 10$, $-2 \leq y \leq 13$.

(a) What was the population of Smallsville when it was founded?

(b) When did Smallsville become a ghost town (nobody lived there anymore)? Give the year and the month.

(c) What was the largest population of Smallsville after 1905? When did Smallsville reach that population? Again, include the month and year. Explain your method.

66. Let $C(x)$ be a firm's total cost, in millions of dollars, for producing a quantity of x thousand units of an item.

(a) Graph $C(x) = (x - 1)^3 + 1$.

(b) Let $R(x)$ be the revenue to the firm (in millions of dollars) for selling a quantity x thousand units of the good. Suppose $R(x) = x$. What does this tell you about the price of each unit?

(c) Profit equals revenue minus cost. For what values of x does the firm make a profit? Break even? Lose money?

67. Allometry is the study of the relative size of different parts of a body as a consequence of growth.[31] The simplest model of allometry is one in which it is assumed that the sizes of two parts x and y are related by a power law of the form

$$y = kx^p,$$

where k and p are positive constants. This equation is often called the *allometric equation*.

(a) Let x be the length of a fish and y be its weight. If L is a typical unit of length, then L^3 is a typical unit of volume. Show that the assumptions that the length x of a fish is proportional to L, and that its weight y is proportional to its volume and therefore to L^3, lead to the equation $y = kx^3$.

(b) Table 11.47 relates the weight y of plaice[32] to its length x. (Plaice is a type of fish.) If $y = kx^3$, what do you expect to happen if you calculate x^3/y for each of the entries in the table? Do this, and estimate the proportionality constant, k.

(c) With this choice of k, plot the function $y = kx^3$ and the data in Table 11.47. Is the function a reasonable model?

---

[31] J. S. Huxley, *Problems of Relative Growth* (Dover, 1972).

[32] Adapted from R. J. H. Beverton and S. J. Holt, "On the Dynamics of Exploited Fish Populations," *Fishery Investigations*, Series II, 19, 1957.

Table 11.47

Length (cm)	33.5	34.5	35.5	36.5	37.5	38.5
Weight (gm)	332	363	391	419	455	500
Length (cm)	39.5	40.5	41.5	42.5	43.5	
Weight (gm)	538	574	623	674	724	

68. The thrust, T, delivered by a ship's propeller is proportional[33] to the square of the propeller rotation speed, R, times the fourth power of the propeller diameter, D.

(a) Write a formula for T in terms of R and D.
(b) What happens to the thrust if the propeller speed is doubled?
(c) What happens to the thrust if the propeller diameter is doubled?
(d) If the propeller diameter is increased by 50%, by how much can the propeller speed be reduced to deliver the same thrust?

69. A function that is not a polynomial can often be approximated by a polynomial. For example, for certain x-values, the function $f(x) = e^x$ can be approximated by the fifth-degree polynomial

$$p(x) = 1 + x + \frac{x^2}{2} + \frac{x^3}{6} + \frac{x^4}{24} + \frac{x^5}{120}.$$

(a) Show that $p(1) \approx f(1) = e$. How good is the estimate?
(b) Calculate $p(5)$. How well does $p(5)$ approximate $f(5)$?

(c) Graph $p(x)$ and $f(x)$ together on the same set of axes. Based on your graph, for what range of values of x does $p(x)$ give a good estimate for $f(x)$?

70. The resolution, $r\%$, of a gamma ray telescope depends on the energy v (in millions of electron volts, or MeVs) of the detected gamma rays.[34] The smaller the value of r, the better the telescope is at distinguishing two gamma ray photons of slightly different energies, and the more detailed observations that can be made. Table 11.48 gives values of r for gamma rays at different energies.

(a) Plot the data in Table 11.48, with r on the vertical axis.
(b) Based on this data, is the telescope better able to distinguish between high-energy photons or low-energy photons?
(c) Fit both power and exponential functions to the data, and give their formulas. Which appears to give the better fit?
(d) The telescope is predicted to grow rapidly worse and worse at distinguishing photons as the energy level drops toward 0 MeV. Which curve, power or exponential, is most consistent with this prediction?

Table 11.48

v, MeV	0.5	0.7	0.9	1.3	1.8	4.0	4.4
r, %	16.0	13.5	12.0	8.5	7.0	4.5	4.0

CHECK YOUR UNDERSTANDING

Are the statements in Problems 1–47 true or false? Give an explanation for your answer.

1. All quadratic functions are power functions.
2. The function $y = 3 \cdot 2^x$ is a power function.
3. Let $g(x) = x^p$. If p is a positive, even integer, then the graph of g passes through the point $(-1, 1)$.
4. Let $g(x) = x^p$. If p is a positive, even integer, then the graph of g is symmetric about the y-axis.
5. Let $g(x) = x^p$. If p is a positive, even integer, then the graph of g is concave up.
6. The graph of $f(x) = x^{-1}$ passes through the origin.
7. The graph of $f(x) = x^{-2}$ has the x-axis as its only asymptote.

8. If $f(x) = x^{-1}$ then $f(x)$ approaches $+\infty$ as x approaches zero.
9. As x grows very large, the values of $f(x) = x^{-1}$ approach zero.
10. The function 2^x eventually grows faster than x^b for any b.
11. The function $f(x) = x^{0.5}$ eventually grows faster than $g(x) = \ln x$.
12. We have $2^x \geq x^2$ on the interval $0 \leq x \leq 4$.
13. The function $f(x) = x^{-3}$ approaches the x-axis faster than $g(x) = e^{-x}$ as x grows very large.

[33]Thomas C. Gillner, *Modern Ship Design* (US Naval Institute Press, 1972).
[34]E. Aprile, et al., *The LXeGRIT Compton Status and Future Prospects*, posted at http://arxiv.org as arXiv:astro-ph/0212005v2, accessed December 4, 2002.

14. The function $f(x) = 3^x$ is an example of a power function.

15. The function $y = 3x$ is an example of a power function.

16. Every quadratic function is a polynomial function.

17. The power of the first term of a polynomial is its degree.

18. Far from the origin, the graph of a polynomial looks like the graph of its highest-power term.

19. A zero of a polynomial p is the value $p(0)$.

20. The zeros of a polynomial are the x-coordinates where its graph intersects the x-axis.

21. The y-intercept of a polynomial $y = p(x)$ can be found by evaluating $p(0)$.

22. For very large x-values $f(x) = 1000x^3 + 345x^2 + 17x + 394$ is less than $g(x) = 0.01x^4$.

23. If $y = f(x)$ is a polynomial of degree n, where n is a positive even number, then f has an inverse.

24. If $y = f(x)$ is a polynomial of degree n, where n is a positive odd number, then f has an inverse.

25. If $p(x)$ is a polynomial and $x - a$ is a factor of p, then $x = a$ is a zero of p.

26. A polynomial of degree n cannot have more than n zeros.

27. The polynomial in Figure 11.65 has a multiple zero at $x = -2$.

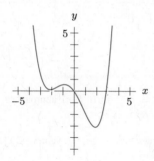

Figure 11.65

28. The polynomial in Figure 11.65 has a multiple zero at $x = 0$.

29. A rational function is the quotient of two polynomials. We assume the denominator is not equal to zero.

30. The function $f(x) = \dfrac{1}{x}$ is a rational function.

31. In order to determine the long-run behavior of a rational function, it is sufficient to consider only the ratio of the highest-power term in the numerator to the highest-power term in the denominator.

32. As x grows through large positive values, $y = \dfrac{x + 18}{x + 9}$ approaches $y = 2$.

33. As x grows through large positive values, $y = \dfrac{2x + 125}{x^2 - 1}$ approaches $y = 0$.

34. As x grows through large positive values, $y = \dfrac{x^3 + 4x^2 - 16x + 12}{4x^3 - 16x + 1}$ has an asymptote at $y = 4$.

35. As x grows through large positive values, $y = \dfrac{1 - 4x^2}{x^2 + 1}$ approaches $y = 0$.

36. As x grows through large positive values, $y = \dfrac{5x}{x + 1}$ approaches $y = -5$.

37. As x grows through large positive values, $y = \dfrac{3x^4 - 6x^3 + 10x^2 - 16x + 7}{-3x + x^2}$ behaves like $y = -x^3$.

38. As x decreases through large negative values, $f(x) = \dfrac{x^3 - 7x^2 + 28x + 76}{-x^2 - 101x + 72}$ approaches positive infinity.

39. A fraction is equal to zero if and only if its numerator equals zero and its denominator does not.

40. The zeros of a function $y = f(x)$ are the values of x that make $y = 0$.

41. The function $f(x) = \dfrac{x + 4}{x - 3}$ has a zero at $x = -4$.

42. The rational function $y = \dfrac{x + 2}{x^2 - 4}$ has a zero at $x = -2$.

43. The rational function $g(w) = \dfrac{12}{(w - 2)(w + 3)}$ has exactly two zeros.

44. If $p(x)$ and $q(x)$ have no zeros in common, then the rational function $r(x) = \dfrac{p(x)}{q(x)}$ has an asymptote at each of the zeros of $p(x)$.

45. In general, the rational function $r(x) = \dfrac{p(x)}{q(x)}$ must have at least one zero.

46. Rational functions can never cross an asymptote.

47. The rational function $g(w) = \dfrac{3w - 3}{(w - 12)(w + 4)}$ has a vertical asymptote at $w = 1$.

SKILLS REFRESHER FOR CHAPTER 11: ALGEBRAIC FRACTIONS

Algebraic fractions are combined in the same way as numeric fractions according to the following rules:

Add numerators when denominators are equal: $\dfrac{a}{c} + \dfrac{b}{c} = \dfrac{a+b}{c}$

Find a common denominator: $\dfrac{a}{b} + \dfrac{c}{d} = \dfrac{a \cdot d}{b \cdot d} + \dfrac{b \cdot c}{b \cdot d} = \dfrac{ad + bc}{bd}$

Multiply numerators and denominators for a product: $\dfrac{a}{b} \cdot \dfrac{c}{d} = \dfrac{ac}{bd}$

To divide by a fraction, multiply by its reciprocal: $\dfrac{a/b}{c/d} = \dfrac{a}{b} \cdot \dfrac{d}{c} = \dfrac{ad}{bc}$

The sign of a fraction is changed by changing the sign of the numerator or the denominator (but not both):

$$-\dfrac{a}{b} = \dfrac{-a}{b} = \dfrac{a}{-b}$$

We assume that no denominators are zero, since we cannot divide by zero; that is, $a/0$ is not defined.

We can simplify a fraction in which either the numerator or denominator is itself a fraction as follows:

$$\frac{a/b}{c} = \frac{a/b}{c/1} = \frac{a}{b} \cdot \frac{1}{c} = \frac{a}{bc} \quad \text{and} \quad \frac{a}{b/c} = \frac{a/1}{b/c} = \frac{a}{1} \cdot \frac{c}{b} = \frac{ac}{b}.$$

Example 1 Perform the indicated operations and express the answers as a single fraction.

(a) $\dfrac{4}{x^2 + 1} - \dfrac{1-x}{x^2+1}$

(b) $\dfrac{M}{M^2 - 2M - 3} + \dfrac{1}{M^2 - 2M - 3}$

(c) $\dfrac{-H^2 P}{17} \cdot \dfrac{\left(PH^{1/3}\right)^2}{K^{-1}}$

(d) $\dfrac{2z/w}{w(w - 3z)}$

Solution (a) $\dfrac{4}{x^2+1} - \dfrac{1-x}{x^2+1} = \dfrac{4 - (1-x)}{x^2+1} = \dfrac{3+x}{x^2+1}$

(b) $\dfrac{M}{M^2 - 2M - 3} + \dfrac{1}{M^2 - 2M - 3} = \dfrac{M+1}{(M^2 - 2M - 3)} = \dfrac{M+1}{(M+1)(M-3)} = \dfrac{1}{M-3}$ if $M \neq -1$.

(c) $\dfrac{-H^2 P}{17} \cdot \dfrac{\left(PH^{1/3}\right)^2}{K^{-1}} = \dfrac{-H^2 P \left(P^2 H^{2/3}\right)}{17 K^{-1}} = -\dfrac{H^{8/3} P^3 K}{17}$

(d) $\dfrac{2z/w}{w(w - 3z)} = \dfrac{2z}{w} \cdot \dfrac{1}{w(w - 3z)} = \dfrac{2z}{w^2(w - 3z)}$

Example 2 Simplify the following expressions, giving your answer as a single fraction.

(a) $2x^{-1/2} + \dfrac{\sqrt{x}}{3}$

(b) $2\sqrt{t + 3} + \dfrac{1 - 2t}{\sqrt{t + 3}}$

Solution

(a) $2x^{-1/2} + \dfrac{\sqrt{x}}{3} = \dfrac{2}{\sqrt{x}} + \dfrac{\sqrt{x}}{3} = \dfrac{2\cdot 3 + \sqrt{x}\sqrt{x}}{3\sqrt{x}} = \dfrac{6+x}{3\sqrt{x}} = \dfrac{6+x}{3x^{1/2}}.$

(b) $2\sqrt{t+3} + \dfrac{1-2t}{\sqrt{t+3}} = \dfrac{2\sqrt{t+3}}{1} + \dfrac{1-2t}{\sqrt{t+3}}$

$\qquad\qquad\qquad\quad = \dfrac{2\sqrt{t+3}\sqrt{t+3} + 1 - 2t}{\sqrt{t+3}}$

$\qquad\qquad\qquad\quad = \dfrac{2(t+3) + 1 - 2t}{\sqrt{t+3}}$

$\qquad\qquad\qquad\quad = \dfrac{7}{\sqrt{t+3}} = \dfrac{7}{(t+3)^{1/2}}.$

Finding a Common Denominator

We can multiply (or divide) both the numerator and denominator of a fraction by the same nonzero number without changing the fraction's value. This is equivalent to multiplying by a factor of $+1$. We are using this rule when we add or subtract fractions with different denominators. For example, to add $\dfrac{x}{3a} + \dfrac{1}{a}$, we multiply $\dfrac{1}{a}\cdot\dfrac{3}{3} = \dfrac{3}{3a}$. Then

$$\frac{x}{3a} + \frac{1}{a} = \frac{x}{3a} + \frac{3}{3a} = \frac{x+3}{3a}.$$

Example 3   Perform the indicated operations:

(a) $3 - \dfrac{1}{x-1}$

(b) $\dfrac{2}{x^2 + x} + \dfrac{x}{x+1}$

Solution

(a) $3 - \dfrac{1}{x-1} = 3\dfrac{(x-1)}{(x-1)} - \dfrac{1}{x-1} = \dfrac{3(x-1) - 1}{x-1} = \dfrac{3x - 3 - 1}{x-1} = \dfrac{3x-4}{x-1}$

(b) $\dfrac{2}{x^2+x} + \dfrac{x}{x+1} = \dfrac{2}{x(x+1)} + \dfrac{x}{x+1} = \dfrac{2}{x(x+1)} + \dfrac{x(x)}{(x+1)(x)} = \dfrac{2+x^2}{x(x+1)}.$

Note: We can multiply (or divide) the numerator and denominator by the same nonzero number because this is the same as multiplying by a factor of $+1$, and multiplying by a factor of 1 does not change the value of the expression. However, we cannot perform any other operation that would change the value of the expression. For example, we cannot add the same number to the numerator and denominator of a fraction nor can we square both, take the logarithm of both, etc., without changing the fraction.

Reducing Fractions: Canceling

We can reduce a fraction when we have the same (nonzero) factor in both the numerator and the denominator. For example,

$$\frac{ac}{bc} = \frac{a}{b}\cdot\frac{c}{c} = \frac{a}{b}\cdot 1 = \frac{a}{b}.$$

Example 4   Reduce the following fractions (if possible).

(a) $\dfrac{2x}{4y}$

(b) $\dfrac{2+x}{2+y}$

(c) $\dfrac{5n-5}{1-n}$

(d) $\dfrac{x^2(4-2x)-(4x-x^2)2x}{x^4}$

Solution

(a) $\dfrac{2x}{4y} = \dfrac{2}{2} \cdot \dfrac{x}{2y} = \dfrac{x}{2y}$

(b) $\dfrac{2+x}{2+y}$ cannot be reduced further.

(c) $\dfrac{5n-5}{1-n} = \dfrac{5(n-1)}{(-1)(n-1)} = -5$

(d)

$$\frac{x^2(4-2x)-\left(4x-x^2\right)2x}{x^4} = \frac{x^2(4-2x)-(4-x)2x^2}{x^4}$$

$$= \frac{(4-2x)-2(4-x)}{x^2}\left(\frac{x^2}{x^2}\right)$$

$$= \frac{4-2x-8+2x}{x^2} = \frac{-4}{x^2}.$$

Complex Fractions

A *complex fraction* is a fraction whose numerator or denominator (or both) contains one or more fractions. To simplify a complex fraction, we change the numerator and denominator to single fractions and then divide.

Example 5   Write the following as simple fractions in reduced form.

(a) $\dfrac{\dfrac{1}{x+h} - \dfrac{1}{x}}{h}$

(b) $\dfrac{a+b}{a^{-2}-b^{-2}}$

Solution

(a) $\dfrac{\dfrac{1}{x+h} - \dfrac{1}{x}}{h} = \dfrac{\dfrac{x-(x+h)}{x(x+h)}}{h} = \dfrac{\dfrac{-h}{x(x+h)}}{\dfrac{h}{1}} = \dfrac{-h}{x(x+h)} \cdot \dfrac{1}{h} = \dfrac{-1}{x(x+h)} \dfrac{(h)}{(h)} = \dfrac{-1}{x(x+h)}$

(b) $\dfrac{a+b}{a^{-2}-b^{-2}} = \dfrac{a+b}{\dfrac{1}{a^2} - \dfrac{1}{b^2}} = \dfrac{a+b}{\dfrac{b^2-a^2}{a^2b^2}} = \dfrac{a+b}{1} \cdot \dfrac{a^2b^2}{b^2-a^2} = \dfrac{(a+b)(a^2b^2)}{(b+a)(b-a)} = \dfrac{a^2b^2}{b-a}$

Splitting Expressions

We can reverse the rule for adding fractions to split up an expression into two fractions,

$$\frac{a+b}{c} = \frac{a}{c} + \frac{b}{c}.$$

Example 6   Split $\dfrac{3x^2 + 2}{x^3}$ into two reduced fractions.

Solution $\dfrac{3x^2 + 2}{x^3} = \dfrac{3x^2}{x^3} + \dfrac{2}{x^3} = \dfrac{3}{x} + \dfrac{2}{x^3}$

Sometimes we can alter the form of the fraction even further if we can create a duplicate of the denominator within the numerator. This technique is useful when graphing some rational functions. For example, we may rewrite the fraction $\dfrac{x+3}{x-1}$ by creating a factor of $(x-1)$ within the numerator. To do this, we write

$$\frac{x+3}{x-1} = \frac{x-1+1+3}{x-1}$$

which can be written as

$$\frac{(x-1)+4}{x-1}.$$

Then, splitting this fraction, we have

$$\frac{x+3}{x-1} = \frac{x-1}{x-1} + \frac{4}{x-1} = 1 + \frac{4}{x-1}.$$

Note: It is not possible to split a sum that occurs in the denominator of a fraction. For example,

$$\frac{a}{b+c} \text{ does not equal } \frac{a}{b} + \frac{a}{c}.$$

Exercises to Skills Review for Chapter 11

For Exercises 1–30, perform the operations. Express answers in reduced form.

1. $\dfrac{3}{5} + \dfrac{4}{7}$

2. $\dfrac{7}{10} - \dfrac{2}{15}$

3. $\dfrac{1}{2x} - \dfrac{2}{3}$

4. $\dfrac{6}{7y} + \dfrac{9}{y}$

5. $\dfrac{-2}{yz} + \dfrac{4}{z}$

6. $\dfrac{-2z}{y} + \dfrac{4}{y}$

7. $\dfrac{2}{x^2} - \dfrac{3}{x}$

8. $\dfrac{3/4}{7/20}$

9. $\dfrac{5/6}{15}$

10. $\dfrac{3/x}{x^2/6}$

11. $\dfrac{3/x}{6/x^2}$

12. $\dfrac{14}{x-1} + \dfrac{13}{2x-2}$

13. $\dfrac{4z}{x^2y} - \dfrac{3w}{xy^4}$

14. $\dfrac{10}{y-2} + \dfrac{3}{2-y}$

15. $\dfrac{8y}{y-4} + \dfrac{32}{y-4}$

16. $\dfrac{8y}{y-4} + \dfrac{32}{4-y}$

17. $\dfrac{8}{3x^2 - x - 4} - \dfrac{9}{x+1}$

18. $\dfrac{15}{(x-3)^2(x+5)} + \dfrac{7}{(x-3)(x+5)^2}$

19. $\dfrac{3}{x-4} - \dfrac{2}{x+4}$

20. $\dfrac{x^2}{x-1} - \dfrac{1}{1-x}$

21. $\dfrac{1}{2r+3} + \dfrac{3}{4r^2+6r}$

22. $u + a + \dfrac{u}{u+a}$

23. $\dfrac{1}{\sqrt{x}} - \dfrac{1}{(\sqrt{x})^3}$

24. $\dfrac{1}{e^{2x}} + \dfrac{1}{e^x}$

25. $\dfrac{a+b}{2} \cdot \dfrac{8x+2}{b^2-a^2}$

26. $\dfrac{0.07}{M} + \dfrac{3}{4}M^2$

27. $\dfrac{1}{r_1} + \dfrac{1}{r_2} + \dfrac{1}{r_3}$

28. $\dfrac{8y}{y-4} - \dfrac{32}{y-4}$

29. $\dfrac{a}{a^2 - 9} + \dfrac{1}{a - 3}$

30. $\dfrac{x^3}{x - 4} \bigg/ \dfrac{x^2}{x^2 - 2x - 8}$

In Exercises 31–40, simplify, if possible.

31. $\dfrac{\dfrac{1}{(x+h)^2} - \dfrac{1}{x^2}}{h}$

32. $\dfrac{a^{-2} + b^{-2}}{a^2 + b^2}$

33. $\dfrac{4 - (x+h)^2 - (4 - x^2)}{h}$

34. $\dfrac{b^{-1}(b - b^{-1})}{b + 1}$.

35. $\dfrac{1 - a^{-2}}{1 + a^{-1}}$.

36. $p - \dfrac{q}{\dfrac{p}{q} + \dfrac{q}{p}}$

37. $\dfrac{\dfrac{3}{xy} - \dfrac{5}{x^2 y}}{\dfrac{6x^2 - 7x - 5}{x^4 y^2}}$

38. $\dfrac{\dfrac{1}{x}(3x^2) - (\ln x)(6x)}{(3x^2)^2}$

39. $\dfrac{2x(x^3 + 1)^2 - x^2(2)(x^3 + 1)(3x^2)}{[(x^3 + 1)^2]^2}$

40. $\dfrac{\frac{1}{2}(2x - 1)^{-1/2}(2) - (2x - 1)^{1/2}(2x)}{(x^2)^2}$

In Exercises 41–46, split into a sum or difference of reduced fractions.

41. $\dfrac{26x + 1}{2x^3}$

42. $\dfrac{\sqrt{x} + 3}{3\sqrt{x}}$

43. $\dfrac{6l^2 + 3l - 4}{3l^4}$

44. $\dfrac{7 + p}{p^2 + 11}$

45. $\dfrac{\frac{1}{3}x - \frac{1}{2}}{2x}$

46. $\dfrac{t^{-1/2} + t^{1/2}}{t^2}$

In Exercises 47–52, rewrite in the form $1 + (A/B)$.

47. $\dfrac{x - 2}{x + 5}$

48. $\dfrac{q - 1}{q - 4}$

49. $\dfrac{R + 1}{R}$

50. $\dfrac{3 + 2u}{2u + 1}$

51. $\dfrac{\cos x + \sin x}{\cos x}$

52. $\dfrac{1 + e^x}{e^x}$

Are the statements in Exercises 53–58 true or false?

53. $\dfrac{a + c}{a} = 1 + c$

54. $\dfrac{rs - s}{s} = r - 1$

55. $\dfrac{y}{y + z} = 1 + \dfrac{y}{z}$

56. $\dfrac{2u^2 - w}{u^2 - w} = 2$

57. $\dfrac{x^2 yz}{2x^2 y} = \dfrac{z}{2}$

58. $x^{5/3} - 3x^{2/3} = \dfrac{x^2 - 3x}{x^{1/3}}$

FUNCTIONS MODELING CHANGE:
A Preparation for Calculus

Third Edition

Produced by the Calculus Consortium and initially funded by a National Science Foundation Grant.

Eric Connally
Harvard University Extension

Deborah Hughes-Hallett
University of Arizona

Andrew M. Gleason
Harvard University

Philip Cheifetz
Nassau Community College

Ann Davidian
Gen. Douglas MacArthur HS

Daniel E. Flath
Macalester College

Brigitte Lahme
Sonoma State University

Patti Frazer Lock
St. Lawrence University

Jerry Morris
Sonoma State University

Karen Rhea
University of Michigan

Ellen Schmierer
Nassau Community College

Pat Shure
University of Michigan

Carl Swenson
Seattle University

Katherine Yoshiwara
Los Angeles Pierce College

Elliot J. Marks

with the assistance of
Frank Avenoso
Nassau Community College

John Wiley & Sons, Inc.

Dedicated to Maria, Ben, Jonah, and Isabel

PUBLISHER	Laurie Rosatone
SENIOR ACQUISITIONS EDITOR	Angela Y. Battle
MARKETING MANAGER	Amy Sell
FREELANCE DEVELOPMENTAL EDITOR	Anne Scanlan-Rohrer
SENIOR PRODUCTION EDITOR	Ken Santor
ASSISTANT EDITOR	Shannon Corliss
MARKETING ASSISTANT	Tara Martinho
COVER DESIGNER	Hope Miller
COVER PHOTO	©Scott Berner/Picture Quest

This book was set in Times Roman by the Consortium using TeX, Mathematica, and the package AsTeX, which was written by Alex Kasman. It was printed and bound by Von Hoffmann Press. The cover was printed by Von Hoffmann Press. The process was managed by Elliot Marks.

This material is based upon work supported by the National Science Foundation under Grant No. DUE-9352905. Opinions expressed are those of the authors and not necessarily those of the Foundation.

ISBN-13 978-0-471-79303-8
ISBN-10 0471-79303-5

Printed in the United States of America

10 9 8 7 6 5 4 3 2 1

Chapter Six

TRIGONOMETRIC FUNCTIONS

Blood pressure in the heart, an alternating electric current, the water level in a reservoir, and the phases of the moon all exhibit repeating behavior. Linear and exponential functions do not adequately model these processes. In this chapter, we introduce the *trigonometric* functions, which model such repetitive behavior.

The Tools Section on page 301 reviews right triangle trigonometry.

6.1 INTRODUCTION TO PERIODIC FUNCTIONS

The World's Largest Ferris Wheel

To celebrate the millennium, British Airways funded construction of the "London Eye," the world's largest ferris wheel.[1] The wheel is located on the south bank of the river Thames, in London, England, measures 450 feet in diameter, and carries up to 800 passengers in 32 capsules. It turns continuously, completing a single rotation once every 30 minutes. This is slow enough for people to hop on and off while it turns.

Ferris Wheel Height As a Function of Time

Suppose you hop on this ferris wheel at time $t = 0$ and ride it for two full turns. Let $f(t)$ be your height above the ground, measured in feet as a function of t, the number of minutes you have been riding. We can figure out some values of $f(t)$.

Let's imagine that the wheel is turning in the counterclockwise direction. At time $t = 0$ you have just boarded the wheel, so your height is 0 ft above the ground (not counting the height of your seat). Thus, $f(0) = 0$. Since the wheel turns all the way around once every 30 minutes, after 7.5 minutes the wheel has turned one-quarter of the way around. Thinking of the wheel as a giant clock, this means you have been carried from the 6 o'clock position to the 3 o'clock position, as shown in Figure 6.1. You are now halfway up the wheel, or 225 feet above the ground, so $f(7.5) = 225$.

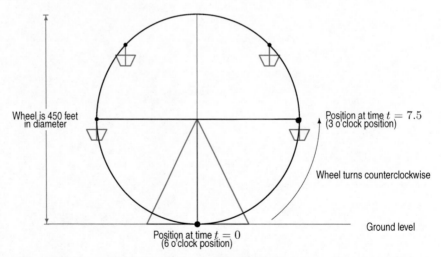

Figure 6.1: The world's largest ferris wheel is 450 ft in diameter and turns around once every 30 minutes. Seats not drawn to scale

After 15 minutes, the wheel has turned halfway around, so you are now at the top, in the 12 o'clock position. Thus, $f(15) = 450$. And after 22.5 minutes, the wheel has turned three quarters of the way around, bringing you into the 9 o'clock position. You have descended from the top of the wheel halfway down to the ground, and you are once again 225 feet above the ground. Thus, $f(22.5) = 225$. (See Figures 6.2 and 6.3.) Finally, after 30 minutes, the wheel has turned all the way around, bringing you back to ground level, so $f(30) = 0$.

---

[1]http://british-airways-london-eye.visit-london-england.com, accessed May 23, 2002.

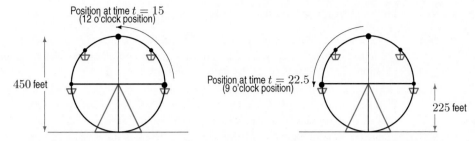

Figure 6.2: At time $t = 15$, the wheel has turned halfway around

Figure 6.3: At time $t = 22.5$, the wheel has turned three quarters of the way around

The Second Time Around On the Wheel

Since the wheel turns without stopping, at time $t = 30$ it begins its second turn. Thus, at time $t = 37.5$, the wheel has again turned one quarter of the way around, and $f(37.5) = 225$. Similarly, at time $t = 45$ the wheel has again turned halfway around, bringing you back up to the very top. Likewise, at time $t = 52.5$, the wheel has carried you halfway back down to the ground. This means that $f(45) = 450$ and $f(52.5) = 225$. Finally, at time $t = 60$, the wheel has completed its second full turn and you are back at ground level, so $f(60) = 0$.

Table 6.1 *Values of $f(t)$, your height above the ground t minutes after boarding the wheel*

t (minutes)	0	7.5	15	22.5	30	37.5	45	52.5	
$f(t)$ (feet)	0	225	450	225	0	225	450	225	
t (minutes)	60	67.5	75	82.5	90	97.5	105	112.5	120
$f(t)$ (feet)	0	225	450	225	0	225	450	225	0

Repeating Values of the Ferris Wheel Function

Notice that the values of $f(t)$ in Table 6.1 begin repeating after 30 minutes. This is because the second turn is just like the first turn, except that it happens 30 minutes later. If you ride the wheel for more full turns, the values of $f(t)$ continue to repeat at 30-minute intervals.

Graphing the Ferris Wheel Function

The data from Table 6.1 are plotted in Figure 6.4. The graph begins at $y = 0$ (ground level), rises to $y = 225$ (halfway up the wheel) and then to $y = 450$ (the top of the wheel). The graph then falls to $y = 225$ and then down to $y = 0$. This cycle then repeats itself three more times, once for each rotation of the wheel.

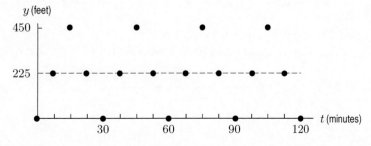

Figure 6.4: Values of $f(t)$, the ferris wheel height function, at 7.5 minute intervals

Filling in the Graph of the Ferris Wheel Function

It is tempting to connect the points in Figure 6.4 with straight lines, but this is not correct. Consider the first 7.5 minutes of your ride, starting at the 6 o'clock position and ending at the 3 o'clock position. (See Figure 6.5). Halfway through this part of the ride, the wheel has turned halfway from the 6 o'clock to the 3 o'clock position. However, as is clear from Figure 6.5, your seat rises less than half the vertical distance from $y = 0$ to $y = 225$. At the same time, the seat glides more than half the horizontal distance. If the points in Figure 6.4 were connected with straight lines, $f(3.75)$ would be halfway between $f(0)$ and $f(7.5)$, which is incorrect.

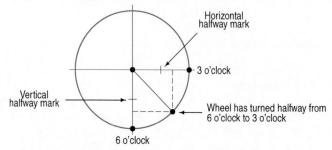

Figure 6.5: As the wheel turns half the way from 6 o'clock to 3 o'clock, the seat rises less than half the vertical distance but glides more than half the horizontal distance

The graph of $f(t)$ in Figure 6.6 is a smooth curve that repeats itself. It looks the same from $t = 0$ to $t = 30$ as from $t = 30$ to $t = 60$, or from $t = 60$ to $t = 90$, or from $t = 90$ to $t = 120$.

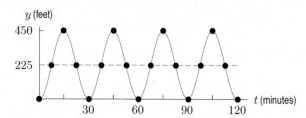

Figure 6.6: The graph of $y = f(t)$ is a smooth wave-shaped curve

Periodic Functions: Period, Midline, and Amplitude

The ferris wheel function, f, is said to be *periodic*. The smallest time interval during which a function completes one full cycle is called its *period* and is represented as a horizontal distance in Figure 6.7.

We can think about the period in terms of horizontal shifts. If the graph of f is shifted to the left by 30 units, the resulting graph looks exactly the same. That is,

$$\underbrace{\text{Graph of } f \text{ shifted left by 30 units}}_{f(t+30)} \quad \text{is the same as} \quad \underbrace{\text{Original graph,}}_{f(t)}$$

so, for all values of t,

$$f(t + 30) = f(t).$$

In general, we make the following definition:

A function f is **periodic** if its values repeat at regular intervals. Graphically, this means that if the graph of f is shifted horizontally by c units, the new graph is identical to the original. In function notation, periodic means that, for all t in the domain of f,

$$f(t + c) = f(t).$$

The smallest positive constant c for which this relationship holds for all values of t is called the **period** of f.

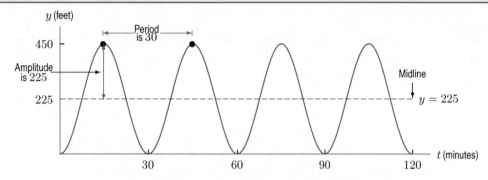

Figure 6.7: The graph of $y = f(t)$ showing the amplitude, period, and midline

In Figure 6.7, the dashed horizontal line is the *midline* of the graph of f. The *amplitude* of a wave-like periodic function is the distance between its maximum and the midline (or the distance between the midline and the minimum). Thus the amplitude of f is 225 because the ferris wheel's maximum height is 450 feet and its midline is at 225 feet. The amplitude is represented graphically as a vertical distance. (See Figure 6.7.) In general:

The **midline** of a periodic function is the horizontal line midway between the function's maximum and minimum values. The **amplitude** is the vertical distance between the function's maximum (or minimum) value and the midline.

Exercises and Problems for Section 6.1

Exercises

In Exercises 1–8, do the functions appear to be periodic with period less than 4?

1.

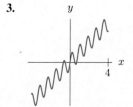

2.

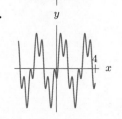

3.

4.

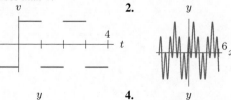

5.

6.

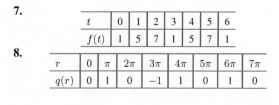

7.

t	0	1	2	3	4	5	6
$f(t)$	1	5	7	1	5	7	1

8.

r	0	π	2π	3π	4π	5π	6π	7π
$q(r)$	0	1	0	-1	1	0	1	0

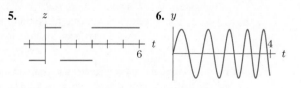

In Exercises 9–12, estimate the period of the periodic functions.

9.

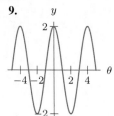

10.

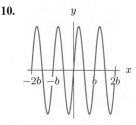

11.

t	0	1	2	3	4	5	6
$f(t)$	12	13	14	12	13	14	12

12.

z	1	11	21	31	41	51	61	71	81
$g(z)$	5	3	2	3	5	3	2	3	5

Problems

You board the London ferris wheel described in this section. In Problems 13–15, graph $h = f(t)$, your height in feet above the ground t minutes after the wheel begins to turn. Label the period, the amplitude, and the midline of each graph, as well as both axes. In each case, first determine an appropriate interval for t, with $t \geq 0$.

13. The London ferris wheel has increased its rotation speed. The wheel completes one full revolution every ten minutes. You get off when you reach the ground after having made two complete revolutions.

14. Everything is the same as Problem 13 (including the rotation speed) except the wheel has a 600 foot diameter.

15. The London ferris wheel is rotating at twice the speed as the wheel in Problem 13.

Problems 16–18 involve different ferris wheels. Graph $h = f(t)$. Label the period, the amplitude, and the midline for each graph. In each case, first determine an appropriate interval for t, with $t \geq 0$.

16. A ferris wheel is 20 meters in diameter and boarded from a platform that is 4 meters above the ground. The six o'clock position on the ferris wheel is level with the loading platform. The wheel completes one full revolution every 2 minutes. At $t = 0$ you are in the twelve o'clock position. You then make two complete revolutions and any additional part of a revolution needed to return to the boarding platform.

17. A ferris wheel is 50 meters in diameter and boarded from a platform that is 5 meters above the ground. The six o'clock position on the ferris wheel is level with the loading platform. The wheel completes one full revolution every 8 minutes. You make two complete revolutions on the wheel, starting at $t = 0$.

18. A ferris wheel is 35 meters in diameter and boarded at ground level. The wheel completes one full revolution every 5 minutes. At $t = 0$ you are in the three o'clock po-

sition and ascending. You then make two complete revolutions and return to the boarding platform.

The graphs in Problems 19–22 describe your height, $h = f(t)$, above the ground on different ferris wheels, where h is in meters and t is time in minutes. You boarded the wheel before $t = 0$. For each graph, determine the following: your position and direction at $t = 0$, how long it takes the wheel to complete one full revolution, the diameter of the wheel, at what height above the ground you board the wheel, and the length of time the graph shows you riding the wheel. The boarding platform is level with the bottom of the wheel.

19.

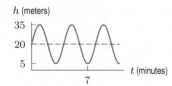

20.

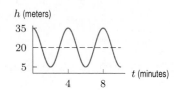

21.

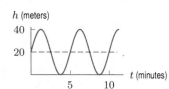

22.

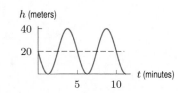

Problems 23–26 concern a weight suspended from the ceiling by a spring. (See Figure 6.8.) Let d be the distance in centimeters from the ceiling to the weight. When the weight is motionless, $d = 10$. If the weight is disturbed, it begins to bob up and down, or *oscillate*. Then d is a periodic function of t, time in seconds, so $d = f(t)$.

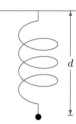

Figure 6.8

23. Determine the midline, period, amplitude, and the minimum and maximum values of f from the graph in Figure 6.9. Interpret these quantities physically; that is, use them to describe the motion of the weight.

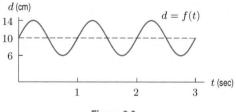

Figure 6.9:

24. A new experiment with the same weight and spring is represented by Figure 6.10. Compare Figure 6.10 to Figure 6.9. How do the oscillations differ? For both figures, the weight was disturbed at time $t = -0.25$ and then left to move naturally; determine the nature of the initial disturbances.

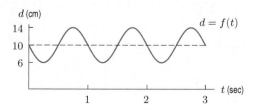

Figure 6.10:

25. The weight in Problem 23 is gently pulled down to a distance of 14 cm from the ceiling and released at time $t = 0$. Sketch its motion for $0 \le t \le 3$.

26. Figures 6.11 and 6.12 describe the motion of two different weights, A and B, attached to two different springs. Based on these graphs, which weight:

(a) Is closest to the ceiling when not in motion?
(b) Makes the largest oscillations?
(c) Makes the fastest oscillations?

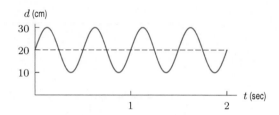

Figure 6.11: Weight A

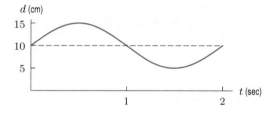

Figure 6.12: Weight B

27. In the US, household electricity is in the form of *alternating current* (AC) at 155.6 volts and 60 hertz. This means that the voltage cycles from -155.6 volts to $+155.6$ volts and back to -155.6 volts, and that 60 cycles occur each second. Suppose that at $t = 0$ the voltage at a given outlet is at 0 volts.

(a) Sketch $V = f(t)$, the voltage as a function of time, for the first 0.1 seconds.
(b) State the period, the amplitude, and the midline of the graph you made in part (a). Describe the physical significance of these quantities.

28. The temperature of a chemical reaction oscillates between a low of $30°C$ and a high of $110°C$. The temperature is at its lowest point when $t = 0$ and completes one cycle over a five-hour period.

(a) Sketch the temperature, T, against the elapsed time, t, over a ten-hour period.
(b) Find the period, the amplitude, and the midline of the graph you drew in part (a).

29. Use a calculator or a computer to decide whether each of the following functions is periodic or not.

   (a) $f(x) = \sin(x/\pi)$ **(b)** $f(x) = \sin(\pi/x)$

   (c) $f(x) = x \sin x$ **(d)** $f(x) = e^{-x} \sin x$

   (e) $f(x) = \pi + \sin x$ **(f)** $f(x) = \sin(e^{-x})$

   (g) $f(x) = \sin(x + \pi)$

30. Table 6.2 gives the number of white blood cells (in 10,000s) in a patient with chronic myelogenous leukemia with nearly periodic relapses. Plot these data and estimate the midline, amplitude and period.

Table 6.2

Day	0	10	40	50	60	70	75	80	90
WBC	0.9	1.2	10	9.2	7.0	3.0	0.9	0.8	0.4
Day	100	110	115	120	130	140	145	150	160
WBC	1.5	2.0	5.7	10.7	9.5	5.0	2.7	0.6	1.0
Day	170	175	185	195	210	225	230	240	255
WBC	2.0	6.0	9.5	8.2	4.5	1.8	2.5	6.0	10.0

31. Table 6.3 gives data from a vibrating string experiment, with time, t, in seconds, and height, $h = f(t)$, in centimeters. Find the midline, amplitude and period of f.

Table 6.3

t	0	.1	.2	.3	.4	.5	.6	.7	.8	.9	1
h	2	2.6	3	3	2.6	2	1.4	1	1	1.4	2

32. Table 6.4 gives the height $h = f(t)$ in feet of a weight on a spring where t is time in seconds. Find the midline, amplitude and period of the function f.

Table 6.4

t	0	1	2	3	4	5	6	7
h	4.0	5.2	6.2	6.5	6.2	5.2	4.0	2.8
t	8	9	10	11	12	13	14	15
h	1.8	1.5	1.8	2.8	4.0	5.2	6.2	6.5

6.2 THE SINE AND COSINE FUNCTIONS

In this section we construct a formula for the ferris wheel function. To do this, we consider points on a unit circle and then riders on the ferris wheel.

The Unit Circle

The *unit circle* is the circle of radius one that is centered at the origin. (See Figure 6.13.) Since the distance from the point P with coordinates (x, y) to the origin is 1, we have

$$\sqrt{x^2 + y^2} = 1,$$

so squaring both sides gives the equation of the circle:

$$x^2 + y^2 = 1.$$

Angles can be used to locate points on the unit circle. Positive angles are measured counterclockwise from the positive x-axis; negative angles are measured clockwise.

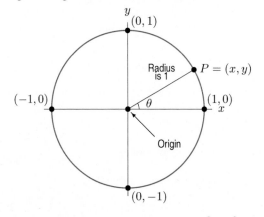

Figure 6.13: The unit circle, with equation $x^2 + y^2 = 1$

Example 1   Figure 6.14 shows the point P determined by $\theta = 90°$. The coordinates of P are $(0,1)$. Figure 6.15 shows the point Q corresponding to $\alpha = 180°$. It has coordinates $(-1,0)$. Figure 6.16 shows the point R determined by the angle $\phi = 210°$. Shortly, we see how to find the coordinates of point R.

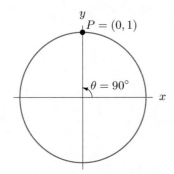

Figure 6.14: The angle $\theta = 90°$ specifies the point $P = (0,1)$ on the unit circle

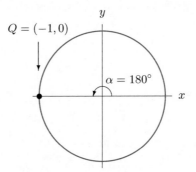

Figure 6.15: The angle $\alpha = 180°$ specifies the point Q on the unit circle

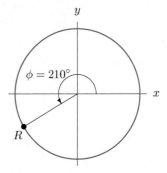

Figure 6.16: The angle $\phi = 210°$ specifies the point R on the unit circle

Definition of Sine and Cosine

In Example 1, angles were used to locate points on the unit circle. The trigonometric functions *sine* and *cosine* give the coordinates of a point in terms of its angle.

> Suppose $P = (x, y)$ is the point on the unit circle specified by the angle θ. We define the functions, **cosine** of θ, or $\cos\theta$, and the **sine** of θ, or $\sin\theta$, by the formulas
>
> $$\cos\theta = x \qquad \text{and} \qquad \sin\theta = y.$$
>
> In other words, $\cos\theta$ is the x-coordinate of the point on the unit circle specified by the angle θ and $\sin\theta$ is the y-coordinate. (See Figure 6.17.)

Notice that we often omit the parentheses around the independent variable, writing $\cos\theta$ instead of $\cos(\theta)$. The independent variable here is θ, not x. In fact, x and y are both functions of θ.

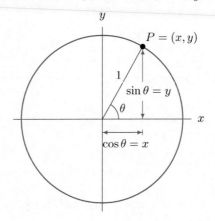

Figure 6.17: For point P, $\cos\theta$ is the x-coordinate and $\sin\theta$ is the y-coordinate

Values of the Sine and Cosine Functions

In principle, we can find values of $\sin\theta$ and $\cos\theta$ for any value of θ. However, there are no easy algebraic formulas for calculating the sine and cosine in terms of θ. So in practice we rely on tables of values, or on calculators and computers. However, there are some values of $\sin\theta$ and $\cos\theta$ we can find on our own.

Example 2   Find the values of $\cos 90°$, $\sin 90°$, $\cos 180°$, $\sin 180°$, $\cos 210°$, $\sin 210°$.

Solution   See Figure 6.14 on page 251. The point P has coordinates $(0, 1)$, so

$$\cos 90° = 0 \qquad \text{and} \qquad \sin 90° = 1.$$

In Figure 6.15, point Q has coordinates $(-1, 0)$, so

$$\cos 180° = -1 \qquad \text{and} \qquad \sin 180° = 0.$$

In Figure 6.16 on page 251, we do not know the coordinates of point R. To find the values of $\cos 210°$ and $\sin 210°$, we use a calculator, which tells us that, approximately

$$\cos 210° = -0.866 \qquad \text{and} \qquad \sin 210° = -0.500.$$

Notice that $\cos 210°$ and $\sin 210°$ are both negative because the point R is in the third quadrant.

Example 3   (a) In Figure 6.18, find the coordinates of the point Q on the unit circle.
(b) Find the lengths of the line segments labeled m and n in Figure 6.18.

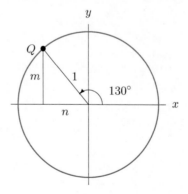

Figure 6.18: The point Q designated by $130°$ on the unit circle

Solution   (a) The coordinates of the point Q are $(\cos 130°, \sin 130°)$. A calculator gives, approximately,

$$\cos 130° = -0.643 \qquad \text{and} \qquad \sin 130° = 0.766.$$

(b) The length of line segment m is the same as the y-coordinate of point Q, so $m = \sin 130° = 0.766$. The x-coordinate of Q is negative because Q is in the second quadrant. The length of line segment n has the same magnitude as the x-coordinate of Q but is positive. Thus, the length of $n = -\cos 130° = 0.643$.

Coordinates of a Point on a Circle of Radius r

Using the sine and cosine, we can find the coordinates of points on circles of any size. Figure 6.19 shows two concentric circles: the inner circle has radius 1 and the outer circle has radius r. The angle θ designates point P on the unit circle and point Q on the larger circle. We know that the coordinates of point $P = (\cos \theta, \sin \theta)$. We want to find (x, y), the coordinates of Q.

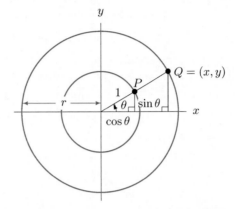

Figure 6.19: Points P and Q on circles of different radii specify the same angle θ

The coordinates of P and Q are the lengths of the sides of the two right triangles in Figure 6.19. Since both right triangles include the angle θ, they are similar and their sides are proportional. This means that the larger triangle is a "magnification" of the smaller triangle. Since the radius of the large circle is r times the radius of the small circle, we have

$$\frac{x}{\cos \theta} = \frac{r}{1} \qquad \text{and} \qquad \frac{y}{\sin \theta} = \frac{r}{1}.$$

Solving for x and y gives us the following result:

The coordinates (x, y) of the point Q in Figure 6.19 are given by

$$x = r \cos \theta \qquad \text{and} \qquad y = r \sin \theta.$$

Example 4   Find the coordinates of the points A, B, and C in Figure 6.20 to three decimal places.

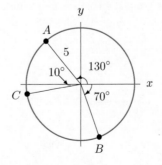

Figure 6.20: Finding coordinates of points on a circle of radius $r = 5$

Solution   Since the circle has radius 5, the coordinates of point A are given by

$$x = 5\cos 130° = 5(-0.643) = -3.214,$$
$$y = 5\sin 130° = 5(0.766) = 3.830.$$

Point B corresponds to an angle of $-70°$, (because the angle is measured clockwise), so B has coordinates

$$x = 5\cos(-70°) = 5(0.342) = 1.710,$$
$$y = 5\sin(-70°) = 5(-0.940) = -4.698.$$

For point C, we must first calculate the corresponding angle, since the $10°$ is not measured from the positive x-axis. The angle we want is $180° + 10° = 190°$, so

$$x = 5\cos(190°) = 5(-0.985) = -4.924,$$
$$y = 5\sin(190°) = 5(-0.174) = -0.868.$$

Example 5   In Figure 6.21, write the height of the point P above the x-axis as a function of the angle θ.

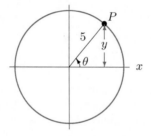

Figure 6.21: Height of point P above x-axis

Solution   We want y as a function of the angle θ. Since the radius of the circle is 5, we have

$$y = 5\sin\theta.$$

Height on the Ferris Wheel as a Function of Angle

Imagine the ferris wheel superimposed on a coordinate system with the origin at the center of the ferris wheel and the positive x-axis extending horizontally to the right. Wherever your seat is on the wheel, we can measure the angle that the line from the center of the wheel to your seat makes with this axis. Figure 6.22 shows the seat in two different positions on the wheel. The first position is at 1 o'clock, which corresponds to a $60°$ angle. The second position is at 10 o'clock, and it corresponds to a $150°$ angle. A point at the 3 o'clock position corresponds to an angle of $0°$.

We now find a formula for the height on the London ferris wheel as a function of the angle θ.

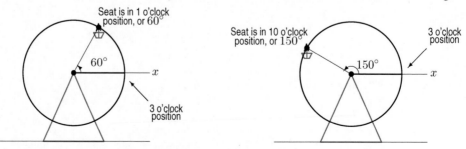

Figure 6.22: The 1 o'clock position forms a $60°$ angle with the positive x-axis, and the 10 o'clock position forms a $150°$ angle

Example 6   The ferris wheel described in Section 6.1 has a radius of 225 feet. Find your height above the ground as a function of the angle θ measured from the 3 o'clock position. What is your height when the angle is $60°$?

Solution   Think of the ferris wheel as a circle centered at the origin, with your position at point P as shown in Figure 6.23. Since $r = 225$, the y-coordinate of point P is given by

$$y = r \sin \theta = 225 \sin \theta.$$

Your height above the ground is given by $225 + y$, so the formula for your height in terms of θ is

$$\text{Height} = 225 + y = 225 + 225 \sin \theta.$$

When $\theta = 60°$, we have

$$\text{Height} = 225 + 225 \sin 60°$$
$$= 225 + 225(0.866) = 419.856 \text{ feet.}$$

So you are approximately 420 feet above the ground.

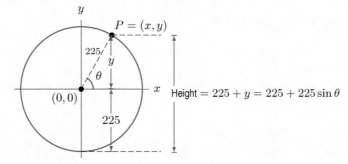

Figure 6.23: Height above the 3 o'clock position is given by the value of y; height above the ground is given by $225 + y$

Exercises and Problems for Section 6.2

Exercises

1. Mark the following angles on a unit circle and give the coordinates of the point determined by each angle.

  (a) $100°$ (b) $200°$ (c) $-200°$
  (d) $-45°$ (e) $1000°$ (f) $-720°$

In Exercises 2–4, what angle (in degrees) corresponds to the given number of rotations around the unit circle?

2. 4   **3.** -2 **4.** 16.4

For Exercises 5–8, sketch and find the coordinates of the point corresponding to each angle on the unit circle.

5. S is at $225°$, T is at $270°$, and U is at $330°$

6. D is at $-90°$, E is at $-135°$, and F is at $-225°$

7. A is at $390°$, B is at $495°$, and C is at $690°$

8. P is at $540°$, Q is at $-180°$, and R is at $450°$

9. Suppose the angles in Exercise 5 are on a circle of radius 5, evaluate the coordinates of S, T and U.

10. Suppose the angles in Exercise 7 are on a circle of radius 3, evaluate the coordinates of A, B and C.

In Exercises 11–24, find the coordinates of the point at the given angle on a circle of radius 3.8 centered at the origin.

11. $90°$ **12.** $180°$ **13.** $-180°$

14. $-90°$ **15.** $-270°$ **16.** $-540°$

17. $1426°$ **18.** $1786°$ **19.** $45°$

20. $135°$ **21.** $225°$ **22.** $315°$

23. $-10°$ **24.** $-20°$

Problems

25. Sketch the angles $\phi = 420°$ and $\theta = -150°$ as a displacement on a ferris wheel, starting from the 3 o'clock position. What position on the wheel do these angles indicate?

26. Find an angle θ, with $0° < \theta < 360°$, that has the same

    (a) Cosine as $240°$ **(b)** Sine as $240°$

27. Find an angle ϕ, with $0° < \phi < 360°$, that has the same

    (a) Cosine as $53°$ **(b)** Sine as $53°$

28. **(a)** Given that $P \approx (0.707, 0.707)$ is a point on the unit circle with angle $45°$, estimate $\sin 135°$ and $\cos 135°$ without a calculator.

    (b) Given that $Q \approx (0.259, 0.966)$ is a point on the unit circle with angle $75°$, estimate $\sin 285°$ and $\cos 285°$ without a calculator.

29. For the angle ϕ shown in Figure 6.24, sketch each of the following angles.

    (a) $180 + \phi$ **(b)** $180 - \phi$ **(c)** $90 - \phi$ **(d)** $360 - \phi$

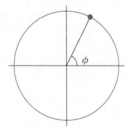

Figure 6.24

30. Let θ be an angle in the first quadrant, and suppose $\sin \theta = a$. Evaluate the following expressions in terms of a. (See Figure 6.25.)

    (a) $\sin(\theta + 360°)$ **(b)** $\sin(\theta + 180°)$
    (c) $\cos(90° - \theta)$ **(d)** $\sin(180° - \theta)$
    (e) $\sin(360° - \theta)$ **(f)** $\cos(270° - \theta)$

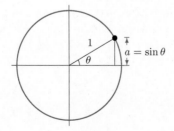

Figure 6.25

31. Explain in your own words the definition of $\sin \theta$ on the unit circle (θ in degrees).

32. You have been riding on the London ferris wheel (see Section 6.1) for 17 minutes and 30 seconds. What is your height above the ground?

33. A ferris wheel is 20 meters in diameter and makes one revolution every 4 minutes. For how many minutes of any revolution will your seat be above 15 meters?

34. A compact disc is 120 millimeters across with a center hole of diameter 15 millimeters. The center of the disc is at the origin. What are the coordinates of the points at which the inner and outer edge intersect the positive x-axis? What are the coordinates of the points at which the inner and outer edges cut a line making an angle θ with the positive x-axis?

35. The revolving door in Figure 6.26 rotates counterclockwise and has four equally spaced panels.

    (a) What is the angle between two adjacent panels?
    (b) What is the angle created by a panel rotating from B to A?
    (c) When the door is as shown in Figure 6.26, a person going outside rotates the door from D to B. What is this angle of rotation?
    (d) If the door is initially as shown in Figure 6.26, a person coming inside rotates the door from B to D. What is this angle of rotation?
    (e) The door starts in the position shown in Figure 6.26. Where is the panel at A after three people enter and five people exit? Assume that people going in and going out do so in the manner described in parts (d) and (c), and that each person goes completely through the door before the next enters.

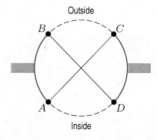

Figure 6.26

36. A revolving door (which rotates counterclockwise in Figure 6.27) was designed with five equally spaced panels for the entrance to the Pentagon. The arcs BC and AD have equal length.

(a) What is the angle between two adjacent panels?

(b) A four-star general enters by pushing on the panel at point B, and leaves the panel at point D. What is the angle of rotation?

(c) With the door in the position shown in Figure 6.27, an admiral leaves the Pentagon by pushing the panel between A and D to point B. What is the angle of rotation?

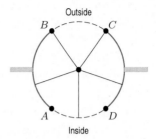

Figure 6.27

6.3 RADIANS

So far we have measured angles in degrees. There is another way to measure an angle, which involves arclength. This is the idea behind radians; it turns out to be very helpful in calculus.

Definition of a Radian

The arc length *spanned*, or cut off, by an angle is shown in Figure 6.28.

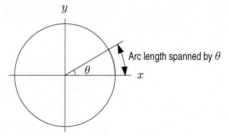

Figure 6.28: Arc length spanned by the angle θ

If the radius of a circle is fixed, (say the radius is 1), the arc length is completely determined by the angle θ. Following Figure 6.29, we make the following definition:

An angle of **1 radian** is defined to be the angle, in the counterclockwise direction, at the center of a unit circle which spans an arc of length 1.

The radius and arc length must be measured in the same units.

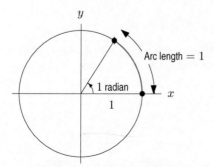

Figure 6.29: One radian cuts off an arc length of one in a unit circle

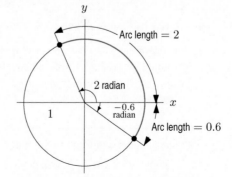

Figure 6.30: Angles of 2 radian and -0.6 radian

An angle of 2 radians cuts off an arc of length 2 in a unit circle; an angle of -0.6 radian is measured clockwise and cuts off an arc of length 0.6. See Figure 6.30. In general:

> The radian measure of a positive angle is the length of the arc spanned by the angle in a unit circle. For a negative angle, the radian measure is the negative of the arc length.

Radians are dimensionless units of measurement for angles (they do not have units of length).

Relationship Between Radians and Degrees

The circumference, C, of a circle of radius r is given by

$$C = 2\pi r.$$

In a unit circle, $r = 1$, so $C = 2\pi$. This means that the arc length spanned by a complete revolution of $360°$ is 2π, so

$$360° = 2\pi \text{ radians.}$$

Dividing by 2π gives

$$1 \text{ radian} = \frac{360°}{2\pi} \approx 57.296°.$$

Thus, one radian is approximately $57.296°$. One-quarter revolution, or $90°$, is equal to $\frac{1}{4}(2\pi)$ or $\pi/2$ radians. Figure 6.31 shows several positions on the unit circle described in radian measure. Since $\pi \approx 3.142$, one complete revolution is about 6.283 radians and one-quarter revolution is about 1.571 radians.

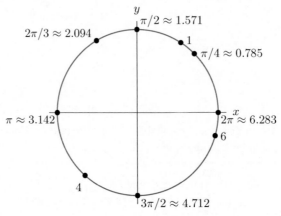

Figure 6.31: Angles in radian measure marked on circle

Example 1   In which quadrant is an angle of 2 radians? An angle of 5 radians?

Solution   Refer to Figure 6.31. The second quadrant includes angles between $\pi/2$ and π, (that is, between 1.571 and 3.142 radians), so 2 radians lies in the second quadrant. An angle of 5 radians is between 4.71 and 6.283, that is, between $3\pi/2$ and 2π radians, so 5 radians lies in the fourth quadrant.

Example 2   The ferris wheel described in Section 6.1 makes one rotation every 30 minutes.

(a) If you start at the 3 c'clock position, find the angle in radians that specifies your position after 10 minutes.

(b) Find the angle that specifies your position after t minutes.

Solution   (a) After 10 minutes, you have completed 1/3 of a revolution, so

$$\text{Angle} = \frac{1}{3}(2\pi) = \frac{2\pi}{3} \text{ radians.}$$

(b) After t minutes, you have completed $t/30$ of a revolution, so

$$\text{Angle} = \frac{t}{30}(2\pi) = \frac{\pi t}{15} \text{ radians.}$$

Converting Between Degrees and Radians

To convert degrees to radians, or vice versa, we use the fact that 2π radians $= 360°$. So

$$1 \text{ radian} = \frac{180°}{\pi} \approx 57.296°.$$

Similarly

$$1° = \frac{\pi}{180} \approx 0.01745 \text{ radians.}$$

Thus, to convert from radians to degrees, multiply the radian measure by $180°/\pi$ radians. To convert from degrees to radians, multiply the degree measure by π radians$/180°$.

Example 3   (a) Convert 3 radians to degrees.   (b) Convert 3 degrees to radians.

Solution   (a) 3 radians $\cdot \dfrac{180°}{\pi \text{ radians}} = \dfrac{540°}{\pi \text{ radians}} \approx 171.887°.$

(b) $3° \cdot \dfrac{\pi \text{ radians}}{180°} = \dfrac{\pi \text{ radians}}{60} \approx 0.052 \text{ radians.}$

The word radians is often dropped, so if an angle or rotation is referred to without units, it is understood to be in radians. We can write, for instance, $90° = \pi/2$ and $\pi = 180°$.

Example 4   Find the arc length spanned by an angle of $30°$ in a circle of radius 1 meter.

Solution   Convert $30°$ to radians, giving

$$30° = 30° \cdot \frac{\pi}{180°} = \frac{\pi}{6}.$$

The definition of a radian tells us that the arc length spanned by an angle of $\pi/6$ in a circle of radius 1 meter is $\pi/6 \approx 0.524$ meter. See Figure 6.32.

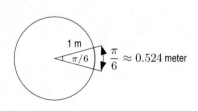

Figure 6.32: Arc length spanned by $30° = \pi/6$ radian in a unit circle

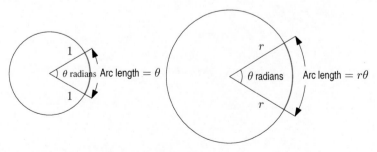

Figure 6.33: Arc length spanned by angle θ is proportional to the radius of the circle

Arc Length

We defined a radian using arc length in a unit circle. However, radians can be used to calculate arc length in a circle of any size. An angle of θ radians spans an arc of length θ in a unit circle. An angle of θ radians spans an arc of length $r\theta$ in a circle of radius r. Figure 6.33 reflects the following result:

> The **arc length**, s, spanned in a circle of radius r by an angle of θ radians, $0 \le \theta \le 2\pi$, is given by
> $$s = r\theta.$$

Thus if the size of an angle is fixed, the arc length it spans is proportional to the radius of the circle. (See Figure 6.34.) Note that θ must be in radians in this arc length formula.

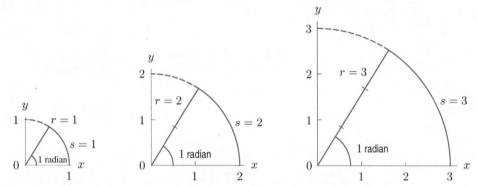

Figure 6.34: On a circle of radius 1, one radian spans an arc of length 1. On a circle of radius 2, it spans an arc of length 2; on a circle of radius 3, it spans an arc of length 3

Example 5   What length of arc is cut off by an angle of $120°$ on a circle of radius 12 cm?

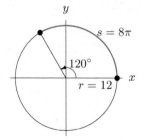

Figure 6.35: An arc cut off by $120°$

Solution   Converting $120°$ to radians gives

$$\text{Angle} = 120° \cdot \frac{\pi}{180°} = \frac{2}{3}\pi \text{ radians,}$$

so

$$\text{Arc length} = 12 \cdot \frac{2}{3}\pi = 8\pi \text{ cm.}$$

Example 6   You walk 4 miles around a circular lake. Give an angle in radians which represents your final position relative to your starting point if the radius of the lake is: (a)   1 mile   (b)   3 miles

Solution   (a)   The path around the lake is a unit circle, so you have traversed an angle in radians equal to the arc length traveled, 4 miles. An angle of 4 radians is in the middle of the third quadrant relative to your starting point. (See Figure 6.36.)

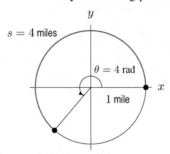

Figure 6.36: Arc length 4 and radius 1, so angle is 4 radians

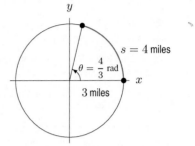

Figure 6.37: Arc length 4 and radius 3, so angle is 4/3 radians

(b)   See Figure 6.37. To find θ, use $s = r\theta$ giving

$$\theta = \frac{s}{r}.$$

The angle you have traversed is

$$\frac{s}{r} = \frac{4}{3} \approx 1.33 \text{ radians}.$$

One-quarter revolution is $\pi/2 \approx 1.571$ radians, so you are nearly one-quarter of the way around the lake.

Sine and Cosine of a Number

We have defined the sine and cosine of an angle. For any real number t, we define $\cos t$ and $\sin t$ by interpreting t as an angle of t radians.

Exercises and Problems for Section 6.3

Exercises

Determine the radian measure of the angles in Exercises 1–4.

1. $60°$ **2.** $45°$ **3.** $100°$ **4.** $17°$

In Exercises 5–8, convert the angle to radians.

5. $150°$ **6.** $120°$ **7.** $-270°$ **8.** $\pi°$

In Exercises 9–13, convert the angle given in radians to degrees.

9. $\frac{7}{2}\pi$ **10.** 5π **11.** 90   **12.** 2   **13.** 45

14. Convert each of the following angles to radians in two forms: as a multiple of π and as a decimal approximation rounded to two decimal places.

(a) $30°$ (b) $120°$ (c) $200°$ (d) $315°$

15. An angle with radian measure $\pi/4$ corresponds to a point on the unit circle in quadrant I. Give the quadrants corresponding to angles with the following radian measures:

(a)   1 radian   (b)   2 radians   (c)   3 radians
(d)   4 radians   (e)   5 radians   (f)   6 radians
(g)   7 radians   (h)   8 radians   (i)   9 radians
(j)   10 radians

In Exercises 16–19, what angle in radians corresponds to the given number of rotations around the unit circle?

16. 1   **17.** -2 **18.** 0.75 **19.** 4.27

In Exercises 20–23, find the arc length corresponding to the given angle on a circle of radius 6.2.

20. $-180°$ **21.** $45°$ **22.** $\dfrac{180°}{\pi}$ **23.** $a°$

Problems

24. What is the radius of a circle in which an angle of 3 radians cuts off an arc of 30 cm?

25. What is the length of an arc which is cut off by an angle of $225°$ in a circle of radius 4 feet?

26. What is the length of an arc cut off by an angle of 2 radians on a circle of radius 8 inches?

27. What is the angle determined by an arc of length 2π meters on a circle of radius 18 meters?

In Problems 28–33, where possible give the radius r, the measure of θ in both degrees and radians, the arc length s, and the coordinates of point P.

28.
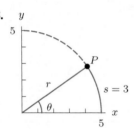

29.
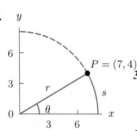

30.
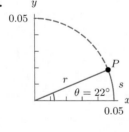

31.
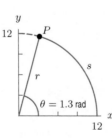

32.
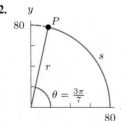

33.
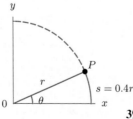

34. A radian can be defined to be the angle at the center of a circle which cuts off an arc of length equal to the radius of the circle. This is because the arc length formula in radians, $s = r \cdot \theta$, becomes just $s = r$ when $\theta = 1$. Figure 6.38 shows circles of radii 2 cm and 3 cm.

(a) Does the angle 1 radian appear to be the same in both circles?

(b) Estimate the number of arcs of length 2 cm that fit in the circumference of the circle of radius 2 cm.

Figure 6.38

35. Without using a calculator, give the sign of each of the following numbers:

(a) $\cos 3$ (b) $\sin 4$ (c) $\sin(-4)$ (d) $\cos 7$

36. Without using a calculator, rank the following in order from smallest to largest.

(a) The angles: $\dfrac{2\pi}{3}, 2.3, \dfrac{2}{3}, -\dfrac{2\pi}{3}$

(b) The numbers:

$$\cos\left(\frac{2\pi}{3}\right), \quad \cos(2.3), \quad \cos\left(\frac{2}{3}\right), \quad \cos\left(-\frac{2\pi}{3}\right)$$

Evaluate $\sin\theta$ and $\cos\theta$ for the angle θ on the unit circle in Problems 37–38.

37.
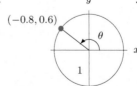

38.
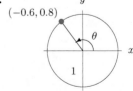

39. An ant starts at the point $(1,0)$ on the unit circle and walks counterclockwise a distance of 3 units around the circle. Find the x and y coordinates (accurate to 2 decimal places) of the final location of the ant.

40. For ϕ in Figure 6.39, sketch the following angles.

   (a) $\pi + \phi$ **(b)** $\pi - \phi$

   (c) $\pi/2 - \phi$ **(d)** $2\pi - \phi$

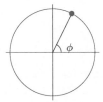

Figure 6.39

41. If a weight hanging on a string of length 3 feet swings through $5°$ on either side of the vertical, how long is the arc through which the weight moves from one high point to the next high point?

42. How far does the tip of the minute hand of a clock move in 35 minutes if the hand is 6 inches long?

43. Using a weight on a string called a plumb bob, it is possible to erect a pole that is exactly vertical, which means that the pole points directly toward the center of the earth. Two such poles are erected one hundred miles apart. If the poles were extended they would meet at the center of the earth at an angle of $1.4333°$. Compute the radius of the earth.

44. Without a calculator, decide which is bigger, t or $\sin t$, for $0 < t < \pi/2$. Illustrate your answer with a sketch.

45. Do you think there is a value of t for which $\cos t = t$? If so, estimate the value of t. If not, explain why not.

6.4 GRAPHS OF THE SINE AND COSINE

Before graphing, we calculate values of the sine and cosine. Some values can be found exactly.

Exact Values of the Sine and Cosine

In Example 2 on page 252, we found sine and cosine of $90°$ and $180°$. Because $90° = \pi/2$ and $180° = \pi$ we have

$$\cos \frac{\pi}{2} = 0, \quad \sin \frac{\pi}{2} = 1, \quad \cos \pi = -1, \quad \sin \pi = 0.$$

Example 1   Evaluate $\sin \theta$ and $\cos \theta$ for $\theta = 0, 3\pi/2$, and 2π.

Solution   Figure 6.40 gives the coordinates of the points on the unit circle specified by $0, 3\pi/2$, and 2π. We use these coordinates to evaluate the sines and cosines of these angles.

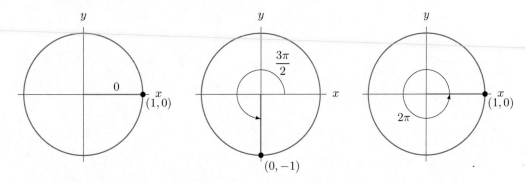

Figure 6.40: The coordinates of the points on the unit circle specified by the angles $0, 3\pi/2$, and 2π

The definition of the cosine function tells us that $\cos 0$ is the x-coordinate of the point on the unit circle specified by the angle 0. Since the x-coordinate of this point is $x = 1$, we have

$$\cos 0 = 1.$$

Similarly, the y-coordinate of the point $(1, 0)$ is $y = 0$ which gives

$$\sin 0 = 0.$$

From Figure 6.40 we see that the coordinates of the remaining points are $(0, -1)$, and $(1, 0)$, so

$$\frac{3\pi}{2} = 0, \qquad \sin \frac{3\pi}{2} = -1, \qquad \text{and} \qquad \cos 2\pi = 1, \qquad \sin 2\pi = 0.$$

In the Tools section on page 301, triangles are used to compute the exact values of the sine and cosine of $30° = \pi/6$, $45° = \pi/4$, $60° = \pi/3$. See also Problem 24 at the end of this section. The results are:

$$\cos 30° = \cos \tfrac{\pi}{6} = \frac{\sqrt{3}}{2} \qquad \cos 45° = \cos \tfrac{\pi}{4} = \frac{1}{\sqrt{2}} \qquad \cos 60° = \cos \tfrac{\pi}{3} = \frac{1}{2}$$

$$\sin 30° = \sin \tfrac{\pi}{6} = \frac{1}{2} \qquad \sin 45° = \sin \tfrac{\pi}{4} = \frac{1}{\sqrt{2}} \qquad \sin 60° = \sin \tfrac{\pi}{3} = \frac{\sqrt{3}}{2}$$

Graphs of the Sine and Cosine Functions

Table 6.5 records values of the sine and cosine functions, using $1/\sqrt{2} \approx 0.7$. The graphs are plotted in Figure 6.41. To model periodic phenomena, we usually work in radians. Thus, the axes are labeled in radians and degrees. Notice that both the sine and cosine functions are periodic with a period of $2\pi = 360°$ and an amplitude of 1.

Table 6.5 *Table of values (rounded) for* $\sin \theta$ *and* $\cos \theta$, *with* θ *in degrees and radians*

θ (degrees)	0°	45°	90°	135°	180°	225°	270°	315°	360°	450°	540°	630°	720°	$\cdots$
θ (radians)	0	$\pi/4$	$\pi/2$	$3\pi/4$	π	$5\pi/4$	$3\pi/2$	$7\pi/4$	2π	$5\pi/2$	3π	$7\pi/2$	4π	$\cdots$
$\sin \theta$	0	0.7	1	0.7	0	-0.7	-1	-0.7	0	1	0	-1	0	$\cdots$
$\cos \theta$	1	0.7	0	-0.7	-1	-0.7	0	0.7	1	0	-1	0	1	$\cdots$

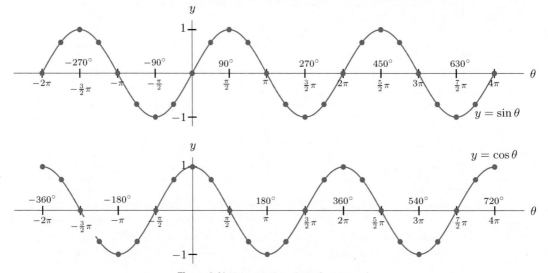

Figure 6.41: The graphs of $\sin \theta$ and $\cos \theta$

Several properties of the sine and cosine functions are illustrated by their graphs. The sine is an odd function and the cosine is an even function. Since the outputs of the sine and cosine functions are the coordinates of points on the unit circle, they lie between -1 and 1. So the range of the sine and cosine are

$$-1 \leq \sin \theta \leq 1 \qquad \text{and} \qquad -1 \leq \cos \theta \leq 1.$$

The domain of both of these functions is all real numbers, since any angle, positive or negative, specifies a point on the unit circle. Both functions are periodic with period 2π, because adding a multiple of 2π (or $360°$) to an angle does not change the position of the point that it designates on the unit circle. The midline of both graphs is $y = 0$ and their amplitude is 1.

Amplitude

We can determine the amplitude of a trigonometric function from its formula. Recall that the amplitude is the distance between the midline and the highest or lowest point on the graph.

Example 2   Compare the graph of $y = \sin t$ to the graphs of $y = 2 \sin t$ and $y = -0.5 \sin t$, for $0 \leq t \leq 2\pi$. How are these graphs similar? How are they different? What are their amplitudes?

Solution   The graphs are in Figure 6.42. The amplitude of $y = \sin t$ is 1, the amplitude of $y = 2 \sin t$ is 2 and the amplitude of $y = -0.5 \sin t$ is 0.5. The graph of $y = -0.5 \sin t$ is "upside-down" relative to $y = \sin t$. These observations are consistent with the fact that the constant A in the equation

$$y = A \sin t$$

stretches or shrinks the graph vertically, and reflects it about the t-axis if A is negative.

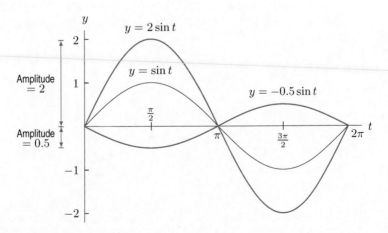

Figure 6.42: The graphs of $y = \sin t$, $y = 2 \sin t$, and $y = -0.5 \sin t$ all have different amplitudes

Midline

Recall that the graph of $y = f(t) + k$ is the graph of $y = f(t)$ shifted vertically by k units. For example, the graph of $y = \cos t + 2$ is the graph of $y = \cos t$ shifted up by 2 units, as shown in Figure 6.43. Notice that the midline of the new graph is the line $y = 2$; it has been shifted up 2 units from its old position at $y = 0$.

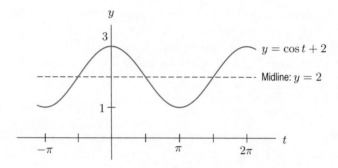

Figure 6.43: The graph of $y = \cos t + 2$ and its midline $y = 2$

Generalizing, we conclude that the graphs of $y = \sin t + k$ and $y = \cos t + k$ have midlines $y = k$. Notice that the expression $\sin t + k$ could also be written as $k + \sin t$; it is *not* the same as $\sin(t + k)$.

Example 3   Graph the ferris wheel function giving your height, $h = f(\theta)$, in feet, above ground as a function of the angle θ:

$$f(\theta) = 225 + 225 \sin \theta.$$

(See Example 6 on page 255.) What are the period, midline, and amplitude?

Solution   Using a calculator, we get the graph in Figure 6.44. The period of this function is $360°$, because $360°$ is one full rotation, so the function repeats every $360°$. The midline is $h = 225$ feet, since the values of h oscillate about this value. The amplitude is also 225 feet, since the maximum value of h is 450 feet.

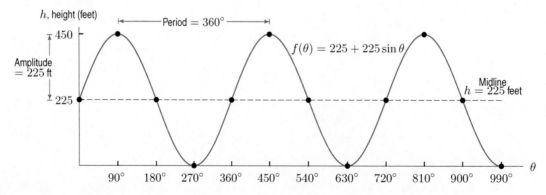

Figure 6.44: On the ferris wheel: Height, h, above ground as a function of the angle, θ

Exercises and Problems for Section 6.4

Exercises

In Exercises 1–8, find the midline and amplitude of the periodic function.

1. $y = \sin(4x)$

2. $y = 6\sin(4x) + 5$

3. $y = -7\cos(2x) - 4$

4.

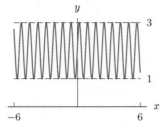

5.

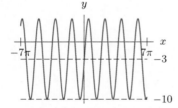

6.

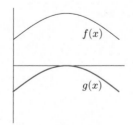

7. The height in cm of the tip of the hour hand on a vertical clock face is a function, $h(t)$, of the time, t, in hours. The hour hand is 15 cm long, and the middle of the clock face is 185 cm above the ground.

8. The height in cm of the tip of the minute hand on a vertical clock face is a function, $i(t)$, of the time, t, in minutes. The minute hand is 20 cm long, and the middle of the clock face is 223 cm above the ground.

9. Graph $y = \sin t$ for $-\pi \le t \le 3\pi$.

   (a) Indicate the interval(s) on which the function is

      (i) Positive   (ii) Increasing (iii) Concave up

   (b) Estimate the t values at which the function is increasing most rapidly.

10. Compare the values of $\sqrt{1/2}$ and $\sqrt{2}/2$ using a calculator. Explain your observations.

11. Compare the values of $\sqrt{3/4}$ and $\sqrt{3}/2$ using your calculator. Explain your observations.

In Exercises 12–15, find an exact value without a calculator.

12. $\cos\dfrac{7\pi}{6}$ **13.** $\sin\dfrac{2\pi}{3}$

14. $\sin\left(-\dfrac{\pi}{3}\right)$ **15.** $\cos\left(\dfrac{-\pi}{6}\right)$

Problems

16. Figure 6.45 shows the graphs of $y = (\sin x) - 1$ and $y = (\sin x) + 1$. Identify which is which.

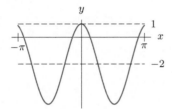

Figure 6.45

17. Figure 6.46 shows $y = \sin x$ and $y = \cos x$ starting at $x = 0$. Which is $y = \cos x$? Find values for a and b.

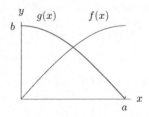

Figure 6.46

18. In Figure 6.47, assume that $\sin A = \sin B$.

    (a) If $A = \pi/8$, find B.   **(b)** If $A = 1$, find B.

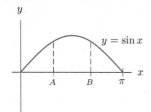

Figure 6.47

19. Figure 6.48 shows $y = \sin(x - \frac{\pi}{2})$ and $y = \sin(x + \frac{\pi}{2})$ starting at $x = 0$. Identify which is which.

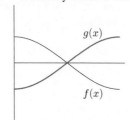

Figure 6.48

20. Match each of the letters A–G in Figure 6.49 to one of the following values of x (in radians): $1, 2, 4, 5, \pi/2, \pi,$ and $3\pi/2$.

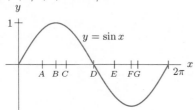

Figure 6.49

21. The graph of $y = \sin \theta$ never goes higher than 1. Explain why this is true by using a sketch of the unit circle and the definition of the $\sin \theta$ function.

22. Compare the graph of $y = \sin \theta$ to the graphs of $y = 0.5 \sin \theta$ and $y = -2 \sin \theta$ for $0 \le \theta \le 2\pi$. How are these graphs similar? How are they different?

23. Find exact values for each of the following:

    (a) $\sin\left(\dfrac{3\pi}{4}\right)$ **(b)** $\cos\left(\dfrac{5\pi}{3}\right)$ **(c)** $\cos\left(\dfrac{7\pi}{6}\right)$

    (d) $\sin\left(\dfrac{11\pi}{6}\right)$ **(e)** $\sin\left(\dfrac{9\pi}{4}\right)$

24. Calculate $\sin 45°$ and $\cos 45°$ exactly. Use the fact that the point P corresponding to $45°$ on the unit circle, $x^2 + y^2 = 1$, lies on the line $y = x$.

25. Find exact values for the coordinates of point W in Figure 6.50.

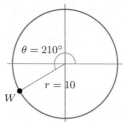

Figure 6.50

26. **(a)** For each of the following angles, sketch an arc of length θ on a unit circle and a line segment of length $\cos \theta$: **(i)** $\theta = 1.1$ **(ii)** $\theta = 5.2$

    (b) Now sketch $y = \cos t$. Mark on your graph of $y = \cos t$ line segments of length θ and $\cos \theta$ for the same values of θ that you used in part (a).

27. **(a)** Match the lengths p, q, r, s marked on the unit circle in Figure 6.51 with the following values:

    (i) $t = 0.8$ **(ii)** $t = \pi - 2.9$

    (iii) $\cos(0.8)$ **(iv)** $-\cos(2.9)$

    (b) On a graph of $y = \cos t$, sketch segments corresponding to each of the values in part (a).

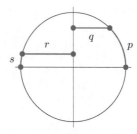

Figure 6.51

28. A circle of radius 5 is centered at the point $(-6, 7)$. Find a formula for $f(\theta)$, the x-coordinate of the point P in Figure 6.52.

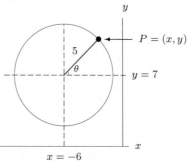

Figure 6.52

29. **(a)** Write an expression for the slope of the line segment joining P and Q in Figure 6.53.
(b) Evaluate your expression for $a = \pi/4$, $b = 4\pi/3$. Give an exact value for your answer.

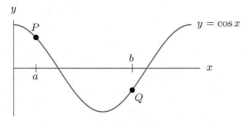

Figure 6.53

30. **(a)** Write an expression for the slope of the line segment joining S and T in Figure 6.54.
(b) Evaluate your expression for $a = 1.7$, $h = 0.05$. Round your answer to two decimal places.

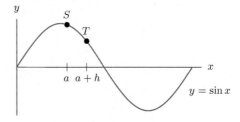

Figure 6.54

6.5   SINUSOIDAL FUNCTIONS

Section 6.1 introduced $f(t)$, your height above the ground while riding a ferris wheel. The graph of f looks like a transformation of $y = \sin t$. Transformations of the sine and cosine are called *sinusoidal* functions, and can be expressed in the form

$$y = A\sin(B(t - h)) + k \qquad \text{and} \qquad y = A\cos(B(t - h)) + k,$$

where A, B, h, and k are constants. Their graphs resemble the graphs of sine and cosine, but may also be shifted, flipped, or stretched. These transformations may change the period, amplitude, and midline of the function as well as its value at $t = 0$.

From Section 6.4 we know the following:

The functions of $y = A\sin t$ and $y = A\cos t$ have **amplitude** $|A|$.

The **midline** of the functions $y = \sin t + k$ and $y = \cos t + k$ is the horizontal line $y = k$.

Period

Next, we consider the effect of the constant B. We usually have $B > 0$.

Example 1   Graph $y = \sin t$ and $y = \sin 2t$ for $0 \le t \le 2\pi$. Describe any similarities and differences. What are their periods?

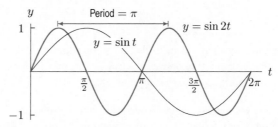

Figure 6.55: The functions $y = \sin t$ and $y = \sin 2t$ have different periods

Solution   The graphs are in Figure 6.55. The two functions have the same amplitude and midline, but their periods are different. The period of $y = \sin t$ is 2π, but the period of $y = \sin 2t$ is π. This is because the factor of 2 causes a horizontal compression, squeezing the graph twice as close to the y-axis.

If $B > 0$ the function $y = \sin(Bt)$ resembles the function $y = \sin t$ except that it is stretched or compressed horizontally. The constant B determines how many cycles the function completes on an interval of length 2π. For example, we see from Figure 6.55 that the function $y = \sin 2t$ completes two cycles on the interval $0 \le t \le 2\pi$.

Since, for $B > 0$, the graph of $y = \sin(Bt)$ completes B cycles on the interval $0 \le t \le 2\pi$, each cycle has length $2\pi/B$. The period is thus $2\pi/B$. In general, for B of any sign, we have:

> The functions $y = \sin(Bt)$ and $y = \cos(Bt)$ have **period** $P = 2\pi/|B|$.

The number of cycles in one unit of time is $|B|/2\pi$, the *frequency*.

Example 2   Find possible formulas for the functions f and g shown in Figures 6.56 and 6.57.

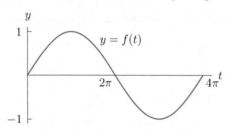

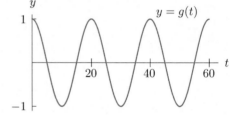

Figure 6.56: This function has period 4π Figure 6.57: This function has period 20

Solution   The graph of f resembles the graph of $y = \sin t$ except that its period is $P = 4\pi$. Using $P = 2\pi/B$ gives

$$4\pi = \frac{2\pi}{B} \qquad \text{so} \qquad B = \frac{1}{2}.$$

Thus, $f(t) = \sin\left(\frac{1}{2}t\right)$.

The function g resembles the function $y = \cos t$ except that its period is $P = 20$. This gives

$$20 = \frac{2\pi}{B} \qquad \text{so} \qquad B = \frac{\pi}{10}.$$

Thus, $g(t) = \cos\left(\frac{\pi}{10}t\right)$.

Example 3   Household electrical power in the US is provided in the form of alternating current. Typically the voltage cycles smoothly between $+155.6$ volts and -155.6 volts 60 times per second.[2] Use a cosine function to model the alternating voltage.

Solution   If V is the voltage at time, t, in seconds, then V begins at $+155.6$ volts, drops to -155.6 volts, and then climbs back to $+155.6$ volts, repeating this process 60 times per second. We use a cosine with amplitude $A = 155.6$. Since the function alternates 60 times in one second, the period is $1/60$ of a second. We know that $P = 2\pi/B = 1/60$, so $B = 120\pi$. We have $V = 155.6\cos(120\pi t)$.

---

[2]A voltage cycling between $+155.6$ volts and -155.6 volts has an average magnitude, over time, of 110 volts.

Example 4   Describe in words the function $y = 300\cos(0.2\pi t) + 600$ and sketch its graph.

Solution   This function resembles $y = \cos t$ except that it has an amplitude of 300, a midline of $y = 600$, and a period of $P = 2\pi/(0.2\pi) = 10$. See Figure 6.58.

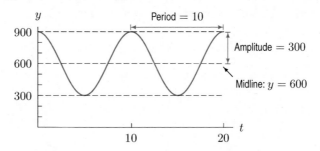

Figure 6.58: The function $y = 300\cos(0.2\pi t) + 600$

Horizontal Shift

Figure 6.59 shows the graphs of two trigonometric functions, f and g, with period $P = 12$. The graph of f resembles a sine function, so a possible formula for f is $f(t) = \sin Bt$. Since the period of f is 12, we have $12 = 2\pi/B$, so $B = 2\pi/12$, so $f(t) = \sin(\pi t/6)$.

The graph of g looks like the graph of f shifted to the right by 2 units. Thus a possible formula for g is

$$g(t) = f(t - 2),$$

or

$$g(t) = \sin\left(\frac{\pi}{6}(t - 2)\right).$$

Notice that we can also write the formula for $g(t)$ as

$$g(t) = \sin\left(\frac{\pi}{6}t - \frac{\pi}{3}\right),$$

but $\pi/3$ is *not* the horizontal shift in the graph! To pick out the horizontal shift from the formula, we must write the formula in factored form, that is, as $\sin(B(t - h))$.

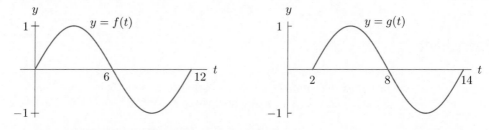

Figure 6.59: The graphs of two trigonometric functions f and g, related by a horizontal shift

The graphs of $y = \sin(B(t - h))$ and $y = \cos(B(t - h))$ are the graphs of $y = \sin Bt$ and $y = \cos Bt$ **shifted horizontally** by h units.

Example 5   Describe in words the graph of the function $g(t) = \cos(3t - \pi/4)$.

Solution   Write the formula for g in the form $\cos(B(t - h))$ by factoring 3 out from the expression $3t - \pi/4$ to get $g(t) = \cos(3(t - \pi/12))$. The period of g is $2\pi/3$ and the graph is the graph of $f = \cos 3t$ shifted $\pi/12$ units to the right, as shown in Figure 6.60.

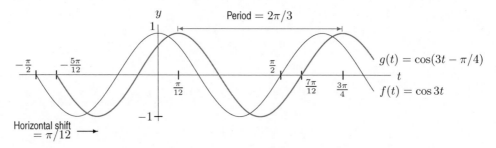

Figure 6.60: The graphs of $g(t) = \cos\left(3t - \frac{\pi}{4}\right)$ and $f(t) = \cos 3t$

Summary of Transformations

The parameters A, B, h, and k determine the graph of a transformed sine or cosine function.

> For the **sinusoidal** functions
>
> $$y = A\sin(B(t - h)) + k \qquad \text{and} \qquad y = A\cos(B(t - h)) + k,$$
>
> - $|A|$ is the amplitude
> - h is the horizontal shift
> - $2\pi/|B|$ is the period
> - $y = k$ is the midline
> - $|B|/2\pi$ is the frequency; that is, the number of cycles completed in unit time.

Phase Shift

In Example 5, we factored $(3t - \pi/4)$ to write the function as $g(t) = \cos(3(t - \pi/12))$. This allowed us to recognize the horizontal shift, $\pi/12$. However, in most physical applications, the quantity $\pi/4$, known as the *phase shift*, is more important than the horizontal shift. We define

$$\text{Phase shift} = \text{Fraction of period} \times 2\pi.$$

The phase shift enables us to calculate the fraction of a full period that the curve has been shifted. For instance, in Example 5, the wave has been shifted

$$\frac{\text{Phase shift}}{2\pi} = \frac{\pi/4}{2\pi} = \frac{1}{8} \text{ of a full period,}$$

and the graph of g in Figure 6.61 is the graph of $f(t) = \cos 3t$ shifted $1/8$ of its period to the right.

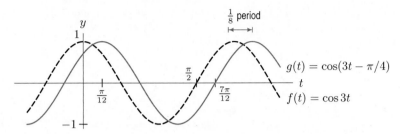

Figure 6.61: The graph of $g(t) = \cos(3t - \frac{\pi}{4})$ has phase shift $\frac{\pi}{4}$ relative to $f(t) = \cos 3t$

Phase shift is significant because in many applications, such as optical interference, we want to know if two waves reinforce or cancel each other. For two waves of the same period, a phase shift of 0 or 2π tells us that the two waves reinforce each other; a phase shift of π tells us that the two waves cancel. Thus, the phase shift tells us the relative positions of two waves of the same period.[3]

For the sinusoidal functions written in the form

$$y = A\sin(Bt + \phi) \quad \text{and} \quad y = A\cos(Bt + \phi),$$

ϕ is the **phase shift**.

Example 6   (a) In Figure 6.62, by what fraction of a period is the graph of $g(t)$ shifted from the graph of $f(t)$?
(b) What is the phase shift?

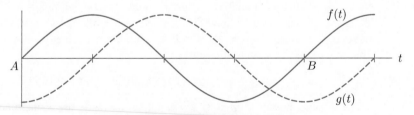

Figure 6.62

Solution   (a) The period of $f(t)$ is the length of the interval from A to B. The graph of $g(t)$ is shifted $1/4$ period to the right.
(b) The phase shift is $\frac{1}{4}(2\pi) = \pi/2$.

Using the Transformed Sine and Cosine Functions

Sinusoidal functions are used to model oscillating quantities. Starting with $y = A\sin(B(t-h))+k$ or $y = A\cos(B(t-h)) + k$, we calculate values of the parameters A, B, h, k.

---

[3]The phase shift which tells us that two waves cancel is independent of their period. The horizontal shift that gives the same information is not independent of period.

Example 7   The temperature, T, in °C, of the surface water in a pond varies according to the graph in Figure 6.63. If t is the number of hours since sunrise at 6 am, find a possible formula for $T = f(t)$.

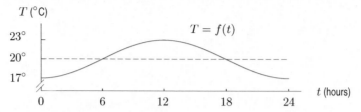

Figure 6.63: Surface water temperature of a pond since sunrise

Solution   The graph of $T = f(t)$ resembles a cosine function with amplitude $|A| = 3$, period $= 24$ and midline $T = 20$. Compared to $y = \cos t$, there is no horizontal shift, but the graph has been reflected across the midline, so A is negative, $A = -3$. We have

$$24 = \frac{2\pi}{B} \qquad \text{so} \qquad B = \frac{2\pi}{24} = \frac{\pi}{12}.$$

So a possible formula for f is

$$T = f(t) = -3\cos\left(\frac{\pi}{12}t\right) + 20.$$

Example 8   A rabbit population in a national park rises and falls each year. It is at its minimum of 5000 rabbits in January. By July, as the weather warms up and food grows more abundant, the population triples in size. By the following January, the population again falls to 5000 rabbits, completing the annual cycle. Use a trigonometric function to find a possible formula for $R = f(t)$, where R is the size of the rabbit population as a function of t, the number of months since January.

Solution   Notice that January is month 0, so July is month 6. The five points in Table 6.6 have been plotted in Figure 6.64 and a curve drawn in. This curve has midline $k = 10,000$, amplitude $|A| = 5000$, and period $= 12$ so $B = 2\pi/12 = \pi/6$. It resembles a cosine function reflected across its midline. Thus, a possible formula for this curve is

$$R = f(t) = -5000\cos\left(\frac{\pi}{6}t\right) + 10,000.$$

There are other possible formulas. For example, we could use a sine function and write

$$R = 5000\sin\left(\frac{\pi}{6}(t-3)\right) + 10,000.$$

Table 6.6   *Rabbit population over time*

t (month)	R
0	5000
6	15,000
12	5000
18	15,000
24	5000

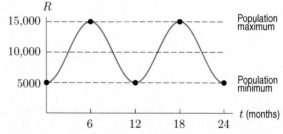

Figure 6.64: The number of rabbits, R, as a function of time in months, t, for $0 \le t \le 24$

Now let's return to the ferris wheel example in Section 6.1.

Example 9   Use the sinusoidal function $f(t) = A\sin(B(t - h)) + k$ to represent your height above ground at time t while riding the ferris wheel.

Solution   The diameter of the ferris wheel is 450 feet, so the midline is $k = 225$ and the amplitude, A, is also 225. The period of the ferris wheel is 30 minutes, so

$$B = \frac{2\pi}{30} = \frac{\pi}{15}.$$

Figure 6.65 shows a sine graph shifted 7.5 minutes to the right because we reach $y = 225$ (the 3 o'clock position) when $t = 7.5$. Thus, the horizontal shift is $h = 7.5$, so

$$f(t) = 225\sin\left(\frac{\pi}{15}(t - 7.5)\right) + 225.$$

Since we can expand and write

$$f(t) = 225\sin\left(\frac{\pi}{15}t - \frac{\pi}{2}\right) + 225,$$

the phase shift is $\pi/2$, corresponding to the fact that we reach $y = 225$ after a quarter of a cycle ($\pi/4$ is a quarter of 2π).

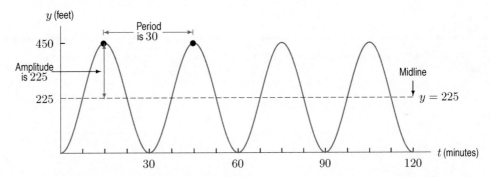

Figure 6.65: Graph of the ferris wheel height function $f(t) = 225\sin(\frac{\pi}{15}(t - 7.5)) + 225$

There are other possible formulas for the function graphed in Figure 6.65. For example, we could have used a cosine reflected about its midline, as in Example 8. (See Problem 32.)

Exercises and Problems for Section 6.5

Exercises

In Exercises 1–4, state the period, amplitude, and midline.

1. $y = 6\sin(t + 4)$

2. $y = 7\sin(4(t + 7)) - 8$

3. $2y = \cos(8(t - 6)) + 2$

4. $y = \pi\cos(2t + 4) - 1$

In Exercises 5–6, what are the horizontal and phase shifts?

5. $y = 2\cos(3t + 4) - 5$

6. $y = -4\cos(7t + 13) - 5$

7. Let $f(x) = \sin(2\pi x)$ and $g(x) = \cos(2\pi x)$. State the periods, amplitudes, and midlines of f and g.

8. Which of the following functions are periodic? Justify your answers. State the periods of those that are periodic.

(a) $y = \sin(-t)$ (b) $y = 4\cos(\pi t)$
(c) $y = \sin(t) + t$ (d) $y = \sin(t/2) + 1$

In Exercises 9–10, estimate the period, amplitude, and midline.

9.

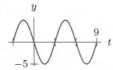

10.

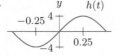

In Exercises 11–18, find formulas for the trigonometric functions.

11.

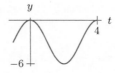

12.

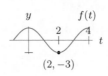

$(2, -3)$

13.

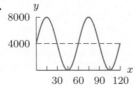

14.

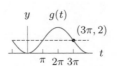

15.

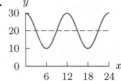

16.

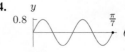

17.

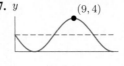

18.

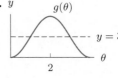

Problems

Without a calculator, graph two periods of the functions in Exercises 19–22.

19. $y = 40\sin\left(\dfrac{2\pi t}{7}\right) + 60$

20. $y = 3 - 2\cos(50\pi t)$

21. $y = 0.001 - 0.003\sin(0.002\pi t)$

22. $y = 12\cos\left(\dfrac{2\pi}{50}t\right) - 24$

For Problems 23–24, you are given a formula for a sinusoidal function f, and graphs of f and a second sinusoidal function g. First, decide by what fraction of a period of f (phase shift) has been shifted to obtain g. Using this, find a formula for g.

23. $f(x) = 3\sin((\pi/4)x)$

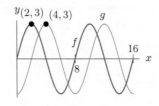

24. $f(x) = 10\sin((\pi/5)x)$

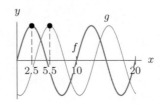

25. Figure 6.66 shows $y = \sin x$ and $y = \sin 2x$. Which graph is $y = \sin x$? Identify the points a to e.

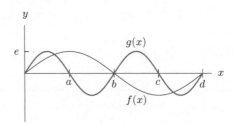

Figure 6.66

26. Describe in words how you can obtain the graph of $y = \cos\left(5t + \dfrac{\pi}{4}\right)$ from the graph of $y = \cos(5t)$.

27. A person's blood pressure, P, (in millimeters of mercury, abbreviated mm Hg) is given, for time, t, in seconds, by

$$P = 100 - 20\cos\left(\frac{8\pi}{3}t\right),$$

Graph this function. State the period and amplitude and explain the practical significance of these quantities.

In Problems 28–29, find a formula, using the sine function, for your height above ground after t minutes on the ferris wheel. Graph the function to check that it is correct.

28. A ferris wheel is 35 meters in diameter and boarded at ground level. The wheel completes one full revolution every 5 minutes. At $t = 0$ you are in the three o'clock position and ascending.

29. A ferris wheel is 20 meters in diameter and boarded in the six o'clock position from a platform that is 4 meters above the ground. The wheel completes one full revolution every 2 minutes. At $t = 0$ you are in the twelve o'clock position.

The graphs in Problems 30–31 show your height h meters above ground after t minutes on various ferris wheels. Using the sine function, find a formula for h as a function of t.

30.

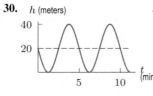

31.

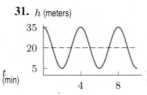

(a) $P = 1500 + 200t$ **(b)** $P = 2700 - 80t$
(c) $P = 1800(1.03)^t$ **(d)** $P = 800e^{-0.04t}$
(e) $P = 230\sin\left(\frac{2\pi}{7}t\right)+3800$

35. A population of animals oscillates between a low of 1300 on January 1 ($t = 0$) and a high of 2200 on July 1 ($t = 6$).

(a) Find a formula for the population, P, in terms of the time, t, in months.
(b) Interpret the amplitude, period, and midline of the function $P = f(t)$.
(c) Use a graph to estimate when $P = 1500$.

36. Find a possible formula for the trigonometric function whose values are in the following table.

x	0	.1	.2	.3	.4	.5	.6	.7	.8	.9	1
$g(x)$	2	2.6	3	3	2.6	2	1.4	1	1	1.4	2

For Problems 37–40, let $f(x) = \sin(2\pi x)$ and $g(x) = \cos(2\pi x)$. Find a possible formula in terms of f or g for the graph.

37.

38.

39.

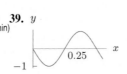

40.

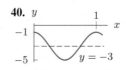

32. Find formula of the form $y = A\cos(B(t - h)) + k$ for the graph in Figure 6.65 on page 275.

33. The London ferris wheel has diameter 450 feet and one complete revolution takes 30 minutes.

(a) Find the rate (in degrees per minute) that the London ferris wheel is rotating.
(b) Let t, the time in minutes, be 0 when you are in the 6 o'clock position. Write θ, measured from the 3 o'clock position, as a function of t.
(c) Find a formula for the ferris wheel function, $h = f(t)$, giving your height in feet above the ground.
(d) Graph $h = f(t)$. What are the period, midline, and amplitude?

34. The following formulas give animal populations as functions of time, t, in years. Describe the growth of each population in words.

41. A company sells $S(t)$ thousand electric blankets in month t (with $t = 0$ being January), where

$$S(t) \approx 72.25 + 41.5\sin\left(\frac{\pi t}{6} + \frac{\pi}{2}\right).$$

Graph this function over one year. Find its period and amplitude and explain their practical significance.

42. The pressure, P (in lbs/ft^2), in a pipe varies over time. Five times an hour, the pressure oscillates from a low of 90 to a high of 230 and then back to a low 90. The pressure at $t = 0$ is 90.

(a) Graph $P = f(t)$, where t is time in minutes. Label your axes.
(b) Find a possible formula for $P = f(t)$.
(c) By graphing $P = f(t)$ for $0 \le t \le 2$, estimate when the pressure first equals 115 lbs/ft^2.

43. A flight from La Guardia Airport in New York City to Logan Airport in Boston has to circle Boston several times before landing. Figure 6.67 shows the graph of the distance, d, of the plane from La Guardia as a function of time, t. Construct a function $f(t)$ whose graph approximates this one. Do this by using different formulas on the intervals $0 \leq t \leq 1$ and $1 \leq t \leq 2$.

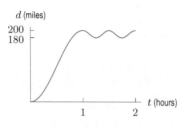

Figure 6.67

44. (a) Graph the data in Table 6.7, which gives the population, P, in thousands, of Somerville, MA, with t in years since 1920.[4]

(b) Based on the data, a researcher decides the population varies in an approximately periodic way with time. Do you agree?

(c) On your graph, sketch in a sine curve that fits your data as closely as possible. Your sketch should capture the overall trend of the data but need not pass through all the data points. [Hint: Start by choosing a midline.]

(d) Find a formula for the curve you drew in part (c).

(e) According to the US census, the population of Somerville in 1910 was $77,236$. How well does this agree with the value given by your formula?

Table 6.7

t	0	10	20	30	40	50	60	70	80
P	93	104	102	102	95	89	77	76	77

45. Table 6.8 shows the average daily maximum temperature in degrees Fahrenheit in Boston each month.[5]

(a) Plot the average daily maximum temperature as a function of the number of months past January.

(b) What are the amplitude and period of the function?

(c) Find a trigonometric approximation of this function.

(d) Use your formula to estimate the daily maximum temperature for October. How well does this estimate agree with the data?

Table 6.8

Month	Jan	Feb	Mar	Apr	May	Jun
Temperature	36.4	37.7	45.0	56.6	67.0	76.6

Month	Jul	Aug	Sep	Oct	Nov	Dec
Temperature	81.8	79.8	72.3	62.5	47.6	35.4

46. The website arXiv.org is used by scientists to share research papers. Figure 6.68 shows usage[6] of this site, $n = f(t)$, the number of new connections on day t, where $t = 0$ is Monday, August 5, 2002.

(a) The graph suggests that f is approximately periodic with a period of 7 days. However, f is not exactly periodic. How can you tell?

(b) Why might the usage of the arXiv.org website lend itself to being modeled by a periodic function?

(c) Find a trigonometric function that gives a reasonable approximation for f. Explain what the period, amplitude, and midline of your function tell you about the usage of the arXiv.org website.

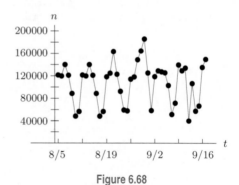

Figure 6.68

47. Table 6.9 gives US petroleum imports, P, in quadrillion BTUs, for t in years since 1900. Plot the data on $73 \leq t \leq 92$ and find a trigonometric function $f(t)$ that approximates US petroleum imports as a function of t.

Table 6.9

t	73	74	75	76	77	78	79	80	81	82
P	14.2	14.5	14	16.5	18	17	17	16	15	14

t	83	84	85	86	87	88	89	90	91	92
P	13	15	12	14	16	17	18	17	16	16

---

[4]From the US census.

[5]Statistical Abstract of the United States.

[6]Data obtained from usage statistics made available at the arXive.org site. Usage statistics for August 28, 2002, are unavailable and have been estimated.

6.6 OTHER TRIGONOMETRIC FUNCTIONS

The Tangent Function

Another useful trigonometric function is called the tangent. Suppose $P = (x, y)$ is the point on the unit circle corresponding to the angle θ. We define the *tangent* of θ, or $\tan \theta$, by

$$\tan \theta = \frac{y}{x}.$$

The graphical interpretation of $\tan \theta$ is as a slope. In Figure 6.69, the slope of the line passing from the origin through P is given by

$$m = \frac{\Delta y}{\Delta x} = \frac{y - 0}{x - 0} = \frac{y}{x},$$

so

$$m = \tan \theta.$$

In words, $\tan \theta$ is the slope of the line passing through the origin and point P.

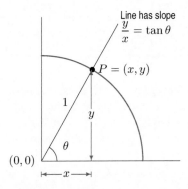

Figure 6.69: The slope of the line passing through the origin and point P is $\tan \theta$

Example 1   Find the slope of the line passing through the origin at an angle of (a) $30°$ (b) $\pi/4$

Solution   (a) A calculator set in degree mode gives

$$\tan 30° \approx 0.577.$$

Thus, the slope of the line is about 0.577.
(b) A calculator set in radian mode gives $\tan(\pi/4) = 1$. This makes sense because an angle of $\pi/4$ describes a ray halfway between the x- and y-axes, or the line $y = x$, which has slope of 1.

Graph of the Tangent Function

Table 6.10 contains values of the tangent function. Figure 6.70 illustrates the connection between an angle θ on the unit circle and the graph of the tangent function. As the angle θ opens from 0 to $\pi/2$, the slope of the line, and therefore the tangent of θ, increases from 0 to $+\infty$. At $\pi/2$, this line

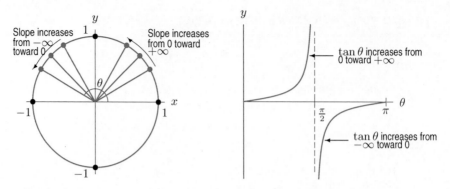

Figure 6.70: The connection between the unit circle and the graph of the tangent function

is vertical, and its slope is undefined. Thus, $\tan(\pi/2)$ is undefined and the graph of $y = \tan\theta$ has a vertical asymptote at $\theta = \pi/2$.

Table 6.10   *Values of tangent function (rounded), with θ in degrees and radians*

θ	$0°$	$30°$	$60°$	$90°$	$120°$	$150°$	$180°$
θ	0	$\pi/6$	$\pi/3$	$\pi/2$	$2\pi/3$	$5\pi/6$	π
$\tan\theta$	0	0.6	1.7	Undefined	-1.7	-0.6	0

For θ between $\pi/2$ and π, the slopes are negative. The line is very steep near $\pi/2$, but becomes less steep as θ approaches π, where it is horizontal. Thus, $\tan\theta$ becomes less negative as θ increases in the second quadrant and reaches 0 at $\theta = \pi$.

For values of θ between π and 2π, observe that

$$\tan(\theta + \pi) = \tan\theta,$$

because the angles θ and $\theta + \pi$ determine the same line through the origin, and hence the same slope. Thus, $y = \tan\theta$ has period π. The completed graph of $y = \tan\theta$ is shown in Figure 6.71.

Notice the differences between the tangent function and the sinusoidal functions. The tangent function has a period of π, whereas the sine and cosine both have periods of 2π. The tangent function has vertical asymptotes at odd multiples of $\pi/2$; the sine and cosine have no asymptotes. Even though the tangent function is periodic, it does not have an amplitude or midline because it does not have a maximum or minimum value.

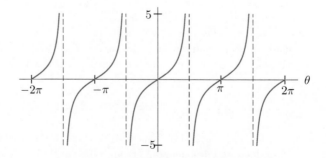

Figure 6.71: The graph of $y = \tan\theta$ in radians

Relationships Between the Trigonometric Functions

There is a relationship among the three trigonometric functions we have defined. If (x, y) are the coordinates of the point P determined by the angle θ on the unit circle, we defined

$$\cos \theta = x \qquad \text{and} \qquad \sin \theta = y.$$

Since $\tan \theta = y/x$, if $x \neq 0$, we have

$$\tan \theta = \frac{\sin \theta}{\cos \theta}.$$

In Problem 26, we see that $\tan \theta$ is an odd function.

Example 2   Calculate the exact value of $\tan(\pi/4)$.

Solution   Since we know $\cos(\pi/4) = \sin(\pi/4) = 1/\sqrt{2}$, we have

$$\tan\left(\frac{\pi}{4}\right) = \frac{\sin(\pi/4)}{\cos(\pi/4)} = \frac{1/\sqrt{2}}{1/\sqrt{2}} = 1.$$

Note that this is the same result as in Example 1.

Because of their definitions in terms of the unit circle, the sine and cosine functions are also related. We have seen that any point on the unit circle has coordinates $(\cos \theta, \sin \theta)$. But we also know that points on the unit circle must satisfy its equation

$$x^2 + y^2 = 1.$$

Substituting $x = \cos \theta$ and $y = \sin \theta$ gives

$$(\cos \theta)^2 + (\sin \theta)^2 = 1,$$

or, writing $\cos^2 \theta$ instead of $(\cos \theta)^2$ and $\sin^2 \theta$ instead of $(\sin \theta)^2$, we have

$$\cos^2 \theta + \sin^2 \theta = 1.$$

If we know which quadrant a given angle is in and we know any one of its three trigonometric values, we can calculate the other two by using these relationships.

Example 3   Check that the relationships between $\sin \theta$, $\cos \theta$, and $\tan \theta$ are satisfied for $\theta = 40°$.

Solution   To three decimal places, a calculator (in degree mode) gives $\sin 40° = 0.643$, $\cos 40° = 0.766$, and $\tan 40° = 0.839$. The fact that

$$\frac{0.643}{0.766} = 0.839,$$

confirms that, to three decimal places,

$$\frac{\sin 40°}{\cos 40°} = \tan 40°.$$

Similarly, to three decimal places, we find that

$$(0.643)^2 + (0.766)^2 = 1,$$

confirming, to the accuracy with which we are working, that

$$\sin^2 40° + \cos^2 40° = 1.$$

Example 4   Suppose that $\cos\theta = 2/3$ and $3\pi/2 \leq \theta \leq 2\pi$. Find $\sin\theta$ and $\tan\theta$.

Solution   Use the relationship $\cos^2\theta + \sin^2\theta = 1$ to find $\sin\theta$. Substitute $\cos\theta = 2/3$:

$$\left(\frac{2}{3}\right)^2 + \sin^2\theta = 1$$

$$\frac{4}{9} + \sin^2\theta = 1$$

$$\sin^2\theta = 1 - \frac{4}{9} = \frac{5}{9}$$

$$\sin\theta = \pm\sqrt{\frac{5}{9}} = \pm\frac{\sqrt{5}}{3}.$$

Because θ is in the fourth quadrant, $\sin\theta$ is negative, so $\sin\theta = -\sqrt{5}/3$. To find $\tan\theta$, use the relationship

$$\tan\theta = \frac{\sin\theta}{\cos\theta} = \frac{-\sqrt{5}/3}{2/3} = -\frac{\sqrt{5}}{2}.$$

The Reciprocals of the Trigonometric Functions: Secant, Cosecant, Cotangent

The reciprocals of the trigonometric functions are given special names. Where the denominators are not equal to zero, we have

$$\text{secant } \theta = \sec\theta = \frac{1}{\cos\theta}.$$

$$\text{cosecant } \theta = \csc\theta = \frac{1}{\sin\theta}.$$

$$\text{cotangent } \theta = \cot\theta = \frac{1}{\tan\theta} = \frac{\cos\theta}{\sin\theta}.$$

The Pythagorean identity, $\cos^2\theta + \sin^2\theta = 1$, can be rewritten in terms of other trigonometric functions. Dividing through by $\cos^2\theta$ gives, provided $\cos\theta \neq 0$,

$$\frac{\cos^2\theta}{\cos^2\theta} + \frac{\sin^2\theta}{\cos^2\theta} = \frac{1}{\cos^2\theta}$$

$$1 + \left(\frac{\sin\theta}{\cos\theta}\right)^2 = \left(\frac{1}{\cos\theta}\right)^2$$

so

$$\boxed{1 + \tan^2\theta = \sec^2\theta.}$$

A similar identity relates $\cot\theta$ and $\csc\theta$. See Problem 27.

Example 5   Use a graph of $g(\theta) = \cos \theta$ to explain the shape of the graph of $f(\theta) = \sec \theta$.

Solution   Figure 6.72 shows the graphs of $\cos \theta$ and $\sec \theta$. In the first quadrant $\cos \theta$ decreases from 1 to 0, so the reciprocal of $\cos \theta$ increases from 1 toward $+\infty$. The values of $\cos \theta$ are negative in the second quadrant and decrease from 0 to -1, so the values of $\sec \theta$ increase from $-\infty$ to -1. The graph of $y = \cos \theta$ is symmetric about the vertical line $\theta = \pi$, so the graph of $f(\theta) = \sec \theta$ is symmetric about the same line. Thus, the graph of $f(\theta) = \sec \theta$ on the interval $\pi \leq \theta \leq 2\pi$ is the mirror image of the graph on $0 \leq \theta \leq \pi$. Note that $\sec \theta$ is undefined wherever $\cos \theta = 0$, namely, at $\theta = \pi/2$ and $\theta = 3\pi/2$. The graph of $f(\theta) = \sec \theta$ has vertical asymptotes at those values.

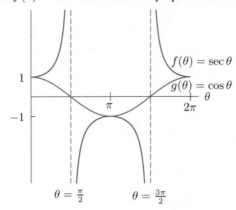

Figure 6.72: Graph of secant

The graphs of $y = \csc \theta$ and $y = \cot \theta$ are obtained in a similar fashion from the graphs of $y = \sin \theta$ and $t = \tan \theta$, respectively. See Figure 6.73 and 6.74.

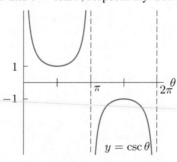

Figure 6.73: Graph of cosecant

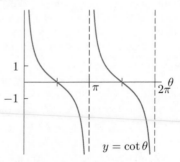

Figure 6.74: Graph of cotangent

Exercises and Problems for Section 6.6

Exercises

1. Find exact values for $\sin 0°$, $\cos 0°$ and $\tan 0°$.

Without a calculator, find exact values for the quantities in Exercises 2–16.

2. $\cos 90°$

3. $\sin 90°$

4. $\tan 90°$

5. $\sin 270°$

6. $\tan 225°$

7. $\tan 135°$

8. $\tan 540°$

9. $\tan \dfrac{5\pi}{4}$

10. $\tan \dfrac{\pi}{3}$

11. $\tan \dfrac{2\pi}{3}$

12. $\tan \dfrac{11\pi}{6}$

13. $\csc \dfrac{5\pi}{4}$

14. $\cot \dfrac{5\pi}{3}$

15. $\sec \left(-\dfrac{\pi}{6}\right)$

16. $\sec \dfrac{11\pi}{6}$

Problems

In Exercises 17–20, give exact answers for $0 \le \theta \le \pi/2$.

17. If $\cos \theta = \frac{1}{2}$, what is $\sec \theta$? $\tan \theta$?

18. If $\cos \theta = \frac{1}{2}$, what is $\csc \theta$? $\cot \theta$?

19. If $\sin \theta = \frac{1}{3}$, what is $\sec \theta$? $\tan \theta$?

20. If $\sec \theta = 17$, what is $\sin \theta$? $\tan \theta$?

In Exercises 21–22, give a possible formula for the function.

21.

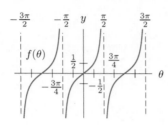

22.

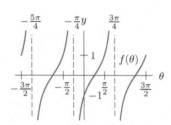

23. **(a)** $\cos \alpha = -\sqrt{3}/5$ and α is in the third quadrant. Find exact values for $\sin \alpha$ and $\tan \alpha$.
   (b) $\tan \beta = 4/3$ and β is in the third quadrant. Find exact values for $\sin \beta$ and $\cos \beta$.

24. **(a)** $\cos \phi = 0.4626$ and $3\pi/2 < \phi < 2\pi$. Find decimal approximations for $\sin \phi$ and $\tan \phi$.
   (b) $\sin \theta = -0.5917$ and $\pi < \theta < 3\pi/2$. Find decimal approximations for $\cos \theta$ and $\tan \theta$.

25. Suppose that $y = \sin \theta$ for $0° < \theta < 90°$. Evaluate $\cos \theta$ in terms of y.

26. Use the fact that sine is an odd function and cosine is an even function to show that tangent is an odd function.

27. Show how to obtain the identity $\cot^2 \theta + 1 = \csc^2 \theta$ from the Pythagorean identity.

Problems 28–31 give an expression for one of the three functions $\sin \theta$, $\cos \theta$, or $\tan \theta$, with θ in the first quadrant. Find expressions for the other two functions. Your answers will be algebraic expressions in terms of x.

28. $\sin \theta = x/3$

29. $\cos \theta = 4/x$

30. $x = 2 \cos \theta$

31. $x = 9 \tan \theta$

32. **(a)** Find an equation for the line l in Figure 6.75.
   (b) Find the x-intercept of the line.

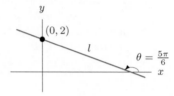

Figure 6.75

33. Use Figure 6.76 to find an equation for the line l in terms of x_0, y_0, and θ.

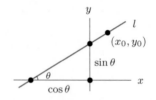

Figure 6.76

34. **(a)** At what values of t does the graph of $y = \tan t$ have vertical asymptotes? What can you say about the graph of $y = \cos t$ at the same values of t?
   (b) At what values of t does the graph of $y = \tan t$ have t-intercepts? What can you say about the graph of $y = \sin t$ at the same values of t?

35. Graph $y = \cos x \cdot \tan x$. Is this function exactly the same as $y = \sin x$? Why or why not?

Find exact values for the lengths of the labeled segments in Problems 36–37.

36.

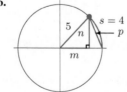

37.

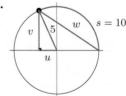

38. Graph the functions $y = \sec x$ and $y = \csc x$, and $y = \cot x$. Describe the behavior of each one.

6.7   INVERSE TRIGONOMETRIC FUNCTIONS

Solving Trigonometric Equations Graphically

A trigonometric equation is an equation that involves trigonometric functions. Consider, for example, the rabbit population of Example 8 on page 274:

$$R = -5000 \cos\left(\frac{\pi}{6}t\right) + 10000.$$

To find when the population reaches 12,000, we need to solve the trigonometric equation

$$-5000 \cos\left(\frac{\pi}{6}t\right) + 10000 = 12{,}000.$$

We can find approximate solutions to trigonometric equations by using a graph. We start with a simpler example.

Example 1   Use a graph to approximate solutions to the equation

$$\cos t = 0.4$$

Solution   We draw a graph of $y = \cos t$ and trace along it on a calculator to find points at which $y = 0.4$ and read off the t-values at these points. In Figure 6.77, the points t_0, t_1, t_2, t_3 represent values of t satisfying $\cos t = 0.4$. If t is in radians, we find $t_0 = -1.159$, $t_1 = 1.159$, $t_2 = 5.12$, $t_3 = 7.44$. We can check these values by evaluating:

$$\cos(-1.159) = 0.40, \quad \cos(1.159) = 0.40, \quad \cos(5.12) = 0.40, \quad \cos(7.44) = 0.40.$$

Notice that because the cosine function is periodic, the equation $\cos t = 0.4$ has infinitely many solutions. The symmetry of the graph suggests that the solutions are related.

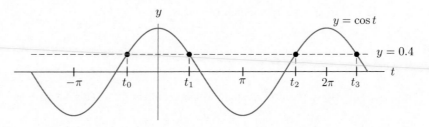

Figure 6.77: The points t_0, t_1, t_2, t_3 are solutions to the equation $\cos t = 0.4$

Solving Trigonometric Equations Using the Inverse Cosine

While trigonometric equations can be solved graphically, there is an another method. Finding a solution to

$$\cos t = 0.4$$

means finding an angle whose cosine is 0.4. In other words, given an output for the cosine function, we want to find the corresponding input. This is what the *inverse cosine*, labeled $\boxed{\cos^{-1}}$ on a calculator, gives us. Evaluating an inverse cosine produces an angle whose cosine is the given value.

A calculator in radian mode gives one of the t-values we found in Example 1:

$$\cos^{-1}(0.4) = 1.159, \qquad \text{where} \qquad \cos(1.159) = 0.4.$$

Notice that the $\boxed{\cos^{-1}}$ key gives only one solution to a trigonometric equation. There are other solutions, which we can find using the symmetry of the cosine graph. Since $t_1 = 1.159$, we see in Figure 6.78 that $t_0 = -1.159$ because the cosine function is symmetric about the y-axis. In addition, the arch of the cosine graph from $-\pi/2$ to $\pi/2$ is exactly the same shape as the arch from $3\pi/2$ to $5\pi/2$, so

$$t_2 = 2\pi - 1.159 = 5.12 \qquad \text{and} \qquad t_3 = 2\pi + 1.159 = 7.44.$$

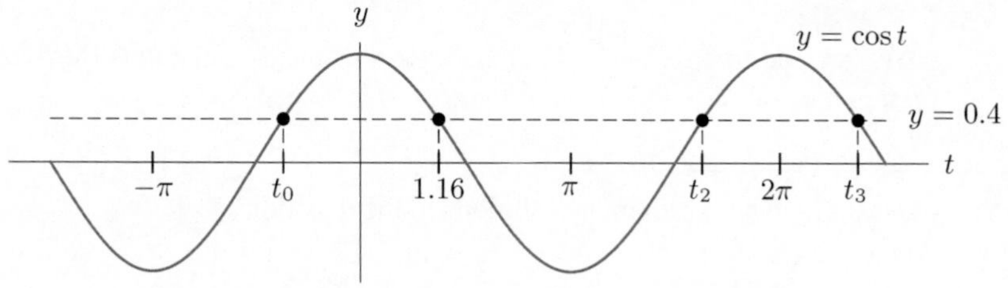

Figure 6.78: Symmetry of cosine graph shows relationship between solutions of $\cos t = 0.4$

Example 2   Use the inverse cosine to estimate when the rabbit population, R, in Example 8 on page 274 reaches 12,000.

Solution   The population is given by

$$R = -5000 \cos\left(\frac{\pi}{6}t\right) + 10000,$$

so we solve the equation

$$-5000 \cos\left(\frac{\pi}{6}t\right) + 10000 = 12000.$$

We first isolate the trigonometric expression $\cos(\pi t/6)$:

$$-5000 \cos\left(\frac{\pi}{6}t\right) = 2000$$

$$\cos\left(\frac{\pi}{6}t\right) = -0.4.$$

To solve for t, we need an angle whose cosine is -0.4. This is what $\cos^{-1}(-0.4)$ gives us. So

$$\frac{\pi}{6}t = \cos^{-1}(-0.4),$$

giving

$$t = \frac{6}{\pi}\cos^{-1}(-0.4).$$

Using a calculator to evaluate $\cos^{-1}(-0.4)$, we see that the solution t_1 in Figure 6.79 is

$$t_1 = \frac{6}{\pi}(1.98) = 3.786.$$

But how do we find the second solution, t_2? Since the graph of R is symmetric about the line $t = 6$, we have

$$t_2 = 12 - t_1 \approx 8.214.$$

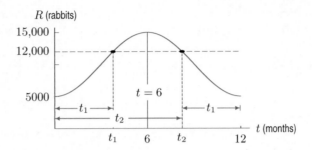

Figure 6.79: By symmetry about the line $t = 6$, we see that $t_2 = 12 - t_1$

The Inverse Cosine Function

As we saw in Figure 6.78 on page 286, the equation

$$\cos t = 0.4$$

has infinitely many solutions. However, the inverse cosine key on a calculator gives only one of them, namely

$$\cos^{-1}(0.4) \approx 1.159,$$

Why does the calculator select this particular solution?

From the graph in Figure 6.80, we see that the angles in the interval $0 \le t \le \pi$ produce all values in the range of $\cos t$ once and once only. By choosing output values for the inverse cosine in this interval, we define a new *function* that assigns just one angle to each possible value of the cosine.[7] (Recall that a function can have only one output for each input value.) This is the function that your calculator evaluates when you press the $\boxed{\cos^{-1}}$ key.

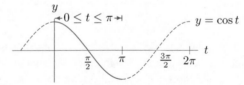

Figure 6.80: The solid portion of this graph represents a function that has only one input value for each output value

The inverse cosine function inputs values of y between -1 and 1 (all possible values of $\cos t$) and outputs angles between 0 and π. We interpret the value of $\cos^{-1}(y)$ as "the angle between 0 and π whose cosine is y." Because an angle in radians determines an arc of the same measure on a unit circle, the inverse cosine of y is sometimes called the *arccosine* of y. We summarize:

The **inverse cosine** function, also called the **arccosine** function, is denoted by $\cos^{-1} y$ or $\arccos y$. We define

$$t = \cos^{-1} y \qquad \text{provided that} \qquad y = \cos t \quad \text{and} \quad 0 \le t \le \pi.$$

In other words, if $t = \arccos y$, then t is the angle between 0 and π whose cosine is y. The domain of the inverse cosine is $-1 \le y \le 1$ and its range is $0 \le t \le \pi$.

---

[7]Other intervals, such as $-\pi \le t \le 0$, could also be used. The interval $0 \le t \le \pi$ has become the agreed upon choice.

Example 3   Evaluate   (a) $\cos^{-1}(0)$ (b) $\arccos(1)$ (c) $\cos^{-1}(-1)$

Solution   (a) $\cos^{-1}(0)$ means the angle between 0 and π whose cosine is 0. Since $\cos(\pi/2) = 0$, we have $\cos^{-1}(0) = \pi/2$.

(b) $\arccos(1)$ means the angle between 0 and π whose cosine is 1. Since $\cos(0) = 1$, we have $\arccos(1) = 0$.

(c) $\cos^{-1}(-1)$ means the angle between 0 and π whose cosine is -1. Since $\cos(\pi) = -1$, we have $\cos^{-1}(-1) = \pi$.

Warning! It is important to realize that the notation $\cos^{-1} y$ does *not* indicate the reciprocal of $\cos y$. In other words, $\cos^{-1} y$ is not the same as $(\cos y)^{-1}$. For example,

$$\cos^{-1}(0) = \frac{\pi}{2} \quad \text{because} \quad \cos\left(\frac{\pi}{2}\right) = 0,$$

but

$$(\cos 0)^{-1} = \frac{1}{\cos 0} = \frac{1}{1} = 1.$$

The Inverse Sine and Inverse Tangent Functions

To solve equations involving sine or tangent, we need an *inverse sine* and an *inverse tangent* function. For example, suppose we want to solve

$$\sin t = 0.8, \qquad 0 \le t \le 2\pi.$$

The inverse sine of 0.8, or $\sin^{-1}(0.8)$, gives us an angle whose sine is 0.8. But there are many angles with a given sine and the inverse sine function specifies only one of them. Just as we did with the inverse cosine, we choose an interval on the t-axis that produces all values in the range of the sine function once and once only.

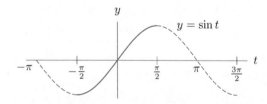

Figure 6.81: The graph of $y = \sin t$, $-\frac{\pi}{2} \le t \le \frac{\pi}{2}$

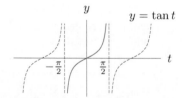

Figure 6.82: The graph of $y = \tan t$, $-\frac{\pi}{2} < t < \frac{\pi}{2}$

Figure 6.81 shows that we cannot choose the same interval that we chose for $\cos t$, which was $0 \le t \le \pi$. However, the interval $-\pi/2 \le t \le \pi/2$ includes a unique angle for each value of $\sin t$. This interval is chosen because it is the smallest interval around $t = 0$ that includes all values of $\sin t$. This same interval, except for the endpoints, is also used to define the inverse tangent function, as illustrated in Figure 6.82.

The **inverse sine** function, also called the **arcsine** function, is denoted by $\sin^{-1} y$ or $\arcsin y$. We define

$$t = \sin^{-1} y \quad \text{provided that} \quad y = \sin t \text{ and } -\frac{\pi}{2} \leq t \leq \frac{\pi}{2}.$$

The domain of the inverse sine is $-1 \leq y \leq 1$ and the range is $-\pi/2 \leq t \leq \pi/2$.
The **inverse tangent** function, also called the **arctangent** function, is denoted by $\tan^{-1} y$ or $\arctan y$. We define

$$t = \tan^{-1} y \quad \text{provided that} \quad y = \tan t \text{ and } -\frac{\pi}{2} < t < \frac{\pi}{2}.$$

The domain of the inverse tangent is $-\infty < y < \infty$ and the range is $-\pi/2 < t < \pi/2$.

Example 4   Evaluate (a) $\sin^{-1}(1)$ (b) $\arcsin(-1)$ (c) $\tan^{-1}(0)$ (d) $\arctan(1)$

Solution   (a) $\sin^{-1}(1)$ means the angle between $-\pi/2$ and $\pi/2$ whose sine is 1. Since $\sin(\pi/2) = 1$, we have $\sin^{-1}(1) = \pi/2$.
(b) $\arcsin(-1) = -\pi/2$ since $\sin(-\pi/2) = -1$.
(c) $\tan^{-1}(0)$ since $\tan 0 = 0$.
(d) $\arctan(1) = \pi/4$ since $\tan(\pi/4) = 1$.

Example 5   Evaluate (a) $\sin^{-1}(-0.5)$ (b) $\arctan(-1)$

Solution   (a) $\sin^{-1}(-0.5)$ is the angle between $-\pi/2 \leq t \leq \pi/2$ whose sine is -0.5. From page 264 we have $\sin(\pi/6) = 0.5$. The sine is an odd function, so $\sin(-\pi/6) = -0.5$, and $\sin^{-1}(-0.5) = -\pi/6$.
(b) The tangent is also an odd function, and $\tan \pi/4 = 1$, so $\tan(-\pi/4) = -1$, and therefore $\arctan(-1) = -\pi/4$.

We can use the inverse sine and inverse tangent to solve equations.

Example 6   While riding the London Eye ferris wheel, how much time during the first turn do you spend above 400 feet?

Solution   Since your first turn takes 30 minutes and your height is given by $f(t) = 225 \sin\left(\frac{\pi}{15}(t - 7.5)\right) + 225$, we must solve the inequality

$$225 \sin\left(\frac{\pi}{15}(t - 7.5)\right) + 225 \geq 400 \qquad \text{for } 0 \leq t \leq 30.$$

This can be simplified as follows:

$$225 \sin\left(\frac{\pi}{15}(t - 7.5)\right) \geq 175$$

$$\sin\left(\frac{\pi}{15}(t - 7.5)\right) \geq \frac{175}{225}.$$

From Figure 6.83, we see that the equation $\sin\left(\frac{\pi}{15}(t-7.5)\right) = \frac{175}{225}$ has two solutions on the interval $0 \leq t \leq 30$. One of them can be found by using the arcsine function:

$$\frac{\pi}{15}(t-7.5) = \arcsin\frac{175}{225}$$

$$t - 7.5 = \frac{15}{\pi}\arcsin\frac{175}{225}$$

$$t = \underbrace{7.5 + \frac{15}{\pi}\arcsin\frac{175}{225}}_{\text{Exact solution}} \approx \underbrace{11.75.}_{\text{Approximate solution}}$$

Since the period of this function is 30, by symmetry the other solution is $30 - 11.75 = 18.25$ minutes. Thus, you spend $18.25 - 11.75 = 6.5$ minutes at a height of 400 feet or more.

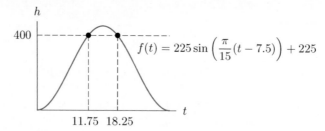

Figure 6.83: On the ferris wheel between $t = 11.75$ minutes and $t = 18.25$ minutes, you are above 400 feet

Solving Equations Using Reference Angles

Because of the symmetry of the unit circle, the values of sine, cosine, and tangent of angles in the first quadrant can be used to find values of these functions for angles in the other three quadrants.

Example 7   Use the values of the sine and cosine of $65°$ to find the sine and cosine of $-65°$, $245°$, and $785°$.

Solution   Let $P = (\cos 65°, \sin 65°) = (0.422, 0.906)$ be the point on the unit circle given by the angle $65°$. In Figure 6.84, we see that $-65°$ gives a point labeled Q that is the reflection of P across the x-axis. Thus, the y-coordinate of Q is the negative of the y-coordinate of P, so $Q = (0.422, -0.906)$. This means that

$$\sin(-65°) = -0.906 \quad \text{and} \quad \cos(-65°) = 0.422.$$

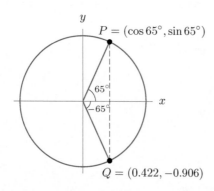

Figure 6.84: The angles $65°$ and $-65°$

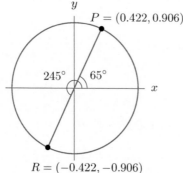

Figure 6.85: The angles $65°$ and $245°$

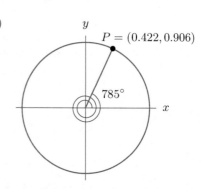

Figure 6.86: The angle $785°$

In Figure 6.85, we see that $245° = 180° + 65°$ gives point R that is diametrically opposite the point P. The coordinates of R are the negatives of the coordinates of P, so $R = (-0.422, -0.906)$. Thus,

$$\sin 245° = -0.906 \quad \text{and} \quad \cos 245° = -0.422.$$

Finally in Figure 6.86, we see that $785° = 720° + 65°$, so this angle specifies the same point as $65°$. This means that

$$\sin 785° = 0.906 \quad \text{and} \quad \cos 785° = 0.422.$$

Because we have used the sine and cosine values of $65°$ to find the sine and cosine values of $-65°$, $245°$, and $785°$, we call $65°$ the *reference angle* for the angles $-65°$, $245°$, and $785°$.

For an angle θ corresponding to the point P on the unit circle, the **reference angle** of θ is the angle between the line joining P to the origin and the nearest part of the x-axis. See Figure 6.87. A reference angle is always between $0°$ and $90°$; that is, between 0 and $\pi/2$.

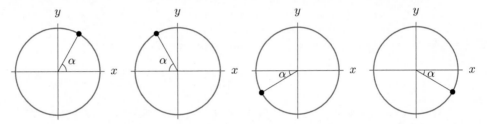

Figure 6.87: In each figure, α is the reference angle for the angle corresponding to P

Example 8   Use reference angles to solve the equations
(a) $\cos \theta = 0.422$ for $0° \le \theta \le 360°$.   (b) $\tan \theta = 2.145$ for $0° \le \theta \le 720°$.

Solution   (a) Since $\cos(65°) = 0.422$, a calculator set in degrees gives $\cos^{-1}(0.422) = 65°$. We see in Figure 6.84 that all the angles with a cosine of 0.422 correspond either to the point P or to the point Q. We want solutions between $0°$ and $360°$, so Q is represented by $360° - 65° = 295°$. Thus, the solutions are

$$\theta = 65° \quad \text{and} \quad \theta = 295°.$$

(b) A calculator gives $\tan^{-1}(2.145) = 65°$. Since $\tan \theta$ is positive in the first and third quadrants, the angles with a tangent of 2.145 correspond either to the point P or the point R in Figure 6.85. Since we are interested in solutions between $0°$ and $720°$, the solutions are

$$\theta = 65°, \quad 245°, \quad 65° + 360°, \quad 245° + 360°.$$

That is

$$\theta = 65°, \quad 245°, \quad 425°, \quad 605°.$$

Example 9   Find all solutions of $\cos \theta = -0.422$ for $0° \leq \theta \leq 720°$.

Solution   Since $\cos^{-1}(-0.422) = 115°$, the angles we want correspond to the points P or Q in Figure 6.88. Both these points have reference angles of $65°$, so the solutions are

$$\theta = 115° \quad \text{and} \quad \theta = 180° + 65° = 245°.$$
$$\theta = 360° + 115° = 475° \quad \text{and} \quad \theta = 360° + 245° = 605°.$$

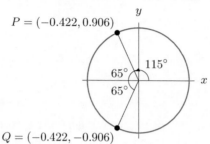

Figure 6.88: Points corresponding to angles with $\cos \theta = -0.422$

Example 10   Use reference angles to solve the equation from Example 6:

$$\sin\left(\frac{\pi}{15}(t - 7.5)\right) = \frac{175}{225} \quad \text{for } 0 \leq t \leq 30.$$

Solution   As in Example 6, the first solution is given by the arcsine. Solving for t in the equation

$$\frac{\pi}{15}(t - 7.5) = \arcsin\frac{175}{225} = 0.891$$

gives $t = 11.75$ minutes. The second solution corresponds to another point on the circle with the same reference angle, 0.891, and a positive value of the sine. This is in the second quadrant, so we have

$$\frac{\pi}{15}(t - 7.5) = \pi - 0.891.$$

Solving for t in this equation gives $t = 18.25$ minutes, as in Example 6.

Exercises and Problems for Section 6.7

Exercises

In Exercises 1–6, find a solution with θ in radians (if possible).   In Exercises 7–14, solve the equation exactly for $0 \leq t \leq 2\pi$.

1. $\tan \theta = 947$

2. $\sin \theta = 4/7$

3. $3\cos \theta = 0.714$

4. $\cos(\theta - 2) = -50$

5. $\tan(5\theta + 7) = -0.241$

6. $2\sin(4\theta) = 0.667$

7. $\sin t = -1$

8. $\sin t = 1/2$

9. $\cos t = -1$

10. $\cos t = 1/2$

11. $\tan t = 1$

12. $\tan t = -1$

13. $\tan t = \sqrt{3}$

14. $\tan t = 0$

15. (a) Use a graph of $y = \cos t$ to estimate two solutions to the equation $\cos t = -0.3$ for $0 \le t \le 2\pi$.
(b) Solve the same equation using the inverse cosine.

16. (a) Find exact solutions to the equation $\cos t = 1/2$ with $-2\pi \le t \le 2\pi$. Plot them on a graph of $y = \cos t$.
(b) Using a unit circle, explain how many solutions to the equation $\cos t = 1/2$ you would expect in the interval $0 \le t \le 2\pi$.

In Exercises 17–24, find the reference angle.

17. $13\pi/6$ **18.** $-7\pi/3$ **19.** $10\pi/3$ **20.** $11\pi/4$

21. $73\pi/3$ **22.** $-46\pi/7$ **23.** 18   **24.** -22

25. Without a calculator, find exact values for
(a) $\cos 120°$ **(b)** $\sin 135°$
(c) $\cos 225°$ **(d)** $\sin 300°$

26. Without a calculator, find exact values for:
(a) $\sin\left(\dfrac{2\pi}{3}\right)$ **(b)** $\cos\left(\dfrac{3\pi}{4}\right)$
(c) $\tan\left(-\dfrac{3\pi}{4}\right)$ **(d)** $\cos\left(\dfrac{11\pi}{6}\right)$

In Exercises 27–29, use a graph to estimate all the solutions of the equations between 0 and 2π.

27. $\sin\theta = 0.65$ **28.** $\tan x = 2.8$ **29.** $\cos t = -0.24$

Problems

In Problems 30–35, find all solutions to the equation for $0 \le x \le 2\pi$.

30. $\cos x = 0.6$ **31.** $2\sin x = 1 - \sin x$
32. $5\cos x = 1/\cos x$ **33.** $\sin 2x = 0.3$
34. $\sin(x - 1) = 0.25$ **35.** $5\cos(x + 3) = 1$

In Problems 36–39, use inverse trigonometric functions to find a solution to the equation in the given interval. Then, use a graph to find all other solutions to the equation on this interval.

36. $\cos x = 0.6$, $0 \le x \le 4\pi$
37. $\sin x = 0.3$, $0 \le x \le 2\pi$
38. $\cos x = -0.7$, $0 \le x \le 2\pi$
39. $\sin x = -0.8$, $0 \le x \le 4\pi$

Find exact solutions to the equations in Problems 40–42.

40. $\sin\theta = -\sqrt{2}/2$ **41.** $\cos\theta = \sqrt{3}/2$
42. $\tan\theta = -\sqrt{3}/3$

43. Find the angle θ, in radians, in the second quadrant whose tangent is -3.
44. Solve for α exactly: $\sec^2\alpha + 3\tan\alpha = \tan\alpha$ with $0 \le \alpha < 2\pi$.

Solve the equations in Problems 45–48 for $0 \le t \le 2\pi$. First estimate answers from a graph; then find exact answers.

45. $\cos(2t) = \dfrac{1}{2}$ **46.** $\tan t = \dfrac{1}{\tan t}$
47. $2\sin t \cos t - \cos t = 0$ **48.** $3\cos^2 t = \sin^2 t$

49. A tree 50 feet tall casts a shadow 60 feet long. Find the angle of elevation θ of the sun.

50. A staircase is to rise 17.3 feet over a horizontal distance of 10 feet. At approximately what angle with respect to the floor should it be built?

51. A company's sales are seasonal with the peak in mid-December and the lowest point in mid-June. The company makes $100,000 in sales in December, and only $20,000 in June.

(a) Find a trigonometric function, $s = f(t)$, representing sales at time t months after mid-January.
(b) What would you expect the sales to be for mid-April?
(c) Find the t-values for which $s = 60,000$. Interpret your answer.

52. In a tidal river, the time between high tide and low tide is 6.2 hours. At high tide the depth of the water is 17.2 feet, while at low tide the depth is 5.6 feet. Assume the water depth is a trigonometric function of time.

(a) Graph the depth of the water over time if there is a high tide at 12:00 noon. Label your graph, indicating the high and low tide.
(b) Write an equation for the curve you drew in part (a).
(c) A boat requires a depth of 8 feet to sail, and is docked at 12:00 noon. What is the latest time in the afternoon it can set sail? Your answer should be accurate to the nearest minute.

53. Approximate the x-coordinates of points P and Q shown in Figure 6.89, assuming that the curve is a sine curve. [Hint: Find a formula for the curve.]

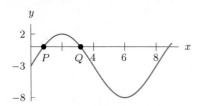

Figure 6.89

54. In your own words, explain what each of the following expressions means. Evaluate each expression for $x = 0.5$. Give an exact answer if possible.

(a) $\sin^{-1} x$ (b) $\sin(x^{-1})$ (c) $(\sin x)^{-1}$.

55. Evaluate the following expressions in radians. Give an exact answer if possible.

(a) $\arccos(0.5)$ (b) $\arccos(-1)$ (c) $\arcsin(0.1)$

56. Use a graph to find all the solutions to the equation $12 - 4\cos 3t = 14$ between 0 and $2\pi/3$ (one cycle). How many solutions are there between 0 and 2π?

57. Approximate the zero(s) of $f(t) = 3 - 5\sin(4t)$ for $0 \le t < \pi/2$.

(a) Graphically.   (b) Using the arcsine function.

58. State the domain and range of the following functions and explain what your answers mean in terms of evaluating the functions.

(a) $f(x) = \sin^{-1} x$ (b) $g(x) = \cos^{-1} x$
(c) $h(x) = \tan^{-1} x$

59. One of the following statements is always true; the other is true for some values of x and not for others. Which is which? Justify your answer with an example.

I. $\arcsin(\sin x) = x$ II. $\sin(\arcsin x) = x$

60. Let k be a positive constant and t be an angle measured in radians. Consider the equation

$$k \sin t = t^2.$$

(a) Explain why any solution to the equation must be between $-\sqrt{k}$ and $\sqrt{k}$, inclusive.
(b) Approximate every solution to the equation when $k = 2$.
(c) Explain why the equation has more solutions for larger values of k than it does for small values.
(d) Approximate the least value of k, if any, for which the equation has a negative solution.

61. You are perched in the crow's nest, C, on top of the mast of a ship, S. See Figure 6.90. You will calculate how far you can see when you are x meters above the surface of the ocean.

(a) Find formulas for d, the distance you can see to the horizon, H, and l, the distance to the horizon along the earth's surface, in terms of x, the height of the ship's mast, and r, the radius of the earth.
(b) How far is the horizon from the top of a 50-meter mast? How far, measured along the earth's surface, is the horizon from the ship's position on the ocean? Use $r = 6{,}370{,}000$ meters.

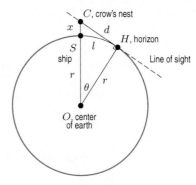

Figure 6.90

62. Let ℓ_1 and ℓ_2 be non-parallel lines of slope m_1 and m_2, respectively, where $m_1 > m_2 > 0$. Find a formula for θ, the angle formed by the intersection of these two lines, in terms of m_1 and m_2. See Figure 6.91.

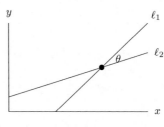

Figure 6.91

CHAPTER SUMMARY

- **Periodic Functions**
  Period: smallest c such that $f(x + c) = f(x)$.

  $$\sin(t+2\pi) = \sin t; \cos(t+2\pi) = \cos t; \tan(t+\pi) = \tan t.$$

- **Sine and Cosine**
  Angles as rotations correspond to points on circle.
  Coordinates on unit circle: $x = \cos\theta; y = \sin\theta$.

- **Radians**
  Definition. Relationship to degrees: 2π radians $= 360°$.
  Arc length: $s = r\theta$.

- **Sinusoidal Functions**
  General formulas

  $$y = A\sin(B(t - h)) + k,$$
  $$y = A\cos(B(t - h)) + k.$$

  Amplitude $= |A|$; period $= 2\pi/|B|$; midline $y = k$.
  Phase shift $= Bh$; horizontal shift $= h$.

- **Other Trigonometric Functions**
  Tangent, secant, cosecant, and cotangent.

- **Identities:**

  $$\tan\theta = \frac{\sin\theta}{\cos\theta};$$
  $$\cos^2\theta + \sin^2\theta = 1.$$

- **Inverse Trig Functions**
  Inverse cosine:

  $$\cos^{-1} y = t \text{ means } y = \cos t \text{ for } 0 \le t \le \pi.$$

  Inverse sine:

  $$\sin^{-1} y = t \text{ means } y = \sin t \text{ for } -\pi/2 \le t \le \pi/2.$$

  Inverse tangent:

  $$\tan^{-1} y = t \text{ means } y = \tan t \text{ for } -\pi/2 \le t \le \pi/2.$$

  Reference angles; solving equations.

REVIEW EXERCISES AND PROBLEMS FOR CHAPTER SIX

Exercises

1. The sinusoidal curves in Figure 6.92 model three different traffic patterns: (i) moderately heavy traffic with some slow-downs; (ii) stop-and-go rush hour traffic; and (iii) light, fast-moving traffic. Which is which?

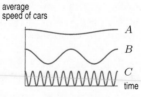

Figure 6.92

2. Find approximations to two decimal places for the coordinates of point Z in Figure 6.93.

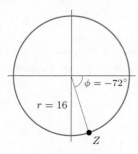

Figure 6.93

3. In which quadrants do the following statements hold?
   (a) $\sin\theta > 0$ and $\cos\theta > 0$
   (b) $\tan\theta > 0$
   (c) $\tan\theta < 0$
   (d) $\sin\theta < 0$ and $\cos\theta > 0$
   (e) $\cos\theta < 0$ and $\tan\theta > 0$

In Exercises 4–7, convert the angle to radians.

4. $330°$ 5. $315°$ 6. $-225°$ 7. $6\pi°$

In Exercises 8–10, convert the angle from radians to degrees.

8. $\frac{3}{2}\pi$ 9. 180 10. $5\pi/\pi$

In Exercises 11–13, what angle in radians corresponds to the given number of rotations around the unit circle?

11. 4   12. -6 13. 16.4

14. If you start at the point $(1, 0)$ on the unit circle and travel counterclockwise through the given angle (in radians), in which quadrant will you be?

   (a) 2   (b) 4   (c) 6   (d) 1.5   (e) 3.2

In Exercises 15–17, find the arc length corresponding to the given angle on a circle of radius 6.2.

15. $17°$ **16.** $-585°$ **17.** $-\dfrac{360°}{\pi}$

18. Without a calculator, match the graphs in Figure 6.94 to the following functions:

(a) $y = \sin(2t)$ (b) $y = (\sin t) + 2$
(c) $y = 2\sin t$ (d) $y = \sin(t + 2)$

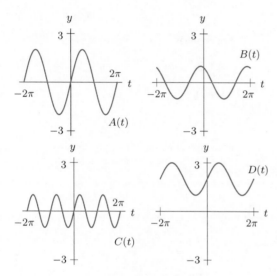

Figure 6.94

In Exercises 19–21, state the period, amplitude, and midline.

19. $y = \cos t + 3$

20. $y = \sin(t + 3) + 7$

21. $6y = 12\sin(\pi t - 7) + 42$

State the amplitude, period, phase shift, and horizontal shifts for the function in Exercises 22–25. Without a calculator, graph the function on the given interval.

22. $y = -4\sin t,\quad -2\pi \le t \le 2\pi$

23. $y = -20\cos(4\pi t),\quad -\frac{3}{4} \le t \le 1$

24. $y = \cos\left(2t + \dfrac{\pi}{2}\right),\quad -\pi \le t \le 2\pi$

25. $y = 3\sin(4\pi t + 6\pi),\quad -\frac{3}{2} \le t \le \frac{1}{2}$

In Exercises 26–29, estimate the amplitude, midline, and period of the sinusoidal functions.

26.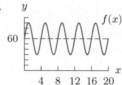

27.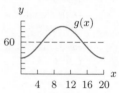

28.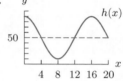

29.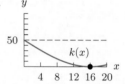

30. Using only vertical shifts, stretches, and flips, and horizontal stretches (but no horizontal shifts or flips), would we start with $y = \sin x$ or $y = \cos x$ if we wanted to find a formula for the functions shown in Problems 26–29?

Without a calculator, graph two periods of the functions in Exercises 31–34.

31. $y = \sin(\frac{1}{2}t)$ **32.** $y = 4\cos(t + \frac{\pi}{4})$

33. $y = 5 - \sin t$ **34.** $y = \cos(2t) + 4$

Problems

In Exercises 35–37, find exact values without a calculator.

35. $\cos 540°$ **36.** $\sin \dfrac{7\pi}{6}$ **37.** $\tan\left(-\dfrac{2\pi}{3}\right)$

38. Find $\tan \theta$ exactly if $\sin \theta = -3/5$, and θ is in the fourth quadrant.

In Exercises 39–40, find a solution with θ in radians (if possible).

39. $\sin \theta = 2/5$ **40.** $\tan(\theta - 1) = 0.17$

41. Find the radian value of x in Figure 6.95.

Figure 6.95

42. (a) Find a sinusoidal formula for the graph in Figure 6.96.
   (b) Find x_1 and x_2.

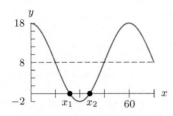

Figure 6.96

43. (a) Find a sinusoidal formula for f in Figure 6.97.
   (b) Find the x-coordinates of the three indicated points.

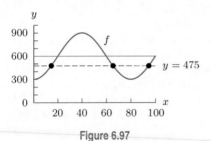

Figure 6.97

For the functions graphed in Problems 44–47, find four possible formulas for the function: $f_1(x) = A\cos(B(x - h)) + k$, where $A > 0$, $f_2(x) = A\cos(B(x - h)) + k$, where $A < 0$, $f_3(x) = A\sin(B(x - h)) + k$, where $A > 0$, and $f_4(x) = A\sin(B(x - h)) + k$, where $A < 0$.

44.

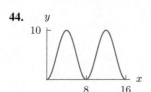

45.

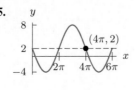

46.

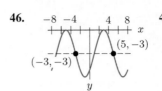

47.

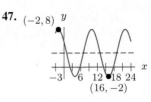

In Problems 48–53, solve the equations with $0 \le \alpha < 2\pi$. Give exact answers if possible.

48. $2\cos\alpha = 1$

49. $\tan\alpha = \sqrt{3} - 2\tan\alpha$

50. $\sin(2\alpha) + 3 = 4$

51. $4\tan\alpha + 3 = 2$

52. $3\sin^2\alpha + 4 = 5$

53. $\tan^2\alpha = 2\tan\alpha$

54. How far does the tip of the minute hand of a clock move in 1 hour and 27 minutes if the hand is 2 inches long?

55. How many miles on the surface of the earth correspond to one degree of latitude? (The earth's radius is 3960 miles.)

56. A person on earth is observing the moon, which is 238,860 miles away. The moon has a diameter of 2160 miles. What is the angle in degrees spanned by the moon in the eye of the beholder?

57. A compact disk is 12 cm in diameter and rotates at 100 rpm (revolutions per minute) when being played. The hole in the center is 1.5 cm in diameter. Find the speed in cm/min of a point on the outer edge of the disk and the speed of a point on the inner edge.

58. Explain in words the difference between the expressions $\sin^2\theta$ and $\sin\theta^2$. Give a specific numerical example illustrating the difference between these expressions.

59. A weather satellite orbits the earth in a circular orbit 500 miles above the earth's surface. What is the radian measure of the angle (measured at the center of the earth) through which the satellite moves in traveling 600 miles along its orbit? (The radius of the earth is 3960 miles.)

60. A weight is suspended from the ceiling by a spring. Figure 6.98 shows a graph of the distance from the ceiling to the weight, $d = f(t)$, as a function of time.

(a) Find a possible formula for $f(t)$.
(b) Solve $f(t) = 12$ exactly. Interpret your results.

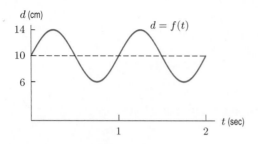

Figure 6.98

61. An animal population increases from a low of 1200 in year $t = 0$, to a high of 3000 four years later and then decreases back to 1200 over the next four years. Model this behavior by a sinusoidal function.

62. Table 6.11 gives the average monthly temperature, y, in degrees Fahrenheit for the city of Fairbanks, Alaska, as a function of t, the month, where $t = 0$ indicates January.

(a) Plot the data points. On the same graph, draw a curve which fits the data.
(b) What kind of function best fits the data? Be specific.
(c) Find a formula for a function, $f(t)$, that models the temperature. [Note: There are many correct answers.]
(d) Use your answer to part (c) to solve $f(t) = 32$. Interpret your results.
(e) Check your results from part (d) graphically.
(f) In the southern hemisphere, the times at which summer and winter occur are reversed, relative to the northern hemisphere. Modify your formula from part (c) so that it represents the average monthly temperature for a southern-hemisphere city whose summer and winter temperatures are similar to Fairbanks.

Table 6.11

t	0	1	2	3	4	5
y	-11.5	-9.5	0.5	18.0	36.9	53.1
t	6	7	8	9	10	11
y	61.3	59.9	48.8	31.7	12.2	-3.3

63. The data in Table 6.12 gives the height above the floor of a weight bobbing on a spring attached to the ceiling. Fit a sine function to this data.

Table 6.12

t, sec	0.0	0.1	0.2	0.3	0.4	0.5
y, cm	120	136	165	180	166	133
t, sec	0.6	0.7	0.8	0.9	1.0	1.1
y, cm	120	135	164	179	165	133

64. In climates that require central heating, the setting of a household thermostat gives the temperature at which the furnace turns on. Water is boiled, and steam is forced into radiators that warm the house. Once the household temperature reaches the thermostat setting, the furnace shuts off. However, the radiators remain hot for some time, and so the household temperature continues rising for a while before it starts to drop. Once it drops back to the thermostat setting, the furnace relights, and the cycle begins anew. As it takes some time for the radiators to reheat, the house continues to cool even after the furnace has turned back on. The household temperature is represented by the graph in Figure 6.99.

(a) The household temperature, T, can be modeled by a trigonometric function. Assume the furnace spends as much time on as it does off. What is the setting on the thermostat?
(b) According to the graph, describe what is happening at $t = 0, 0.25, 0.5, 0.75, 1$.
(c) Give a formula for $T = f(t)$, the temperature in terms of time, t, in hours.
(d) Describe the physical significance of the period, the amplitude, and the midline.
(e) The house described in this problem takes as much time to heat up as it does to cool down. Suppose another house takes 15 minutes to heat up but 45 minutes to cool. Sketch (roughly) its temperature over one hour. Label any significant points (such as times the furnace turns on or off). Is this the graph of a trigonometric function?

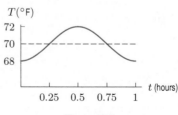

Figure 6.99

CHECK YOUR UNDERSTANDING

Are the statements in Problems 1–11 true or false for all values of x? Give an explanation for your answer.

1. $\sin(-x) = -\sin x$

2. $\cos(-x) = -\cos x$

3. $\sin(-x) = \sin x$

4. $\cos(-x) = \cos x$

5. $\sin(x + \pi) = -\sin x$

6. $\cos(x + \pi) = \sin x$

7. $\cos(x + 4\pi) = \cos x$

8. $2\cos x = \cos(2x)$

9. $\cos\left(\dfrac{1}{x}\right) = \dfrac{\cos 1}{\cos x}$

10. $\sec^2 x + 1 = \tan^2 x.$

11. $\cos(x + 1) = \cos x + \cos 1$

Are the statements in Problems 12–87 true or false? Give an explanation for your answer.

12. If $f(t)$ and $g(t)$ are periodic functions with period A and $f(t) = g(t)$ for $0 \le t < A$, then $f(t) = g(t)$ for all t.

13. The function $\sin x$ has period 2π.

14. The function $\sin(\pi x)$ has period π.

15. A parabola is a periodic function.

16. If f is a periodic function, then there exists a constant c such that $f(x + c) = f(x)$ for all x in the domain of f.

17. The smallest positive constant c for which $f(x + c) = f(x)$ is called the period of f.

18. The amplitude of a periodic function is the difference between its maximum and minimum values.

19. The midline of a periodic function is the horizontal line $y = \dfrac{\text{Maximum} + \text{Minimum}}{2}.$

20. A unit circle may have a radius of 3.

21. The angle $\theta = 180°$ specifies the point $(0, -1)$ on the unit circle.

22. The point $(1, 0)$ on the unit circle corresponds to $\theta = 0°$.

23. If $P = (x, y)$ is a point on the unit circle and θ is the corresponding angle then $\sin \theta = y$.

24. The coordinates of the point of intersection of the terminal ray of a $240°$ angle with a circle of radius 2 are $(-\sqrt{3}, -1)$.

25. If a point (x, y) is on the circumference of a circle of radius r and the corresponding angle is θ, then $x = r\cos\theta$.

26. In Figure 6.100, the points P and Q on the unit circle correspond to angles with the same cosine values.

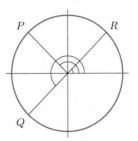

Figure 6.100

27. In Figure 6.100, the points P and R on the unit circle correspond to angles with the same sine values.

28. The point on the unit circle whose coordinates are $(\cos 200°, \sin 200°)$ is in the third quadrant.

29. The point on the unit circle whose coordinates are $(\cos(-200°), \sin(-200°))$ is in the third quadrant.

30. An angle of one radian is about equal to an angle of one degree.

31. The radian measure of an angle is the length of the arc spanned by the angle in a unit circle.

32. An angle of three radians corresponds to a point in the third quadrant.

33. To convert an angle from degrees to radians you multiply the angle by $\dfrac{180°}{\pi}$.

34. The length of an arc s spanned in a circle of radius 3 by an angle of $\dfrac{\pi}{3}$ is 180.

35. An angle of $2\pi/3$ radians corresponds to a point in the second quadrant.

36. In a unit circle, one complete revolution about the circumference is about 6.28 radians.

37. The cosine of $30°$ is the same as $\sin(\pi/3)$.

38. $\sin(\pi/6) = \sqrt{3}/2.$

39. $\sin(\pi/4) = \cos(\pi/4).$

40. $-\sin(\pi/3) = \sin(-\pi/3).$

41. The value of $\cos 315°$ is $-\sqrt{2}/2.$

42. The function in Figure 6.101 appears to be periodic with period less than 5.

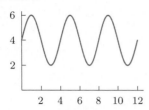

Figure 6.101

43. In Figure 6.101, the amplitude of the function is 6.

44. In Figure 6.101, the period of the function is 4.

45. In Figure 6.101, the midline has equation $y = 4$.

46. In Figure 6.101, the function $g(x) = f(2x)$ has the same period as f.

47. The amplitude of $y = -3\sin(2x) + 4$ is -3.

48. The amplitude of $y = 25 + 10\cos x$ is 25.

49. The period of $y = 25 + 10\cos x$ is 2π.

50. The maximum y-value of $y = 25 + 10\cos x$ is 10.

51. The minimum y-value of $y = 25 + 10\cos x$ is 15.

52. The midline equation for $y = 25 + 10\cos x$ is $y = 35$.

53. The function $\cos x$ is a sinusoidal function.

54. The function $y = -2\sin x + k$ has amplitude -2.

55. The graph of the function $y = 3\cos x - 4$ is the graph of the function $y = \cos x$ reflected across the x-axis.

56. The function $f(t) = \sin(2t)$ has period π.

57. The function $f(x) = \cos(3x)$ has a period three times as large as the function $g(x) = \cos x$.

58. Changing the value of B in the function $y = A\sin(Bx) + k$ changes the period of the function.

59. The graph of $y = A\sin(2x + h) + k$ is the graph of $y = A\sin(2x) + k$ shifted to the left by h units.

60. A sinusoidal function that has a midline of $y = 5$, an amplitude of 3, and completes 4 cycles in the interval $0 \leq x \leq 2\pi$ could have the equation $y = -3\cos(4x) + 5$.

61. The function graphed in Figure 6.102 could have the equation $y = \frac{1}{2}\sin(2x) + 1$.

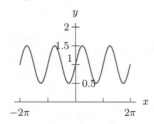

Figure 6.102

62. The function graphed in Figure 6.102 could have the equation $y = -0.5\cos(2x + \frac{\pi}{3}) + 1$.

63. For all values of θ where $\cos\theta \neq 0$, we have $\tan\theta = \dfrac{\sin\theta}{\cos\theta}$.

64. The tangent function is defined everywhere on the interval $0 \leq x \leq 2\pi$.

65. The tangent function has a period of π.

66. The tangent of $\pi/2$ is infinite.

67. For any value x, we have $\sin^2 5x + \cos^2 5x = 1$.

68. If θ is in the second quadrant, then $\tan\theta$ could equal $\frac{3}{4}$.

69. The value of $\sec\pi = -1$.

70. Since the value of $\sin\pi = 0$, the value of $\csc\pi$ is undefined.

71. The reciprocal of the sine function is the cosine function.

72. If $y = \arccos 0.5$, then $y = \frac{\pi}{3}$.

73. If $y = \arctan(-1)$, then $\sin y = -\sqrt{2}/2$.

74. $\sin^{-1}(\sqrt{3}/2) = \pi/3$.

75. $\cos(\cos^{-1}(2/3)) = 2/3$.

76. If $y = \sin^{-1} x$ then $y = \dfrac{1}{\sin x}$.

77. The domain of the inverse cosine is all real numbers.

78. If $\cos t = 1$, then $\tan t = 0$.

79. The reference angle for $120°$ is $30°$.

80. The reference angle for $300°$ is $60°$.

81. If $\arcsin x = 0.5$ then $x = \pi/6$.

82. If $\cos\theta = \dfrac{\sqrt{2}}{2}$ then θ must be $\dfrac{\pi}{4}$.

83. For all angles θ in radians, $\arccos(\cos\theta) = \theta$.

84. For all values of x between -1 and 1, $\cos(\arccos x) = x$.

85. If $\tan A = \tan B$, then $\dfrac{A - B}{\pi}$ is an integer.

86. If $\cos A = \cos B$, then $\sin A = \sin B$.

87. If $\cos A = \cos B$, then $B = A + 2n\pi$ for some integer n.

TOOLS FOR CHAPTER 6: RIGHT TRIANGLES

For most of recorded history, people have used the properties of triangles to make indirect measurements of the world around them. In the fourth century BC, the Greek mathematician Eudoxus used trigonometry (which means, literally, *triangle measurement*) to calculate the radius of the earth. Today scientists and engineers, surveyors, and contractors still use trigonometry.

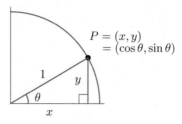

Figure 6.103: A right triangle shown with the unit circle

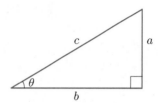

Figure 6.104: A triangle which is similar to the triangle in Figure 6.103

There is a relationship between the trigonometric functions and right triangles. An angle θ determines a point P on the unit circle in Figure 6.103. The angle θ also determines the right triangle with hypotenuse of length 1; the other sides of this triangle have lengths $x = \cos\theta$ and $y = \sin\theta$. The right triangle in Figure 6.104 also has an angle θ, so these two triangles are similar. Therefore, the ratios of the lengths of their corresponding sides are equal:

$$\frac{a}{c} = \frac{\sin\theta}{1} = \sin\theta \qquad \text{and} \qquad \frac{b}{c} = \frac{\cos\theta}{1} = \cos\theta.$$

In addition,

$$\frac{a}{b} = \frac{\sin\theta}{\cos\theta} = \tan\theta.$$

The side directly across from the angle θ is referred to as the *opposite* side, and the other side, which forms one side of the angle θ, is called the *adjacent* side. Using this terminology we have:

> If θ is an angle in a right triangle (other than the right angle),
>
> $$\sin\theta = \frac{\text{Opposite}}{\text{Hypotenuse}}, \qquad \cos\theta = \frac{\text{Adjacent}}{\text{Hypotenuse}}, \qquad \tan\theta = \frac{\text{Opposite}}{\text{Adjacent}}.$$

Special Angles: 30°, 45°, 60°

We use right triangles to calculate exact values of the sine, cosine, and tangent of 30°, 45°, and 60°.

Example 1   Figure 6.105 shows the point $P = (x, y)$ corresponding to the angle 45° on the unit circle. A right triangle has been drawn in. The triangle is isosceles; it has two equal angles (both 45°) and two equal sides, so $x = y$. Therefore, the Pythagorean theorem $x^2 + y^2 = 1$ gives

$$x^2 + x^2 = 1$$
$$2x^2 = 1$$
$$x = \sqrt{\frac{1}{2}} = \frac{1}{\sqrt{2}}.$$

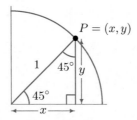

Figure 6.105: This triangle has two equal angles and two equal sides, so $x = y$

We know that x is positive because P is in the first quadrant. Since $x = y$, we see that $y = 1/\sqrt{2}$ as well. Thus, since x and y are the coordinates of P, we have $\cos 45° = 1/\sqrt{2}$, $\sin 45° = 1/\sqrt{2}$, and $\tan 45° = 1$.

Example 2   Figure 6.106 shows the point $Q = (x, y)$ corresponding to the angle $30°$ on the unit circle. A right triangle has been drawn in, and a mirror image of this triangle is shown below the x-axis. Together these two triangles form the triangle $\triangle OQA$. This triangle has three equal $60°$ angles and so has three equal sides, each side of length 1. The length of side $\overline{QA}$ can also be written as $2y$, and so we have $2y = 1$, or $y = 1/2$. By the Pythagorean theorem,

$$x^2 + y^2 = 1$$
$$x^2 + \left(\frac{1}{2}\right)^2 = 1$$
$$x^2 = \frac{3}{4}$$
$$x = \sqrt{\frac{3}{4}} = \frac{\sqrt{3}}{2}.$$

Note that x is positive because Q is in the first quadrant. Since x and y are the coordinates of Q, this means that $\cos 30° = \sqrt{3}/2$, $\sin 30° = 1/2$, and $\tan 30° = 1/\sqrt{3}$.

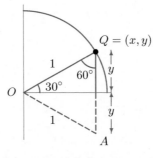

Figure 6.106: The triangle $\triangle OQA$ has three equal angles and three equal sides, so $2y = 1$

A similar argument shows that $\cos 60° = 1/2$, $\sin 60° = \sqrt{3}/2$, and $\tan 60° = \sqrt{3}$.

It is worth memorizing the values of sine and cosine for these special angles. See Table 6.13. As the following example shows, special angles and reference angles[8] can be used to calculate exact values of the trigonometric functions of some angles greater than $90°$ or less than $0°$.

Table 6.13 *Trigonometric functions of special angles*

θ	$\cos \theta$	$\sin \theta$	$\tan \theta$
$30°$	$\sqrt{3}/2$	$1/2$	$1/\sqrt{3}$
$45°$	$1/\sqrt{2}$	$1/\sqrt{2}$	1
$60°$	$1/2$	$\sqrt{3}/2$	$\sqrt{3}$

Example 3 Find the exact coordinates of a point B designated by $315°$ on a circle of radius 6.

Solution Point B is in the fourth quadrant, where $\cos 315°$ is positive and $\sin 315°$ is negative. See Figure 6.107. The reference angle for $315°$ is $45°$, so $\cos 315° = \cos 45°$ and $\sin 315° = -\sin 45°$.

The coordinates of point B are given by

$$x = r \cos \theta \qquad\qquad\text{and}\qquad\qquad y = r \sin \theta$$
$$= 6 \cos 315° \qquad\qquad\qquad\qquad = 6 \sin 315°$$
$$= 6 \left(\frac{\sqrt{2}}{2} \right) = 3\sqrt{2} \qquad\qquad\qquad = 6 \left(\frac{-\sqrt{2}}{2} \right) = -3\sqrt{2}$$

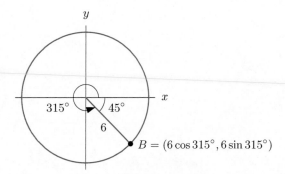

Figure 6.107: Exact coordinates of B found using reference angle of $45°$

Thus, the coordinates of B are $(3\sqrt{2}, -3\sqrt{2})$.

[8]See page 291.

Exercises on Tools for Chapter 6

---

1. Use Figure 6.108 to find the following exactly:

   (a) $\tan\theta$ **(b)** $\sin\theta$ **(c)** $\cos\theta$

Figure 6.108

2. Find exact values of the sine, cosine and tangent for the angles θ and ϕ in Figure 6.109.

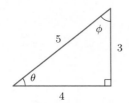

Figure 6.109

3. Using Figure 6.110, find exactly:

   (a) $\sin\theta$ **(b)** $\sin\phi$ **(c)** $\cos\theta$

   (d) $\cos\phi$ **(e)** $\tan\theta$ **(f)** $\tan\phi$

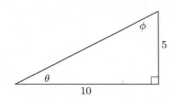

Figure 6.110

4. Find the lengths h and x in Figure 6.111.

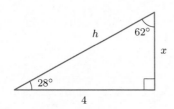

Figure 6.111

In Exercises 5–10, use Figure 6.112 to find exactly

   (a) $\sin\theta$ **(b)** $\cos\theta$ **(c)** $\tan\theta$

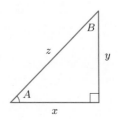

Figure 6.112

5. $x = 2$, $z = 7$, $A = \theta$ **6.** $x = 9$, $y = 5$, $A = \theta$

7. $y = 8$, $z = 12$, $A = \theta$ **8.** $z = 17$, $A = \theta$, $B = \theta$

9. $y = 2$, $z = 11$, $B = \theta$ **10.** $x = a$, $y = b$, $B = \theta$

In Exercises 11–16, use Figure 6.113 to find exact values of q and r.

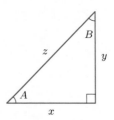

Figure 6.113

11. $A = 17°$, $B = 73°$, $x = q$, $y = r$, $z = 7$

12. $A = 12°$, $B = 78°$, $x = q$, $y = 4$, $z = r$

13. $A = 37°$, $B = 53°$, $x = 6$, $y = q$, $z = r$

14. $A = 40°$, $x = q$, $y = r$, $z = 15$

15. $B = 77°$, $x = 9$, $y = r$, $z = q$

16. $B = 22°$, $x = \lambda$, $y = q$, $z = r$

Find the missing sides and angles in the right triangles in Problems 17–20, where a is the side across from angle A, b across from B, and c across from the right angle.

17. $a = 20$, $b = 28$

18. $a = 20$, $c = 28$

19. $c = 20$, $A = 28°$

20. $a = 20$, $B = 28°$

21. You have been asked to build a ramp for Dan's Daredevil Motorcycle Jump. The dimensions you are given are indicated in Figure 6.114. Find all the other dimensions.

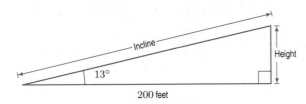

Figure 6.114

22. A kite flier wondered how high her kite was flying. She used a protractor to measure an angle of 38° from level ground to the kite string. If she used a full 100 yard spool of string, how high, in feet, was the kite? (Disregard the string sag and the height of the string reel above the ground.)

23. The top of a 200-foot vertical tower is to be anchored by cables that make an angle of 30° with the ground. How long must the cables be? How far from the base of the tower should anchors be placed?

24. Find approximately the acute angle formed by the line $y = -2x + 5$ and the x-axis.

25. The front door to the student union is 20 feet above the ground, and it is reached by a flight of steps. The school wants to build a wheel-chair ramp, with an incline of 15 degrees, from the ground to the door. How much horizontal distance is needed for the ramp?

26. A ladder 3 meters long leans against a house, making an angle α with the ground. How far is the base of the ladder from the base of the wall, in terms of α? Include a sketch.

27. A plane is flying at an elevation of 35,000 feet when the Gateway Arch in St. Louis, Missouri comes into view. The pilot wants to estimate her horizontal distance from the arch, so she notes the angle of depression, θ, between the horizontal and a line joining her eye to a point on the ground directly below the arch. Make a sketch. Express her horizontal distance to that point as a function of θ.

28. You see a friend, whose height you know is 5 feet 10 inches, some distance away. Using a surveying device called a transit, you determine the angle between the top of your friend's head and ground level to be 8°. You want to find the distance d between you and your friend.

(a) First assume you cannot find your calculator to evaluate trigonometric functions. Find d by approximating the arc length of an 8° angle with your friend's height. (See Figure 6.115.)

(b) Now assume that you have a calculator. Use it to find the distance d. (See Figure 6.116.)

(c) Would the difference between these two values for d increase or decrease if the angle were smaller?

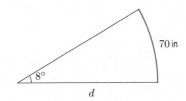

Figure 6.115: Arc of 70 in with 8° angle

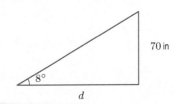

Figure 6.116: Triangle with side 70 in and angle 8°

29. Hampton is a small town on a straight stretch of coast line running north and south. A lighthouse is located 3 miles off-shore directly east of Hampton. The light house has a revolving search light that makes two revolutions per minute. The angle that the beam makes with the east-west line through Hampton is called ϕ. Find the distance from Hampton to the point where the beam strikes the shore, as a function of ϕ. Include a sketch.

30. You are parasailing on a rope that is 125 feet long behind a boat. See Figure 6.117.

(a) At first, you stabilize at a height that forms a 45° angle with the water. What is that height?

(b) After enjoying the scenery, you encounter a strong wind that blows you down to a height that forms a 30° angle with the water. At what height are you now?

(c) Find c and d, i.e. the horizontal distances between you and the boat, in parts (a) and (b).

31. A bridge over a river was damaged in an earthquake and you are called in to determine the length, d, of the steel beam needed to fill the gap. (See Figure 6.118.) You cannot be on the bridge, but you are able to drop a line from T, the beginning of the bridge, and measure a distance of 50 ft to the point P. From P you find the angles of elevation to the two ends of the gap to be 42° and 35°. How wide is the gap?

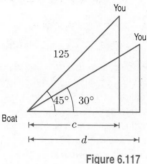

Figure 6.117

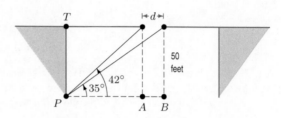

Figure 6.118: Gap in damaged bridge

Section 1.1

S1 $(2/3)c$

S3 $6\pi r^2$

S5 $51/2$

S7 $3/2$

S9 $A = (-2, 8)$

1 (a) 2
  (b) 2
  (c) About 12 hours

3 $w = f(c)$

5
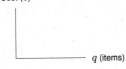

7

9 (a) 4
  (b) 3
  (c) 2
  (d) 2 and 4

11 2.9

13 0, 4, 8

15 (a) w
  (b) $(-4, 10)$
  (c) $(6, 1)$

17 (a) Yes
  (b) No

19

21 (a) 100.3 m. own phones in 2000
  (b) 20 m. own phones a years after 1990
  (c) b m. own phones in 2010
  (d) n m. own phones t years after 1990

23 (a) Most: Hannah; least: Madison
  (b) Most: Madison; least: Alexis

25 (a) 10.71 gallons
  (b) 0.25 gallons
  (c) 55 mph

27 (a) 72π ft^3
  (b) 45π ft^3
  (c) $V(h) = 9\pi h$

29 (a) 69°F
  (b) July 17 and 20
  (c) Yes

(d) No

31 (a) No
  (b) Yes
  (c) In 1981, record was 3 min 47.33 sec
  (d) 1967, record of 3 min 51.1 sec

33 (a) $x + y$
  (b) $0.15x + 0.18y$
  (c) $(15x + 18y)/(x + y)$

35 $A(r) = \pi r^2$
  21%

37 (b) $C = 2 + (0.5)l$

Section 1.2

S1 -2

S3 -2

S5 -1

S7 $-3x^2 - 4ax - a^2$

S9 $x + y$

1 (a) $80/3$ CDs per year
  (b) -20 CDs per year
  (c) 0 CDs per year

3 Decreasing

5 0.513

7 0.513

9 (a) Negative
  (b) Positive

11 $F(-2) > F(2)$

13 (a) $A = (10, 30)$
    $B = (30, 40)$
    $C = (50, 90)$
    $D = (60, 40)$
    $E = (90, 40)$

  (b) Point F is on the graph.
  (c) Increasing: 6–21,
    36–51, 66–81
  (d) Decreasing: 22–35,
    52–65, 82–96

15 (a) 2
  (b) Increasing
  (c) Increasing everywhere

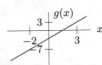

17 (a) Town B
  (b) Town A

19 24.5 degrees/minute

21 (a) 162 calories
  (b) Swimmer
  (c) Increases

23 (a) 9
  (b) $\dfrac{n - k}{m - j}$
  (c) $6x + 3h$

25 (a) 10, 10, 10, 10, 7, 1
  (b) 30, 30.5, 53.6, 33.9, 15.5, -5
  (c) No; $\Delta G/\Delta t$ not constant
  (d) Recycling and composting program in US

Section 1.3

S1 $f(0) = 5, f(3) = 7$

S3 5

S5 $y = 3; x = 3/4$

S7 $7/2, -2$

S9 $-ab + a + 3, a - 3$

1 Not linear

3 No

5 Yes

7 (a) $y = 7 + 2x$
  (b) $y = 8 - 15x$

9 Vert int: 54.25 thousand; Slope: $-2/7$ thousand/yr

11 Vert int: $-\$3000$; Slope: $\$0.98$/item

13 (a) $r = f(v)$ could be linear
  (b) \$5 increase/mph
  (c)
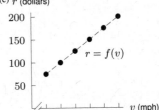

15 $V = 21,500 - 3200t$

17 (b)
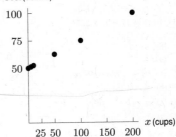

  (c) 0.25
  (d) Start-up cost

19 $\pi(n) = -10,000 + 127n$

21 $c = 4000 + 80r$

23 (a) Radius and circumference
  (c) 2π

25 (a) No
  (b) Looks linear

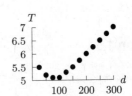

(c) $\Delta T/\Delta d = 0.01°C/\text{meter}$

27 (a) $T = \$1900$
(b) $C = 7$
(d) Twelve credits
(e) Fixed costs that do not depend on the number of credits taken

29 (a) $r = 5/2, s = 16$
(b) $k = 0.2, j = -3$

33 No

Section 1.4

S1 $y = 26$

S3 $x = 2$

S5 $y = -17/16$

S7 $F = (9/5)C + 32$

S9 $x = (c - ab)/(2a)$

1 $y = 4/5 - x$

3 $y = 180 - 10x$

5 $y = -0.3 + 5x$

7 $y = -40/3 - 2/3x$

9 $y = 21 - x$

11 Yes; $F(P) = 13 + (-1/8)P$

13 Yes; $C(r) = 0 + 2\pi r$

15 Yes; $f(x) = n^2 + m^2 x$

17 $y = 8 + 3x$

19 $y = (11 + 2x)/3$

21 $y = 0.03 + 0.1x$

23 $f(x) = 3 - 2x$

25 $q = 2500 - 2000p$

27 $y = 459.7 + 1x$

29 $u = (1/12)n$

31 $f(x) = -12.5 - 1.5x$

33 $h(t) = 12,000 + 225t$

35 (a) $\$11,375$
(b) $\$125$
(c) $\$5$

37 $C(n) = 10,500 + 5n$

39 (b) $v = 40 - 32t$

41 (a) $q = 210 - 50p$

43 $y = -4 + 4x$

45 $y = \frac{16+5\sqrt{7}}{2+\sqrt{7}} - \frac{3}{2+\sqrt{7}}x$ or
$\quad y = (1 + 2\sqrt{7}) + (2 - \sqrt{7})x$

47 (a) $p = 0.1t - 1$, and $t \geq 10$
(b) 11
(d) $t = 10p + 10$
(e) 2 hours 40 minutes

49 (a) $i(x) = 2.5x$
(b) $i(0) = 0$

51 $w(r) = \pi x^2 - s\sqrt{x} + (-3x - 4s)r$;
$\quad b = \pi x^2 - s\sqrt{x}; m = -3x - 4s$

53 (a) $r = 0.005H - 0.03$
(b) $S = 200$

Section 1.5

S1 $x = -2, y = 5$

S3 No solution

S5 $x = 7, y = 4$

S7 $x = 3/2, y = 3/2$

1 (a) (V)
(b) (VI)
(c) (I)
(d) (IV)
(e) (III)
(f) (II)

5 (a)

(b) Yes $(y = 3 + 0x)$, No

7 Perpendicular

9 Neither

11 Parallel

13 $y = 6 - (3/5)x$

15 Parallel line:
$\quad y = -4x + 9$
Perpendicular line:
$\quad y = 0.25x + 4.75$

17 $(1, 0)$

19 (a) 5 years

21 (a) $y = 9 - \frac{2}{3}x$
(b) $y = -4 + \frac{3}{2}x$
(c)

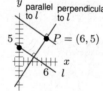

23 (a) $P = (a, 0)$
(b) $A = (0, b), B = (-c, 0)$
$\quad C = (a + c, b), D = (a, 0)$

27 $3 < \beta < 6$

29 (a) $y = -\sqrt{3}x$
(b) $y = (1/\sqrt{3})x + 4/\sqrt{3}$

31 $y = x/3 + 2/3$.

Section 1.6

1 $r = 0.93$ is reasonable.

3 $r = 1$ is not reasonable.

5 $r = 1$ is not reasonable.

7 (a) $r = 1$
(b) $r = 0.7$

(c) $r = 0$
(d) $r = -0.98$
(e) $r = -0.25$
(f) $r = -0.5$

9 (a) and (b)

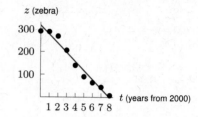

(c) $z = -40t + 314$
(e) Strong negative correlation $(r = -0.983)$

11 (a) nonpreferred hand strength (kg)

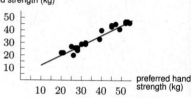

(c) $y = 3.623 + 0.825x$
(d) ≈ 34
(e) ≈ 40

Chapter 1 Review

1 Neither

3 Both

5 Neither

7 (a)

x	0	1	2	3
$f(x)$	10	5	2	1

(b) $x = 0$; smallest x-value

9 (a) #2
(b) #1, #3
(c) #3

11 (a) Owens: 12 yards/sec horse: 20 yards/sec
(b) 6 seconds

13 Yes

15 $f(t) = 2.2 - 1.22t$

17 (a) (ii)
(b) (iii)
(c) (i)

19 (a) $y = 3 + 4x$
(b) $y = 5 - 2x$

21 Neither

23 Perpendicular

25 120

27 500 m

29 distance of bug from light

time

31 temperature

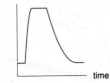

time

33 $T(d) = d/5 + (10 - d)/8$

35 $s = 1440 - w$

37 (a) (i) 1/2

  (ii) 1/2

  (iii) 1/2

  (b) Always 1/2

39 (a) $0°\text{C}/\text{meter}$

  (b) $-0.008°\text{C}/\text{meter}$

  (c) $0.009°\text{C}/\text{meter}$.

41 (a) $5350, $5700, $6750,
    $8500, $12,000

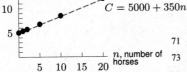

  (b) $C = 5000 + 350n$

  (c) $350/\text{horse}$

43 $h(t) = 254 - 248t$

45 (a) 1000, 990.2, 980.4, 970.6, 960.8

  (b) v decreasing at constant rate

  (c) Slope: -9.8 meter/sec^2

    v-intercept: 1000 meters/sec

    t-intercept: 102.04 sec

49 (a) $S = -100 + 100p$

  (c) Yes, $1

  (d) $4

51 $g(x) = -2 - 2x$

53 $y = 2.8 - 0.1x$

55 $d = 60 + 50t$

57 $g(x) = 32 - (3/5)x$

59 (a) $Y_A = 0.37x$

    $Y_B = 13.95 + 0.22x$

    $Y_C = 50$

  (c) $93 < x \le 163$

61 (a) hours of TV

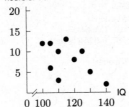

IQ

  (b) $r \approx -1/2$

  (c) $y = 27.5139 - 0.1674x$

    $r = -0.5389$

63 (a)

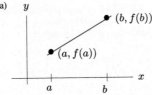

  (b) $(f(b) - f(a))/(b - a)$

65 $y = 0.75/(0.75 - 1) - (\sqrt{0.5})^2 x; p = 0.75, r = \sqrt{0.5}$

67 (a) y-intercept: c/q

    x-intercept: c/p

  (b) $-(p/q)$

69 hair length

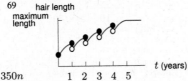

  t (years)

71 $g(x) = 17/5 + 6/(5\pi) \cdot x$

73 $g(54) = 8^{1/5} = \sqrt[5]{8}$

Ch. 1 Understanding

1 False

3 True

5 True

7 True

9 True

11 True

13 True

15 True

17 False

19 False

21 False

23 True

25 True

27 False

29 True

31 False

33 False

35 True

37 False

39 False

41 True

43 False

45 True

47 True

49 False

51 True

53 True

Ch. 1 Skills: Linear Equations

1 $x = 5$

3 $z = 11/2$

5 $w = -11$

7 $t = 45/13$

9 $t = 10/7$

11 $B = -2$

13 $l = A/w$

15 $a = 2(h - v_0 t)/t^2$

17 $v = (3w - 2u - z)/(u + w - z)$

19 $x = -a(b + 1)/(ad - c)$

21 $y' = 4/(y + 2x)$

23 $x = 4, y = 3$

25 $x = -55, y = 39$

27 $x = 1, y = a$

29 $x = 3, y = 6$

31 $A = (-4, 7)$

33 $A = (2, 9), B = (10, 1)$

35 $A = (-7, 8), B = (-3, 4)$

Section 2.1

S1 $5x - 15$

S3 $4m^2 - 38m + 90$

S5 $(3x + 3)/3$

S7 $x = \pm 3$

S9 $(18 \pm \sqrt{285})/3$

1 (a) -4

  (b) ± 2

3 (a) $-1/2$

  (b) -1

5 $3/2$

7 54

9 $(0, 2)$

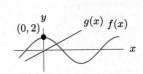

11 Intersect at $x = 2$

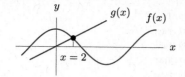

13 100

15 $f(1/3) = 3.222$; $f(1)/f(3) = 0.238$; Not equal

17 (a) (i) $1/(1-t)$
    (ii) $-1/t$
  (b) $x = 3/2$

19 (a) 48 feet for both
  (b) 4 sec, 64 ft

21 (a) $s(2) = 146$
  (b) Solve $v(t) = 65$
  (c) At 3 hours

23 (a) \$4261
  (b) $T(x) = 0.8x$
  (c) $L(x) = 0.0548x - 397$
  (d) \$4261

27 (a) $h(1) = b + c + 1$
  (b) $h(b+1) = 2b^2 + 3b + c + 1$

29 $a/2$

31 $a/(a - a^2 + 1)$

33 (a) (i) 6
    (ii) 5
    (iii) Not defined
  (b) (i) $50 \le s \le 75$
    (ii) $76 \le s \le 125$

35 (a) 7000
  (b) 8500; 4 weeks after the beginning of the epidemic
  (c) $w = 1, w = 10$
  (d) $1.5 \le w \le 8$

Section 2.2

S1 $x = 3$
S3 $x < 15$
S5 $x > 8$
S7 $n < 0$
S9 $x > 5$ or $x < -5$.

1 $f(x) \le -(1/2)$ or $f(x) \ge (1/2)$
3 $-4 \le f(x) \le 5$
5 D: all real numbers $\ne -3$
7 D: all real numbers $\ne -3$
9 Domain: $x > 4$
   Range: $y > 0$
11 D: $x \ge 2$ or $x \le -2$
13 D: all real numbers
15 D: all real numbers
    R: all real numbers
17 $a = 3$
19 $a = -3$
21 D: $1 \le x \le 7$; R: $2 \le f(x) \le 18$
23 $y = 1/((x+5)\sqrt{-x})$
25 D: $0 \le t \le 12$
    R: $0 \le f(t) \le 200$

27 Domain: integers $0 \le n \le 200$
    Range: $0, 4, 8, \ldots, 800$

29 (a) 162 calories
   (c) (i) Calories = $0.025 \times$ weight

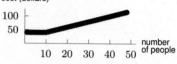

   (ii) (0,0) is the number of calories burned by a weightless runner
   (iii) Domain $0 < w$; range $0 < c$
   (iv) 3.6

31 D: all real numbers;
    R: $h(x) \ge 6$

33 (a) $p(0) = 50$
      $p(10) \approx 131$
      $p(50) \approx 911$
   (c) $50 \le p(t) < 1000$

35 (a) 800; 200; -200
   (b)
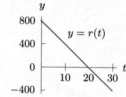
   (c) $t = 20$; $t = 0$
   (d) Domain: $0 \le t \le 30$
      Range: $-400 \le r(t) \le 800$

Section 2.3

S1 $x > 0$
S3 $2 \le x \le 3$
S5 $x \le -1$ or $x \ge 2$
S7 Domain: $2 \le x < 6$
    Range: $3 \le x < 5$
S9 Domain: $-2 \le x \le 3$
    Range: $-2 \le x \le 3$

1
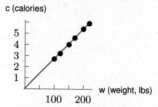

3
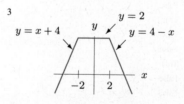

5 Domain: all reals;
   Range: $G(x) < 0$ and $G(x) \ge 3$

7 $y = \begin{cases} 5 - x & \text{for } x < 3 \\ -1 + (1/2)x & \text{for } x \ge 3 \end{cases}$

9 $y = \begin{cases} 4 - \frac{1}{2}x & \text{for } 1 \le x \le 3 \\ -9 + 2x & \text{for } 5 \le x \le 8 \end{cases}$

11 (a) Yes
   (b) No
   (c) $y = 1, 2, 3, 4$

13 (c) Domain: all x, $x \ne 0$
      Range: -1 and 1
   (d) False, $u(0)$ is undefined

15 (a)
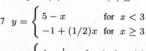

   (b) Integers from 1 to 50
      Even integers from 40 to 120

17 (a) \$1.01
   (b) $y = \begin{cases} 1 + x & \text{for } 0 < x < 0.1 \\ 10x + x & \text{for } 0.1 \le x \le 0.5 \\ 5 + x & \text{for } x > 0.5 \end{cases}$
   (c) \$4
   (d)
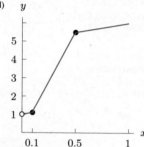

19 (b) 13-69

21 (a) $f(x) = \begin{cases} 2x - 6 & \text{for } x \ge 3 \\ 6 - 2x & \text{for } x < 3 \end{cases}$
   (b)
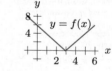

23 (a) $f(0) = 0, f(3) = 1$
   (b) Domain: $-1 \le x \le 5$;
      Range: $-3 \le f(x) \le 3$.

25 $y = \begin{cases} x^2 & \text{for } x < 0 \\ x - 1 & \text{for } x \ge 0 \end{cases}$

Section 2.4

S1 $y = (x + 4)/3$

S3 $y = (2x + 1)/(x - 2)$

S5 $y = \sqrt[3]{x + 4}$

S7 x

S9 $3y^2 - 12y + 5$

1 Area in sq cm at time t

3 Price for diameter d

5 0

7 -10

9 $9x - 4$

11 Year pop is P; years

13 Days for N inches snow; days

15 Diameter in inches of pizza costing c dollars

17 $f^{-1}(Q) = (Q - 3)^{1/3}$

19 $g^{-1}(y) = 1/(y - 1)$

21 (a) b
   (b) a
   (c) a
   (d) b

23 $n = f(100) = 0.4$ gal
   $A = f^{-1}(100) = 25{,}000$ ft^2

25 (a)   (i) 2
     (ii) 1
     (iii) 1
     (iv) 2
  (b) $f(0) = 2$ means $f^{-1}(2) = 0$
  (c) $f(1) = 0$ means $f^{-1}(0) = 1$

27 (a) 5000 loaves cost \$653
  (b) 620 loaves \$80
  (c) \$790 for 6300 loaves
  (d) 1200 loaves for \$150

29 (a) 12, perimeter for $s = 3$
  (b) 5; side for $P = 20$
  (c) $f^{-1}(P) = P/4$

31 $t = f^{-1}(H) = \frac{9}{5}H + 32 = t$

33 $20 + (50/9)2^{-n}$;
  $H = f(g(n))$ is temperature in °C at time n

35 (a) $A = f(r) = \pi r^2$
  (b) $f(0) = 0$
  (c) $f(r + 1) = \pi(r + 1)^2$
  (d) $f(r) + 1 = \pi r^2 + 1$
  (e) Centimeters

37 $f(t) = 4\pi(50 - 2.5t)^3/3$

39 $f(t) = \pi(2t - 0.1t^2)^2$

41 (a) 2 lbs cost \$2.80
  (b) 0.5 lb costs \$0.70
  (c) \$0.35 buys 1/4 lb
  (d) \$7 buys 5 lb

43 $23/4$; -2

45 $f^{-1}(y) = (y - 1)^{1/3}$

47 D: all real numbers
  R: all real numbers

49 D: all real numbers < 3
  R: all real numbers > 0

Section 2.5

1 Concave down

3 Concave up

5 Concave up

7 Concave up

9 Rates of change: 2.889, 1.417, 1.167; Concave down

11 Possible graph:

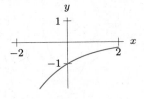

13 Increasing;
  concave up

15 Increasing;
  concave up then down

17 Increasing;
  concave up then down

19 (a) E, III
  (b) G, I
  (c) F, II

21 No

23 (a) Larger swims twice as fast
  (b) Increasing, concave down

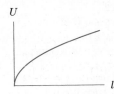

  (c) $\sqrt{l}$ increasing
  (d) $\sqrt{l}$ concave down;
    greater

Chapter 2 Review

1 $f(-7) = -9/2$

3 $-3/31$; 1

5 32; $\sqrt[3]{9/4}$

7 (a) 1
  (b) $-1/2$

9 -8

11 (a) $2, 0, -2$
  (b) $x = -1$

13 Domain: $x \geq 3$ or $x \leq -3$
  Range: $q(x) \geq 0$

15 Domain: all real numbers
  Range: all real numbers

17 D: all real numbers
  R: all real numbers

21 (a) $2(1 - x)$
  (b) $2 - x$
  (c) x
  (d) $(1 - x)^2$
  (e) 0

(f) $\sqrt{1 - x}$

23 $(3x - 7)^3 + 1$

25 Period in sec at time t

27 26

29 7

31 $2x^2 + 5$

33 $4x + 9$

35 Interest rate for \$$I$ interest; %/year

37 D: all real numbers $\geq b$;
  R: all real numbers ≥ 6

39 $f^{-1}(P) = (P + 2)/14$.

41 Time, yrs, at which pop is P mil

43 Rates of change: 4.35, 4.10, 3.80; Concave down

45 8; 81

47

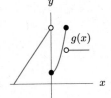

49 (a) -22
  (b) $3 - a^2$
  (c) $-a^2 + 10a - 22$
  (d) $-a^2 - 2$
  (e) $-a^2 + 25$

51 (a) $t = 6$
  (b) $t = 1, t = 2$

53 (a) -1
  (b) $x = \pm 3$
  (c) 0
  (d) -1
  (e) 3, -3

55 $g^{-1}(7) = 1, g^{-1}(12) = 2, g^{-1}(13) = 3,$
  $g^{-1}(19) = 4, g^{-1}(22) = 5$

57 (a) $s = f(A) = +\sqrt{\frac{A}{6}}$
  (b) $V = g(f(A)) = \left(\sqrt{A/6}\right)^3$.

59 (a) $C(3.5) = \$6.25$
  (b) $C^{-1}(\$3.5) \approx 1.67$

61 (a) $d/\sqrt{2}$
  (b) s^2
  (c) $d^2/2$
  (d) $h(d) = g(f(d))$

63 (a) $(-2, 2)$
  (b) $(-2\sqrt{2}, -2), (2\sqrt{2}, -2)$
  (c)

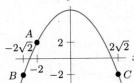

  (d) -3

65 (a) $t(400) = 272$
(d) $t(2x) = t(x)/2$
69 $y = \sqrt{x-4} + 1/(x-8)$
71 (a) Increasing until year 60, then decreasing
(c) Appears concave up
(d) Greatest between 40 and 60; smallest between 60 and 70
(f) 1840; potato famine

Ch. 2 Understanding

1 False
3 False
5 False
7 False
9 True
11 True
13 False
15 False
17 True
19 True
21 True
23 False
25 True
27 True
29 True
31 True
33 False
35 True
37 True
39 True
41 True

Section 3.1

S1 $-200t$
S3 $u(u-2)$
S5 $(3x-4)(x+1)$
S7 $(4x-1)(4x+1)$
S9 $x = -6$ or $x = -1$
1 Yes; $f(x) = 2x^2 - 28x + 99$
3 Yes; $g(m) = -2m^2 + \sqrt{3}m + 42$
5 Not quadratic
7 Yes; $T(n) = (\sqrt{3} - 1/2)n^2 + \sqrt{5}$
9 $x \approx -0.541$ and $x \approx 5.541$
11 $x = 2, 3/2$
13 $x = 2, x = -1$
15 $x = (-1 \pm \sqrt{6})/5$
17 No zeros
19 $y = (7/4)(x-1)(x-4)$
21 3 sec
23 $f(x) = a(x-1)(x-2)$ for any constant a
25 For example $y = (x+2)(x-3)$

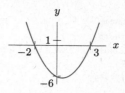

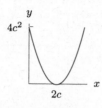

27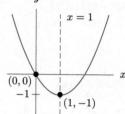

29 $y = -(5/12)x^2 - (5/3)x + 5$
31 $k = -30, r = 8, s = 0.2$
33 (a) 4 meters per second
(b) 2 seconds
(c) Concave up
35 -2.4% in 2004
37 (a) 5 km
(b) 4430 m
(c) $h \approx -0.000000255d^2 + 5$

Section 3.2

S1 $(y-6)^2 - 36$
S3 $(c+3/2)^2 - 37/4$
S5 $r = 4, 2$
S7 $q = 1/5 \pm \sqrt{41}/5$
S9 $n = -5, 1$
1 $(1, 2)$; $x = 1$; opens upward
3 Vertex: $(-11/2, -137/4)$
Axis of symmetry: $t = -11/2$
5 (a) $a = 1, b = 0, c = 3$
Axis of symmetry: y-axis
Vertex: $(0, 3)$
No zeros
y-intercept: $y = 3$

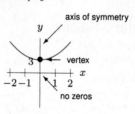

(b) $a = -2, b = 4, c = 16$
Axis of symmetry: $x = 1$
Vertex: $(1, 18)$
Zeros: $x = -2, 4$
y-intercept: $y = 16$

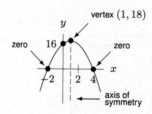

7 $k = 4$
9 $y = -(3/16)(x-4)^2 + 7$
11 $y = \frac{7}{9}(x-3)^2 - 5$
13 $f(x) = (x+4)^2 - 13$;
Vertex: $(-4, -13)$; axis: $x = -4$
15 $p(t) = 2(t - 0.03)^2 + 0.0982$, vertex $(0.03, 0.0982)$, axis of symmetry $t = 0.03$
17 $(1/2)x^2 - (1/2)x - 6$;
$(1/2)(x - 1/2)^2 - (49/8)$;
$(1/2)(x-4)(x+3)$
19 $2s^2 - 7s - 15$;
$2(s - 7/4)^2 - (169/8)$;
$2(s-5)(s+3/2)$
21 $y = (1/4)(x-4)^2 + 2$
23 $y = (-2/49)(x-4)^2 + 2$
25 (a)

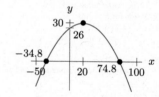

(b) $y = (x-1)^2 - 1$ or $y = x^2 - 2x$
(c) Range: $y \geq -1$
(d) The other zero is $(2, 0)$
27 Vertex: $(20, 30)$

29 12.5 cm by 12.5 cm; $k/4$ by $k/4$
31 (b) Maximum height: $t = T/2$

Chapter 3 Review

1 $f(x) = -2x^2 + 13x - 15$; $a = -2, b = 13, c = -15$
3 $w(n) = 3n^2 + 6n + 0$; $a = 3, b = 6, c = 0$
5 $x = -1/3$
7 No zeros
9 2 and 5
11 There are no real zeros
13 $y = -3(x-1)^2 - 2$
15 $(1/4)(x-7)^2 + 3$
17 $y = 4(x+1)(x-2)$
19 $y = (x+1)(x-3)$

21 $y = -(x-2)^2$

23 Vertex is $(3/4, -2/3)$, axis of symmetry is $x = 3/4$, y-intercept $y = 11/24$, concave up

25 Vertex is $(0.6, 0)$, axis of symmetry is $x = 0.6$, y-intercept is $y = 0.36$, concave up

27 $y = 0.3(x-6)(x+4)$, zeros at $x = 6$ and $x = -4$, vertex at $(1, -7.5)$

29 $y = -3(x-6)(x-2)$, vertex is $(4, 12)$, zeros at $x = 6$ and $x = 2$

31 Rates of change: $-4, 0, 4$; Concave up

33 1/2 second

Ch. 3 Understanding

1 True

3 False

5 False

7 False

9 False

11 True

13 False

15 True

Ch. 3 Skills: Factoring

1 $6x - 14$

3 $12x + 12y$

5 $2x^2 + 5x$

7 $-50r^2 - 60r^2 s$

9 $5xz - 10z - 3x + 6$

11 $x^2 + 4x - 12$

13 $yz + 3y + z + 3$

15 $5xz - 10z - 3x + 6$

17 $x - 25$

19 $Pp^2 - 6Ppq + 9Pq^2$

21 $-2x - 2\sqrt{2x} - 1$

23 $2(x+3)$

25 $5(z-6)$

27 $5(2w-5)$

29 $3u^2(u^5+4)$

31 $7rs(2r^3 s - 3t)$

33 $(x-2)(x-1)$

35 Cannot be factored

37 Cannot be factored

39 $(2x+1)(x+2)$

41 $(x+7)(x-4)$

43 $x(x+3)(x-1)$

45 $(x+2y)(x+3z)$

47 $(ax-b)(ax+b)$

49 $(B-6)(B-4)$

51 Cannot be factored.

53 $(t-1)(t+7)$

55 $(a-2)(a^2+3)$

57 $(d+5)(d-5)(c+3)(c-3)$

59 $(r+2)(r-s)$

61 $xe^{-3x}(x+2)$

63 $P(1+r)^3$

65 $(k+2m)(d-3e)$

67 $(2g-3h)(4s+5m)$

69 $x = (-3 \pm \sqrt{249})/8$

71 $x = 7/4$

73 $t = 3 \pm \sqrt{6}$

75 $x = 2, x = -4/3$

77 $N = 3, N = 1$

79 $x = 1 \pm \sqrt{2}$

81 $t = 3 \pm \sqrt{6}$

83 $a = -10, \pm 2\sqrt{5}/5$

85 $z = -7/2$

87 $L = \pm 1/2$

89 $r = \pm 5$

91 $x = 0, x = 36$

93 $x = -4/3, x = 2$

95 $b = \sqrt[5]{C/A}$

97 $x = 4m$

99 $x = 1/2$ and $y = 2$, or $x = -1/2$ and $y = -2$

101 $x = -3$ and $y = -5$, or $x = 1$ and $y = 3$

103 $(0, 0)$ and $(3, 9)$

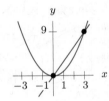

105 $(-5, 25), (3, 9)$

Ch. 3: Completing Square

1 $(x+4)^2 - 16$

3 $2(r+5)^2 - 50$

5 $(a-1)^2 - 5$

7 $3(r+3/2)^2 - 43/4$

9 $(x-1)^2 - 4$

11 $-(x-3)^2 + 7$

13 $(-3, -6)$

15 $(-4, 18)$

17 $(1/2, -23/4)$

19 $(1, -2)$

21 $(7/4, -25/8)$

23 $g = 6, -4$

25 $d = 2, -1$

27 $s = -5/2 \pm \sqrt{27}/2$

29 $p = -9/10 \pm \sqrt{101}/10$

31 $y = -1/2, -2$

33 $w = (-1 \pm \sqrt{17})/2$

35 $q = (-3 \pm \sqrt{15})/2$

37 $s = \left(-3 \pm \sqrt{13}\right)/2$

39 $u = (3 \pm \sqrt{5})/5$

41 $y = 1 \pm \sqrt{7}$

43 $w = 3, 2, -2$

45 $m = (-5 \pm \sqrt{3})/7$

Section 4.1

S1 0.06

S3 0.12%

1 Yes; $g(w) = 2(1/2)^w$

3 Yes; $f(x) = (1/4)9^x$

5 Yes; $q(r) = -4(1/3)^r$

7 Yes; $Q(t) = 2^t$

9 Not exponential

11 1.28 (per decade)

13 0.20 (per century)

15 $a = 34.3; b = 0.788; r = -21.2\%$

17 $a = 0.0022; b = 0.0811; r = -91.89\%$

19 \$109,272.70

21 (a) (ii)
    (b) (i)
    (c) (iv)
    (d) (ii)
    (e) (iii)
    (f) (i)

23 (a) $Q = 35(0.92)^t$
    (b) 15.204

25 (a) $Q = 5.35(1.008)^t$
    (b) 5.794

27 (a) $Q = 0.2(0.995)^t$
    (b) 0.190

29 $P = 70(1.019)^t$

31 $f(n) = P_0(0.8)^n$

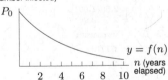

33 (a) $P = 7.50(1.035)^t$
    (b) $\approx \$14.92$

35 (a) $C = 100(0.84)^t$
    (b) 41.821 mg

37 (a) 14.026 m; 19.371 m
    (b) 2030-55 larger; graph concave up

39 (a) $P = 1.15(1.0135)^t$
    (b) 1.230 billion; 1.315 billion
    (c) 15.525 million people per year
    (d) About 29 people per minute

41 (a) 31,532 megawatts; 62.3 megawatts
    (b) 8.1%; 0.2%

43 $5 \cdot 4^{-\frac{1}{6} \cdot t}; a = 5, k = -1/6$

45 (a) $N = 13.4(1.05)^t$
    (b) 17.957 million; 11.024 million

47 (a) $N(r) = 64(1/2)^r$

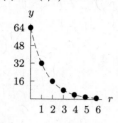

(b) 6

49 9.712%

51 (a) \$444 per month
(b) \$286.20 per month
(c) \$506.40 per month
(d) \$11,232
(e) \$23,112

53 366.875 miles

55 0.5

57 b_0

59 t_0 decreases

61 (a) $R = Nr$
(b) $A = R/P = Nr/P$
(c) $N_{new} = 1.02N$
$r_{new} = 1.03r$
(d) $R_{new} = 1.0506R$; 5.06%
(e) $A_{new} = (0.9728)A$; average revenue falls by 2.7%

Section 4.2

S1 b^{10}

S3 $6a^7b^{10}$

S5 5.6; 6.354

S7 $x = 1.710$

S9 $x = 1.393$

1 (a) $p = 2.50 + 0.03t$
(b) $p = 2.50 - 0.07t$
(c) $p = 2.50(1.02)^t$
(d) $p = 2.50(0.96)^t$

3 B, C, D exponential

5 $Q = 70.711(0.966)^t$

7 $f(x) = 2(1/3)^x$

9 $Q = 0.7746 \cdot (0.3873)^t$

11 $y = 50(0.833)^x$

13 $y = 2(3/2)^x$

15 $y = 160(0.983)^x$

17 Not exponential

19 $g(t) = 5.7(0.315)^t$

21 f is exponential, h is linear, g is neither

23 (a) $g(x)$ is linear
(b) $g(x) = 2x$

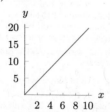

25 (a) $i(x)$ is linear
(b) $i(x) = 18 - 4x$

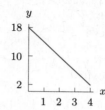

27 $x < -1.69$ and $x > 2$

29 $p = 20(1.0718)^x$; $q = 160(0.8706)^x$

31 Exponential,
$R(t) = 2.001(1.030)^t$

33 (a) $P = 1154.160(1.20112)^t$
(b) \$1154.16
(c) 20.112%

35 $P = 1046(0.798)^t$; decreasing by 20.2%/yr

37 (a) $W = 43.45 - 0.126t$; 40.43 seconds
(b) $W = 43.45(0.997057)^t$; 40.48 seconds

39 (a) $P = 3500 - 180t$; -180 fish/year
(b) $P = 3500(0.93)^t$; -7%/year
(c)

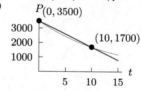

41 (a) Linear
(b) $L = 0.25t + 75.85$
(c) 88.35 years

43 (a) $N = 84 + 11.3684t$;
increasing by 11.3684 million people per year
(b) $N = 84(1.0693)^t$;
increasing by 6.93% per year
(c) Linear: 425.0520 million; Exponential: 626.9982 million

45 (a) Neither
(b) Not possible

Section 4.3

1 (b)

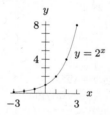

3 $h(x)$ top; $g(x)$ middle; $f(x)$ bottom

5 Yes

7 No

9 No

11 D

13 D

15 (a) 13 ft^3
(b) 3.2 weeks

17 $q = 5.662$

19 $t = 2.452$

21 Zero

23

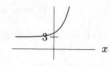

25

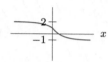

27

29 (a) $-\infty$
(b) $-\infty$

31 (a) All
(b) b
(c) b, a, c, p
(d) $a = c$
(e) d and q

33 Increasing: $b > 1, a > 0$ or $0 < b < 1, a < 0$;
Decreasing: $0 < b < 1, a > 0$ or $b > 1, a < 0$;
Concave up: $a > 0, 0 < b < 0$ or $b > 1$.

35 y_0 decreases, $y_0 > b$

37 (a) $P = 651(0.9925)^t$
(b) 603,790
(c) $t = 22.39$

41 (a) $P \approx 0.538$ millibars
(b) $h \approx 0.784$ km

43 (a)

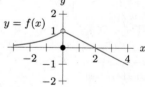

(b) $f(x) < 1$
(c) $(0, 0)$ $(2, 0)$
(d) As $x \to +\infty$, $f(x) \to -\infty$
As $x \to -\infty$, $f(x) \to 0$
(e) Increasing for $x < 0$, decreasing for $x > 0$

45 (a)

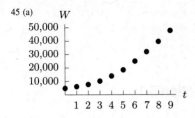

(b) $W = 4710(1.306)^t$; answers may vary
(c) 30.6%/yr

Section 4.4

1 (a) 8.300%
(b) 8.322%
(c) 8.328%

3 165.3%

5 (a) $1270.24
(b) $1271.01
(c) $1271.22

7 (a) $505
(b) $505.02
(c) $505.03

9 (a) $525
(b) $525.62
(c) $525.64

11 (a) Nom: 1% Eff: 1%
(b) Nom: 1% Eff: 1.004%
(c) Nom: 1% Eff: 1.005%

13 (a) Nom: 3% Eff: 3%
(b) Nom: 3% Eff: 3.034%
(c) Nom: 3% Eff: 3.045%

15 34.392%

17 7.352%

19 1.628%

21 (i) (b)
(ii) (a)
(iii) (c)
(iv) (b), (c) and (d)
(v) (a) and (e)

Section 4.5

S1 1.073

S3 1.433

S5 2.3; 7.636

S7 161.6; 202.027

S9 $f(t) = 27e^{0.12t}$

S11 $Q = 1{,}096.633e^{-3t}$

S13 $m(x) = \frac{7}{\sqrt{3}}e^{-0.3x}$

S15 $H(r) = \frac{1}{6}e^{0.65r}$

1 Bottom to top:
$y = e^x, y = 2e^x, y = 3e^x$

3 (a)=(II); (b)=(III); (c)=(IV); (d)=(I)

5 $f(x) = e^{-x}$
$g(x) = e^x$
$h(x) = -e^x$

7 (a)=(I); (b)=(II); (c)=(III); (d)=(IV)

9 0

11 2

13 $a > 0, k > 0$

15 (a) $Q_0 = 2.7$
(b) Decreasing
(c) −88%
(d) Not continuous

17 (a) $Q_0 = 0.01$
(b) Decreasing
(c) −20%
(d) Continuous

19 (a) $Q_0 = 1$
(b) Increasing
(c) 100%
(d) Not continuous

21 (a) $Q = 8(1.12)^t$; 24.847
(b) $Q = 8e^{0.12t}$; 26.561

23 (a) (i) 23.183
(ii) 23.645
(b) Continuous growth faster

25 (a) $P = 3000 + 200t$
(b) $P = 3000(1.06)^t$
(c) $P = 3000e^{0.06t}$
(d) $P = 3000 - 50t$
(e) $P = 3000(0.96)^t$
(f) $P = 3000e^{-0.04t}$

27 (a) $P(t) = 22{,}000e^{0.071t}$
(b) ≈ 7.358%

31 54.931 years

33 (a) $24,102.64
(b) 124.323 years

35 Eff. yield: 20.925%
Cont. rate: 19%

37 5.127%

39 (a) (i) 6.14%
(ii) 6.17%
(iii) 6.18%
(iv) 6.18%
(b) 1.0618
The highest possible APR is 6.18%.

41 From best to worst: B, C, A

43 (a) $G = 145.8e^{0.051t}$
(b) 5.23%
(c) $G = 145.8(1.0523)^t$
(d) The two formulas have the same graph

45 $143.70

47 $a = b > 1$
$0 < k < 1$
$l < 0$

49 (a) $A = 50e^{-0.14t}$
(b) 12.330 mg
(c) 2025

51 $27,399.14

53 (a) 2.708333333
(b) 2.718055556
(c) 2.718281828; thus (a) is correct to 2 correct digits, while (b) is correct to 4 digits
(d) 13 terms

Chapter 4 Review

1 550

3 495

5 411.8

7 $P = 2200(0.968)^t$

9 20%; 2%.

11 Linear: $p(r) = 10 + 3r$

13 Neither

15

Yr	2010	2011	2012	2013	2014
$	95	101.65	108.77	116.38	124.53

17 (a) 4.2%
(b) ≈ 4.28%
(c) ≈ 4.29%

19 $h(x) = 3(5)^x$

21 $g(x) = 2(4)^x$

23 $g(x) = 14.20(0.6024)^x$

25 (a) $f(x) = \frac{31}{8}x + \frac{49}{4}$
(b) $f(x) = 5(2)^x$

27 $y = (1/2)^x$

29 $y = \frac{1}{5}(3)^x$

31 $y = 2(0.8)^x$

33 (a) $P(t) = 2.58 + 0.09t$,
increases by 90,000 people per year
(b) $P(t) = 2.68(1.026)^t$,
increases by 2.6% per year

35 0

37 15

39 −∞

41 $N = 10(1.13)^t$; 13%/yr

43 (a) $S = 128.4(1.13)^t$
(b) Increasing by 13%/yr
(c) No

45

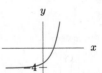

47

49 f

51 $y = 2$

55 (a) Initial balance = $1100
Effective yield = 5%
(b) Initial balance = $1500
Effective yield ≈ 5.13%

57 $p(x) = 7e^x \sqrt{e}/20$

59 $s(w) = (v - 4t + kv)j^w$
$a = v - 4t + kv, b = j$

61 $g(n) = 1000(0.7071)^n$

65 $d > b$

67 f matches (ii) and (iv); g matches (i) and (iii)

69 (a)

$$8 + \quad f(x) = 2^x$$

x

$-3 \quad 3$

(b) 0.69
(c) 1.10
(d) $e \approx 2.72$

71 $V = 12,000e^{0.042t}$

73 $y = -13.1x + 2090$

75 $a = 12,000;\ k = -12.2\%;\ b = 0.8851;$
$r = -11.49\%$

77 (a) $15.269(1.122)^t$
(b) 108,066
(c) Not useful

79 t_0 decreases

81 (a)

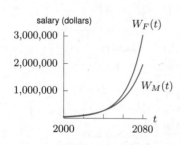

salary (dollars)

30,000

20,000

10,000

Male

Female

1950   2000

year

(b) $W_F(t) = 953e^{0.062(t-1950)}$ (women)
$W_M(t) = 2570e^{0.051(t-1950)}$ (men)

(c) salary (dollars)

30,000

20,000

10,000

$W_M(t)$

$W_F(t)$

1950   2000 t

salary (dollars)

3,000,000

2,000,000

1,000,000

$W_F(t)$

$W_M(t)$

2000   2080 t

(d) Yes, in about 2060
(e) Not reliable

83 50.7%

Ch. 4 Understanding

1 True

3 True

5 False

7 True

9 True

11 False

13 False

15 True

17 True

19 False

21 True

23 False

25 True

27 False

29 True

31 False

Ch. 4 Tools: Exponents

1 25

3 10,000

5 5

7 1

9 4

11 4

13 16

15 -121

17 2100

19 2

21 32

23 100,000

25 -6

27 4

29 $1/(3\sqrt{3})$

31 $1/625$

33 0.5

35 y^4

37 $x^{5/2}y^2$

39 $5x^{3/2}z^2$

41 $r^{3/2}$

43 $8s^{7/2}$

45 $4\sqrt{3}u^5v^6y^{5/2}$

47 $16S^2xt^2$

49 $A^3/\left(3B^3\right)$

51 $(M+2)^2$

53 $3a$

55 $25(2b+1)^{20}$

57 -8

59 Not a real number

61 $1/512$

63 Not a real number

65 $x = \pm 1.690$

67 $(2.5, 31.25)$

69 False

71 True

73 True

75 $x = r + s$

77 $x = 5/a$

79 $x = 3/a$

81 $x = b/a$

Section 5.1

S1 $x = 6$

S3 $z = 3/2$

S5 No solution

S7 $t = 14/9$

S9 $t = -1/8$

1 $19 = 10^{1.279}$

3 $26 = e^{3.258}$

5 $P = 10^t$

7 $8 = \log 100,000,000$

9 $v = \log \alpha$

11 (a) 3
(b) 1.5
(c) 0
(d) 1/2
(e) 5
(f) 2
(g) $-1/2$
(h) 100
(i) 1
(j) 0.01

13 $(\log 11)/(\log 2) = 3.459$

15 $(\ln 100)/(0.12) = 38.376$

17 $(\log(48/17))/(\log(2.3)) = 1.246$

19 (a) $2x$
(b) x^3
(c) $-3x$

21 (a) $3, 3$
(b) $5, 5$
(c) $-1, -1$
(d) $-1, -1$
(e) $2, 2$
(f) $3, 3$
Both answers equal

23 (a) True
(b) False
(c) False
(d) True
(e) True
(f) False

25 $x = 57.002$

27 $x = (a - \log M)/(\log N)$

29 $x = 2.714$

31 (a) 10; 15%
(b) $t \approx 10.5$
(c) $t = (\ln 0.2)/(-0.15) = 10.730$

33 (a) $\log 15 - \log 5$
(b) $2\log 5$
(c) $\log 15 + \log 5$

35 $(\log(91/46))/(\log(1.1))$

37 $(\ln 6/0.044)$

39 $x = \ln 10 - 4$

41 $\log(35/2)/\log(2/27)$

43 $t = \ln(500/400)/0.02$

45 $\ln 10 - 4$

47 $(\ln Q - \ln P)/k$

49 $x = -2, \dfrac{1}{3},$ or $-\dfrac{1}{3}$

51 $-2, 1/3, -1/3$

53 The log increases by 0.3010

55 $\log \sqrt{vw} = (\log v + \log w)/2$

57 $B > A$

Section 5.2

S1 $(5x)^{-1}$

S3 $t^2/2$

S5 $x = (\log 9)/(\log 4) = 1.585$

S7 $x = \ln(13/2) = 1.872$

S9 $x = 93/2$

1 $y = 25(1.0544)^t$,
 5.44%/yr, 5.3%/yr

3 $y = 6000e^{-0.1625t}$,
 −15%/yr, −16.25%/yr

5 $Q = 4 \cdot 1096.633^t$

7 $Q = (14/5)1.030^t$

9 $Q = 12e^{-0.105t}$

11 $Q = 14e^{-0.208t}$

13 $a = 230, r = 18.2\%, k = 16.72\%$

15 $a = 0.81, r = 100\%,$ and $k = 69.31\%$

17 $a = 12.1, r = -22.38\%, k = -25.32\%$

19 $a = 5.4366, b = 0.4724, r = -52.76\%, k = -3/4$

21 $t \approx 3.466$

23 About 26 years

25 About 12.3 years

27 6.301 minutes

29 (a) 7.70%
 (b) 6.18%

31 27.756 years

33 (a) 4.729%
 (b) 4.621%

35 −34.7% per hour

37 23.1%/yr; $W = 90e^{0.231t}$

39 (a) 10; 30; and 70 yrs
 (b) 14.207; 28.413; and 42.620 yrs

41 (a) 4 hours
 (b) −17.3% per hour; $Q = 150e^{-0.173t}$

45 (a) 300; 600
 (b) 34.739 years

47 (a) 27.465 years
 (b) 28.011 years

49 (a) $R(t) \approx 200(0.8909)^t$
 (b) ≈ 4.422 hours
 (c) concave up

51 5092.013 years ago

53 (a) $f(x) = \frac{1}{2}(4)^x$
 $g(x) = 4\left(\frac{1}{3}\right)^x$
 $h(x) = x + 2$
 (b) $x = \log 8/\log 12$
 (c) $x = 1.378$ or $x = -1.967$

57 (a) 20, 395, 954
 (b) 5.615 years, 7.2 years

(c) 1000 toads

59 $t = -10\ln(-2\ln 0.5) = -3.266$

61 (a) $v = \log 1.12, w = \log 6.3$
 (b) $t = w/v; t = 16.241$

Section 5.3

S1 -4

S3 $\log 100,000 = 5$

S5 $x = e^{-12}$

S7 $\ln x + 3\ln(7 - x)$

S9 $\ln x^5$

1 $y = 0, y = 0, x = 0$

3 $A: y = 10^x, B: y = e^x$
 $C: y = \ln x, D: y = \log x$

5

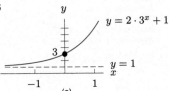
(a)

7

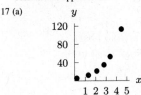
(c)

9 Vertical asymptote at 3,
 Domain $(3, \infty)$

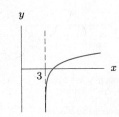

11 (a) 0
 (b) $-\infty$

13 (a) $-\infty$
 (b) $-\infty$

15 0.1 moles/l

17 3.162×10^{-5} moles/l

21 (a) $t(x)$
 (b) $r(x)$
 (c) $s(x)$

23 100 watts/cm^2

25 37

27 79,432,823

29 $M_2 - M_1 = \log(W_2/W_1)$

31 (a) $10^{-2}, 10^{-4}, 10^{-7}$

(b) Less

33 (a) 0.005 moles/liter
 (b) 3.3×10^{-4} moles H$^+$ ions
 1.987×10^{20} ions

35 $y = b^x, 0 < b < 1$

37 $y = \ln x$

39 $y = -b^x, b > 1$

Section 5.4

S1 1.455×10^6

S3 6.47×10^4

S5 3.6×10^{-4}

S7 $10^4 < \log 12,500 < 10^5$

S9 $10^{-1} < 1/3 < 10^0$

1 Log

3 Linear

7 (a) $y = -3582.145 + 236.314x; r \approx 0.7946$
 (b) $y = 4.797(1.221)^x; r \approx 0.9998$
 (c) Exponential is better fit

9 $10^{-3.65}$ million years ago

11 A: \$1.58
 B: \$6.31
 C: \$31.62
 D: \$630.96
 E: \$10,000.00
 F: \$125,892.54
 G: \$6,309,573.45
 Answers are approximate.

17 (a)

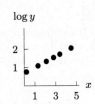

 (b) Exponential
 (c) Linear

19 Yes

21 (a) $a \approx -7.787, b \approx 86.283$
 (b)

(c) $69,918.342$ minutes ≈ 45 days
0.172 minutes ≈ 10 seconds

(d)

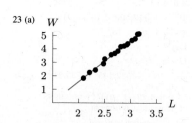

23 (a)

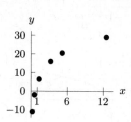

(b) $W = 3.06L - 4.54$
(c) $w = 0.011\ell^{3.06}$

Chapter 5 Review

1 $Q = 7(0.0000454)^t$
3 $Q = 4e^{1.946t}$
5 $Q = 4e^{2.703t}$
7 $(\log 3)/(\log 1.04)$
9 $(\log(14/3))/(\log 1.081)$
11 $(\log(12/5))/(3\log 1.014)$
13 $(\log 1.6)/(\log 1.031)$
15 47
17 2.324
19 $(1/0.049) \cdot \ln(25/13) \approx 13.345$
21 $x = 1000$
23 $2(x+1)$
25 $\ln(AB)$
27 Domain: $x > 20$; Asymptote: $x = 20$
29 Domain: $x < 300$; Asymptote: $x = 300$
31 Domain: $x > -15$; Asymptote: $x = -15$
33 3.7
35 2.2
37 0.6
39 (a) $q + 4p$
(b) $-q$
(c) p/q
(d) $3q$
41 (a) $\ln 8 - 3 \approx -0.9206$
(b) $\log 1.25/\log 1.12 \approx 1.9690$
(c) $-\dfrac{\ln 4}{0.13} \approx -10.6638$
(d) 105
(e) $\frac{1}{3}e^{3/2} \approx 1.4939$
(f) $e^{1/2}/(e^{1/2}-1) \approx 2.5415$
(g) -1.599 or 2.534
(h) 2.478 or 3
(i) 0.653

43 158.5 times larger
45 15.85 times larger
47 (a) Initial balance: $1100
Effective yield: 5%
(b) Initial balance: $1500
Effective rate: 5.127%/yr
(c) Continuous rate: 4.879%/yr
49 (a) 1412 bacteria
(b) 10.011 hours
(c) 1.005 hours
51 (a) 7 years
(b) 10.4%
53 $\ln(1.5)/0.2 = 2.027$
55 $t = (\ln 2)/0.22$
57 (a) Domain: all x
Range: $y > 0$
Asymptote: $y = 0$
(b) Domain: all $x > 0$
Range: all y
Asymptote: $x = 0$
59 (a) Log function

(b)

(c) Linear; $y = 4 + 9.9z$
(d) $y = 4 + 9.9\ln x$
(e) $x = 0.67e^{0.1y}$;
Exponential function of y
61 (a) $Q(t) = 2e^{-0.04t}$
(b) 3.921%
(c) After 51.986 hours
(d) 54.931 hrs after second injection
63 (a) $\approx 33.517\%$
(b) $k \approx 4.082\%$, continuous hourly decay rate
65 (a) 10
(b) 50
(c) 10^{50}
67 $\sqrt[8]{k}$

Ch. 5: Understanding

1 False
3 True
5 True
7 True

9 True
11 False
13 False
15 False
17 True
19 False
21 False
23 True
25 True
27 True
29 True
31 True
33 False
35 False
37 False

Ch. 5 Skills: Logs

1 0
3 8
5 0
7 2
9 $\log 0.0001 = -4$
11 $\ln 0.135 = -2$
13 $10^{-2} = 0.01$
15 $e^{x^2} = 4$
17 Cannot be rewritten
19 $\log(x^2+1) - 3\log x$
21 Cannot be rewritten
23 Cannot be rewritten
25 $\log 12x$
27 $\log(\sqrt{x}y^4)$
29 $\log\left((x+1)^3(x+4)^2\right)$
31 $\log(9 - x^2)$
33 Cannot be simplified
35 0
37 $4z$
39 $-\ln(e^x + 1)$
41 $x = (\log 3)/(\log 5) \approx 0.683$
43 $x = -(\ln 9)/5 \approx -0.439$
45 $x = (\log 77)/(6\log 19 - 4\log 7) \approx 0.440$
47 $x = (10^{3/2} - 17)/9 \approx 1.625$
49 $x = (e+1)/6 \approx 0.620$

Section 6.1

S1 2
S3 -1
S5 $x = 0$
S7 $x = -8$
S9 (a) Shift right 4 units
(b) Shift down 7 units
(c) Shift left $\sqrt{2}$ units
(d) Shift right 3 units and up 5 units
1 (a) $-3, 0, 2, 1, -1$
One unit right

(b) $-3, 0, 2, 1, -1$
One unit left
(c) $0, 3, 5, 4, 2$
Up three units
(d) $0, 3, 5, 4, 2$
One right and three up

3 (a) $(3, 1)$
(b) $(-2, -4)$
(c) $(6, -6)$

5
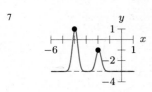

7
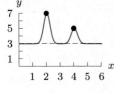

11 $-50 \leq R(s) - 150 \leq 50$
13 $(1/2)n^2 + 1$
15 $(1/2)n^2 - 3.7$
17 $(1/2)n^2 + \sqrt{13}$
19 $(1/2)n^2 + 3n + 23/2$
21 $3^w - 3$
23 $3^w + 1.8$
25 $3^{w+2.1} - 1.3$
27 (a) (i) 248
(ii) 142
(iii) 4
(iv) 12
(v) 378
(vi) -18
(vii) 248
(viii) 570
(ix) 13
(b) (i) $x = 2$
(ii) $x = 8$
(iii) $x = 7$
(c) $x = 1, 4$
29 $y = f(x - 2) - 6$
31 (a) $g(x) + 3$
(b) $g(x - 2)$
33 (a) Population 100 people larger than original
(b) Population same as 100 years earlier
35 Average for 7 mos, 10 mos
Above average
37 Up 1, right 3
39 Vertical shifts

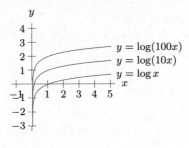
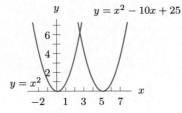

41 Shift $y = x^2$ right by 5 units to get $y = (x-5)^2 = x^2 - 10x + 25$

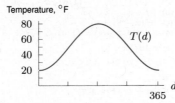

43 Shift up 3
45 Shift left 4
47 Shift left b, down a
49 (a) $T(d) = S(d) + 1$
(b) $P(d) = S(d - 1)$
51 $w(x) = v(x - 5) - 7; h = 5, k = -7$
53 (a) $t(x) = 20 + 7x$ for $x \geq 0$
(b) $n(x) = t(x) + 5$
(c) $p(x) = t(x - 2) + 10$ for $x \geq 2$
55 (a)
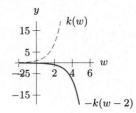
57 $H(t) - 37$

Section 6.2

S1 20.086
S3 0.050
S5 (a) $f(-x) = 2x^2$
(b) $-f(x) = -2x^2$
S7 (a) $f(-x) = -2x^3 - 3$
(b) $-f(x) = -2x^3 + 3$
S9 (a) $f(-x) = 3x^4 + 2x$
(b) $-f(x) = -3x^4 + 2x$
1 (a) $(-2, -3)$
(b) $(2, 3)$
3 -7
5 Domain: $t < 0$
Range: $-4 \leq Q(-t) \leq 7$

7 Domain: $t < 0$
Range: $-7 \leq -Q(-t) \leq 4$
9 $y = -e^x$
13 Reflected across x-axis;
$-g(x) = -(1/3)^x$
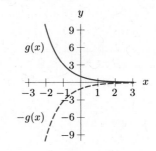
15 $-m(n) = -(n)^2 + 4n - 5$
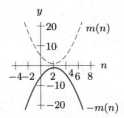
17 $m(-n) + 3 = n^2 + 4n + 8$
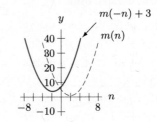
19 $-k(w) = -3^w$
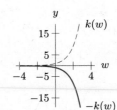
21 $-k(w - 2) = -3^{w-2}$
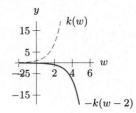

23 Odd

25 Neither

27 (a) $y = 2^{-x} - 3$

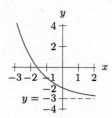

(b) $y = 2^{-x} - 3$

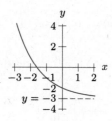

(c) Yes

29 (a) $g(-x) = -\sqrt[3]{x}$
(c) Odd

31 Reflections across x-axis

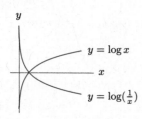

33 (i) b
(ii) c
(iii) d
(iv) e
(v) a

35 (a)

(b)

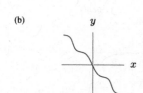

(c)

37 (a) Odd
(b) Unless $f(x) = 0$ or $g(x) = 0$, $k(x)$ is neither.
(c) Even

39 $y = x$. $y = -x + b$, where b is an arbitrary constant

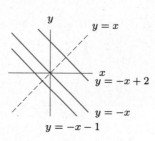

43 No

45 If $f(x)$ is odd, then $f(0) = 0$

49 Yes, $f(x) = 0$

Section 6.3

S1 (a) 72
(b) -18
(c) 177
(d) 25/4

S3 (a) $-(1/3)f(x) = -(1/3)\sqrt{x}$
(b) $5f(-x) = 5\sqrt{-x}$
(c) $6f(x - 8) = 6\sqrt{x - 8}$
(d) $(1/4)f(2 - x) = (1/4)\sqrt{2 - x}$

1 $y = 10f(x - 2)$

3 $-0.25 \le 0.25C(x) \le 0.25$

5 $R(n) = -5P(n)$

7 $T(n) = 1/4P(n + 7)$

9

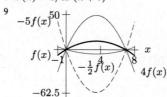

11

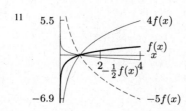

13 (d) All three

15

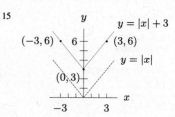

17

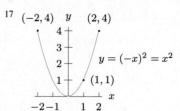

19

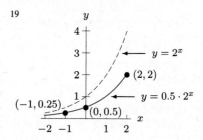

21 Stretch vertically by a factor of 2, Shift left 1 unit

23

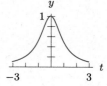

25

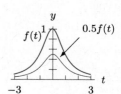

27

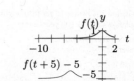

29 I is (b)
II is (d)
III is (c)
IV is (h)

31 $1.3C(t)$

33

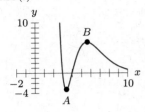

37 (a) $h(x) = 1/2f(x)$
(b) $k(x) = f(-x)$
(c) $m(x) = f(x) - 4$

39 (a) $y = -2f(x)$
(b) $y = f(x) + 2$
(c) $y = 3f(x - 2)$

43 -7

Section 6.4

S1 $8x^3 - 5$

S3 $(-x^3)/27 - 5$

S5 $4e^{2t}$

S7 $4e^{12t} + 11$

1 $(1, 3)$

3 Same function values for
$x = -6, -4, -2, 0, 2, 4, 6$

5

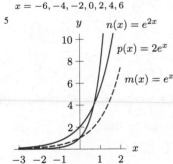

7

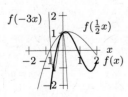

9

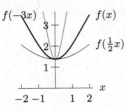

11 (a) -0.33

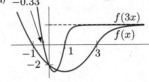

(b)

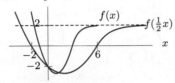

(c)

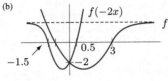

13 (a) Domain: $-6 \le x \le 6$;
Range: $0 \le l(2x) \le 3$
(b) Domain: $-24 \le x \le 24$;
Range: $0 \le l((1/2)x) \le 3$

15

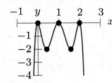

17 $T(1000x)$

19 (a) $A(s/60)$
(b) A(60 h)

21 $r(t)$: half the level
$s(t)$: half the rate

23 (a) III
(b) II
(c) I
(d) IV

25 $y = -f(-\frac{1}{2}x)$

27

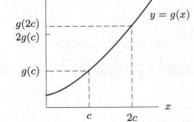

29 (a) $-24 \le x \le 8$
(b) $-3/4$

31 (a) $-2 \le x \le 6$
(b) 3

Section 6.5

S1 -3

S3 $10/3$

S5 (a) -1
(b) $8\sqrt[3]{-2}$
(c) 5
(d) -16
(e) $-2\sqrt[3]{2}$
(f) $\sqrt[3]{5}$

S7 $A = 1, B = -2, h = 0, k = 9$

S9 $A = 6, B = -1/3, h = -27, k = 0$

1 A horizontal compression by a factor of $1/3$ and
then a horizontal shift right by $2/3$ units.

3 (a) $(3, -14)$
(b) $(6, -26)$
(c) $(18, 17)$
(d) $(-33, -25/2)$

7 (a)

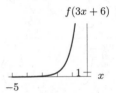

(b)

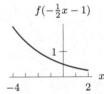

(c)

0.4f(-x + 1) - 2

(d)

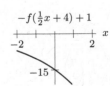

9

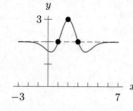

11

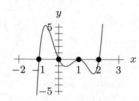

13 $t = -2.5, y = 5$

15

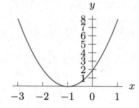

17 (a)

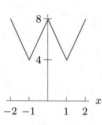

(b)

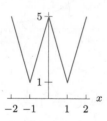

(c) The graphs are not the same.

19 No; down 10 units

21 $g(x) = -3f(x+4) + 6$

23 $h(x) = -2f(-x+3) - 4$

25 $(-9, 7), (3, 0), (39, -4)$

27

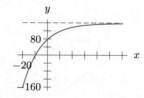

29 All four transformations are equivalent.

31 (a) $+1$

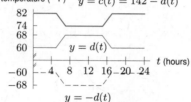
$g(x) = \log(10x)$
$f(x) = \log x$

(b) $\log(10x) = 1 + \log x$
(c) $k = \log a$

33 A vertical compression by a factor of e^{-k}.

35 (a) Vertical; stretch by 2, shift by 8
(b) Vertical; shift by 4, stretch by 2

37 (b) $d(t)$ reflected about the t-axis and then raised 142

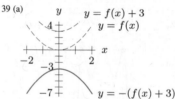
temperature ($^\circ$ F)
$y = c(t) = 142 - d(t)$
$y = d(t)$
t (hours)
$y = -d(t)$

39 (a)

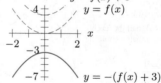
$y = f(x) + 3$
$y = f(x)$
$y = -(f(x) + 3)$

(b)

$y = f(x) + 3$
$y = f(x)$
$y = -(f(x) + 3)$

41 (a) $y = mx, m > 1$
(b) $y = mx + b, \; m > 1$ and b an arbitrary constant

43 Yes; $g(x) = (rb + j) + (rms) \cdot x, B = rb + j, M = rms$

45 Yes; $g(x) = (ras^2) \cdot (x - h/s)^2 + (rk + j), A = ras^2, H = h/s, K = rk + j$

Chapter 6 Review

1 (a) 4
(b) 1
(c) 5
(d) -2

3 (a) $(6, 5)$
(b) $(2, 1)$
(c) $(1/2, 5)$
(d) $(2, 20)$

5 Odd

7 Neither

9 Even

11 (a) $f(2x) = 1 - 2x$
(b) $f(x + 1) = -x$
(c) $f(1 - x) = x$
(d) $f(x^2) = 1 - x^2$
(e) $f(1/x) = (x - 1)/x$
(f) $f(\sqrt{x}) = 1 - \sqrt{x}$

13

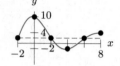

15 $y = f(t + 4) - 8$

17 (a) A horizontal reflection about the y-axis.
(b) A horizontal shift 6 units to the right.

19 (a) VI
(b) V
(c) III
(d) IV
(e) I
(f) II

21 (a) $-16t^2 + 23$
$-16t^2 + 48t + 2$

(b)

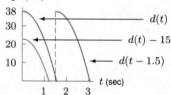
height (feet)
$d(t)$
$d(t) - 15$
$d(t - 1.5)$
t (sec)

(d) 1.541 secs
1.199 secs
(e) 3.041 secs

23 $y = -(x + 1)^3 + 1$

25 $y = (1/2)h(x + 6) + 1$

27 $p \approx 15, q \approx 7190$

31

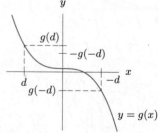
$g(d)$
$-g(-d)$
$g(-d)$
$y = g(x)$

33 $y = 3h(x)$

35 $y = -h(2 - 2x)$

37 $y = 2f(x/2) + 3$

41

d	20	45	70	95
$h(d)$	5.5	5.2	5.1	5.1
d	120	145	170	195
$h(d)$	5.3	5.5	5.75	6

43

d	25	50	75	100
$n(d)$	8.25	7.8	7.65	7.65
d	125	150	175	200
$n(d)$	7.95	8.25	8.63	9

45

d	25	50	75	100
$q(d)$	10.25	9.8	9.65	9.65
d	125	150	175	200
$q(d)$	9.95	10.25	10.63	11

Ch. 6: Understanding

1 True

3 True

5 True

7 False

9 True

11 False

13 False

15 True

17 True

19 False

21 False

23 True

Section 7.1

1 (I), (II), (IV)

3 90 m

5 90 m

7 b

9 41

11 12 o'clock position; 165 m

13 6 o'clock position; 15 m

15

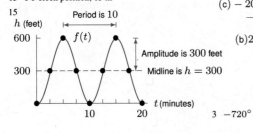

17

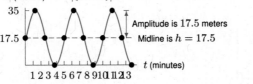

19

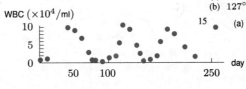

21 12 o'clock; descending; 4 minutes;
    30 meters; 5 meters; 10 minutes

23 3 (or 9) o'clock; descending;
    5 minutes; 40 meters; 0 meters;
    11.25 minutes

27 (a) Weight B
    (b) Weight A
    (c) Weight A

29 Midline: $y = 5.55$;
    Amplitude: 5.15 WBC $\times 10^4$/mL;
    Period: 72 days

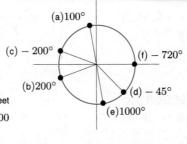

Section 7.2

1 (a) $(-0.174, 0.985)$
   (b) $(-0.940, -0.342)$
   (c) $(-0.940, 0.342)$
   (d) $(0.707, -0.707)$
   (e) $(0.174, -0.985)$
   (f) $(1, 0)$

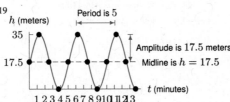

3 $-720°$

5 $D = (0, -1)$, $E = (-0.707, -0.707)$,
   $F = (-0.707, 0.707)$

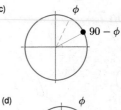

7 (a) 0.923
   (b) 0.385

9 (a) 0.447
   (b) 0.894

13 (a) 307°
    (b) 127°

15 (a)

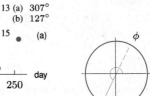

(b)

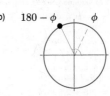

(c)

(d)

19 (a) 72°
   (b) 180°
   (c) 216°
21 (a) All are equal
   (b) $KP = 1/2$
   (c) $OP = \sqrt{3}/2$
   (d) $(\sqrt{3}/2, 1/2)$
   (e) $\cos 30° = \sqrt{3}/2$;
       $\sin 30° = 1/2$
   (f) $\cos 60° = 1/2$;
       $\sin 60° = \sqrt{3}/2$
23 $d = 3\cos\alpha$ meters

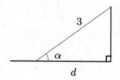

Section 7.3

1 Mid: $y = 2$; Amp: 1
3 Mid: $y = -3$; Amp: 7
5 Mid: $i(t) = 223$ cm; Amp: 20 cm
7 $(0, 3.8)$
9 $(-3.8, 0)$
11 $(0, 3.8)$
13 $(3.687, -0.919)$
15 $(3.8\sqrt{2}/2, 3.8\sqrt{2}/2)$ or $(2.687, 2.687)$
17 $(-3.8\sqrt{2}/2, -3.8\sqrt{2}/2)$
   $(-2.687, -2.687)$
19 $(3.742, -0.660)$
21 $(-5\sqrt{3}, -5)$
23 period 50, midline $y = 12$, amplitude 5
25 period 24, midline $y = -500$, amplitude 2000
27 period 25, midline $y = 30$, amplitude 25
29 $g(x) = \cos x, a = 90°, b = 1$
33 $f(x) = \sin(x + 90°)$
   $g(x) = \sin(x - 90°)$
35 $(60, 0), (7.5, 0)$
   $(60\cos\theta, 60\sin\theta)$
   $(7.5\cos\theta, 7.5\sin\theta)$
37 $h(\theta) = 2.5 + 2.5\sin\theta$.

Section 7.4

1 $0, 1, 0$
3 (a) $\tan\theta = 2$
   (b) $\sin\theta = 2/\sqrt{5}$
   (c) $\cos\theta = 1/\sqrt{5}$
5 (a) $\sqrt{45}/7$
   (b) $2/7$
   (c) $\sqrt{45}/2$
7 (a) $8/12$
   (b) $\sqrt{80}/12$
   (c) $8/\sqrt{80}$
9 (a) $\sqrt{117}/11$
   (b) $2/11$

(c) $\sqrt{117}/2$
11 $r = 7\sin 17°$; $q = 7\cos 17°$
13 $r = 6/\cos 37°$; $q = 6\tan 37°$
15 $r = 9/\tan 77°$; $q = 9/\sin 77°$
17 0
19 Undefined
21 1
23 0
25 $h = 400$ feet; $x = 346.410$ feet
27 $d = 35000/\tan\theta$ feet

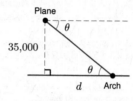

29 $d \approx 15.877$ feet

Section 7.5

1 61.164°
3 7.012°
5 no solution
7 89.190°
9 $\theta = 60°$
11 $\theta = 60°$
or 13 $\theta = 45°$
15 $c = 34.409$; $A = 35.538°$, $B = 54.462°$
17 $B = 62°$; $a = 9.389$; $b = 17.659$
19 The angle is k; a represents the value
21 The angle is c; the value is $1/d$
23 The angle is n; the value is p
25 (a) 0.009
   (b) 30°
   (c) 114.593
27 (a) $\sqrt{2} + 1$
   (b) $2\sqrt{2} + 1$
   (c) 90.008°
29 $\theta = 33.557°$
31 No solution
33 9°
35 30°
37 15.859°
39 39.806°
41 $\approx 39.806°$
43 (a) $a = 4$; $c = 2$; $B = 60°$
   (b) $A \approx 73.740°$; $B \approx 16.260°$; $b = 7$

Section 7.6

1 $x \approx 19.121$
3 $b \approx 5.120$, $c \approx 6.497$; $\beta = 52°$
5 $a \approx 11.818$, $b \approx 2.084$; $\theta = 80°$
7 $a = 10.450$; $\theta = 16.560°$, $\psi = 143.440°$

9 $A = 25.922°$, $B = 37.735°$, $C = 116.343°$
11 $b = 31.762$, $A = 38.458°$, $C = 60.542°$
13 $c = 10.954$, $A = 54.010°$, $B = 45.990°$
15 $c = 7.2605$; $A = 21.4035°$; $B = 126.597°$
17 $a = 15.860$, $b = 2.569$, $C = 66°$
19 $a = 10.026$, $b = 6.885$, $C = 61°$
21 $a = 2.079$, $b = 3.090$, $B = 18°$
23 $a = 1.671$, $b = 4.639$, $B = 166°$
25 $a = 13.667$, $A = 90.984°$, $C = 17.016°$
27 $a = 12.070$, $A = 135.109°$, $C = 27.891°$
   or
   $a = 3.231$, $A = 10.891°$, $C = 152.109°$
29 $b = 0.837$ m, $c = 2.720$ m; $\gamma = 143.7°$

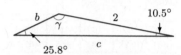

31 $\alpha \approx 41.410°, \beta \approx 82.819°, \gamma \approx 55.771°$

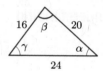

33 (a) $\sin\theta = 0.282$
   (b) $\theta \approx 16.374°$
   (c) 12.077 cm^2
35 B closer by 2.387 miles
37 396.004 miles
39 $(18.876, 10.071)$
43 (a) First; 3.062 feet closer
   (b) 157.279 feet to home
       113.218 feet to third
45 158.926 feet
47 4 rolls

Chapter 7 Review

1 Yes
3 No
5 No
7 Yes
9 $S = (-0.707, -0.707)$, $T = (0, -1)$, $U = (0.866, -0.5)$

15 True

17 True

19 False

21 True

23 False

25 True

27 False

29 True

Section 10.1

1 $2^{x/(x+1)}$

3 $\sin(4\sqrt{x})$; $\sqrt{\sin 4x}$

5 $w(x) = 4x + 3$

7 $s(0) = 2, s(1) = 5, s(2) = 8,$
$s(3) = 3, s(4) = 1, s(5) = 4$

9 $9x$

11 $27x^2 - 2$

13 $3888x^2 - 1728x + 192$

15 $\ln(x^2 + 4)$

17 $\cos 2x$

19 Area in terms of time

21 Revenue in terms of fertilizer

23 $u(x) = 1/(x - 1),$
$v(x) = x^2$

25 $g(x) = \sqrt{x}$, $h(x) = 1 + \sqrt{x}$

27 $g(x) = 1/x^2$, $h(x) = x + 4$

29

x	$f(x)$	$g(x)$	$h(x)$
0	2	1	3
1	1	0	0
2	4	3	2
3	0	4	1
4	3	2	4

31 $f(x) = 2x$

33 $f(x) = \ln x$

35 $(\sqrt{x + h} - \sqrt{x})/h$

37 $(2^{x+h} - 2^x)/h$

39 (a) 4
(b) 1
(c) 4
(d) 0

41 (a)

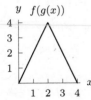

(b) $0 < x < 2$
(c) $2 < x < 4$

43

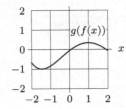

45

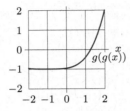

47 $v(x) = x + 1/x$

49 (a) $u(x) = (1 + x)/(2 + x)$
(b) $u(x) = x/(1 + x)$

51 (a) $v(x) = -x$
(b) $u(x) = \sqrt{1 - x}$

53 (a) $v(x) = \sin x$
(b) $u(x) = \sin^2(\sqrt{x})$

55 (a) (i) 3
(ii) 4
(iii) 3
(iv) 4
(b) 5

57 1/2

59 All real numbers;
All real numbers greater than or equal to zero

61 $q(x) = 2^x$

63 $g(x) = -1$, provided $x \neq -3$

65 (a) and (e)

Section 10.2

1 Not invertible

3 Not invertible

5 Not invertible

11 Yes, $f(f^{-1}(x)) = f^{-1}(f(x)) = x$

13 Yes, $f(f^{-1}(x)) = f^{-1}(f(x)) = x$

15 $f^{-1} = x - 5$

17 $h^{-1} = x^2$

19 $f^{-1}(x) = (x + 7)/3$

21 $l^{-1} = \sqrt{(1 - x^2)/2}$

23 $n^{-1} = \sqrt{\sqrt{x} - 1}$

25 $j^{-1}(x) = (x^2 - 1)^2$

27 $k^{-1}(x) = (3 - 2x)^2/(x + 1)^2$

29 $h^{-1}(x) = (5 + 4 \cdot 10^x)/(10^x - 1)$

31 $g^{-1}(x) = \arcsin(\ln x / \ln 2)$

33 Time at which pop is P; years

35 (a) $f^{-1}(R) = (1/5)R - 30$

37 (a) $f(3) = 5^3 = 125$; $f^{-1}(\frac{1}{25}) = -2$

(b) $f^{-1}(10) \approx 1.43086$

39 $f^{-1}(3) < f(3) < 0 < f(0) < f^{-1}(0) < 3$

41 $f^{-1}(P) = 50\ln(P/10)$

43 (a) $f(t) = 800 - 14t$ gals
(b) (i) 800 gals
(ii) 57.143 days
(iii) 28.571 days
(iv) 14t

45 (a) $f(g(x)) = g(f(x)) = x$; inverses
(b) Line $y = x$

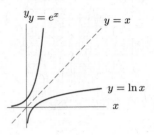

47 (a) $P(t) = 150(1.1)^t$
(b) $P^{-1}(N) =$
$(\log(N) - \log(150))/(\log(1.1))$
(c) 10.3 years

49 (a) $H(t) = 200e^{-1.15129t}$
(b) Dropped 50.021°C in the first 15 mins, 37.532°C in the next 15 mins
(c) $H^{-1}(y) = -\ln(y/200)/1.15129$
(d) About 3 hours and 12 minutes
(e) Brick's temperature approaches room temperature

51 $f^{-1}(x) = \left(0.5x^{-1} - A^{-1}\right)^{-1}$

53 $W(-1/e) = -1, W(0) = 0, W(e) = 1$

55 (a) $f(t) = 7.112(1.08998)^t$
(b) $f^{-1}(P) =$
$(\log(P/7.112))/(\log 1.08998)$
(c) $f(25) = 61.299$
$f^{-1}(25) = 14.590$

57 (a) $C(0) = 99\%$
(b) $C(x) = (99 - x)/(100 - x)$
(c) $C^{-1}(y) = (99 - 100y)/(1 - y)$

Section 10.3

1 (a) $f(x) + g(x) = 3x^2 + x + 1$
(b) $f(x) - g(x) = -3x^2 + x + 1$
(c) $f(x)g(x) = 3x^3 + 3x^2$
(d) $f(x)/g(x) = (x + 1)/(3x^2)$

3 (a) $f(x) + g(x) = 2x$
(b) $f(x) - g(x) = 10$
(c) $f(x)g(x) = x^2 - 25$
(d) $f(x)/g(x) = (x + 5)/(x - 5)$

5 (a) $f(x) + g(x) = x^3 + x^2$
(b) $f(x) - g(x) = x^3 - x^2$
(c) $f(x)g(x) = x^5$
(d) $f(x)/g(x) = x$

7 $f(x) = x$

9 $h(x) = 7x - 5$

11 $k(x) = 1 - 2x + x^2$

13 $f(x) = e^x(2x + 1) = 2xe^x + e^x$

15 $h(x) = 4e^{2x} + 4e^x + 1$

17 $\sin x + x^2$

19 $(\sin x)/x^2$

21 $\sin^2 x$

25 (a) $p(t) = f(t) + g(t)$
   (b) $m(t) = g(t) \cdot h(t)$

27 4550

31
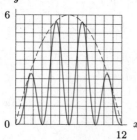

35 $17.50

37
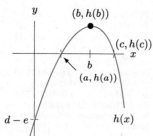

39 (a) Yes

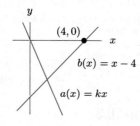

(b) The function has no zeros

41 $H(x) = (e^{-x^2})/(x^4)$,
   $h(x) = (-2x^5 e^{-x^2} - 4x^3 e^{-x^2})/(x^8)$

43 (b) $p(t) = (f_{CA}(t) \cdot g_{CA}(t) + f_{FL}(t) \cdot g_{FL}(t))/(f_{US}(t) \cdot g_{US}(t))$

45 40

47 $g(2000) = 100$, the dollar cost per square foot for building 2000 square feet of office space

49 $g(q) < g(p) < f(p) < f(q)$

51 $j(x) = x/h(x)$

Chapter 10 Review

1 $2^{x^2}; 4^x$

3 $1/(x^2 - 2)$

5 $\sqrt{x^2 + 1}$

7 $1/(x - 2)$

9 (a) Not invertible
   (b) Not invertible
   (c) Invertible

11 $h^{-1}(x) = x/(1 - 2x)$

13 $g^{-1}(x) = \frac{1}{3}\ln(x - 1)$

15 $h^{-1}(x) = \frac{1}{2}(1 - e^x)$

17 $g^{-1}(x) = (3x + 2)/(1 - 2x)$

19 $f^{-1}(x) = (11x - 3)^2/(1 + x)^2$

21 $s^{-1}(x) = 10^{(3/x) - 2}$

23 Not invertible

25 Not invertible

27 $r^{-1}(y) = \ln(y + 7)$

31 $2e^x - 1$

33 $4x - 3$

35 $\sqrt{x}e^{2x-1}$

37 (a) $f(2x) = 4x^2 + 2x$
   (b) $g(x^2) = 2x^2 - 3$
   (c) $h(1 - x) = (1 - x)/x$
   (d) $(f(x))^2 = (x^2 + x)^2$
   (e) $g^{-1}(x) = (x + 3)/2$
   (f) $(h(x))^{-1} = (1 - x)/x$
   (g) $f(x)g(x) = (x^2 + x)(2x - 3)$
   (h) $h(f(x)) = (x^2 + x)/(1 - x^2 - x)$

39 $x/(1 + e^{2x})$

41 $3x^2 + x$

43 $2x\sqrt{x + 2}$

45 $3x/2 - 1/2$

47 $x^{3/2}\tan 2x$

49 $\tan((3x - 1)^2/2) - 27x^{3/2}$

51

t	$p(t)$	$q(t)$	$r(t)$
0	4	3	5
1	5	2	1
2	3	4	0
3	2	0	4
4	1	5	2
5	0	1	3

53 $u(x) = \sqrt{x}, v(x) = 3 - 5x$

55 $u(x) = x^2, \quad v(x) = \sin x$

57 $u(x) = x^3, v(x) = 2x + 5$

59 $u(x) = 3^x, v(x) = 2x - 1$

63 (a) $r(x) = (x - 1)/(x - 2)$
   (b) $s(x) = x + 1$ and $t(x) = 1/x$
   (c) $p(p(a)) = (2a + 1)/(a + 1)$

65

x	$f(x)$	$g(x)$	$h(x)$
0	9	1	0
1	0	2	1
2	1	0	9

67 (a) $f^{-1}(P) = 2.5P - 50$
   (b)

t	$P = f(t)$
0	20
5	22
10	24
15	26
20	28

P	$t = f^{-1}(P)$
20	0
22	5
24	10
26	15
28	20

69 Velocity for time t; mph

71 $1 - t^2$

73 $x = (\ln 3/\ln 2) - 5$

75 $x = e^{1.8} - 3$

77 $x = (19 - \sqrt{37})/2$

79 (a) $A = \pi r^2$
   (b)
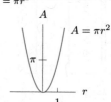

   (c) $r \geq 0$

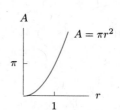

   (d) $f^{-1}(A) = \sqrt{A/\pi}$
   (e)
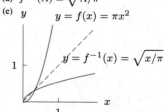

(f) Yes

81 (a) $f(g(a)) = a$
   (b) $g(f(c)) = b$
   (c) $f^{-1}(b) - g^{-1}(b) = -c$
   (d) $0 < x \le a$

83 $2\sqrt{x} - 9$

85 $(3 \pm \sqrt{17})/4$

87
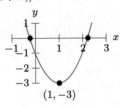
$(1, -3)$

89 (a) Only to $(u(x))^2$.
   (b) $u((v(x))^2)$ and $u(w(v(x)))$
   (c) (i) $1 + \sin 2x$
      (ii) 1
      (iii) $\cos(x^2) + \sin(x^2)$

91 $y = f(g(x))$
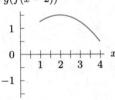

93 $y = g(f(x-2))$
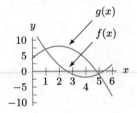

95 (a)
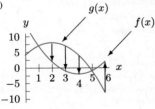

(c)
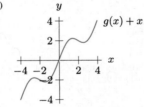

(f) $f(x) = x^2 - 8x + 14$;
   $g(x) = -x^2 + 4x + 4$;
   $f(x) - g(x) = 2x^2 - 12x + 10$
(g) Yes

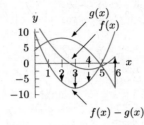
$f(x) - g(x)$

97 (a) $f(x) = 2x + 4, g(x) = \frac{1}{3}x - 1$
   (b)
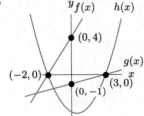

99 (a)
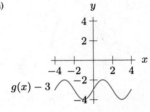
$g(x) - 3$

(b)
$g(x) + x$

101 False

103 $g(x) = (x+2)/2 = 0.5x + 1$

105 (a) $f(x) = e^x, g(x) = 6x, G(x) = 3x^2$
   (b) $f(x) = \sin x, g(x) = -1/(2\sqrt{x})$,
      $G(x) = \sqrt{x}$

107 (a) True
   (b) False
   (c) False
   (d) True

109 Increasing

111 Can't tell

113 (a) $f(8) = 2, f(17) = 2$,
     $f(29) = 2, f(99) = 0$
   (b) $f(3x) = 0$

(c) No
(d) $f(f(x)) = f(x)$
(e) No

115 $f^{-1}(L) = -\frac{1}{k} \ln(1 - L/L_\infty)$
   $f^{-1}(L) = $ Age of fish of length L
   Domain: $0 \le L \le L_\infty$

Ch. 10 Understanding

1 False
3 True
5 True
7 True
9 True
11 False
13 False
15 True
17 False
19 False
21 False
23 False
25 True
27 True
29 True
31 False
33 True
35 True
37 True

Section 11.1

S1 $6|t|$
S3 $0.16x^2y^4$
S5 $x = 0.585$
S7 False
S9 False

1 Yes; $g(x) = (-1/6)x^9$
3 No
5 Not a power function
7 $y = \frac{48}{30625} \cdot x^{-2}, a = \frac{48}{30625}, p = -2$
9 Even
11 Fractional
13 $y = 3x^{1.058}$
15 $f(x) = (3/2) \cdot x^{-2}$
17 $k = 5; c = 5d^2; c = 125$
19 $k = 3/2; y = (3x)/2; x = 5.33$
21 $f(x) = 3x^2$
23 $j(x) = 2x^3$
25 (a) 0
   (b) 0
29 (a) $x^{-3} \to +\infty, x^{1/3} \to 0$
   (b) $x^{-3} \to 0, x^{1/3} \to \infty$
31 Formula not unique
33 v, w, f, g
35 $f(x) = -1/(3\sqrt[3]{7}) \cdot x^{-4/3}$
37 (a) $C(x) = kx$
   (b) $k = 9.5; C(x) = 9.5x$

(c)

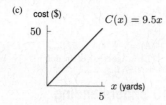

cost ($)

$C(x) = 9.5x$

50

5 x (yards)

(d) $52.25

39 (b) 16 times greater

41 $P = k/\sqrt{\rho}$

43 $h = 192.5/v; 64.167$ mph

45 (a) $d = 1.7, 3.4, 20.4, 102$
$d = 0.34t$
(b) 9.8 mins
(c) $A = 9.1, 36.3, 1307, 32685$
$A = 0.363t^2$
(d) $P = 11.25t^2$
(e) 298 sec, or approx 5 min

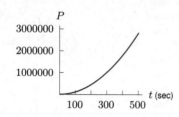

P

3000000

2000000

1000000

100 300 500 t (sec)

47 (a) $t = 4875/w$
(b) 19.5, 16.25, 9.75, 7.5 mins
(c) t (mins)

20

10

500 1000 w (watts)

(d) 1 min

49 (a) p even: all positive real numbers
p odd: all nonzero real numbers
(b) p even: symmetric about the y-axis
p odd: symmetric about the origin.
(c) p even: $y \to \infty$ as $x \to 0^-$ or $x \to 0^+$
p odd: $y \to -\infty$ as $x \to 0^-$ and $y \to \infty$
as $x \to 0^+$
(d) $y \to 0$ as $x \to \pm\infty$

51 (a) $p < 0, x \neq 0$
(b) $p > 0, y \geq 0$;
$p < 0, y > 0$;
$p > 0, y$ is any real;
$p < 0, y \neq 0$
(c) p even: y-axis symmetry;
p odd: origin symmetry

Section 11.2

1 No

3 Yes, 2

5 No

7 Degree: 3; Terms: 3;
$x \to -\infty: y \to -\infty$;
$x \to +\infty: y \to +\infty$

9 Degree: 3; Terms: 4;
$x \to -\infty: y \to +\infty$;
$x \to +\infty: y \to -\infty$

11 $x \approx 0.718, x \approx 1.702$.

15 $y = \frac{1}{2}x - 1$

17 (a) $-3 \leq x \leq -1, -5 \leq y \leq 5$
(b) $-3 \leq x \leq 4, -35 \leq y \leq 15$
(c) $1.25 \leq x \leq 2.35, -0 \leq y \leq 6$
(d) $-8 \leq x \leq 8, -50 \leq y \leq 2000$

19 $-1.1 \leq x \leq -0.9, -0.121 \leq y \leq 0.081$

21 $-20 \leq x \leq 20, -7600 \leq y \leq 8400$

23 $-1.764 < x < 0.875$, or $x > 3.889$

25 (a)

y

10
8
6
4
2
-2   2 4 6 8 t

(b) 100 people
(c) July of 1897
(d) 1010; February of 1893
(e) -115.7; not reasonable

27 (a)

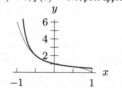

Volume

1
0.8
0.6
0.4
0.2

$V(t)$

1 2 3 4 5 t (sec)

(b) $V \approx .886$ at $t \approx 3.195$
(c) $(0, 0)$ and $(5, 0)$;
Lungs empty at beginning and end

29 Yes

31 (a) False
(b) False
(c) False
(d) True

33 (a) $p(0.5) \approx 0.65625$; 2 dec pl
(b) $p(1) = 0, f(1) = 0.5$; poor approx
(c)

y

6
4
2

-1   1 x

Section 11.3

1 $0, -4, -3$

3 $-3, 2, -7$

5 $h(x) = x(x + 2)^2(x - 3)$

7 $f(x) = (x + 2)(x - 2)^3$

9 $y = (-1/8)(x + 2)(x - 2)^2(x - 5)$;
$y = (-1/20)(x + 2)(x - 2)(x - 5)^2$

11

500

-5   4 5

13 (a) $f(x) = (x + 5)(x + 1)(2x - 1)(x - 1)$
(b) $-7 \leq x \leq 2, -150 \leq y \leq 10$

15 C

17 $f(x) = 1$

19 $f(x) = -\frac{1}{2}(x + 3)(x - 1)(x - 4)$

21 $p(x) = x^2 + 2x - 3$

23 $f(x) = -(x + 1)(x - 1)^2$

25 $f(x) = kx^3(x + 1)(x - 2)$ for $k > 0$

27 $f(x) = 3x(x + 1)(x - 1)^2$

29 $h(x) = (x + 2)(x + 1)^2(x - 1)$

31 $g(x) = -\frac{1}{3}(x^2)(x + 2)(x - 2)$

33 $x = \pm\frac{1}{2}$

35 $6, 2, 3$

37 None

39 $r = -1, s = 2, g(x) = k(x + 5)^2$ or
$r = -5, s = 2, g(x) = k(x + 5)(x + 1)$,
$k \neq 0$

41 (a) $V(x) = x(6 - 2x)(8 - 2x)$
(b) $0 < x < 3$
(c) y

25
20
15
10
5

$V(x) = x(6 - 2x)(8 - 2x)$

1 2 3 x

(d) ≈ 24.26 in^3

43 7.83 by 5.33 by 1.585 inches

45 $x \geq c$ and $a \leq x \leq b$

47 (a) $f(x) = \frac{2}{15}(x + 2)(x - 3)(x - 5)$
(b) $f(x) = -\frac{2}{75}(x + 2)(x - 3)(x - 5)^2$
(c) $f(x) = \frac{1}{15}(x + 2)^2(x - 3)(x - 5)$

Section 11.4

S1 $(6y^2 + 7)/y^3$

S3 $x^3/2$

S5 $(-18x^2 + 18x + 41)/((x - 2)^2(x + 1))$

S7 $1/2$

S9 $1/(x - 1)$

1 Rational; $(x + 2)/(x^2 - 1)$

3 Rational; $(x^3 + 2)/(2x)$

5 Not rational

7 Not rational

9 ∞

11 0

13 $y = 1$

15 As $x \to \pm\infty, f(x) \to 1, g(x) \to x$, and
$h(x) \to 0$

19 (a)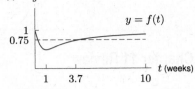

(c) Approaches 1
(d) About 3.73 weeks

21 (a) $f(x) = (3 + x)/(12 + x)$
  (b) (i) 28%
       (ii) 25%
       (iii) $\approx 18.2\%$
       (iv) 6
       (v) -3
  (c) concentration of copper in alloy

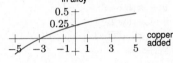

  (d)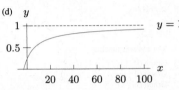

23 2011; Never

25 (a) $f(x) = x/(x + 5)$
  (b) $f(7) = 7/12 \approx 58.333\%$
  (c) $x = 0$
  (d) $y = 1$

27 (a) $C(n_0)/n_0$
  (b) Slope is average cost for n_0 units

29 (a) $C(x) = 30000 + 3x$
  (b) $a(x) = 3 + 30000/x$
  (c)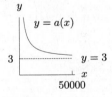

  (f) $a^{-1}(y) = 30000/(y - 3)$
  (g) 15,000

Section 11.5

1 Zeros: $x = 4$;
  Asymptote: $x = \pm 3$;
  $y \to 0$ as $x \to \pm\infty$

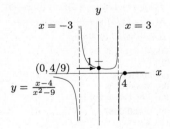

3 Zero: $x = -3$;
  Asymptote: $x = -5$;
  $y \to 1$ as $x \to \pm\infty$

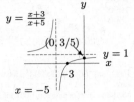

5 x-int: $x = \pm 2$
  y-int: None
  Horiz asy: $y = 0$
  Vert asy: $x = 0, x = -4$

7 x-int: $x = 2$
  y-int: $y = 1/2$
  Horiz asy: $y = 1$
  Vert asy: $x = 4$

9 (c) Horizontal: $y = 2$
      Vertical: $x = -4$

$G(x) = \dfrac{2x}{x+4}$

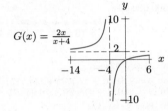

11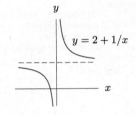

13 (a) $-\infty$
   (b) $+\infty$

15 (a) (iii)
   (b) (i)
   (c) (ii)
   (d) (iv)
   (e) (vi)
   (f) (v)

17 (a) 0, 0
   (b) $\lim_{x \to -2^+} f(x) = \infty$;
       $\lim_{x \to -2^-} f(x) = \infty$

19 (a) Small
   (b) Large
   (c) Undefined
   (d) Positive
   (e) Negative

21 (a)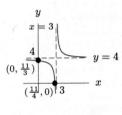

(b)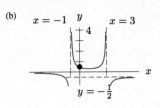

23 (a) $y = -1/(x + 2)$
   (b) $y = -1/(x + 2)$
   (c) $(0, -1/2)$

25 $p = 1, (0, 11/3), (11/4, 0)$
   $x = 3, y = 4$

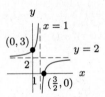

27 $p = 1, (0, 3), (3/2, 0)$
   $x = 1, y = 2$

29 (a) $y = 1/x$
   (b) $y = x/(2x - 4)$

31 (a) $1/x$
   (b) $y = (1/x) + 2$

33 $y = -(x + 1)/(x - 2)$

35 $y = -(x - 3)(x + 2)/((x + 1)(x - 2))$

37 $y = (x - 2)/((x + 1)(x - 1))$

39 $y = x - 9; (2, -7)$

41 $h(x) = (x^4 - 2x^3)/(x - 2)$

43 $g(x) = (x - 5)/((x + 2)(x - 3))$

Section 11.6

1 $p(x) = 25^x$

3 Neither

5 $r(x) = 2(\frac{1}{9})^x$

7 A - (i)
B - (iv)
C - (ii)
D - (iii)

11 $y = 6x^{35}$

13 $y = 50x^{1.1}$

15 $y = e^{-x}$

17 (a) $f(x) = 720x - 702$
(b) $f(x) = 2(9)^x$
(c) $f(x) = 18x^4$

19 (a) $f(x) = y = \frac{63}{4}x + \frac{33}{2}$
(b) $f(x) = 3 \cdot 4^x$
(c) $f(x) = \frac{3}{4}x^6$

21 A: $kx^{5/7}$; B: $kx^{9/16}$;
C: $kx^{3/8}$; D: $kx^{3/11}$;

23 $m = 2, t = 4, k = \frac{1}{4}$

25 $y \to 0$ as $x \to \pm\infty$

27 $y \to 0$ as $t \to \infty$
$y \to 7/9$ as $t \to -\infty$

29 $y \to \infty$ as $x \to \infty$
$y \to -\infty$ as $x \to -\infty$

31 $y \to 0$ as $x \to \infty$

33 $y \to \infty$ as $x \to \infty$
$y \to -\infty$ as $x \to -\infty$

35 $y \to \infty$ as $x \to \infty$
$y \to 0$ as $x \to -\infty$

37 $f(x) = 2\sin(\frac{\pi}{2}x) + 4$ (trigonometric);
$g(x) = -\frac{5}{2}x^3$ (power function);
$h(x) = \frac{1}{3}(\frac{1}{2})^x$ (exponential)

39 (a) $p_5(r) = 1000[(1 + r)^5 + (1 + r)^4 + (1 + r)^3 + (1 + r)^2 + (1 + r) + 1]$;
$p_{10}(r) = 1000[(1 + r)^{10} + (1 + r)^9 + (1 + r)^8 + (1 + r)^7 + (1 + r)^6 + (1 + r)^5 + (1 + r)^4 + (1 + r)^3 + (1 + r)^2 + (1 + r) + 1]$
(b) 20.279%

Section 11.7

1 $f(x) = x^{\ln c / \ln 2}$

3 $g(x) = 2x^{1.2}$

5 (a) $f(x) = 201.353x^{2.111}$
(b) $f(20) = 112,313.62$ gm
(c) $x = 18.930$ cm

7 $y = x^{3/2}$

9 $y = (3/2)x$

11 $y = e^{0.4x}$

13 (a) $y = -83.039 + 61.514x$; superb fit
(b) Good only for close values

15 $a \approx 3.49$

17 (b) $R(p) = -0.0565p^2 + 72.9981p + 4749.85$
(c) $p = \$646, R = \$28,349$

19 (a) $C(t) = 841.368(1.333)^t$
(b) 33.3% per year
(c) Slower growth; concave down

21 (a)
Population (thousands)

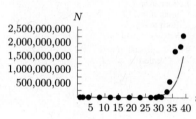

(b) $P(t) = 56.108(1.031)^t$, answers may vary
(c) 56.108 is 1650 population, 1.031 means 3.1% annual growth
(d) $P(100) = 1194.308$, slightly higher
(e) $P(150) = 5510.118$, higher

23 (a) $N = 1148.55e^{0.3617t}$

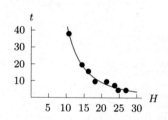

(b) About 1.92 years

25 (a) $y = 0.310t^2 - 12.177t + 144.517$
(b) $y = 3.01t^2 - 348.43t + 10,955.75$

27 (b) Points lie on a line

29 (a) Quadratic
(b) $y = -34.136x^2 + 3497.733x - 39,949.714$; answers may vary
(c) \$42,734; answers may vary
(d) Age 10, $-\$386$, not reasonable; answers may vary

31 (a) $t = 8966.1H^{-2.3}$

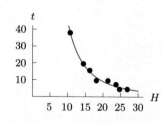

(b) $r = 0.0124H - 0.1248$

(c) $H = 0°C$; $H = 10.1°C$; model (b)

Chapter 11 Review

1 Yes; $k = 1/6$ and $p = -7$

3 No

5 No

7 Yes; $y = x^2$

9 Even

11 Odd

13 Odd

15 $k = 2\sqrt[3]{7}, p = 11/15$

17 4th degree

19 $y \to \infty$; like $4x^4$

21 $y \to \infty$; like $2x^9$

23 $x = (3 \pm \sqrt{33})/4$

25 Not rational

27 $y = 4/e^{-x}$

29 (a) 2
(b) 5/6

31 Not a power function

33 Graph (i): J;
Graph (ii): L;
Graph (iii): O;
Graph (iv): H

35 $y = -\frac{3}{2}(x + 4)(x + 2)(x - 2)$

37 $y = \frac{1}{2}(x + \frac{1}{2})(x - 3)(x - 4)$

39 $y = -x(x + 3)(x - 2)$

41 $y = (x + 3)x^2$

43 $y = (x + 3)(x + 2)(x + 1) + 4$

45 (a) $y = 1/(x - 2)^2 - 1$
(b) $y = (-x^2 + 4x - 3)/(x^2 - 4x + 4)$
(c) $(0, -3/4)$, $(1, 0)$ and $(3, 0)$

47 (a) $y = -1/(x - 3)^2$
(b) $y = -1/(x^2 - 6x + 9)$
(c) $(0, -1/9)$

49 (a) $-2, -3$; None
(b) $-2, -3$; No; $r(x) \to 1$ as $x \to \pm\infty$
(c) No; Yes at $x = -2$ and $x = 3$;
$s(x) \to 1$ as $x \to \pm\infty$

51 (a) False
(b) False
(c) True
(d) False

53 $f(x) = (x + 3)(x - 2)/((x + 5)(x - 7))$

55 $f(x) = (x + 1)/(x - 1)$

57 $f(x) = (-1/5)(x + 3)(x - 2)(x - 5)$

59 $h(x) = (1/5)(x + 5)(x + 1)(x - 4) + 7$

61 $d = 0.1x$; 32.5 miles

63 (a) 20 lbs; 1620 lbs
(b) 3/10

65 (a) 500 people
(b) May of 1908
(c) 790; February of 1907

67 (b) $k \approx 0.0087$
(c) Yes

33 Yes; $k \approx 0.2$; $P = 0.2D^{3/2}$

69 (c)

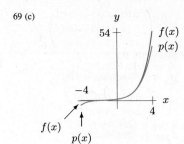

Ch. 11 Understanding

1 False
3 True
5 True
7 False
9 True
11 True
13 False
15 True
17 False
19 False
21 True
23 False
25 True
27 True
29 True
31 True
33 True
35 False
37 False
39 True
41 True
43 False
45 False
47 False

Ch. 11 Skills: Fractions

1 $41/35$
3 $(3 - 4x)/6x$
5 $-2(1 - 2y)/yz$
7 $(2 - 3x)/x^2$
9 $1/18$
11 $x/2$
13 $(4y^3z - 3wx)/(x^2y^4)$
15 $(8(y + 4))/(y - 4)$
17 $(-27x + 44)/((x + 1)(3x - 4))$
19 $(x + 20)/(x^2 - 16)$
21 $1/2r$
23 $(x - 1)/(\sqrt{x})^3 = x\sqrt{x} - \sqrt{x}/x^2$
25 $(4x + 1)/(b - a)$
27 $(r_2r_3 + r_1r_3 + r_1r_2)/(r_1r_2r_3)$
29 $(2a + 3)/((a + 3)(a - 3))$

31 $(-2x - h)/\left(x^2(x + h)^2\right)$
33 $-2x - h$
35 $1 - (1/a)$
37 $x^2y/(2x + 1)$
39 $(2x - 4x^4)/(x^3 + 1)^3$
41 $13/x^2 + 1/(2x^3)$
43 $(2/l^2) + (1/l^3) - 4/(3l^4)$
45 $1/6 - 1/(4x)$
47 $1 - 7/(x + 5)$
49 $1 + 1/R$
51 $1 + \sin x/\cos x$
53 False
55 False
57 True

Section 12.1

1 Scalar
3 Vector
5 Scalar
7 Vector
9

11

13

15 $\vec{p} = 2\vec{w}$
$\vec{q} = -\vec{u}$
$\vec{r} = \vec{u} + \vec{w}$
$\vec{s} = 2\vec{w} - \vec{u}$
$\vec{t} = \vec{u} - \vec{w}$

17 (a) 1.710 miles
(b) 5.848 miles

19 5.116 miles; 14.639° east of north

21 14,705 meters;
angle of 17.819° from horizontal

23 (a) 14.3373
(b) Veers right
(c) Not possible

Section 12.2

1 $-3\vec{i} - 4\vec{j}$
3 $\vec{w} \approx -0.725\vec{i} - 0.95\vec{j}$
5 $\vec{i} + 3\vec{j}$
7 $0.3\vec{i} - 1.8\vec{j} + 0.03\vec{k}$
9 $\sqrt{11} \approx 3.317$
11 7.649
13 $-5\vec{i} + 10\vec{j}$ knots
15 45° or $\pi/4$
17 90° or $\pi/2$
19 $-140.847\vec{i} + 140.847\vec{j} + 18\vec{k}$
21 $21\vec{j} + 35\vec{k}$
23 (a) 50 km/hr
(b) Horizontal: 43.301; vertical: 25
25 (a) $3.536(\vec{i} + \vec{j})$.
(b) $3.536\vec{i} + 4.736\vec{j}$
27 (a) (i) $\vec{m} = 3\vec{j}, \vec{h} = 2\vec{j}$

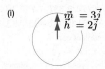

(ii) $\vec{m} = 3\vec{j}, \vec{h} = 2\vec{i}$

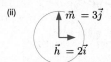

(iii) $\vec{m} = 3\vec{j}, \vec{h} = \vec{i} + \sqrt{3}\vec{j}$

(iv) $\vec{m} = -3\vec{j}, \vec{h} = \sqrt{2}\vec{i} + \sqrt{2}\vec{j}$

(b) $3\vec{j} - 2\vec{i}$

(c) $\sqrt{2}\vec{i} + (\sqrt{2}-3)\vec{j}$

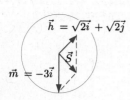

$$\vec{h} = \sqrt{2}\vec{i} + \sqrt{2}\vec{j}$$
$$\vec{S}$$
$$\vec{m} = -3\vec{i}$$

29 $\vec{k}$

31 $\vec{i} + \vec{k}$

Section 12.3

1 $(2, 2, 4, 6, 10, 16)$

3 $(-4, -5, -5, -5, -4, -2)$

5 $(5, 6, 7, 8, 9, 10)$

7 $(13/6, 5/2, 10/3, 25/6, 11/2, 22/3)$

9 $(3.63, 1.44, 6.52, 1.43, 1.20, 0.74)$

11 $(3.467, 1.277, 6.357, 1.267, 1.037, 0.577)$

13 $(79.000, 79.333, 89.000, 68.333, 89.333)$

15 $3.378°$ north of east

17 (a) $\vec{v} = 4.330\vec{i} + 2.500\vec{j}$
For the second leg of his journey, $\vec{w} = x\vec{i}$

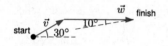

(b) $x = 9.848$
(c) 14.397

19 (a) $\vec{F}_{net} = (8, 7)$
(b) $\vec{F}_4 = (-8, -7)$

21 $\vec{q}_a = 1.065\vec{i} + 1.966\vec{j}$; $(1.065, 1.966)$
$\vec{q}_b = 2.703\vec{i} + 3.113\vec{j}$; $(2.703, 3.113)$
$\vec{q}_c = 2.129\vec{i} + 3.933\vec{j}$; $(2.129, 3.933)$
$\vec{q}_d = 0.491\vec{i} + 2.785\vec{j}$; $(0.491, 2.785)$

Section 12.4

1 -7

3 -38

5 14

7 -2

9 $28\vec{j} + 14\vec{k}$

11 238

13 $108.435°$

15 2100 ft-lbs

17 1.911 radians $(109.471°)$

19 For both, max $= 11$, min $= 3$

21 No

25 (a) $\vec{a} = (3, 2, 4)$; $\vec{c} = (c_b, c_e, c_m)$
$3c_b + c_e + 4c_m = 40$, or $\vec{a} \cdot \vec{c} = 40$
(c) The "freshness-adjusted" cost is cheaper at Beta

27 $43.297°$

29 (a) Width
(b) Height
(c) Perimeter

Section 12.5

1 (a) $\begin{pmatrix} 15 & 35 \\ 10 & -5 \end{pmatrix}$

(b) $\begin{pmatrix} -2 & 10 \\ 0 & -16 \end{pmatrix}$

(c) $\begin{pmatrix} 4 & 2 \\ 2 & 7 \end{pmatrix}$

(d) $\begin{pmatrix} -8 & -26 \\ -6 & 11 \end{pmatrix}$

(e) $\begin{pmatrix} 13 & 45 \\ 10 & -21 \end{pmatrix}$

(f) $\begin{pmatrix} k & -5k \\ 0 & 8k \end{pmatrix}$

3 (a) $\begin{pmatrix} 12 & 8 & 20 & 4 \\ 16 & 24 & 28 & 12 \\ 4 & 36 & 20 & 32 \\ 0 & -8 & 16 & 24 \end{pmatrix}$

(b) $\begin{pmatrix} -2 & -12 & -8 & -4 \\ -6 & -10 & 2 & -14 \\ -18 & -8 & -14 & -6 \\ -4 & -16 & -8 & -10 \end{pmatrix}$

(c) $\begin{pmatrix} 2 & -4 & 1 & -1 \\ 1 & 1 & 8 & -4 \\ -8 & 5 & -2 & 5 \\ -2 & -10 & 0 & 1 \end{pmatrix}$

(d) $\begin{pmatrix} 6 & -12 & 3 & -3 \\ 3 & 3 & 24 & -12 \\ -24 & 15 & -6 & 15 \\ -6 & -30 & 0 & 3 \end{pmatrix}$

(e) $\begin{pmatrix} 4 & 8 & 9 & 3 \\ 7 & 11 & 6 & 10 \\ 10 & 13 & 12 & 11 \\ 2 & 6 & 8 & 11 \end{pmatrix}$

(f) $\begin{pmatrix} 10 & -4 & 12 & 0 \\ 10 & 14 & 30 & -2 \\ -14 & 28 & 6 & 26 \\ -4 & -24 & 8 & 14 \end{pmatrix}$

5 (a) $(51, 15, 38)$
(b) $(-8, -11, 33)$
(c) $(70, 20, 22)$
(d) $(11, -6, 17)$
(e) 681

(f) $\begin{pmatrix} 24 & 60 & 84 \\ 48 & -72 & 36 \\ 192 & -60 & 0 \end{pmatrix}$

7 (a) Defined
(b) Not defined
(c) Not defined
(d) Not defined
(e) Defined
(f) Not defined

9 (a) $\mathbf{T} = \begin{pmatrix} 0.90 & 0 & 0 \\ 0.10 & 0.50 & 0.02 \\ 0 & 0.50 & 0.98 \end{pmatrix}$

(b) $\vec{p_1} = (1.8, 0.2, 0)$,
$\vec{p_2} = (1.62, 0.28, 0.1)$,
$\vec{p_3} = (1.458, 0.304, 0.238)$

11 (a) $\mathbf{T} = \begin{pmatrix} 0.97 & 0.05 \\ 0.03 & 0.95 \end{pmatrix}$

(b) $\vec{p}_{2006} = (214, 386)$,
$\vec{p}_{2007} = (226.88, 373.12)$.

13 (a) $\vec{v} = \begin{pmatrix} 11 \\ 19 \end{pmatrix}$

(b) $\vec{v} = \begin{pmatrix} 5 \\ 11 \end{pmatrix}$

(c) $\vec{v} = \begin{pmatrix} 2a+b \\ 3a+2b \end{pmatrix}$

15 (a) $\lambda_2 = -1$
(b) $\lambda_3 = -1$
(c) $\mathbf{A}\vec{v} = \lambda\vec{v}$, and $\mathbf{A}\vec{v}$ is parallel to $\vec{v}$

17 (a) $\begin{pmatrix} 3 & 5 \\ 2 & 4 \end{pmatrix}\begin{pmatrix} a \\ b \end{pmatrix} = a\begin{pmatrix} 3 \\ 2 \end{pmatrix} + b\begin{pmatrix} 5 \\ 4 \end{pmatrix}$

(b) $\vec{v} = \begin{pmatrix} -8.5 \\ 5.5 \end{pmatrix}$

(c) $\vec{v} = -8.5\vec{c_1} + 5.5\vec{c_2}$

Chapter 12 Review

1 $(3, 3, 6)$

3 $(-3, -2, 9)$

5 $(7, 8, -21)$

7 $(4, -2, 18)$

9 $-4.5\vec{i} + 8\vec{j} + 0.5\vec{k}$

11 13

13 6

15 $6\vec{i} + 6\vec{j} + 6\vec{k}$

17 $\vec{a} = \vec{b} = \vec{c} = 3\vec{k}$
$\vec{d} = 2\vec{i} + 3\vec{k}$
$\vec{e} = \vec{j}$
$\vec{f} = -2\vec{i}$

19 $\|\vec{u}\| = \sqrt{6}$
$\|\vec{v}\| = \sqrt{5}$

21 (a) Yes
(b) No

23 (a) $\vec{L} = (11, 7, 11, 7, 13)$
(b) $\vec{F} = (32, 36, 21, 8, 4)$,
$\vec{G} = (3, 3, 2, 0, 7)$

25 $F = g\sin\theta$

29 $0.4v\vec{i} + 0.693v\vec{j}$

31 (a) $\overrightarrow{AB} = 2\vec{i} - 2\vec{j} - 7\vec{k}$
$\overrightarrow{AC} = -2\vec{i} + 2\vec{j} - 7\vec{k}$
(b) $\theta = 44.003°$

35 $\overrightarrow{AB} = -\vec{u}$; $\overrightarrow{BC} = 3\vec{v}$;
$\overrightarrow{AC} = \overrightarrow{AB} + \overrightarrow{BC} = -\vec{u} + 3\vec{v}$; $\overrightarrow{AD} = 3\vec{v}$

TABLE OF GREEK LETTERS

Name	Capital	Lowercase
Alpha	A	α
Beta	B	β
Gamma	Γ	γ
Delta	Δ	δ
Epsilon	E	ϵ
Zeta	Z	ζ
Eta	H	η
Theta	Θ	θ
Iota	I	ι
Kappa	K	κ
Lambda	Λ	λ
Mu	M	μ
Nu	N	ν
Xi	Ξ	ξ
Omicron	O	o
Pi	Π	π
Rho	P	ρ
Sigma	Σ	σ
Tau	T	τ
Upsilon	Υ	υ
Phi	Φ	ϕ
Chi	X	χ
Psi	Ψ	ψ
Omega	Ω	ω

TRIGONOMETRIC IDENTITIES

- **Tangent identity:**

$$\tan t = \frac{\sin t}{\cos t}$$

- **Periodicity:**

$$\sin(t + 2\pi) = \sin t \quad \cos(t + 2\pi) = \cos t \quad \tan(t + \pi) = \tan t$$

- **Pythagorean identity:**

$$\sin^2 t + \cos^2 t = 1$$

- **Double-angle formula for sine:**

$$\sin 2t = 2 \sin t \cos t$$

- **Double-angle formula for cosine** (expressed in three different ways):

$$\cos 2t = 1 - 2 \sin^2 t$$
$$\cos 2t = 2 \cos^2 t - 1$$
$$\cos 2t = \cos^2 t - \sin^2 t$$

- **Double-angle formula for tangent:**

$$\tan 2t = \frac{2 \tan t}{1 - \tan^2 t}$$

- **Negative angle identities:**

$$\sin(-t) = -\sin t \quad \cos(-t) = \cos t \quad \tan(-t) = -\tan t$$

- **Identities relating sine and cosine:**

$$\sin t = \cos\left(t - \frac{\pi}{2}\right) \qquad \cos t = \sin\left(t + \frac{\pi}{2}\right)$$

- **Sum-of-angle and difference-of-angle formulas for sine and cosine:**

$$\sin(\theta + \phi) = \sin\theta \cos\phi + \cos\theta \sin\phi$$

$$\sin(\theta - \phi) = \sin\theta \cos\phi - \cos\theta \sin\phi$$

and

$$\cos(\theta + \phi) = \cos\theta \cos\phi - \sin\theta \sin\phi$$

$$\cos(\theta - \phi) = \cos\theta \cos\phi + \sin\theta \sin\phi.$$

- **Sum and difference of sine and cosine:**

$$\cos u + \cos v = 2 \cos \frac{u+v}{2} \cos \frac{u-v}{2} \qquad \sin u + \sin v = 2 \sin \frac{u+v}{2} \cos \frac{u-v}{2}$$

$$\cos u - \cos v = -2 \sin \frac{u+v}{2} \sin \frac{u-v}{2} \qquad \sin u - \sin v = 2 \cos \frac{u+v}{2} \sin \frac{u-v}{2}$$

9   $(c + 3/2)^2 - 37/4$

11   $4(s + 1/8)^2 + 31/16$

13   $(x - 1)^2 - 4$

15   $-(x - 3)^2 + 7$

17   $(-3, -6)$

19   $(-4, 18)$

21   $(1/2, -23/4)$

23   $(1, -2)$

25   $(7/4, -25/8)$

27   $r = 4, 2$

29   $p = 1 \pm \sqrt{7}$

31   $d = 2, -1$

33   $s = -5/2 \pm \sqrt{27}/2$

35   $r = 3/14 \pm \sqrt{177}/14$

37   $n = 6, -2$

39   $k = -1/3, -3/2$

41   $z = -2 \pm \sqrt{10}$

43   $r = 4, -2$

45   $n = -5, 1$

47   $z = -2, \pm\sqrt{3}$

49   $u = (3 \pm \sqrt{5})/5$

51   $y = 1 \pm \sqrt{7}$

53   $w = 3, 2, -2$

55   $m = (-5 \pm \sqrt{3})/7$

Section 6.1

1   Yes

3   No

5   No

7   Yes

9   4

11   3

13

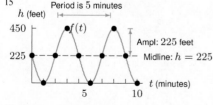

15

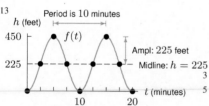

17

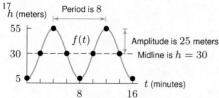

19   3 (or 9) o'clock; rising; 4 minutes;
30 meters; 5 meters; 11 minutes

21   3 (or 9) o'clock; upward; 5 minutes;
40 meters; 0 meters; 11.25 minutes

23   Midline: $y = 10$;
Period: 1;
Amplitude: 4;
Minimum: 6 cm;
Maximum: 14 cm

25   Graph is same except starts at a peak

27 (b)   Period: 1/60 seconds;
Amplitude: 155.6 volts;
Midline: $V = 0$

29 (a)   Periodic
  (b)   Not periodic
  (c)   Not periodic
  (d)   Not periodic
  (e)   Periodic
  (f)   Not periodic
  (g)   Periodic

31   Midline: $h = 2$;
Amplitude: 1;
Period: 1

Section 6.2

1 (a) $(-0.174, 0.985)$
  (b) $(-0.940, -0.342)$
  (c) $(-0.940, 0.342)$
  (d) $(0.707, -0.707)$
  (e) $(0.174, -0.985)$
  (f) $(1, 0)$

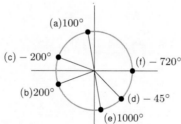

3   $-720°$

5   $S = (-0.707, -0.707)$, $T = (0, -1)$,
$U = (0.866, -0.5)$

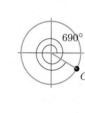

7   $A = (0.866, 0.5)$, $B = (-0.707, 0.707)$,
$C = (0.866, -0.5)$

9   $S = (-3.536, -3.536)$
$T = (0, -5)$
$U = (4.330, -2.5)$

11   $(0, 3.8)$

13   $(-3.8, 0)$

15   $(0, 3.8)$

17   $(3.687, -0.919)$

19   $(3.8\sqrt{2}/2, 3.8\sqrt{2}/2)$ or $(2.687, 2.687)$

21   $(-3.8\sqrt{2}/2, -3.8\sqrt{2}/2)$ or
$(-2.687, -2.687)$

23   $(3.742, -0.660)$

27 (a) $307°$
  (b) $127°$

29   (a)

(b)

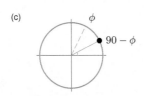

$180 - \phi$ ϕ

(c)

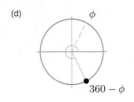

ϕ

$90 - \phi$

(d)

ϕ

$360 - \phi$

33   4/3 minutes

35 (a) $90°$
    (b) $90°$
    (c) $180°$
    (d) $180°$
    (e) A

Section 6.3

1   $\pi/3$

3   1.7453 radians

5   $5\pi/6$

7   $-3\pi/2$

9   $630°$

11   $16{,}200/\pi \approx 5156.620°$

13   $8100/\pi \approx 2578.310°$

15 (a)   I
    (b)   II
    (c)   II
    (d)   III
    (e)   IV
    (f)   IV
    (g)   I
    (h)   II
    (i)   II
    (j)   III

17   -4π

19   8.54π

21   $6.2\pi/4 \approx 4.869$

23   $6.2a\pi/180$

25   5π feet

27   $\pi/9$ radians or $20°$

29   $r = \sqrt{65}$; $\theta = 0.5191$ rad $= 29.7449°$; $s = 4.185$; $P = (7, 4)$

31   $r = 12$; $\theta = 1.3$ rad $= 74.485°$; $s = 15.6$; $P = (3.2100, 11.5627)$

33   $\theta = 0.4$ rad $= 22.918°$; $P = (0.9211r, 0.3894r)$

35 (a)   Negative
    (b)   Negative
    (c)   Positive
    (d)   Positive

37   $\sin \theta = 0.6$; $\cos \theta = -0.8$

39   $(-0.99, 0.14)$

41   $\pi/6$ feet

43   3998.310 miles

45   $t \approx 0.739$

Section 6.4

1   Mid: $y = 0$; Amp: 1

3   Mid: $y = -4$; Amp: 7

5   Mid: $y = -2$; Amp: 3

7   Mid: at 185 cm; Amp: 15cm

9 (a)   (i) $0 < t < \pi$ and $2\pi < t < 3\pi$
      (ii) $-\frac{\pi}{2} < t < \frac{\pi}{2}$ and $\frac{3\pi}{2} < t < \frac{5\pi}{2}$
      (iii) $-\pi < t < 0$ and $\pi < t < 2\pi$
   (b) $t = 0, 2\pi$

11   They are equal

13   $\sqrt{3}/2$

15   $\sqrt{3}/2$

17   $g(x) = \cos x$, $a = \pi/2$, $b = 1$

19   $f(x) = \sin(x + \frac{\pi}{2})$
     $g(x) = \sin(x - \frac{\pi}{2})$

23 (a) $1/\sqrt{2}$
    (b) $1/2$
    (c) $-\sqrt{3}/2$
    (d) $-1/2$
    (e) $1/\sqrt{2}$

25   $(-5\sqrt{3}, -5)$

27 (a)   (i) p
      (ii) s
      (iii) q
      (iv) r
   (b)

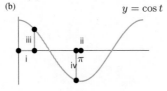

$y = \cos t$

29 (a) $m = (\cos b - \cos a)/(b - a)$
    (b) $-6(1 + \sqrt{2})/(13\pi)$

Section 6.5

1   Mid: $y = 0$; Amp: 6; Per: 2π

3   Mid: $y = 1$; Amp: $1/2$; Per: $\pi/4$

5   Hor: $-4/3$; Phs: -4

7   Both f and g have periods of 1, amplitudes of 1, and midlines $y = 0$

9   Period: 6; Amp: 5; Mid: 0

11   $h(t) = 4\sin(2\pi t)$

13   $g(t) = -2\cos(t/2) + 2$

15   $y = 4000 + 4000\sin((2\pi/60)x)$

17   $y = -2\sin(\pi\theta/6) + 2$

19

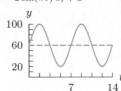

21

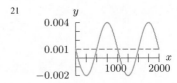

23   $1/4$, $g(x) = 3\sin((\pi/4)x - \pi/2)$

25   $f(x) = \sin x$, $a = \pi/2$, $b = \pi$, $c = 3\pi/2$, $d = 2\pi$, $e = 1$

27   Amplitude: 20
     Period: $3/4$ seconds

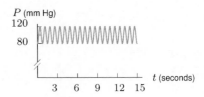

29   $f(t) = 14 + 10\sin(\pi t + \pi/2)$

31   $f(t) = 20 + 15\sin((\pi/2)t + \pi/2)$

33 (a) $12°$/min
    (b) $\theta = (12t - 90)°$
    (c) $f(t) = 225 + 225\sin(12t - 90)°$
    (d)   Amp = Midline = 225 feet
        Period = 30 min

35 (a) $P = f(t) = -450\cos(\pi t/6) + 1750$
    (c) $t_1 \approx 1.9$; $t_2 \approx 10.1$

37   $y = 3f(x)$

39   $y = -f(2x)$

41   Amplitude: 41.5;
     Period: 12 months

blanket sales (thousands)

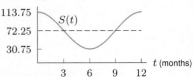

43   $f(t) = -100\cos(\pi t) + 100$ (for $0 \le t \le 1$)
     $10\cos(4\pi t) + 190$ (for $1 < t \le 2$)

45 (a)

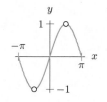

$T(°F)$

Midline Temperature

t (months)

(b) $23.2°$; 12 months
(c) $T = f(t) = -23.2\cos((\pi/6)t) + 58.6$
(d) $T = f(9) \approx 58.6°$

47 $f(t) = 3\sin((\pi/6)(t - 74)) + 15$

BTU (quadrillions)

year (since 1900)

Section 6.6

1 $0, 1, 0$

3 1

5 -1

7 -1

9 1

11 $-\sqrt{3}$

13 $-\sqrt{2}$

15 $2/\sqrt{3}$

17 $\sec\theta = 2$
$\tan\theta = \sqrt{3}$

19 $\sec\theta = 3/\sqrt{8}$
$\tan\theta = 1/\sqrt{8}$

21 $f(\theta) = (1/2)\tan\theta$

23 (a) $\sin\alpha = -\sqrt{22}/5$,
$\tan\alpha = \sqrt{22/3}$
(b) $\sin\beta = -4/5$,
$\cos\beta = -3/5$

25 $\cos\theta = \sqrt{1 - y^2}$

29 $\sin\theta = \sqrt{x^2 - 16}/x$,
$\tan\theta = \sqrt{x^2 - 16}/4$

31 $\cos\theta = 9/\sqrt{x^2 + 81}$,
$\sin\theta = x/\sqrt{x^2 + 81}$

33 $y = y_0 + (\tan\theta)(x - x_0)$

35 No

y

$-\pi$

π

x

37 $u = -5\cos 2$
$v = 5\sin 2$
$w = 5\sqrt{2(1 - \cos 2)}$

Section 6.7

1 1.570

3 1.330

5 -1.447

7 $3\pi/2$

9 π

11 $\pi/4, 5\pi/4$

13 $\pi/3, 4\pi/3$

15 (a) $1.88, 4.41$
(b) $1.88, 4.41$

17 $\pi/6$

19 $\pi/3$

21 $\pi/3$

23 0.850

25 (a) $-1/2$
(b) $\sqrt{2}/2$
(c) $-\sqrt{2}/2$
(d) $-\sqrt{3}/2$

27 $\theta = 0.708, 2.434$

29 $t = 1.813, 4.473$

31 $0.340, 2.802$

33 $0.152, 2.989, 3.294, 6.131$

35 $1.914, 4.653$

37 $0.305, 2.837$

39 $4.069, 5.356, 10.352, 11.639$

41 $\theta = \pi/6 + 2\pi k, 11\pi/6 + 2\pi k$, k an integer

43 $\theta \approx 1.893$

45 $t = \pi/6, 5\pi/6,$
$7\pi/6$, or $11\pi/6$

47 $t = \pi/2, 3\pi/2,$
$\pi/6$, or $5\pi/6$

49 $\approx 39.806°$

51 (a) $f(t) = 40,000\cos\left(\frac{\pi}{6}t + \frac{\pi}{6}\right) + 60,000$
(b) $f(3) = \$40,000$
(c) Mid-March and mid-September

53 $P: x \approx 0.819$;
$Q: x \approx 3.181$

55 (a) $\pi/3$
(b) π
(c) ≈ 0.1

57 (a) $t_1 \approx 0.161$ and $t_2 \approx 0.625$.
(b) $t_1 = \arcsin(3/5)/4$ and
$t_2 = \pi/4 - \arcsin(3/5)/4$

59 Statement II is always true;
statement I is not always true

61 (a) $d = \sqrt{2rx + x^2}$
(b) $d = 25,238.776$ meters

Chapter 6 Review

1 (i) is B; (ii) is C; (iii) is A

3 (a) I
(b) I and III
(c) II and IV
(d) IV

(e) III

5 $7\pi/4$

7 $\pi^2/30 \approx 0.329$

9 $32,400/\pi \approx 10,313.240°$

11 8π

13 32.8π

15 $6.2 \cdot 17\pi/180 \approx 1.840$

17 12.4

19 Mid: 3; amp: 1; per:2π

21 Mid: 7; Amp: 2; Per: 2

23 Amplitude: 20
Period: 1/2
Phase shift: 0
Horizontal shift: 0

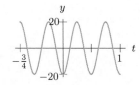

25 Amplitude: 3;
Period: 1/2;
Phase Shift: -6π;
Horizontal Shift: $-3/2$ (left)

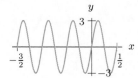

27 Amp: 30; mid: $y = 60$; per: 20

29 Amp: 50; mid: $y = 50$; per: 64

31

y

33

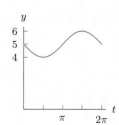

y

35 -1

37 $\sqrt{3}$

39 0.412

41 0.979

43 (a) $y = 600 - 300\cos(2\pi x/80)$
   (b) $x = 14.5279, 65.4721, 94.5279$

45 $f_1(x) = 6\cos((1/2)(x - 3\pi)) + 2, f_2(x) = -6\cos((1/2)(x - \pi)) + 2, f_3(x) = 6\sin((1/2)(x - 2\pi)) + 2, f_4(x) = -6\sin((1/2)x) + 2;$ answers may vary

47 $f_1(x) = 5\cos((\pi/6)(x+2))+3, f_2(x) = -5\cos((\pi/6)(x - 4)) + 3, f_3(x) = 5\sin((\pi/6)(x - 7)) + 3, f_4(x) = -5\sin((\pi/6)(x - 1)) + 3;$ answers may vary

49 $\pi/6, 7\pi/6$

51 2.897, 6.038

53 0, π, 1.107, 4.249

55 69.115 miles

57 Outer edge: 3770 cm/min; Inner edge: 471 cm/min

59 0.1345 radians

61 $f(t) = -900\cos((\pi/4)t) + 2100$

63 $y = 30\sin(105t - \pi/2) + 150$

Ch. 6 Understanding

1 True
3 False
5 True
7 True
9 False
11 False
13 True
15 False
17 True
19 True
21 False
23 True
25 True
27 True
29 False
31 True
33 False
35 True
37 True
39 True
41 False
43 False
45 True
47 False
49 True
51 True
53 True
55 False
57 False
59 False
61 True
63 True

65 True
67 True
69 True
71 False
73 True
75 True
77 False
79 False
81 False
83 False
85 True
87 False

Chapter 6 Tools

1 (a) $\tan\theta = 2$
  (b) $\sin\theta = 2/\sqrt{5}$
  (c) $\cos\theta = 1/\sqrt{5}$

3 (a) $5/\sqrt{125}$
  (b) $10/\sqrt{125}$
  (c) $10/\sqrt{125}$
  (d) $5/\sqrt{125}$
  (e) $1/2$
  (f) 2

5 (a) $\sqrt{45}/7$
  (b) $2/7$
  (c) $\sqrt{45}/2$

7 (a) $8/12$
  (b) $\sqrt{80}/12$
  (c) $8/\sqrt{80}$

9 (a) $\sqrt{117}/11$
  (b) $2/11$
  (c) $\sqrt{117}/2$

11 $r = 7\sin 17°; q = 7\cos 17°$

13 $r = 6/\cos 37°; q = 6\tan 37°$

15 $r = 9/\tan 77°; q = 9/\sin 77°$

17 $c = 34.409; A = 35.538°, B = 54.462°$

19 $B = 62°; a = 9.389; b = 17.659$

21 Height = 46.174 ft; Incline = 205.261 ft

23 $h = 400$ feet; $x = 346.410$ feet

25 74.641 feet

27 $d = 35000/\tan\theta$ feet

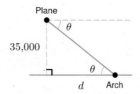

29 $d = 3\tan\phi$ miles

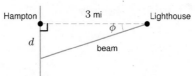

31 $d \approx 15.877$ feet

Section 7.1

1 $A = 25.922°, B = 37.735°, C = 116.343°$

3 $b = 31.762, A = 38.458°, C = 60.542°$

5 $c = 10.954, A = 54.010°, B = 45.990°$

7 $c = 7.2605; A = 21.4035°; B = 126.597°.$

9 $a = 15.860, b = 2.569, C = 66°$

11 $a = 10.026, b = 6.885, C = 61°$

13 $a = 2.079, b = 3.090, B = 18°$

15 $a = 1.671, b = 4.639, B = 166°$

17 $a = 13.667, A = 90.984°, C = 17.016°$

19 $a = 12.070, A = 135.109°, C = 27.891°$
   or
   $a = 3.231, A = 10.891°, C = 152.109°$

21 $b = 0.837$ m, $c = 2.720$ m; $\gamma = 143.7°$

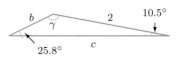

23 $\alpha \approx 41.410°, \beta \approx 82.819°, \gamma \approx 55.771°$

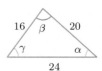

25 (a) $\sin\theta = 0.282$
   (b) $\theta \approx 16.374°$
   (c) 12.077 cm^2

27 Length of arc ≈ 0.174533 feet; Length of chord ≈ 0.174524 feet

29 B closer by 2.387 miles

31 396.004 miles

33 $(18.876, 10.071)$

37 (a) First; 3.062 feet closer
   (b) 157.279 feet to home
       113.218 feet to third

39 158.926 feet

Section 7.2

1 $\sin x$

3 $2\sin\alpha$

5 $\cos t - \sin t$

7 0

9 $\cos^2\theta + \sin^2\theta = 1; \cos 2\theta = \cos^2\theta - \sin^2\theta = 2\cos^2\theta - 1 = 1 - 2\sin^2\theta$

17 $\pi/2, 7\pi/6, 11\pi/6$